AN INTRODUCTION TO
THE STUDY OF
PROTOZOA

THE CILIUM AND THE KINETY

(cf. Fig. 112 in the text)

Above, longitudinal section of a cilium of *Paramecium*. Electron micrograph by Dr. A. W. Sedar and Dr. K. R. Porter, the Rockefeller Institute, New York. On the right, longitudinal section of a kinety of *Stentor*. Electron micrograph by Professor J. T. Randall, F.R.S., and Dr. S. Fitton Jackson, King's College, London.

AN INTRODUCTION TO
THE STUDY OF
PROTOZOA

BY THE LATE

DORIS L. MACKINNON

*sometime Professor of Zoology in the
University of London King's College
and Honorary Research Associate of
University College London*

AND

R. S. J. HAWES

*Lecturer in Zoology in the
University of Exeter*

OXFORD
AT THE CLARENDON PRESS

Oxford University Press, Ely House, London W. 1

GLASGOW NEW YORK TORONTO MELBOURNE WELLINGTON
CAPE TOWN SALISBURY IBADAN NAIROBI DAR ES SALAAM LUSAKA ADDIS ABABA
BOMBAY CALCUTTA MADRAS KARACHI LAHORE DACCA
KUALA LUMPUR SINGAPORE HONG KONG TOKYO

FIRST PUBLISHED 1961

REPRINTED LITHOGRAPHICALLY IN GREAT BRITAIN
AT THE UNIVERSITY PRESS, OXFORD
BY VIVIAN RIDLER
PRINTER TO THE UNIVERSITY
1966, 1970

PREFACE

When Doris Mackinnon retired from the Chair of Zoology at King's College, she was elected an Honorary Research Associate of University College London, and there she settled, in 1949, to write a book about the Protozoa. As time went on, her work became more and more interrupted by illness, and in June 1956 she invited me to become her collaborator. But before we could meet to discuss her proposals, she suffered a paralysing stroke, and in the following September she died. Thus, with the consent and encouragement of her executors, I became responsible for the revision and completion of a work which at that time I had never seen. This book is the result. It is in some ways different from the book which Professor Mackinnon might have written, and an explanation is owing.

It happened that for some decades Professor Mackinnon was almost the only protozoologist of established reputation to teach undergraduate classes in England. Her teaching remains unforgettable; it was also inimitable. Her work on the present book, begun twelve years ago, often rewritten by herself, revised by me, and then incorporated in the context of my own contribution, cannot possibly convey the impact of her style. She was a conscious stylist, speaking and writing with crisp authority. What she said always seemed to come very naturally. Yet the flow of her originality was governed by a privately cultivated discipline. For example, she offered courses in protozoology (and in many other subjects) for thirty years in the same college, and she never repeated a lecture. Every one was composed for its own occasion. She composed with deliberate taste, disliking both the cliché and the touch of flamboyance. She was by nature serious, and at the same time took obvious pleasure in work, and whether she was speaking formally, or sitting at the microscope, she could convey her interest and seriousness and delight. When you take a drop of water from an infusion, she would say, and look at it, you are seeing something no one has ever seen before, and when you discard it, no one will ever see it again. She thought that life was wonderful, and she was full of common sense about it. Few zoologists can have read more widely than she, and to all her scientific work she brought a remarkably educated versatility which could easily have become overwhelming, and yet much of her success as a teacher was due to her modesty and to the consideration she showed to her pupils; she taught with habitual good manners.

The book now lacks her touch, but I have kept to her plan. Her approach was practical, based on her long experience of the needs of teachers and students of protozoology. She very well understood the gap between what the expert and what the novice can see when each looks down the same microscope, and she knew how to narrow it. Her intention was to describe a number of representative species of Protozoa, and likely substitutes for them, and to put down what the student with patience and sound advice may be expected to see for himself, first in the living, and then in fixed and stained preparations. This method of dividing a description tends to be repetitious, and sometimes irritating, but to the inexperienced it is very helpful at the laboratory bench, and I have retained it. Most Protozoa are seen at their best when alive, but the comparison of fresh with fixed material is nearly always necessary.

By the time of her last illness, Professor Mackinnon had compiled descriptions of her types for various versions of Chapters I, II, and III, and of some ciliates, but she had written little else. My principal alterations and additions have been as follows. I have tried to bring the book up to date as far as I could, and this has in places called for extensive rewriting, e.g. the sections on amoebae in Chapter I are almost entirely new. I have assumed that teachers in modern laboratories would make use of cultures as well as collections, and this has allowed a wider range of types for treatment than Professor Mackinnon admitted, e.g. I have inserted *Entamoeba invadens* into the text. In Chapter II, I have rewritten the sections on Trypanosomidae and Trichomonadida, and, as termites are now obtainable in this country, I have introduced a section on their flagellates. I have greatly expanded the treatment of the Archigregarina in Chapter III in the hope of drawing attention to the merits of these interesting and easily accessible animals, which are very rewarding to study; that much of what we now know about archigregarines is due to the work of Professor Mackinnon and her pupils has added to my pleasure in writing about them. In one respect I have not repaired an omission which I knew to be deliberate. The genus *Plasmodium* and the entire subject of malaria are omitted. To anyone who cares for protozoological studies it will be obvious that this decision must have been difficult. I was swayed by knowing that the scale of this book would have allowed only a sketchy account of a subject which deserved better and which was more appropriately dealt with in textbooks of medical protozoology. I thought it useful, having described any parasite as a type, to include in their systematic places at least brief notes of other parasites likely to be encountered in the same host. This called for more additions to the text; yet even so I have not achieved completeness, e.g. I have

included many of the parasites so conveniently offered to us by *Eisenia
foetida*, but I have not exhausted the resources of its seminal vesicles.
Finally, I have written the introductions to the four main chapters, and
added those sections which bear my name in the table of contents.

Of these sections, the longest is the chapter on the Ciliata. In 1950
Professor Emmanuel Fauré-Fremiet, in a modest paper, revised the
classification of ciliates, and during the last decade his suggestions have
been fortified and extended by the lucid interpretations and additions of
Professor John O. Corliss. The impact of their writings has been twofold.
In the first place they have established the outlines of a taxonomy which is
firmly based in the study of phylogeny and homology. In the second, they
have obliged the systematist to take into account, not only the facts of
morphology, but all that is known of the life-histories and, above all, the
morphogenetics, of the animals they are classifying. The 'new systematics'
of ciliates is of interest to zoologists generally, as well as being acceptable
to taxonomic experts. Yet, as far as I am aware, it has never been presented
to the general reader or the undergraduate student. In expounding the
classification here I have been obliged to relate the main facts of development for each group. It is my regret that I have not been able to do
justice to the subject, but I hope that I shall arouse enough interest in the
new approach to ciliate studies to send the reader to some of the excellent
summarizing articles quoted in the text. My debt to Professor Corliss,
who has helped me through many difficult passages, will be obvious to
anyone who knows the extent of the literature.

The passage on *Paramecium* is very long. Perhaps some historian of our
subject will one day explain by what mischance this genus was adopted as a
type for elementary study, a role for which it is ill adapted. *Paramecium*
is an extremely specialized member of a peculiar and imperfectly investigated suborder. Its structure is difficult to observe and almost impossible to demonstrate to the inexperienced. Very few people understand
how it feeds. Only recently has it found a tenable taxonomic position. Year
after year examination candidates pour out, as if they were incantations,
traditional misunderstandings about the functions of its nuclei. We use it
to illustrate to elementary classes the general features of the Protozoa (or
the Ciliata) with about as much sense of proportion as if we introduced the
Phylum Arthropoda with compulsory dissections of *Drosophila*. Is it too
much to hope that one day it will be abandoned as a morphological type
in favour of some more generalized ciliate such as *Tetrahymena*? But though
it fails in the role it is generally cast for, *Paramecium*, like *Drosophila*, claims
the attention of all zoologists as one of the most important experimental

animals known, and to neglect the fact is frivolous. For this reason I do not apologize for the space devoted to *Paramecium*: I regret only that I could touch but briefly on the kind of zoology which its study illuminates.

I wish that controversies about nomenclature could have been ignored throughout this book, for Protozoa are more interesting than their names. But many of them are entirely asexual, so that the limits of species cannot be ascertained by tests of reproductive isolation; further, there are in protozoology no type specimens. These and other circumstances make the Protozoa singularly vulnerable to the emending proclivities of scholarly— and, indeed, of unscholarly—authors. In some places where the literature is bedevilled by nomenclatorial disputation I have been forced into brief explanations of the usage adopted. I know that my judgement will not meet with the approval of all experts, but I hope that it will be intelligible enough for its purpose.

There are 795 drawings in the figures, of which 74 (marked D. L. M. in the legends) are by Professor Mackinnon; the rest are mine. Nearly 150 of these are original; the sources of the rest are acknowledged in a following section and their authors are named in the legends. All the drawings are in line and stipple, a style which cannot convey the delicacy and beauty of Protozoa. But it does make for clarity, and I hope I may be forgiven the crudities which, especially in my hands, it is prone to. Those who take pleasure in the combination of design and scientific accuracy which the style can achieve are recommended to examine Miss Boatwright's work for Professor Corliss at the University of Illinois or almost any illustrations published by Professor K. G. Grell of Tübingen.

It is a pleasure to acknowledge the help I have received. Nearly all of this book was written, first by Professor Mackinnon and then by myself, at University College London, where, during all the vacations of three consecutive years, I enjoyed the hospitality of Professor P. B. Medawar, F.R.S.; it is true to say that but for the kindness of him and his colleagues there would have been no book. Dr C. A. Hoare, F.R.S., has read the passages on trypanosomes and Coccidia, Dr R. A. Neal those on amoebae, Dr J. A. Kitching, F.R.S., the section on Suctorida, Dr C. Horton-Smith read that on *Eimeria tenella* and kindly supplied me with material for sectioning and drawing. Professor L. A. Harvey and Mr G. F. Lothian read the section on microscopy, and Dr Keith Vickerman that on *Naegleria*. The most wearisome task was undertaken by Professor Corliss, who answered many questions about ciliates, supplied me with literature, and finally read the whole of Chapter IV. To all these gentlemen I am most grateful for advice and corrections. They, and many others who have helped me, have saved me from mistakes. But I have not always taken advice, and responsibility for the text, including the mistakes which remain in it, is mine. I am grateful, too, to the librarians of the Foster Court Library, University College, London, and especially to Mrs Blamire and her colleagues, and to Mrs Whalen, at the Wellcome Laboratories of Tropical Medicine, for all their kind and efficient help. Professor Mackinnon's executors have given me all possible encouragement and assistance, and without the care taken by Mrs Hilda Lindars and Mrs Jane Spicer to see that all the relevant papers left by Professor Mackinnon came into my hands it would have been difficult even to begin work. It is indeed a pleasure to record my gratitude to Mrs Rosemary Marchant, who typed the manuscript, undertook much of the more laborious work of checking, read the proofs, and, in startling acts of supererogation, corrected slips far outside the scope of her acknowledged responsibilities.

R. S. J. H.

London, 1960

ACKNOWLEDGMENTS

THE following journals, publishers, and societies have kindly granted permission for the use of illustrations (the names of the authors are given below the individual figures): Academic Press Inc. (Figs. 143, 144 from *Recent Advances in Genetics*); Akademische Verlagsgesellschaft (Figs. 80C, 101, 119 from *Zeitschrift für wissenschaftliche Zoologie*; Figs. 111M, 168F from *Zoologischer Anzeiger*); American Microscopical Society (Figs. 77C, 95 C, D, 98A, 134 A, B, D, 136, 138 (1–8), B, 150B, 151 A–E from *Transactions of the American Microscopical Society*); *Archives d'Anatomie microscopique* (Fig. 123); *Archives de Zoologie expérimentale* (Figs. 48C, 66 B, D, 68 A–F, 92, 93 A, B, E, F, 95 A, B, 96, 98E, 99E, 116A, 125 B, E–H, 149 G–J, 155 C, D, 160, 163 C–F, 164A); *Atti della Società italiana di Scienze naturali* (Fig. 111D); Baillière, Tindall, & Cox (Figs. 71 *a, b*, 74, 78 C, D, 79C from Wenyon, *Protozoology*); *Biological Bulletin* (Figs. 53A, 121D, 134 E, F, 135 E, F, 140, 149 A, B); Blackie & Son Ltd. (Fig. 176 from Martin and Johnson, *Practical Microscopy*); Blackwell Scientific Publications Ltd. (Figs. 172, 174 from Barer, *Lecture Notes on the Use of the Microscope*); *Botanisk Tidsskrift* (Fig. 45D); *Bulletin biologique* (Figs. 58, 59, 130, 135A, 166A, 168 D, E, 170); *Bulletin scientifique de la France et de la Belgique* (Figs. 111 A–C, E, G, I, J, L, 150H); Cambridge University Press (Fig. 15C from *Journal of General Microbiology*; Figs. 23, 24, 25, 70 A, B, 89 C, D, 90 C, G, I, 98 B–D, 99 D, 111 F, H, 133 C, E, 137 D, 145A, 177 from *Parasitology*); Columbia University Press (Fig. 139 from Jennings, *Behavior of the Lower Organisms*); Commonwealth Bureau of Animal Health (Fig. 72 from *Veterinary Reviews and Annotations*); Company of Biologists Ltd. (Fig. 13 *a–g* from *Journal of Experimental Biology*); Gauthier-Villers (Figs. 87D, 154 from *Comptes Rendus de l'Academie des Sciences, Paris*); Johns Hopkins Press (Figs. 106 A–D, 107 from *American Journal of Hygiene*); *Journal of Parasitology* (Figs. 76G, 164 D, E); *Journal of Protozoology* (Figs. 9 C, D, 10, 113, 132, 153); Macmillan & Co. Ltd. (Figs. 3B, 54 from *Nature*); Marine Biological Association (Fig. 56 A–D from Lebour, *The Dinoflagellates of Northern Seas*); Masson & Cie Editeurs (Figs. 124, 125 A, C, D, 126 C, E, 127, 128, 129 B, C, 155B, 158 F–I, 159 A–C from *Annales des Sciences naturelles*; Fig. 110A from Grassé, *Traité de Zoologie*); Oxford University Press (Figs. 17, 18, 55, 71 *c–e, h*, 77A, 99H, 114A, 163G, 168C from *Quarterly Journal of Microscopical Science*); Rockefeller Institute (Figs. 112 B, E, G, 114 B, C, and Frontispiece from *Journal of Biophysical and Biochemical Cytology*; Fig. 65 from *Journal of General Physiology*); Royal Microscopical Society (Fig. 30 from *Journal of the Royal Microscopical Society*); Springer-Verlag, Heidelberg (Fig. 49 F, G from *Archiv für Mikrobiologie*; Fig. 116 C, D from *Zeitschrift für Parasitenkunde*); Springer-Verlag, Vienna (Fig. 3A from *Protoplasma*); *Systematic Zoology* (Fig. 137B); University of California Press (Fig. 56 E, F from *Memoirs of the University of California*; Figs. 52, 60, 85, 86, 167, 169 from *University of California Publications in Zoology*); University of Illinois Press (Figs. 103 B–G, I, 110 H, I from *Illinois Biological Monographs*); VEB Gustav Fischer Verlag (Figs. 2, 4, 5, 6, 9B, 15 A, B, 26, 31, 33, 39, 40,

45 A–C, 50, 62, 63, 64, 66C, 71 *f, g, i, j,* 76F, 80 A, B, D, 81, 82, 87 H, I, 93 C, D, 94, 99 F, G, 100, 102 C–F, K–O, 110 B–G, J, K, 116B, 118 B, C, 120, 121 A–C, 122 D, 126 A, B, D, 133D, 135 B–D, 137 A, C, E–H, 138A, 142, 145 B, C, 148, 150 C–G, 151 F–H, 159 D, 161 B, C, 162A, 165, 166 B, C, 171 from *Archiv für Protistenkunde*; Fig. 118 A, D from Dahl, *Die Tierwelt Deutschlands*; Figs. 29, 111K from Doflein and Reichenow, *Lehrbuch der Protozoenkunde*); Wistar Institute of Anatomy and Biology (Fig. 152 from *Journal of Experimental Zoology*; Figs. 13*h*, 14, 67, 76E, 141, 162 B–E, 164B, 168 A, B from *Journal of Morphology*); Zoological Society of London (Figs. 46, 70C from *Proceedings of the Zoological Society*).

CONTENTS

CONTENTS

    B

LIST OF ABBREVIATIONS
IN THE TEXT

Ag   silver (nitrate)
AZM   adoral zone of membranellae
B   Bouin's Fluid
D.H.   Delafield's Haematoxylin
DNA   deoxyribonucleic acid
DZM   dorsal zone of membranellae
E.M.   electron microscope
F+   Feulgen positive
F−   Feulgen negative
H.H.   Heidenhain's Haematoxylin
RNA   ribonucleic acid
S   Schaudinn's Fluid
S+A   Schaudinn's Fluid with acetic acid
UM   undulating membrane (of ciliates only)

Abbreviations in the figures are given in the legends

THE PHYLUM PROTOZOA

THE name Protozoa means 'first animals' or, by implication, simple, primitive animals. In all respects it is a misleading name. Some Protozoa are not animals, but plants. The meaning to be attached to 'first' is ambiguous. A glance through this book will show that most Protozoa are extremely complicated, and the apparent simplicity of some of them turns out on examination to be delusory. If we seek by the study of protozoology to assemble the living image of some ancestral organism existing in a state of primitive simplicity and from which the later complexities of the animal kingdom arose, we shall deserve and shall discover only disappointment. Simplicity of structure, where it does occur, is rarely allied to simplicity of life-history, as might be expected of some primordial creature; both are commonly secondary. For example, the life-history of *Amoeba proteus* is certainly simple; it grows and it divides. But it is almost certain that the monotony of this existence has been derived from an ancestral life-history enlivened by encystation and sexual reproduction, both of which are lost to the modern amoeba (see p. 14). And the type of nucleus and its mitosis seen in *A. proteus* labels it firmly as the specialized end and not the primitive starting-point of an evolutionary excursion. Likewise, such flagellates as the leptomonads (p. 112) unite their simplicity of structure with a high degree of ecological specialization. And, as already said, most Protozoa are very complicated either in life-history or in structure, or in both.

These considerations alone should disabuse us of the belief that the Protozoa as we now know them—and of their past little is sure except what can be gleaned from collections of fossilized shells—lie, so to speak, 'at the beginning' of the animal kingdom, as 'first animals'. The expression carries an implication that on some remote occasion an autotrophic organism lost its photosynthetic pigment and survived as the ancestor of animals. It is a naïve conception of evolutionary history and it is not supported by the facts. Photosynthesizing organisms have repeatedly lost their pigments in the past, providing even within a single order a variety of colourless genera of different ancestries whose descendants we recognize among the living Protozoa; and the process continues today (see p. 72). It is for this reason that it is not desirable to distinguish plant-like organisms and evict them from the phylum in order to compile a homogeneously zoological taxon. Among the Phytomastigina the photosynthesizing organisms and their colourless derivatives remain naturally linked to each other by their community of organization, reflecting a common ancestry, and to separate them would be not only to violate a natural taxonomy but also to destroy a character of the group. If we here refuse to recognize fixed differences between plants and animals, it is because the differences are not fixed.

The phylum is often called a sub-kingdom, and its status is held to be entrenched in the doctrine that Protozoa are not composed of cells. Some of the Cnidosporidia in fact are multicellular during parts of their life-cycles (Fig. 110); perhaps they ought not to be included among the Protozoa, but if they are it is certain that they are atypical. The Protozoa as a group are not multicellular and this sets them apart from the great majority of plants and animals. It also raises the question, are they unicellular, or are they of a distinct nature, lying outside the range of organisms for which the cell is the natural unit of structure and so to be regarded as acellular or non-cellular? It must at once be said that many Protozoa have much in common with single cells, and when the experimentalist employs a culture of amoebae instead of one of fibroblasts and draws conclusions about 'cells' it is only pedantry to deny his right to the word. Yet after 50 years of discussion* the general question remains unsettled. The clearest statement of the case for an acellular nature is found in an influential essay published by Clifford Dobell in 1911. Much of his argument is directed against views of recapitulation and evolution and the place of the Protozoa in them which are now discredited and to that extent is wasted for lack of a target. We no longer suppose, for example, that 'the amoeba' is an ancestral type still represented in metazoan ontogeny by the zygote. But a residue of Dobell's discussion remains fresh. For him, a cell acquires its nature by being part of an organism. The zygote is not a cell, nor is the body of a protozoan. The latter is a complete organism and so far as it corresponds to anything metazoan it corresponds to the complete metazoan organism and not to any cell which is a part of it.

Evidently to define a cell as part of an organism prejudges the issue.† Supporters of the view that the Protozoa are unicellular would insist on a morphological criterion of homology and argue that the nucleus, the cytoplasm, and inclusions such as mitochondria are homologous in the metazoan cell and protozoan body and conclude that the two wholes are homologous. All are cells morphologically. It is really no reply to say that the protozoan organism is a whole organism, the equivalent of the metazoan whole organism, and cannot be equal to both the whole and the part. The neatness of the reply slips attention away from its fallacy, which is that the

* See especially Dobell (1911), Baker (1948), and a correspondence between Boyden, Corliss, and others in *Science* (1957), **125**, 155 and 988.

† The problem of definition is illustrated by one proposed by Baker (1948), who calls a cell 'a mass of protoplasm, largely or completely surrounded by a membrane, and containing within it a single nucleus formed by the telophase transformation of a haploid or diploid set of anaphase chromosomes'. If the reader will pause to apply this to a selection of Protozoa he will discover that some are unicellular, some multicellular, and some acellular.

principle violated is mathematical and the subject is not. We cannot think of an amoeba, for instance, as mathematically 'equal' to anything at all. There seems to be no reason why a cell should not be a part in one context and a whole in another and still be a cell. The proposition that Protozoa are unicellular ought to be dismissed, if at all, not by adopting a definition of cells which must exclude the Protozoa, or by invoking concepts of 'equality' which fail to apply, but by other means. Of these, possibly the most hopeful is to insist that the very high degree of organization found in numerous Protozoa so far exceeds anything recognizable in a metazoan cell that we have to strain our concept of homology beyond usefulness if we are to apply it throughout the phylum. This seems to say that even if it be granted that some Protozoa are homologous with cells many of them have developed beyond the point when they are still recognizable as such.

From the above it should be clear that it is very difficult to define the Protozoa. Because they include many Phytomastigina they are limited only by an arbitrary convention and in practice the realms of the botanists and zoologists overlap. One of the most interesting and experienced of living protozoologists opens his subject with the words, 'The Protozoa include a variety of microorganisms which, by general agreement of protozoologists, are currently assigned to the phylum.' One might insert the word 'nucleated'. Even so, the definition would not satisfy the taxonomist who wishes to see his categories clearly defined or the student seeking some clue to the nature of the Protozoa. The former cannot be satisfied; it is to be hoped that the latter will find something of what he seeks in the rest of this book.

I

CLASS RHIZOPODA

THE rhizopod Protozoa are distinguished by their pseudopodia, which are temporary organs of locomotion and feeding. The name means 'root feet', but the pseudopodia are by no means always root-like, and, as explained in the succeeding sections, their form is, on the whole, characteristic in the different orders. They are typically blunt, with rounded ends, in the Amoebina, and the form of the pseudopodium when fully formed can vary from one genus to another (cf. Figs. 1, 7, 8). In the Heliozoa (Figs. 37, 39) and Radiolaria, they are long, fine, and stiff, and project radially from the body. In the Foraminifera they are likewise fine and delicate but anastomose to form an extensive feeding net outside the body. The familiar pseudopods of *Amoeba*, with their rounded extremities, are known as lobopodia. The finer, more filamentous organs of some Testacea are filopodia, and fine pseudopodia which branch are rhizopodia. All these are temporary structures which can apparently form anywhere on the surface of the animal. The stiff pseudopodia of many Heliozoa (Fig. 37 A, B) possess a well-defined and essentially fibrillar axis and have a more regularly organized disposition about the body, and these are known as axopodia. The names are useful when the pseudopodia clearly fall within the definitions, but transitional types occur; further, some pseudopodia, as in many Radiolaria, are so delicate that it is difficult to determine whether they are really axopodia or filopodia.

Many rhizopods form shells or tests, and these may be rough constructions of casually affixed sand-grains or other debris, or they may be beautifully finished and sometimes highly complicated (Foraminifera, Radiolaria). The shell may be an organic secretion (*Arcella*, Fig. 27) or have an organic base covered with inorganic particles (*Difflugia*, Fig. 28) or it may be purely inorganic, as in the calcareous and siliceous shells of Foraminifera and Radiolaria (Figs. 32, 34, 41–43). Regular shells impose regular shapes upon the bodies which produce them. Many of the naked forms (e.g. Heliozoa, some Radiolaria) are spherical and, although the amoebae are sometimes referred to as formless, distinctive differences in outline may, with a little experience, be detected among them (cf. Figs. 1, 7, 8, 10). The Rhizopoda include the largest of Protozoa; the extinct *Nummulites*, with the body supported by a shell, could reach the size of a shilling, and the naked *Pelomyxa* may, though exceptionally, be as much as a centimetre and a half long.

Most Rhizopoda are uninucleate, but *Pelomyxa* (p. 20) has very numerous nuclei, and some Heliozoa and Radiolaria are multinucleate in the main phase of the life-cycle. Binary fission is very common throughout the class. Sexual reproduction is unknown in the Amoebina, but usual and diverse in some other orders (Foraminifera and Heliozoa); the life-histories of the Radiolaria are so incompletely known that, though no sexual process has yet been seen among them, its absence is by no means certain.

Rhizopods are typically phagotrophic, living off bacteria, algae, and other Protozoa. They occur in fresh water, the soil, and the sea; a number of Amoebina are entozoic (p. 32). The freshwater forms have contractile vacuoles, absent from marine and entozoic species. They often produce cysts, the properties of which would repay further investigation—as it is, they are assumed, on not very much evidence, to be resistant to various adverse environmental conditions; most entozoic forms produce cysts, which constitute the distributive phase.

The class Rhizopoda, sometimes called the Sarcodina, may be divided on the broad characters of the pseudopodia and, where present, the test, as follows:

Order Amoebina—naked, with broad pseudopodia having rounded ends (lobopodia). Asexual. Freshwater, marine, terrestrial, and entozoic. *Amoeba, Entamoeba.*

Order Testacea—with a monolocular test which is pseudochitinous or has a pseudochitinous base. Nearly all freshwater. They are the testate amoebae of some authors. *Arcella, Difflugia.*

Order Foraminifera—with a test which is nearly always polythalamous and calcareous. Typically marine. *Elphidium.*

Order Heliozoa—the sun animalcules, with axopodia. With or without a test. Usually freshwater, but some marine. *Actinosphaerium, Actinophrys.*

Order Radiolaria—with a central capsule separating the ectoplasm and endoplasm, and usually with a siliceous skeleton. Marine. *Sphaerozoum.*

Order Acantharia—central capsule, if present, lying entirely in the ectoplasm. Skeleton said to be of strontium sulphate. Marine. *Acanthometra.*

Two orders are here omitted: the **Rhizomastigina**, a small group with permanent flagella as well as pseudopodia, are sometimes classed with the Mastigophora and are in any event difficult of access for class work, and the **Mycetozoa**, which are the Myxomycetes of the botanists.

ORDER AMOEBINA

Amoebae in active progression are constantly changing the shapes of their bodies and much of this change is due to the growth and withdrawal of the lobopodia, which themselves vary in outline from one instant to another. In a famous and frequently quoted experiment Verworn (1899) showed that the form of the pseudopodium is affected by the environment; thus a *limax* amoeba (p. 23), on the addition of potassium hydroxide to the medium, developed, in place of its normally single lobopodium, a number of slender radiating pseudopodia. On the face of it, characters as dependent and variable as pseudopodia would appear to have little taxonomic value. But this is not so. Under normal conditions, when extended in movement, many amoebae do have characteristic outlines; for example, the conical pseudopodia connected by ectoplasmic webs, found in *Mayorella* (Fig. 7), are unmistakable, and so are the ectoplasmic 'warts' of the *verrucosa* amoebae (Fig. 8). The pseudopodial pattern may be very stable. Thus, '*Amoeba discoides*' forms many short pseudopodia and so displays a more serrated outline than *A. proteus* and this distinction is retained even after an exchange of nuclei (Lorch and Danielli, 1953 *a, b*, and see p. 12). The form of the nucleus, the mitotic figure, and the cyst are unquestionably reliable and useful in taxonomy, but information about these is, for very many species, either imperfect or totally lacking, and consequently the systematics of the order, and particularly of the free-living forms, is uncertain and confused.

Amoebae reproduce asexually and binary fission is typical. They occur in the sea, but more abundantly in the soil and fresh water, probably because the bacteria on which they, or their protozoan prey, mainly feed, are more numerous there. There are both coprozoic and entozoic species, and a few of the latter (*Entamoeba invadens, E. histolytica*, pp. 32f.) are in some hosts pathogenic.

Purely for descriptive purposes, it is convenient to consider amoebae as falling into three main groups, which cut across any formal taxonomic classification. They are (i) the small *limax* amoebae, common in soil, and progressing by means of a single large lobopodium, (ii) the large freshwater amoebae usually studied in the classroom, and (iii) the entozoic amoebae. The second group is here taken first, as its best known representative, *A. proteus*, is familiar to all zoologists.

Amoeba proteus (Leidy)*

A. proteus is commonest in the sheltered parts of not too stagnant pools or streams where gentle currents supply food and oxygen. A good growth

---

* The familiar name is here retained for the organism now sometimes called *Chaos diffluens*. A complicated controversy about the correct name turns upon the difficulty of

of diatoms or desmids is often an indication of its whereabouts. It frequently occurs on the under sides of the leaves of aquatic plants. Water and plant material from such sources are distributed into shallow containers (e.g. tongue jars or finger bowls), the vegetation being gently scraped and shaken, and left for a fortnight. It may help to add a few boiled wheat grains and, at the start, to leave the vessels under a slowly dripping tap. Amoebae are picked out under the binocular dissecting microscope and mounted under cover slips supported at the corners by fragments of No. 1 or No. 2 slips to prevent crushing.

The living organism

The transparent body of the amoeba (Fig. 1) constantly changes its shape as it thrusts out pseudopodia, which in this species are large, comparatively few, and, on the whole, elongate and club-shaped. Rapid outline sketches made at intervals of 2 minutes should be compared.

The ectoplasm is hyaline, firm and consistent, elastic, and bears superficially a number of longitudinal ridges marking the lobopodia; the ridges are characteristic of the species. The endoplasm is much more fluid, as is seen in a long, extended pseudopodium, where it is, as it were, encased in a tube of stiffer ectoplasm. The endoplasm contains a variety of inclusions, such as mitochondria, Neutral Red granules, fat globules, and crystals. The last are plate-like or, more commonly, bipyramidal and truncate; each is contained in its own vacuole (Fig. 2); according to Mast and Doyle (1935a), the plate-like crystals are probably leucine and the bipyramidal ones are closely related to a magnesium salt of a glycine. Their function is unknown. They do not arise from food vacuoles; they are not food reserves, for they increase in number in starved specimens, and their numbers also vary with the diet, being commoner when the amoebae are fed on certain ciliates, such as *Paramecium* or *Colpoda* (Williamson, 1944, and see Andresen, 1956). According to Bernheimer (1938), who studied the crystals of *Cochliopodium bilimbosum*, a testate form, they are eventually lost from their vacuoles to the exterior, where they quickly dissolve.

Amoeboid movement, which of course occurs not only in *Amoeba* but in other Protozoa and some amoeboid cells of Metazoa, has been the subject of many investigations and hypotheses meant to explain it (see especially the reviews of De Bruyn, 1947, and Noland, 1957). Pseudopodia grow at their tips, where the ectoplasm solates and extends fan-wise; into it the endoplasm then flows with a fountain-like movement (Fig. 3 A–D). It has been suggested that the forward movement was assisted by a contraction of

deciding what exactly it was that Rösel von Rosenhoff saw under his microscope over 200 years ago and which in 1755 he called 'der kleine Proteus'. The question is discussed by Schaeffer (1916b), Mast and Johnson (1931), and Kudo (1959).

the ectoplasm posteriorly and laterally, where it gelated, forming a tube of
plasma gel along which the internal plasma sol was forced. There is no
doubt that gelation and solation of the cytoplasm occur as described, but
it is unlikely that the contraction upon gelation, which is slight, would
supply the force capable of moving an amoeba. Goldacre and Lorch (1950,
and see references in Noland's review) have offered a more hopeful hypothesis, for which some evidence is presented, and which has the additional

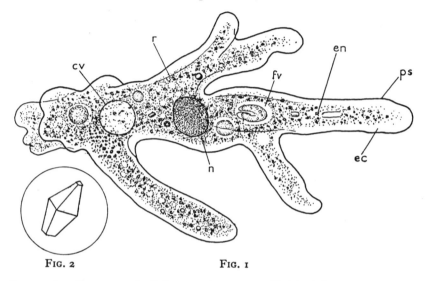

FIG. 2   FIG. 1

FIG. 1. *Amoeba proteus*: the living organism. ×250. (Original: D. L. M.)

cv, contractile vacuole; *ec*, ectoplasm; *en*, endoplasm; *fv*, food vacuole; *n*, nucleus; *ps*, pseudopodium; *r*, ectoplasmic ridge.

FIG. 2. *Amoeba proteus*. Bipyramidal crystal within fluid-filled vacuole. (After Mast
and Doyle.)

attraction of placing the contractility involved in amoeboid movement on
a similar basis to that found in muscle-fibres (Fig. 3). Nearly all proteins
gel when their molecules unfold if they are in the concentrations actually
found in cells. In the endoplasm of the amoeba, which is fluid, the molecules
are thought to be folded compactly. At the tip of a pseudopodium the
molecules unfold, and some of the side-chains used in holding them
together in the folded state are now free to embrace neighbouring molecules
so that a layer of straightened and attached molecules is formed, and this is
the recognizable plasma gel of the animal's ectoplasm over most of its
length. Posteriorly, the protein molecules begin to fold again, and, because
they are interlocked, they impart a contraction; it is suggested that they
so contract under the influence of adenosine triphosphate (or a similar
substance) which supplies the energy for muscle contraction, and the

injection of adenosine triphosphate into amoebae has produced contraction. With further unfolding they lose their grip on each other, so to speak, and pass forward, after solating, in the endoplasm. One effect, if the hypothesis is true, would be to produce osmotic work. Unfolded protein molecules, as already mentioned, expose more free bonds than folded ones, and some of these could unite with other substances while some engaged neighbouring protein molecules likewise unfolded. Such molecules ought, therefore,

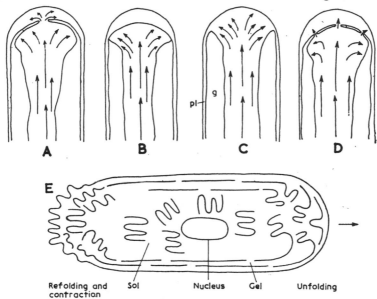

Fig. 3. Amoeboid movement. A–D, formation of pseudopodial tip, according to Mast. Contraction of the tube of ectoplasm (g) when it gelates below the plasmalemma (pl) was supposed to force the cylinder of solated endoplasm along the paths of the arrows to stream through a large gap (c) or a number of small apertures (D). In E, the movement of the amoeba is explained by the unfolding of protein molecules anteriorly to supply a gelated jacket which solates and contracts again posteriorly: see text for further explanation. (A–D after Mast; E after Goldacre and Lorch.)

to attract substances from the sides of the amoeba, and release them when they fold again to accumulate in the posterior of the animal, and this is what is observed to happen when amoebae are kept in 0·01–0·001 per cent solutions of Neutral Red. Additional evidence is given in the original paper and in Noland's summary.

There are very numerous food vacuoles of different sizes in the endoplasm. *A. proteus* feeds on other Protozoa, small algae, and bacteria, which it captures with its pseudopodia. These do not embrace their prey like pincers, but flow over it, so that the food comes to lie in a water-filled cup, which narrows at its aperture until it is nipped off as a vacuole (Schaeffer, 1916*a*). The newly ingested organisms may be active for some time within the large primary food vacuoles so formed. Within an hour or so these break down into smaller and secondary vacuoles, which then subdivide into the numerous minute vacuoles which in well-fed specimens form much of the endoplasmic content. Digestion begins in the primary vacuoles (Pappas, 1954). The undigested remains are left behind (defecated), usually at the posterior end of the animal.

Amoebae do not only eat; they also drink. The peculiar process by which they do so, now called pinocytosis, was seen and clearly described in 1934 by Mast and Doyle,* but only recently has it received the study which, as a widespread physiological activity of first importance, it deserves (see the general review by Holter, 1959 a, b, and also Holter and Marshall, 1954; Bennett, 1956; Chapman-Andresen and Prescott, 1956; Schumaker, 1958; Brandt, 1958; Marshall, Schumaker, and Brandt, 1959; Terra and Rustad, 1959). Pinocytosis, or cell drinking, occurs only in the presence of certain substances, of which the best known are salts and some proteins; Mast and Doyle used 3 per cent egg albumen. When placed in an appropriate solution, the amoeba is arrested, it contracts, and its surface rapidly becomes wrinkled by many folds and crevices. The folds are not stationary and their edges tend to touch and adhere and so to form little pockets, or much more commonly tubes leading from the surface, at which they remain open to the medium. Very commonly the mouth of a tube is raised away from the surface of the amoebae on the tip of a papillate pseudopodium. Most of the tubes are a few microns in diameter, and 15 to 30 μ long, and there may be 50 to 100 of them. They form very rapidly, are completed within a few seconds, and each lasts for several minutes before it disappears. During their short existence the flexible lips of their openings expand and contract so as to gulp droplets of the medium, which widen the tubes at intervals along their lengths. The droplets are usually pinched off as vacuoles at the base of a tube, or occasionally a whole tube disintegrates into vacuoles; these enter the cytoplasm and are lost sight of. Pinocytosis is an intermittent phenomenon; the active phase lasts for about half an hour, and during it there is not a steady acceptance of liquid, but a series of sips or gulps which actively take up droplets one by one into the tubes.

Two considerations strongly suggest that the process described above is one of major importance in the general physiology of the cell. Firstly, the quantities involved are large. An amoeba drinks about 30 per cent of its own volume in 3 hours, and at some concentrations of protein it can very rapidly take up enough solution to increase its dry weight by 5 per cent. It is true that the substances which induce pinocytosis form a list which does not suggest any obvious relevance to the needs of the organism. Some proteins induce; some do not. The best known inducers, besides

---

* It is possible that, as sometimes asserted, the behaviour reported by Edwards in 1925 was pinocytosis; if so, it was not typical.

salt solutions, include rabbit gamma-globulin, gelatin, Na-glutamate, ribo-nuclease, and cytochrome c. Carbohydrates and nucleic acids are non-inducers. But it is important to note that substances, such as carbohydrates, can be accepted during the pinocytosis which they cannot provoke. It may well appear that although the name pinocytosis means cell-drinking it is not the solvent but the materials in solution which contribute significantly to cellular economy. Secondly, it is now recognizable that the drinking of an amoeba, such as *A. proteus* or the giant amoeba, *Chaos chaos*, which is visible with ordinary optical apparatus, is a performance on a large scale of an activity occurring very generally among many types of cell, but usually at a submicroscopic level. Indeed the name pinocytosis was suggested to Lewis (1931) by his observations on macrophages, and by now the process has been identified repeatedly during tissue-culture studies. (For example, the brush border of some epithelial elements may be adaptations for facilitating pinocytosis.) These facts have led Bennett (1956) to the hypothesis that pinocytosis is a general process by which the cell obtains ions (and other particles) to which its bounding layer is impermeable, and which are first engaged at the cell surface, invaginated along the lining of the drinking tubes, and thence discharged in vacuoles into the cytoplasm. It is not clear how the substances obtained are liberated to the organism. In amoebae, for example, the plasmalemma is impermeable to the inducer substances, and it has been confirmed that the concentrations at which they operate show no relation to their osmotic properties. The tubes and, presumably, the walls of the vacuoles, are themselves constructed from invaginated plasmalemma. Soon after their formation, the walls of the tubes lose their impermeability, so that the contents are made available to the cytoplasm, but the means by which this barrier is overcome—and this is the crux of both the purpose and the problem of pinocytosis—have not yet been discovered.

The large, normally single, contractile vacuole circulates, also in the endoplasm. It generally begins its formation, probably by the fusion of a number of smaller vacuoles, at the hind end of the amoeba and then, as this solates, passes forwards in the endoplasmic stream. As it continues to grow, it commonly comes to lie in the peripheral plasmagel layer, where it remains as the amoeba flows onwards, and so it is left to burst in the tail (see Kitching, 1952c). Its pulsations should be timed with a stop watch; if the amoeba is normal there is a regular rhythm. Contractile vacuoles are found in almost all freshwater Protozoa and it is supposed that their main function is to regulate the osmotic pressure by pumping out excess water collected from the hypotonic medium.* It may be that the vacuole

* This opinion has been disputed by Hopkins (1946): but see a discussion by Kitching (1951). There seems to be no doubt that in many Protozoa the contractile vacuoles are in fact osmoregulators.

incidentally rids the animal of some dissolved toxins, but from such a small and permeable surface the main means of excretion must be diffusion.

The nucleus (Figs. 1, 5) may be seen as it rolls over and over in the endoplasm to be discoidal, slightly biconcave, and opaque; especially in older animals it may have a folded outline. It is bounded by a membrane, and immediately within this is a lining of refringent granules. The centre is occupied by a structureless sap. The 'karyosome'* commonly illustrated in the books is an artefact of fixation and does not exist in the living animal. The nucleus shows up more plainly if a drop of fixative, e.g. Bouin or Methyl Green (p. 424), is run under the cover slip, when the 'karyosome' appears.

We are beginning to know something of the roles played by nucleus and cytoplasm in determining the inherited characters of amoebae. Danielli and his collaborators have transferred nuclei between *A. proteus* and the closely related species *A. discoides* (if it is a species) and between differing clones of the same species; such compound amoebae may survive and some of them establish clones to which of course they transmit the nucleus of one 'species' or clone and the cytoplasm of another. To which 'species', the nuclear or cytoplasmic donor, will the characters inherited belong? The following shows the results of heterotransfers between the 2 species (P and D) and between 2 clones of *A. proteus* (T and Z) in which members of pairs differed in maximum nuclear size. ($P_c . D_n$ means an amoeba having a *discoides* nucleus in *proteus* cytoplasm or its descendants, and so on.)

	Normal	Heterotransfers		Normal
	$P_n . P_c$	$P_c . D_n$	$D_c . P_n$	$D_n . D_c$
$d(\mu)$	45	44	38·6	38·2
	38	40·3	41	44·5
	$T^4{}_n . T^4{}_c$	$T^4{}_c . Z_n$	$T^4{}_n . Z_c$	$Z_n . Z_c$

In the first case the size of the nucleus very plainly follows the cytoplasm and the effect of the nucleus seems to be negligible. In the second, the transfers are intermediates but the cytoplasm is at least as important as the nucleus in determining the character studied. Similar results have been obtained with other characters such as the distribution of nuclear sizes in a clone or the type of outline (few large or many small pseudopodia) during locomotion, and the influence of the cytoplasm may be maintained over very long periods, in one example over 8 years. Some characters (e.g. adaptation to anti-sera) are determined always and absolutely by the nuclei,

* The term karyosome (the endosome of some authors) is here used descriptively as the name of any conspicuous, deeply staining body lying in the nuclear sap, without regard to its constitution. Undoubtedly some karyosomes are really nucleoli (*Trichomonas vaginalis*) and they disappear during mitosis; others play an important part in that process (*Naegleria*) and some are Feulgen positive (*Trichomonas sanguisugae*).

on others the cytoplasm has always a marked and sometimes a decisive effect. (For details and for a possible interpretation of the results see Lorch and Danielli, 1950, 1953 *a*, *b*; Danielli, Lorch, Ord, and Wilson, 1955; Danielli, 1958, 1959). The exposition of this work is slightly clouded but not at all vitiated by a taxonomic uncertainty lying in its background. Few protozoologists would now accept *A. discoides* as a good species. The authors themselves point out that two strains of *A. proteus*, stemming in the first place from one laboratory, differed more from each other than

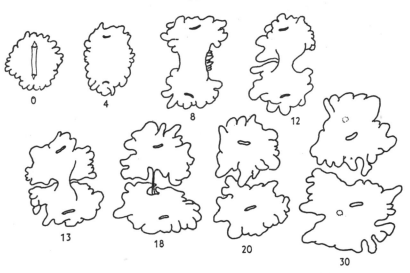

Fig. 4. *Amoeba proteus.* Outlines of a living amoeba in division, with times given in minutes. × *c.* 100. (After Liesche.)

from a strain of *A. discoides* from the same source (where all three were originally determined), and the characters they studied do not seem to have been distributed throughout the 'species'. But this is not the point. The real claim is not that the nucleus of one species survives in the cytoplasm of another—the asexual species used in these experiments would at the best be no more than subjective, in any event—but that nuclei and cytoplasm of clones showing distinctive, stable differences, determined in each case, are interchangeable, with effects which are equally distinctive, stable, and determinable, and the gain lies in what is learnt from the results, not in the achievement of an interspecific transfer.

Binary fission (Fig. 4) may be observed, especially in young cultures. According to Taylor (1947), dividing stages of *A. kerrii*, a member of the *proteus* group, are obtained if cultures are kept in Petri dishes 'as cold as possible' and then examined at about 23° C. Amoebae about to divide may be recognized at a magnification of about 30 diameters. They are sluggish, spherical, with a hyaline exterior covered with radially arranged small pseudopodia so that they resemble translucent blackberries. Such fission spheres are distinguished by their pseudopodia from degenerating amoebae, which are also rounded, but with smooth surfaces. In the middle of each sphere is a relatively clear spot marking the position of the nucleus. The contractile vacuole disappears early, at prophase, and mitosis proceeds within the sphere to the end of anaphase. At telophase the body of the amoeba lengthens and a constriction appears in its middle. The pseudopodia become fewer, larger, and regain their activity, the two halves draw apart and the constriction narrows to a cytoplasmic thread which eventually snaps. At 24° C the process takes some 20 to 30 minutes. For stages in nuclear division not visible in the living organism, see p. 16.

Life history and encystation

A. proteus grows and divides and under fairly constant conditions of culture its life is very regular. Dividing, say, every 24 hours at 23° C, it grows rapidly after division, then rather less rapidly for most of the time, and during the last few of the 24 hours (known as predivision) it neither feeds nor grows, though its nucleus increases in size. It is not possible to attribute the onset of division to the attainment of a given size, for this is reached 4 hours earlier than division. Yet size and division are related: small amoebae take longer to reach division and very large ones take shorter than normal sizes, but the lengthening of time for small ones is proportionally far greater than the shortening of it due to starting large. Further, if cell division is inhibited after mitosis, and one daughter nucleus removed, we have an amoeba which, if size were the guide, is ready to divide at once; in fact it will begin to divide after 14 to 18 hours, which is 60 to 75 per cent of a normal interphase.* Nor does the stimulus to division seem to lie in some state reached by the nucleus after a given interval (in this case, 24 hours). In a paper on 'experimental immortality of the individual', Max Hartmann (1928) described how, by repeatedly removing some of the cytoplasm from the same amoeba during its interphase, he was able to inhibit all division for periods of about 4 months, during which control specimens had undergone some 65 divisions. The cell seemed to be immortal, but when left alone at the end of the experiments it resumed binary fission at a normal rate.

The life-history appears to consist of no more than growth and binary fission. This is indeed a pattern of simplicity, and the question is: is it normally or can it ever be complicated by the events commonly observed

---

* The facts cited are obtained by finding the reduced weights of single amoebae in a Cartesian diver balance itself weighing 2 μg and with a cup only 400 μ wide. For discussion and more information see Prescott (1955, 1959). Under Prescott's conditions an amoeba grows from about half a million to a million μ^3 during its life.

in other rhizopod life-cycles? It is doubtful if any modern support could be found for older workers who described sexual phenomena among amoebae. On the other hand, belief in an encysted phase, which may or may not be reproductive, is still remarkably persistent, though it has little more to commend it than a literary tradition. A cyst was first described and figured by Scheel (1899 a, b) who claimed that within it the contents divided into some 500 to 600 amoebulae, which eventually hatched. Carter (1915) also described a cyst of A. proteus, but felt uncertain whether she and Scheel had seen the same object. The difficulty with the cysts of these authors is to believe, on the evidence offered, that they had any part at all in the life-history of A. proteus; the nuclei figured by Carter as those of the hatching amoebulae resemble no known stage in the development of that species and all the nuclei figured by Scheel are unrecognizable (see also Doflein, 1918). Nor, in all the years that have passed since their publication have the claims been confirmed. No author has traced the development of any organism from a cyst into an unquestionable adult A. proteus; small amoebae appearing in cultures exhausted of large specimens of A. proteus have never been shown to be descended from the latter or to grow into them, and such small forms may have been contaminants. Finally, it should be mentioned that, according to Taylor and her associates, portions of the nucleus ('chromidia') of A. proteus and related species escape into the cytoplasm and there give rise to numerous cysts which escape from the disintegrating 'mother' amoeba and hatch. But the evidence for this unusual view is not convincing; the metacystic amoebae, so far as their development has been described, differ strikingly from A. proteus, the nucleus of which was misinterpreted by Taylor herself, and, without more support than has yet been made available, it is difficult to accept her radical revision of the life-cycle (see Taylor, 1925, 1956 a, b; Taylor and Hayes, 1944). If the positive evidence for encystation is contradictory and unconvincing, that against it must be taken seriously. Johnson (1930) found that once cultures were truly exhausted of large amoebae (A. proteus) these never reappeared; cultures readily become infected by small amoebae such as A. dofleini, or the amoeboid stages of Myxomycetes, but none of the amoebulae detected ever gave rise to A. proteus. Halsey (1936) allowed over 400 specimens of A. proteus and the closely related A. dubia to degenerate; they never formed cysts and he could discover no means of reorganization except binary fission. Liesche (1938) kept A. proteus for 800 vegetative generations and Dawson (1954) for 28 years without detecting cysts. These considerations gain weight from the fact that A. proteus has been kept for many decades in hundreds of laboratories all over the world and observed by thousands of teachers and students and yet it is never possible to demonstrate this widely credited stage in its life-history. It is, of course, very difficult to prove a general negative but it is fair to assert that on the present evidence we have no reason to believe that *A. proteus* ever reproduces except by binary fission and every reason to believe that it has lost the capacity to form cysts.

Permanent preparations: nucleus and mitosis

A rich culture in a Petri dish is gently disturbed and the bottom strewn with No. o cover slips and left overnight. The amoebae creep on to the slips and next day these are carefully and slowly removed with fine forceps and dropped face downwards on to fixative in watch-glasses. The shape of the watch-glass prevents friction which might scrape off the amoebae. If material is restricted the amoebae must be pipetted one by one on to

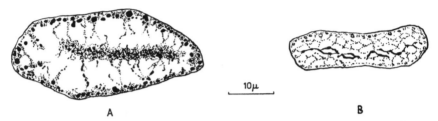

10μ

A　　　　　　　　　　　　　　　　　　　B

FIG. 5. *Amoeba proteus*: sections of interphase nuclei, showing the effects of different fixatives and stains. (After Liesche.)

A, fixed B and stained Iron Haematoxylin, with peripheral granules and apparent 'karyosome'; B, fixed Flemming and stained Feulgen, showing distribution of chromatin (the F+ chromatin is black on a dotted background).

slips in as little water as possible; they are left on the bench for some 5 minutes until the amoebae are well extended in natural attitudes and are then rapidly inverted and dropped into fixative (B or warm S+A) as above, and stained in DH or HH. The natural shape of the body is often better maintained by a preliminary fixation in the fumes of osmic acid. The amoebae are allowed to expand on cover slips in a Petri dish and then a drop of a 2 per cent aqueous solution of osmium tetroxide is put in the dish, out of contact with the slips, and the lid put on for 1 to 2 minutes. Remove, invert, and drop into B or S+A, and so on.

Among fairly recent accounts of the nucleus and mitosis, that by Chalkley and Daniel (1933) affords good pictures of cytokinesis, but is misleading on the subject of mitosis, while those of Chalkley (1936), Dawson, Kessler, and Silberstein (1937), and especially Liesche (1938), based on more critical cytological methods, give clearer and more accurate details of nuclear division.

The interphase nucleus of *A. proteus* (Fig. 5) is, as mentioned, a slightly biconcave disk, like a human erythrocyte. After appropriate fixation the 'karyosome' appears as a centrally placed, flattened mass, more or less granular or reticulate, according to the fixative used. It is the sole source of the F+ material from which the chromosomes will eventually be formed.* The erroneous expression 'peripheral chromatin' is apparently due to a misinterpretation of the nature of the peripheral granules, which stain vigorously with iron haematoxylin but are consistently F—.

At the outset of division (Fig. 6) the nucleus enlarges and becomes more spherical. The peripheral granules move inwards from the membrane and they eventually disappear. By the end of prophase the very numerous chromosomes, of which there are some 500 to 600, are recognizable as they

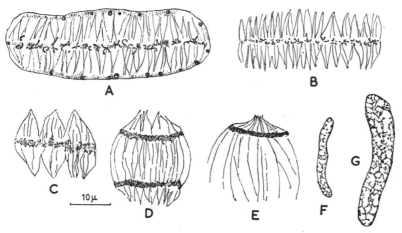

Fig. 6. *Amoeba proteus*: mitosis as seen in sections of dividing amoebae. (After Liesche.)

A, prophase; B, metaphase; C–E, early, middle, and late anaphase; F–G, early and late telophase.

are now at their maximum length, which is about 2 μ; the spindle fibres already foreshow the multipolar arrangement which subsequently becomes more marked. The nuclear membrane persists till metaphase. According to Liesche there is, at anaphase, a true splitting of the chromosomes, although, on account of their small size, it is difficult to observe. As anaphase proceeds the spindle elongates until it stretches across nearly the whole diameter of the organism (Fig. 4 at o) and at the same time its many poles, hitherto separate, converge to compose a conventional mitotic pattern (Fig. 6 D, E). It disappears at telophase, a nuclear membrane is formed, within which the contents are at first reticular, and the refringent granules reappear. Each daughter organism possesses a small, flattened nucleus, with numerous peripheral granules and otherwise homogeneous

* More specifically, Mercer (1959), in an E.M. study which provides a good general report on the fine structure of *A. proteus*, has suggested that minute clusters of well-formed helices found in the nucleus may be DNA bodies. Their structure would not be visible by light microscopy.

contents which coagulate on fixation to form the so-called 'karyosome' as in the parent amoeba.

For some account of the cytoplasmic inclusions of *A. proteus* and methods of study see Brown (1930*a*), Mast and Doyle (1935 *a*, *b*), and Singh (1938), and for E.M. studies see Pappas (1959) and Mercer (1959).

Culture

A rough and ready method, generally successful, is as follows. Boil wheat grains for about 5 minutes. Add three or four to some 50 ml boiled pond or rain-water in small finger bowls or tongue jars; the water should be 2 or 3 inches deep. When a whitish growth of moulds or bacteria appears round the seeds introduce the amoebae, which feed on the organisms in the growth. The colourless flagellates *Chilomonas paramecium* are commonly present and *A. proteus* will engulf 50 to 100 of them daily. The cultures should be kept covered at about 24° C and away from bright light: not only does *A. proteus* occur in shaded places in nature but there is always the possibility of some algae being brought over from the original catch, and their growth must not be encouraged.

The amoebae are plentiful in 2 to 3 weeks. Pour off the water and replace, adding freshly boiled wheat grains every few weeks. Sub-culture by introducing amoebae into newly prepared medium as for the initial culture at 2 to 3 monthly intervals or when small Metazoa (oligochaetes, crustaceans, rotifers) become common.

The medium described on pp. 400–1 is more precise and reliable.

Some other freshwater amoebae

Other amoebae, worth comparing with *A. proteus*, may be collected, especially in the early spring and autumn from drainage cuttings in birch, elder, and willow woods, from rain or snow pools, or from moss clumps which have stood for some time under water. Some of the species may also be found in soil, including the damp soil and weed at the bottoms of tanks used for keeping amphibians. From such sources collect sediment, some soil, decaying leaves, filamentous algae and water, dispose the samples in shallow glass vessels with some boiled wheat grains and treat as for *A. proteus* (*v. sup.*).

Many of the amoebae found will be difficult or impossible to identify specifically, though often they may be allocated to a genus or a group of genera. Points to be noted are the structure of the nucleus, shape of the pseudopodia, nature of food and other inclusions, commonest position of the contractile vacuole, and the appearance of the hind end of the organism. The last is often more or less drawn out into a number of processes, varying from short papillae to long filaments, constituting the so-called uroid; it is a region of posterior gelation, usually sticky and trailing material behind it. The presence of a uroid behind and an actively advancing end in front confers on a moving amoeba some degree of polarity and this may be very striking (see pp. 22 and 26), but it is doubtful whether the polarity of most progressing amoebae is anything but temporary (cf. the views of Bovee (1949), and Kudo (1952)). The taxonomic works by Leidy (1879), Penard (1902), Cash *et al.* (1905, 1919), Schaeffer (1926), and Bovee (1953) may be consulted, but the student must bear in mind that many species have been imperfectly described in the past, few have been adequately studied and there is undoubtedly a great deal of overlapping among the species of the literature. Two contrasting and fairly well-defined forms are offered here as examples.

Mayorella vespertilio (Penard)

This is a large amoeba, about 200 μ long, said to prefer marshy places, but certainly found elsewhere, in fresh water and in soil, including that of potted plants. When not actively moving about, it extrudes long, slender, radiating and usually hyaline pseudopodia. When on the crawl (Fig. 7), the pseudopodia are conical, connected by a clear web of ectoplasm, suggesting the outline of a bat's wing (and hence the name, *vespertilio*). It is very voracious and the endoplasm may be crammed with food, commonly diatoms and green algae, but sometimes other Protozoa (for cannibalism, see Lapage, 1922). According to Lapage, *M. vespertilio* captures its food in the same way as *Amoeba proteus*, but Ivanić (1933d, 1936a) claimed that there was a more or less deeply excavated protoplasmic invagination or temporary cytostome through which food was ingested; the question deserves more attention. There may be several contractile vacuoles which as they grow tend to be confined to the posterior end of the animal, and as one bursts its place is taken by another, formed by the growth of one or of the fusion of several smaller vacuoles (Hyman, 1936). The nucleus is conspicuous, with a glimmering, highly refringent karyosome, very striking in the living organism; the membrane is not easy to detect; between it and the karyosome is a clear zone containing a few granules. A spherical cyst with a gelatinous envelope was described by Doflein (1907).

Thecamoeba verrucosa (Ehrenberg)

When extended in motion, this large amoeba (100–200 μ long) is oval or roughly oblong in shape (Fig. 8). It progresses by means of a single large ectoplasmic pseudopodium, which fans out in front. The ectoplasm may occupy a very extensive area, so that the endoplasm is, so to speak, left on one side or to the rear of the animal. The characteristic feature of the genus is the presence of ectoplasmic excrescences, pulled out into wavy lines over the surface of the body, or contracted, when the amoeba is stationary, into

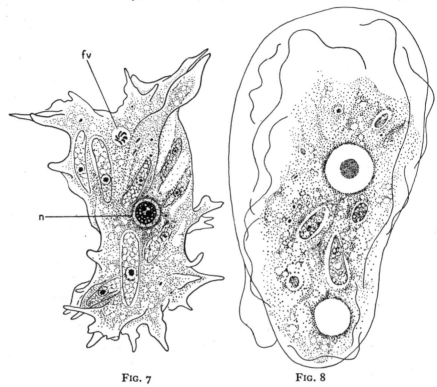

FIG. 7   FIG. 8

FIG. 7. *Mayorella vespertilio*. Fixed B, stained Dobell's Iron Haematin. × 500.
(Original: D. L. M.)

fv, food vacuole; *n*, nucleus.

FIG. 8. *Thecamoeba verrucosa*. The living animal. × 500. (Original.)

hyaline warts. The nucleus is spherical, with a karyosome, less conspicuous than in the foregoing species, but unquestionably recognizable in the living organism. The species usually feeds on algae. but is also carnivorous.

Permanent preparations

As for *Amoeba proteus* (p. 16).

Pelomyxa palustris Greeff

This highly distinctive and sometimes gigantic amoeba may be found in sediment from stagnant water rich in organic matter. Debris and water from suitable ponds should be brought to the laboratory and allowed to settle for several days, then 'the organisms . . . buried in different parts of the debris move up to the surface of the bottom mud . . . and crawl on the

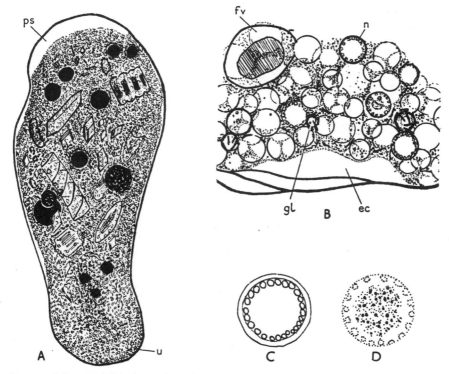

FIG. 9. *Pelomyxa palustris*. A, the living animal ×c. 100; B, portion of margin with part of pseudopodium ×c. 1000; C, living nucleus in optical section with peripheral granules and clear central zone; D, the same after fixation and Feulgen's reaction, showing appearance of central body containing F+ granules (cf. Fig. 5B). (A modified after Leidy; B simplified after Okada; C and D after Kudo.)

ec, ectoplasm; *fv*, food vacuole; *gl*, glycogen bodies surrounded with bacteria; *n*, nucleus; *ps*, pseudopodium; *u*, uroid.

glass wall of the container day and night. After a week or so, the organisms descend to, and remain on, the surface of the mud' (Kudo, 1957, whose paper gives much valuable information).

*P. palustris** (Figs. 9, 10) usually measures from 0·5 to 2·5 mm when outstretched, though considerably greater lengths have been reported. The

* The giant amoeba called *P. carolinensis*, though multinucleate, is closely related to *Amoeba proteus*, with which it shares the peculiar multipolar mitotic spindle (Kudo, 1947) and many other characters (Andresen, 1956); the two forms should be more closely united. The position of *P. palustris* is at present difficult to decide but the work of Kudo (1957) at least suggests, from the nuclear cytology, a closer affinity with the *Amoeba proteus* group than at first glance appears; see p. 23.

animal moves forward by means of a single broad hyaline pseudopodium, so short as to appear a narrow crescent in front of the dark, opaque endoplasm. The opposite end is often more or less constricted from the rest of the animal by a waist and forms a bulbous uroid or urosphere, very viscous and commonly drawn out into a fringe of papillate or digitiform processes (Mast, 1934); though sometimes collected under the name *P. villosa* such stages are really no more than forms often assumed by *P. palustris*. With a single anterior pseudopodium, a distinct uroid, and a constant endoplasmic flow from posterior to anterior, *P. palustris* displays a well-defined polarity, and this reflects an axial gradient demonstrable by increasing

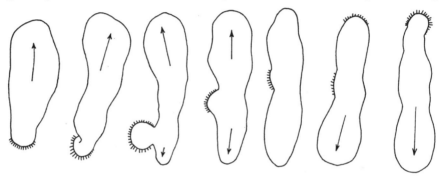

FIG. 10. *Pelomyxa palustris*. Outlines of a moving animal during reversal, showing loss of the old and development of the new uroid with their villous appendages. The arrows show the direction of endoplasm flow. ×*c.* 25. (After Kudo.)

sensitivity, maximal in the uroid, to Neutral Red and other vital dyes (Hollande and Guilcher, 1945). The polarity can be destroyed, as when the animal reverses its direction and the uroid, with its villi, disappears from one end and is formed at the other (Fig. 10); if the uroid is cut off and reattached to the anterior end, the endoplasmic flow is again reversed (Okada, 1930, 1932).

The endoplasm, which is opaque, and grey, green, yellow, or brown, is very fluid and remarkable for the number and density of its inclusions (Fig. 9B). The animal ingests everything it comes across and in the food vacuoles may be detected the remains of desmids, diatoms, ciliates, rotifers, entomostracan crustaceans, with scraps of decaying leaves, wood fibres, sand grains, and mud particles. All this is taken in at the viscous posterior end of the body from which hyaline processes extend to clasp the food (e.g. filamentous algae), one end of which becomes involved in the forward endoplasmic flow, so that the rest is gradually drawn in. Ingestion is very slow and Kudo thought that the animal could deal only with inactive material. The endoplasm also contains numerous shiny, oval glycogen bodies, and often associated with these, and with the nuclei, are rod-like bacteria, *Cladothrix pelomyxae*, which are said to be symbiotic (Leiner and Wohlfeil, 1953). There are many fluid-filled vacuoles, but none is contractile. The nuclei (Fig. 9 C, D) are very numerous and small. The inner surface of the nuclear membrane is lined with peripheral granules and the centre of the living nucleus appears clear or faintly reticular, but on fixation a central mass is precipitated which contains F + material (Kudo, 1957); the structure resembles that of *Amoeba proteus* (pp. 12, 16). A remarkable feature is the rarity of mitosis which has scarcely ever been seen even in studies extending over many years.

Pelomyxa multiplies by plasmotomy, breaking up into 2, 3, or occasionally more masses measuring anything between 50 and 200 μ and each containing a number of nuclei. According to Hollande, cysts with a diameter of 225 μ are formed at times; they have a very tough envelope and contain 'symbiotic' bacteria.

The life-cycle is known but sketchily. At one time it was supposed that *Pelomyxa* produced little amoebulae internally and that they escaped and became gametes. Undoubtedly the large amoeba is liable to infection with parasites, which break out at intervals; one of these, *Vahlkampfia* (? *Naegleria*) *pelomyxae*, is a *limax* type of amoeba with a flagellated phase and the other, *Amoebophilus destructor*, a pathogen of uncertain systematic position; it seems likely, as maintained by Hollande, that failure to recognize these organisms has given rise to misunderstanding in the past (see Hollande, 1945; Hollande and Guilcher, 1945).

Culture

In jars of its original water and debris, *P. palustris* may live from 1 to 8 weeks. Most workers have had difficulty in maintaining it in the laboratory, but Kudo (1957) established mass and clone cultures by the following simple method. The type of container is important. For mass cultures, a Carrel tissue-culture flask, 5 cm in diameter and 1·4 cm high, was filled with filtered lake water (from the source of the collection); *Spirogyra*, ground or cut into minute pieces, was added as food; and 30 to 50 well-fed amoebae introduced. The flasks were kept at 18° to 24° C in moist chambers in diffuse daylight. Other filamentous algae make suitable food.

The *limax* amoebae

Small amoebae, ranging from about 3 μ to 15 μ in length, and creeping forward by means of a single large hyaline pseudopodium (Fig. 11), are very commonly seen in infusions of hay, leaves, or faeces. The bodies are usually round and compact, apart from the conspicuous pseudopodium, and contain a single vesicular nucleus in which is a large, refringent karyosome, visible in the living animal and heavily basophil in permanent preparations.

Many amoebae, the amoeboflagellates, have transient stages in which they produce a small number of flagella (Fig. 13). Most, if not all, form spherical, strongly walled cysts, often with pores and very resistant (Fig. 12). Such small, slug-like forms are collectively known as *limax* amoebae. They are very common in soil, in fresh and especially in stagnant and foul waters, and in infusions; a few are marine; some are parasitic, e.g. in tipulid larva (Mackinnon, 1914*a*), on fish gills (Chatton, 1910), in the alimentary canal of lizards (Dobell, 1914) or in other Protista, such as diatoms (Zuelzer, 1927) and foraminiferans (Le Calvez, 1940). Owing to the viability of their cysts and the readiness with which they hatch and multiply in a great variety of media, they are common contaminants of insufficiently protected cultures of other Protozoa. It is important to be able to detect them.

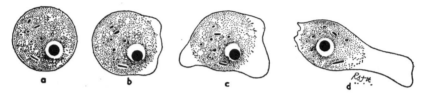

FIG. 11. A *limax amoeba*. Inception of movement from the resting state. Pseudopodia are protruded at various points on the periphery. Some are withdrawn but one elongates in the direction of movement. At *d* the animal has attained the characteristic *limax* facies with a single conspicuous ectoplasmic pseudopodium, uroid, and vesicular nucleus. × 1750. (Original.)

This is not difficult. *Limax* amoebae are easily recognized as such. It is much more difficult, and it is sometimes impossible, to identify them specifically. The term *limax* refers to the habit and it cuts across the taxonomic classification to include amoebae drawn from a number of genera in at least two families. Nearly all the trophic forms are practically identical with very similar cysts; both stages are small. Classification is awkwardly based on stages in the life-history which may be brief and rarely encountered, as, for instance, the shape of the mitotic figure and the number of flagella in the flagellated phase. Few of the life-histories have been fully reported. The family Vahlkampfiidae includes all those forms with promitosis, that is, a nuclear division in which the membrane and the karyosome persist and the latter plays an important part in division (Fig. 14); there are generally supposed to be 3 genera, *Naegleria* (p. 26), with usually 2 flagella and no cytostome, *Tetramitus*, with 4 flagella and a cytostome, and *Vahlkampfia*, which is like *Naegleria* but has no flagellated phase (Calkins, 1913). Against this, Grassé (*Traité*, 1953, I. ii, p. 46, footnote) considers that all the forms adequately studied are really amoeboflagellates, so that the genus *Vahlkampfia* really consists of *limax* amoebae with a promitosis in which the flagellated phase has not yet been seen. Some *limax* species belong to the family Hartmannellidae, having a conventional mitotic figure with a spindle (for taxonomy, see Volkonsky, 1931). As already stated, accurate determination of these most common animals is extremely difficult and uncertain and there is a great deal of overlapping among the named forms. An attempt at classification of some of the soil species is offered by Singh (1952).

Culture

Limax amoebae are very easy to cultivate. They do well on nutrient agar, on liquid media such as *hsm* (p. 417) where they multiply profusely in the bacterial mat which forms as a surface scum, and in hay infusions or faecal suspensions (p. 404); in general, they should be sub-cultured every 7 to 10 days. They may be isolated from soil by the method given on p. 408. They may be grown in monaxenic culture on *Aerobacter* as food and may be isolated from other bacteria by the migration procedure given by Neff for obtaining *Acanthomoeba* in axenic culture; the only difference is that here a monaxenic culture is obtained (see Neff, 1957).

Wet and permanent preparations

A small amount of the surface scum from 3 or 4 day Petri dishes or tubes is sucked up in a pipette with a little of the underlying liquid, distributed on No. o cover slips, inverted on to cavity slides or over polythene rings, and sealed. Within a few minutes very numerous amoebae begin to emerge from the specks of bacterial scum and creep about in the surrounding liquid; they are now firmly attached to the slips and may be watched for hours or, when well extended, fixed in their natural positions (see below).

To obtain flagellated stages from amoebae, it is simply necessary to flood with distilled or pond water, but the time taken to enflagellate depends on the time of year, temperature, and condition of the culture. Cover slopes with water, or remove scum from the top of a liquid medium, place in the bottom of a tube and dilute five or six times with water. Examine hourly. Some amoebae may have grown flagella at the end of an hour and most should have done so in 4 hours (for details see under *Naegleria*, p. 26, and Willmer, 1956).

For permanent preparations fix well-expanded populations in B or S+A, or, for better cytoplasmic preservation, weak Flemming. Stain in H.H. The extrakaryosomatic material in the nucleus is difficult to reveal and is faithfully shown only by Feulgen or a similar technique, such as Azure A or Thionine with SO_2 after hydrolysis (for methods, see p. 437), though it may be shown in haematoxylin preparations of some of the larger forms such as *Naegleria gruberi*.

Naegleria gruberi (Schardinger)

This large amoeboflagellate is easily obtained from well-manured soil (see p. 408) and is likely to appear in cultures containing invertebrate or vertebrate faeces. All stages of the living organism may be plainly seen in hanging drops on No. o cover slips; they adhere well to the slips and make good material for permanent preparations. (For methods, see p. 428.) Good accounts exist of the morphology (Wilson, 1916), nuclear division (Rafalko, 1947), and enflagellation (Willmer, 1956).

The living organism and permanent preparations

After mounting in a hanging drop, the animals must be given a few minutes to recover from the mechanical shock. At rest, the amoeba is a granular ball; in movement, it glides in typical *limax* fashion by means of a single, large pseudopodium (Figs. 11; 12A). It may attain a length of 40 μ but smaller forms, 6 to 10 μ long, are quite common. The nucleus is prominent, with a single, conspicuous karyosome, surrounded by a halo. In most *limax* amoebae, this is all that can be seen under ordinary optical conditions, but in *N. gruberi* it is ordinarily possible to distinguish a ring of fine granules outside the halo; these constitute the only F + material in the nucleus. At the posterior end there is a uroid, which appears to be sticky and relatively stiff. In the moving organism, the sequence of *limax* pseudopodium, nucleus, contractile vacuole(s), and uroid confers on the body an apparent polarity, but it is doubtful whether this is to any degree lasting. *Naegleria*, when it comes to rest, withdraws its pseudopodia and becomes spherical, or from time to time it floats freely in water with five or six pseudopodia radiating bluntly from it; it has never been determined whether the anterior end which it forms after passing through these experiences is the same as the one which it lost before them.

Enflagellation is induced by flooding the solid slopes or diluting the liquid medium on which the amoeboid stages have been growing with distilled water (see p. 25). The first phase of transformation is an extension of the uroid by long, filiform ectoplasmic processes, which come and go, are retracted, bent, and reformed as the animal moves (Fig. 13, *a–c*), and the flagella appear among these as thicker filaments, which immediately begin to beat, while the filopodia are withdrawn (*d, e*) as also are the anterior lobopodia. Wilson (1916) and Rafalko (1947) regarded 2 as the normal number of flagella in this species (*h*), but Willmer found that 3 or 4 were commoner; it is possible that strains vary in this respect. The flagella become longer and finer and migrate in a group from their point of origin to the old anterior end, while the contractile vacuole remains behind in its typical position, so that the former polarity is resumed (*f, g*). As the flagella

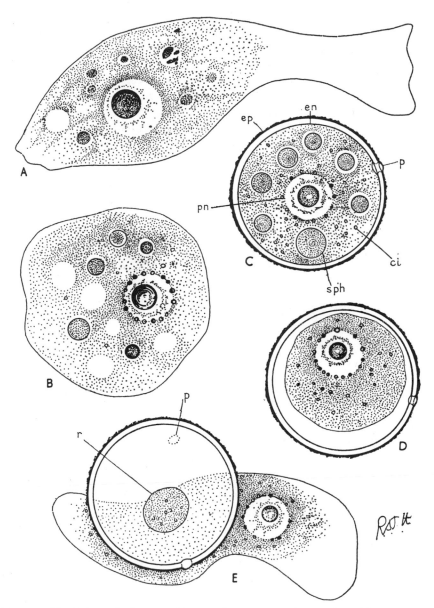

Fig. 12. *Naegleria gruberi.* A, trophic amoeba; B, precystic amoeba with perinuclear granules and Neutral Red spherules; C, young cyst, with contained amoeba filling the cavity and still with spherules; D, mature cyst, with contracted amoeba which has exhausted its spherules; E, excysting amoeba: the karyosome, as in the encysted forms, has smaller proportions than in the trophic form, and note some cytoplasm still in the cyst. ×4,000. (Original, after material supplied by Dr. K. Vickerman.)

ci, cytoplasmic inclusion; *en,* endocyst; *ep,* epicyst; *p,* pore; *pn,* perinuclear granule; *r,* cytoplasm still in cyst; *sph,* Neutral Red spherule.

beat faster and faster, the body spins and at last breaks free of the substrate
and swims freely in the water. It seems doubtful whether in this stage the
animal normally feeds, though once Rafalko observed a flagellate ingesting
bacteria. The stage is brief. Under experimental conditions it appears as a
response to dilution of food and other elements in the medium and it is
generally thought of as a transient development enabling the organism to
move rapidly out of an environment which is in some way defective, for
example, in food or salts. The flagella are rarely retained for more than

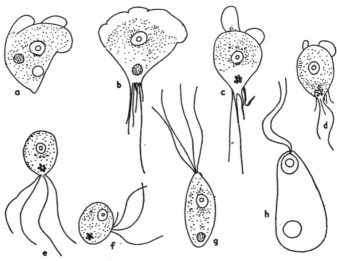

FIG. 13. *Naegleria gruberi*. Enflagellation. *a–c*, amoeboid phase: *b* and *c* have long
filiform extensions behind the uroid; *d*, the first 2 flagella appear among the filiform appendages, which shorten; *e*, 4 flagella have developed posteriorly: *f*, the flagella are moving
towards the anterior pole; *g*, the definitive flagellated form which has regained the polarity
of the amoeboid phase, with locomotor organs anterior, nucleus more or less central, and
contractile vacuole posterior; *h*, flagellate phase with 2 flagella. (Somewhat simplified: *a–g* after Willmer; *h* after Rafalko.)

24 hours, at the end of which time the organism settles and puts out a
pseudopodium. The flagella are absorbed, they may either swell at the base
with an accompanying loss of length until they are totally withdrawn, or
they may play against the body and eventually fuse with it from the base
outwards.

N. *gruberi* very readily forms cysts.* In liquid media, encystation is continuous, that is, amoebae and cysts formed by them are always present; on
agar plates, encystation is a mass phenomenon. At 25° C on 0·5 per cent
peptone agar, the full cycle of excystation, trophic life of the amoeba, and

* I am much indebted to Dr. Keith Vickerman for permission to draw upon his
unpublished accounts of encystation, the cyst, and excystation in this species, and for use
of his drawings in preparing Fig. 12. R. S. J. H.

encystation is completed in 24 hours, and strains grown in this way provide the simplest means of study. Before encystation there is rapid growth and division and most of the precystic amoebae accumulate in their cytoplasm spheres of some substance that stains readily with Neutral Red. Their significance is uncertain; they are not invariably present and they may occur in the medium outside the organisms; possibly they represent compacted food, lying in vacuoles, which in some cases is ejected and in others retained and finally used up within the cyst. The organism stops moving and feeding and loses volume by the active discharge of water from numerous contractile vacuoles. The cytoplasm becomes more refractile. There is a slight diminution in the size of the nucleus, more especially of the karyosome, while, at the same time, refringent granules are formed at the nuclear membrane (Fig. 12B). A tough outer membrane is formed first; it is not perfectly smooth and appears to be sticky, with debris adhering to it. The thicker inner wall is formed later from the refractile cortex of the encysted organism, and there are some 3 to 6 pores, each closed with a plug. The wall is completely hyaline and the contents can be seen through it (Fig. 12C). Cysts are almost invariably spherical and vary in diameter, even within the same clone; they measure 6 to 16 μ, with a mean of 10 μ. In the newly formed cyst (C), the organism fills the whole cavity. The refractile neutral red spherules disappear after 24 to 30 hours and the cytoplasm is then seen to be highly granular. The body of the animal retracts from the cyst wall and, after loss of all the spherules, is ripe, that is, ready to excyst.

Excystation may sometimes be induced simply by spreading ripe cysts on a thin film of fresh 0·5 per cent peptone agar. Portions of the film are cut out, covered with No. 0 slips, and examined at hourly intervals. The contained amoeba swells to occupy most of the cavity and emerges through one of the pores; it may at first attempt evacuation through 2 pores at the same time, eventually settling on one or the other. The plugs are sometimes seen within a vacated cyst but may also be discharged outwards. Violent streaming movements within the extruded pseudopodium assist in extracting more of the amoeba which then finds some purchase on the substrate or on part of the external cyst wall; then the rest of the body is withdrawn during a period which may last up to an hour, in which the organism may drag the almost empty cyst around with it. The metacystic amoeba is small, the karyosome larger than in the encysted form, and the perinuclear granules less evident: their eventual fate is unknown but they are not seen in the normal trophic amoeba.

Permanent preparations of cysts are less easy to obtain than of trophic amoebae, owing to the thickness of the wall. Fix in Carnoy. After staining, dehydration must be slow and gradual or the contents collapse. Haematoxylin staining shows that the karyosome, perinuclear granules, and spherules are intensely basophil; the chromatin outside the karyosomatic halo stains poorly. A better picture is obtained by staining in 0·25 per cent Thionine for 10 minutes; examine in water: the perinuclear granules and karyosome stain pale blue, and the circle of chromatin granules rose pink. Cysts stained in this way should be examined in water or mounted in glycerine jelly.

The nuclear division of *Naegleria* is promitotic and in essentials is as follows (Fig. 14). The karyosome persists throughout division, divides itself, and plays an important part in the separation of the chromosomes; likewise, the nuclear membrane persists. Both these structures are F— and the only F+ material, the source of the chromosomes, is found in the perikaryosomatic granules already figured for the interphase nucleus (Fig. 12A). In prophase the karyosome elongates and narrows at the waist,

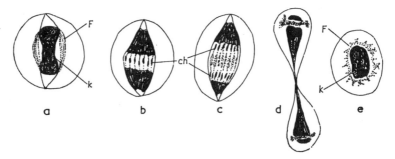

FIG. 14. *Naegleria gruberi*. Promitosis. *a*, the nucleus in prophase; *b*, metaphase; *c*, anaphase; *d*, telophase; *e*, return to the interphase state (cf. Fig. 12A). (Simplified, after Rafalko.)

ch, chromosomes; *F*, F+material; *k*, karyosome (basophil and F—).

forming a dumb-bell; this structure is highly basophil and is very commonly the only evidence of the occurrence of promitosis seen in ordinary haematoxylin preparations and therefore represents the sole means of diagnosing a member of the family Vahlkampfiidae. Besides the dumb-bell, lying in its waist, the F+ granules arrange themselves as strands and from these the chromosomes are formed (Fig. 14, *a*, *b*). Metaphase and anaphase (*c*) are rapid and rarely seen; telophase figures (*d*) are commoner. There are said to be 14 to 16 chromosomes. Rafalko (1947) reports a wealth of detail which few, if any, students will have an opportunity to confirm.

Incertae Sedis: *Leptomyxa reticulata* Goodey

This is a gigantic amoeboid organism encountered in soil samples (for methods, see p. 408) and belonging to the little-known group, called the Protomyxidea, of doubtful position (see Valkanov, 1940; Singh, 1948 *a*, *b*; Grassé's *Traité*, I, ii).

The living organism

In good cultures, *L. reticulata* may reach a size of 3 mm or more, though in the soil it is more likely to be nearer to 1 mm. Like *Pelomyxa* it is multi-nucleated, but otherwise resembles no other amoeba so far considered. Its body is spread out as a thin sheet of almost transparent protoplasm with branching, finely pointed, delicate pseudopodia which tend to inter-lace and fuse so as to form a network (Fig. 15A). At the advancing edge of the body, clear ectoplasm is distinct from the more granular endoplasm: but, in general, the organism shows little progressive movement in a given

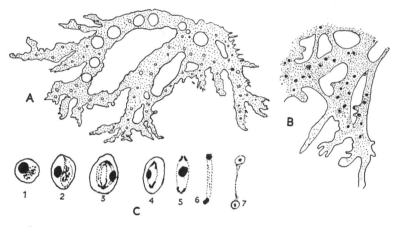

FIG. 15. *Leptomyxa reticulata.* A, living organism, spread out in water. ×150. Note spaces enclosed by converging pseudopodia and very numerous small contractile vacuoles. B, Portion of marginal region, stained Iron Haematoxylin: most of the dark dots are karyo-somes of nuclei. ×450. C, Some stages in nuclear division, stained Iron Haematoxylin. ×1,100. The nuclear membrane persists until late anaphase. (A and B after Goodey; C after Singh.)

direction. There are very numerous, tiny contractile vacuoles distributed all through the body. *Leptomyxa* will eat small amoebae and flagellates; but probably its main food is bacterial. When in the active condition it multi-plies by plasmotomy; that is, its body breaks up into a number of parts, each taking with it a quota of nuclei and contractile vacuoles. In culture, individuals may come together and fuse; but this phenomenon, plasmo-gamy, does not imply any sexual union. Nuclear division (Fig. 15C), which is mitotic, is rarely seen, but it has been briefly described by Singh (1948b). Multinucleate cysts with double envelopes may be developed in clusters: up to 40 of these may be formed from one individual. Sometimes cysts are formed by part of a trophic *Leptomyxa* and left behind it while it flows on. Transplantation of the cysts to fresh culture media usually brings about the hatching of the enclosed organisms.

Permanent preparations and culture

See Singh (1948 *a*, *b*).

Entozoic amoebae

The term 'entozoic' is applied to an organism that is found living within another, its host, without implying any special degree of dependence or pathogenicity in the relationship, and is on that account to be preferred to the word 'parasitic' which, though still generally useful where no ambiguity is possible, may suggest that the entozoic organism is somehow harmful to its host. In fact, as is now well known, the great majority of 'parasites' are perfectly harmless, being well adapted to their habit, and this with few exceptions is true of the amoebae. Most of the entozoic amoebae are grouped in a single family, the Entamoebidae, a procedure which gives a misleading impression of their phylogeny, for many of them have practically no more in common than the facts that they are amoebae and are parasitic.

Almost all of them produce cysts (Figs. 16 c, d; 20)—*Entamoeba gingivalis* from the human mouth is an exception—and their size, shape, and the number of their nuclei when mature are good taxonomic characters. For many species cysts are the most accessible stage in the life-history and hence are widely used in diagnosis.

Entamoeba histolytica, the causal organism of amoebic dysentery in man, is undoubtedly the most studied of all parasitic amoebae, but for various reasons it is not the most suitable form with which to introduce the group in the laboratory. *E. invadens*, from snakes and other reptiles, is morphologically indistinguishable from *E. histolytica* at every stage in its life-history, and has the advantages that it is cultivable and active at room temperatures and cannot infect human beings.

Entamoeba invadens* Rodhain

This interesting amoeba, first noted in 1934 by Rodhain, has now been described from a variety of reptiles from Zoological Gardens, in which it is highly pathogenic, producing lesions in the stomach, intestine, and liver; little is known of wild infections. The life-history is well described by Geiman and Ratcliffe (1936) and for a host list see Hill and Neal (1953). Cultures of *E. invadens* (see p. 416) may be initiated from faeces of diseased

---

* *sic*—the type species is *E. coli* Casagrandi and Barbagallo. The generic name *Endamoeba* sometimes used for the *histolytica* group is, in fact, the name of a different genus of which *Endamoeba blattae* Leidy (see p. 40) is the type. See the *Memorandum on the genus Entamoeba* which forms an appendix to Dobell (1938) and Opinion 312, dated 17 December 1954, rendered by the International Commission on Zoological Nomenclature.

snakes or from fragments of infected tissues taken at autopsy, but those who have no opportunity to try this method should obtain strains from research institutes.

The living organism

A small quantity of material from the bottom of a 2 to 7-day culture should be mounted and sealed at once. The amoeba (Fig. 16 A, B), measuring on the average some 10 μ to 20 μ, is very active, thrusting out clear

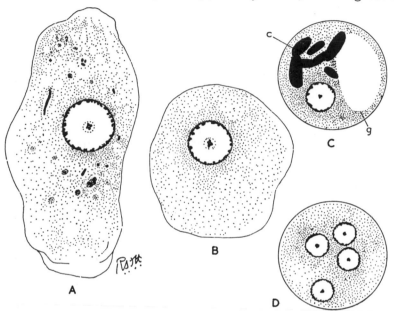

FIG. 16. *Entamoeba invadens.* A, trophic amoeba. ×4,000; B, precystic amoeba. ×4,000; C, young cyst. ×2,000; D, ripe cyst. ×2,000. (Original.)

c, chromatoid body; g, glycogen vacuole.

pseudopodia explosively except when pursuing a course, when the motion is more slug-like, though still lively; the pseudopodia are shorter than those of *Amoeba proteus* and smaller than the single advancing pseudopodium of a *limax* amoeba. Endoplasmic streaming is very pronounced. The contractile vacuole, characteristic of forms living in a hypotonic medium, is here missing. The amoeba engulfs bacteria and starch grains and it may take to cannibalism and consume its own cysts. The nucleus is vesicular and it is usually possible to observe the fine, refringent, hyaline peripheral granules and the central karyosome.

In natural infections, cysts more often occur in the diseased liver and colon than in the stomach and intestine. In culture, amoebae will not encyst freely unless supplied with adequate carbohydrate in an acceptable form, which is ordinarily rice starch (p. 414). Encysting amoebae may be distinguished from the trophic forms by their smaller size, absence of food inclusions, and clear cytoplasm; such precystic amoebae contain diffuse glycogen, which may be revealed by mounting in Lugol's Iodine Solution (p. 424), which colours it brown. The glycogen soon becomes more localized and the edges of its mass better defined while, at the same time, a number of chromatoid bodies, usually blunt rods with rounded ends, appear in the cytoplasm; these chromatoid bodies, which are characteristic of some entozoic cysts and are stained an opaque black, are very conspicuous in iron haematoxylin preparations; in living cysts, they are refringent, faintly silvery. Barker and Deutsch (1958) have produced evidence that they consist of RNA together with unspecified proteins. The young cyst is generally spherical, hyaline, and smaller than a trophic amoeba (about 14μ on the average with a range of 11 to 20 μ, according to Geimann and Ratcliffe): it contains a large glycogen vacuole, a number of chromatoid bodies, and a single nucleus (Fig. 16 c). This last divides, typically twice, to produce 4 nuclei (D). The chromatoid bodies and glycogen eventually disappear and the ripe cyst must soon afterwards hatch or die. The reserves of the similar cysts of *E. histolytica* are ordinarily exhausted after a fortnight at room temperature and few survive much longer (Dobell, 1927, 1928; Dobell and Laidlaw, 1926). It is to be noted that the cysts of the *histolytica* group are relatively delicate, thin-walled structures; they are, of course, the distributive, infective phase of the life-history, but they are not drought-resistant and drying kills them at once (Dobell, 1928; Hill and Neal, 1953).

The process of excystation is highly characteristic of *E. invadens* and its relatives and it may be observed *in vitro* from 6 to 8 hours after transferring cysts, which should be mature and numerous, from old to fresh medium. The first sign of activity is a streaming movement in the encysted amoeba, which pulls away from the cyst wall and begins to move about within it. Hyaline pseudopodia travel round the organism, exploring the wall, as it were, until one of them becomes applied to a point on its internal surface. Shortly afterwards the tip of the pseudopodium appears outside the cyst, and some of the organism squeezes after it, through a previously invisible pore; by thrusting itself backwards and forwards, the whole of the organism, or all except the tip of the tail, works its way out of the cyst. The entire process takes about a quarter of an hour at room temperature. What emerges is a single quadrinucleate amoeba, not a number of uninucleate amoebulae, and the excysted organism by mitosis and division gives rise to 8 young amoebae which, in nature, set up new infections.

Trophic and precystic amoebae and cysts in all stages of development may be seen in cultures fed on rice starch and the process of hatching may be followed as explained in the previous paragraph, but it is improbable that much, if anything at all, will be seen of metacystic development, which has been described by Geiman and Ratcliffe from material taken from infected animals. By mixing a small drop of material from a culture, or from an autopsy or faecal specimen, with a drop of iodine solution, the nuclei and glycogen vacuoles are shown up plainly after a few minutes; the chromatoid bodies, unstained, are best seen mounted in the culture medium or saline solution. As many cysts as possible should be drawn with the aid of a camera lucida and their measurements recorded: examination for cysts is the usual means of diagnosing infections of entozoic amoebae.

Permanent preparations

Leave spreads of living material to settle while the amoebae expand in natural attitudes on the cover slips, but do not allow to dry. Fix by dropping face downwards on to S+A or B; stain in Heidenhain's Iron or Dobell's Phosphotungstic Haematoxylin, and differentiate until the peripheral granules in the nucleus appear plainly.

Cultures

E. invadens is most conveniently cultivated in hsm+S (p. 417) at room temperature (10° to 20° C). It is anaerobic and lives in the bottom of the tube. Sub-culture every 7 to 10 days. Cysts may be stored in the refrigerator.

The histolytica group of amoebae

A considerable number of amoebae described under various names so closely resemble Entamoeba histolytica as to be morphologically indistinguishable from it at any of the known stages of their life-cycles. They are widely distributed and, with the exception of E. moshkovskii, which occurs in sewage and has not yet been connected with any host (Neal, 1953), they are entozoic. They have the following characters in common. The nucleus of the trophic form is vesicular, with a small, central karyosome; the peripheral granules are fine and, as seen in optical section, are arranged in a delicate chain. The cysts are spherical, refringent, typically developing 4 nuclei, though irregular numbers (most often 8 in E. histolytica) may occur; there is a glycogen vacuole; the chromatoid bodies are usually thick rods with bluntly rounded ends. In those forms in which excystation has been studied (E. histolytica, Dobell, 1928; E. invadens, E. moshkovskii, Neal, 1953) a single quadrinucleate, metacystic amoeba emerges by working its way through a minute pore in the cyst wall, and each of its nuclei then divides and so does the cytoplasm and in such a way that the products of each nuclear division are separated at the next cytoplasmic division, so that finally 8 uninucleate amoebulae result. The best account of the life-history is that of *E. histolytica* itself by Dobell (1928), and this paper, already a classic of protozoology, should be consulted.

Members of the *histolytica* group infect both invertebrate and vertebrate hosts, e.g. *E. aulostomi* occurs in the horse-leech, *Haemopis sanguisugae* (Bishop, 1932); *E. thomsoni* in the cockroach, *Periplaneta americana* (Lucas, 1927); *E. minchini* in tipulid larvae (Mackinnon, 1914 *a*, *b*); *E. invadens* in reptiles, *E. ranarum* (Figs. 17, 18) in frogs (Sanders, 1931), and *E. histo-*

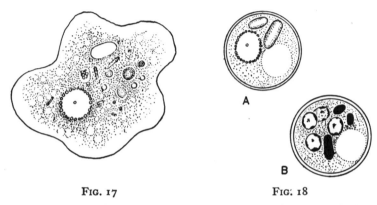

FIG. 17   FIG. 18

FIG. 17. *Entamoeba ranarum*: trophic amoeba. ×2,350. (After Dobell.)

FIG. 18. *Entamoeba ranarum*. A, living uninucleate cyst; B, quadrinucleate cyst, stained Iron Haematoxylin. ×1,350. (After Dobell.)

lytica in various Primates (Dobell, 1931) and in rats (Neal, 1948). Most of these amoebae live harmlessly in the gut and of the two pathogenic species it must be remembered that *E. histolytica* is characteristically a gut commensal, and only in a minority of cases causes symptoms of disease (Hoare, 1952 *a*, *b*, 1957*c*); our knowledge of the pathology of *E. invadens* is based almost entirely on studies on animals in captivity and more information is needed about wild infections.

The existence of a group of organisms so much alike that they would, on morphological grounds, be classified as members of a single species, though they often go by different names and even may exhibit biological differences which are genetically stable, raises the question, what is their status? In the first place, names have often been applied to identical amoebae for no other reason than that they have been observed in different hosts, and in some of these cases it can be shown experimentally that strains derived from one host can infect another; *E. histolytica* from man, for example, can infect various species of macaque monkeys, in which it is indistinguishable from the strains naturally occurring, sometimes under different names, in simian hosts; in fact, the *histolytica* forms of man and macaques are one and the same species, and ought to be known by the same name, that is *E. histolytica*, of which the various names like *E. nuttalli* and *E. duboscqi*, applied in the past to strains from monkeys, are synonyms (Dobell, 1931). In other cases, the facts are not established; for example, a *histolytica* form occurs as a parasite of opalinids from the rectum of various amphibians in both the Old and New Worlds (Carini and Reichenow, 1935; Chen and Stabler, 1936; Stabler and Chen, 1936); it has long been known that the rectum of amphibians is itself infected with a similar amoeba named *E. ranarum* (Figs. 17, 18), the life-history of which has been outlined by Sanders (1931), and it seems very possible that the amoeba of opalinids is either *E. ranarum* itself or a derivative distinguished from it by some biological characters so far undetermined. On the other hand, *E. ranarum* and *E. histolytica* are different at least to the extent that the trophic stages of the latter cannot survive at the same temperatures as the former, nor can its cysts infect tadpoles (Dobell, 1918). On these grounds Dobell regarded the 2 strains as good species, but systematists may be reluctant to adopt host-specificity as a useful taxonomic character if only because it is so laborious to determine.

The members of the group, isolated in different hosts by some degree of physiological disparity, are assumed to be evolving along divergent lines; but speciation is slow, partly because the hosts provide very stable environments, partly because speciation presumably does tend to be slow in asexually reproducing organisms. The degrees of difference between entozoic (or other) amoebae, just because they do reproduce asexually, cannot be submitted to any test of reproductive isolation; no group of amoebae may be thought of as possessing a common gene pool. For these reasons, the species are open to be named on a basis of convenience, and it might seem the wiser to require clear and readily observed differences between them. Yet in practice, names like *E. ranarum* and *E. invadens* and others of uncertain provenance are used for organisms showing only slight differences, which can be elicited only by experiment. The problem in general has been discussed by Hoare (1943, 1952c) and Sonneborn (1957); in approaching it, the student may be steadied by practical experience of some of the material in the laboratory. With this in mind, as many members of the *histolytica* group of amoebae as possible should be collected, drawn, and measured.

Culture and permanent preparations

E. aulostomi was grown by Bishop (1932) on inspissated horse serum slopes covered with 1 part inactivated horse serum to 10 parts of 0·5 per cent NaCl plus sterile rice starch, that is, on a sort of invertebrate version of HShs+S (see p. 414).

For *E. thomsoni*, see p. 416.

For *E. ranarum*, see p. 416.

E. histolytica grows at 37° C on *hsm*+S and the modifications of Boeck and Drobhlav's media proposed by Dobell and Laidlaw (1926). It should be noted that some strains of this species encyst *in vitro* only in the hands of very experienced workers.

Permanent preparations should be made as for *E. invadens* except that a different technique is needed to obtain well-expanded amoebae from homoiothermic hosts (Fig. 177, p. 415).

Entamoeba muris (Grassi) and the *coli* group of amoebae

Just as for *E. histolytica*, so a number of amoebae morphologically indistinguishable from *E. coli*, a common and harmless commensal of man and other Primates, have been described from various hosts, and we take as an example *E. muris* (see Neal, 1950). It occurs most abundantly in the caecum, but also elsewhere in the intestinal tract, of rats and mice, and similar amoebae have been reported from other rodents. Very different figures are given by the authors for the incidence of *E. muris* in wild rats (usually *Rattus norvegicus*) but between 10 and 20 per cent may be taken as reasonable; Elton, Ford, Baker, and Gardner (1931) found that of 597 wild mice and voles (*Apodemus sylvaticus*, *Clethrionomys* (*Evotomys*) *glareolus*, and *Microtus agrestis* (*M. hirtus*)) examined, nearly half were infected.

The amoebae of homoiothermic animals are far more difficult to observe in a natural state than those of poikilothermic hosts, as the former, on cooling, soon withdraw their pseudopodia and begin to deteriorate. Nevertheless, even without a warm stage, something may be seen of the living animal by using glassware kept in an incubator at 37° C till required and making rapid examinations.

Open a mouse or rat, dry, in a dish, remove the gut from just above the caecum to the posterior end and place it in a warm Petri dish. Keep it moist with warm Ringer's Solution. Open the caecum and dilute a little of its contents on a slide with Ringer's Solution; if positive, make mounts in iodine solution and warm Ringer's Solution and examine.

E. muris (Fig. 19) is commonly some 25 to 30 μ in diameter when rounded but considerably longer when extended. It moves by means of broad, ectoplasmic pseudopodia, and the endoplasm is stuffed with food vacuoles containing bacteria, yeasts, and flagellates from the alimentary canal of the host. The nucleus is larger and somewhat coarser than that of a *histolytica* type of amoeba, and has the karyosome eccentrically placed; the peripheral material tends to be in larger clumps than the delicate granules of *E. invadens*. The nucleus is often hidden by other endoplasmic contents but can usually be revealed by mounting in iodine.

The cysts, produced by precystic amoebae of relatively small size and with almost homogeneous cytoplasm, may occur among the trophic amoebae or in the posterior gut generally. Two races, producing cysts ranging about mean diameters of 17 μ and 14 μ respectively, were recognized by Neal. The typical cyst (Fig. 20) of the *coli* group is usually spherical, somewhat larger than a *histolytica* cyst, and rather more opaque. The glycogen vacuole is, at any rate in young cysts, less definite in outline. The chromatoid bodies are often flaky or splintered in appearance or, if rodlike, commonly have

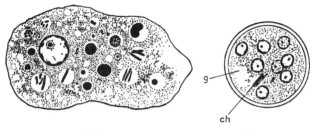

FIG. 19   FIG. 20

FIG. 19. *Entamoeba muris*: trophic amoeba. ×1,500. Stained Iron Haematoxylin. (Original: D. L. M.)

FIG. 20. *Entamoeba muris*: cyst. ×1,500. Stained Iron Haematoxylin. (Original: D. L. M.)

ch, chromatoid body; *g*, glycogen reserve.

irregular rather than rounded ends. The mature cyst has 8, rarely 16, nuclei. The metacystic development of *E. muris* is so far unknown, but in *E. coli* a multinucleate amoeba hatches by breaking down an extensive area of the cyst wall and then divides without mitoses into amoebulae (Dobell, 1938).

Permanent preparations

As for *E. histolytica* (p. 38).

NOTE. *The entozoic amoebae of man* are far better treated in textbooks of medical protozoology than they could be here, and the student should consult those of Hoare (1949) and Wenyon (1926) as well as Dobell's *The Amoebae Living in Man*, London (1919).

The entozoic amoebae of cockroaches

The hind-gut of cockroaches (*Blatta orientalis* and *Periplaneta americana*) harbours, in addition to various flagellates and ciliates (see *cockroaches*, under *host-lists* in Index), representatives of 4 genera of amoebae, and provides therefore very suitable material for class-work. Newly caught cockroaches are probably more often infected than those kept for some time in captivity; in the latter, Morris (1936) found that meat and other high protein foods, such as milk powder, helped to maintain good infections.

Remove the hind-gut of a cockroach, moisten with 0·5 per cent NaCl and clean away any adherent fat. To observe the living organisms, mounts, under No. 0 cover-slips, should be diluted with the salt solution; cysts should be examined in iodine.

Directions for staining all species will be found on p. 43.

Endamoeba blattae Leidy

The amoeba occurs in both the common cockroaches named above as well as in *Periplaneta australasiae*; it is said to be commoner in *Blatta*

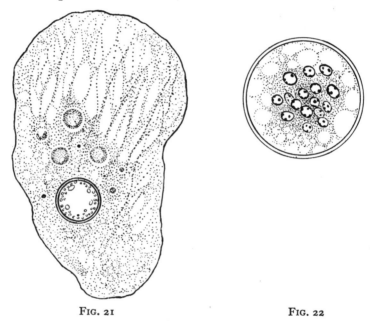

FIG. 21   FIG. 22

FIG. 21. *Endamoeba blattae*: trophic amoeba. × 1,000. (Original: D. L. M.)
FIG. 22. *Endamoeba blattae*: cyst. × 3,350. (Original: D. L. M.)

orientalis than in other species and in females than in males; 5 to 20 per cent of the animals may be infected.

The adult amoebae (Fig. 21) are usually about 50 μ in diameter, but may sometimes reach 150 μ; they are sluggish animals, often rounded up and motionless, but ovoid when in motion, and with a sticky uroid to which detritus adheres. Every now and then the amoeba anchors itself by this end and engulfs the attached food, mainly yeasts and bacteria. In action, and more particularly when forming pseudopodia, the amoeba displays a characteristic fibrous appearance, as if there were a supporting network of denser material through which the more liquid parts of the endoplasm stream fountain-wise from the uroid in the direction of the animal's movement; the streaming is not steady, but occurs in explosive surges.

The nucleus, 15 to 25 μ, may be spherical, but frequently shows a small papillate eminence at some point on its circumference. The membrane is thick and contains peripherally a zone of refringent granules and larger masses of siderophile material; there is no karyosome and the central region of the nucleus is clear and homogeneous in the living animal (Kudo, 1926c). The interphase nucleus is F— and the origin of the chromosomes is unknown; mitosis has been described by Meglitsch (1940).

Multiplication is by binary fission. The cysts (Fig. 22) are formed from small precystic amoebae containing as many as 16 or even more nuclei; further nuclear division occurs after encystation and the mature cyst may contain 30 or more nuclei.

It will be evident from the foregoing that *E. blattae* is an unusual amoeba, and a convincing account of its life-history is very much needed, the more especially as it is the type species of its genus (see Thomson and Lucas, 1926, and p. 32, footnote). The existing accounts should be treated with reserve; some include descriptions of sexual phenomena which cannot be accepted without better proofs, while others appear to be confused by the importation into the life-history of stages that almost certainly belong to other amoebae, which may accompany it in nature. A successful solution to the problem could presumably be based on the study of a 'pure' line *in vitro*, but so far it has proved impossible to cultivate this species. In our present ignorance, it is difficult to determine the relationship between *E. blattae* and various amoebae described by Kirby (1927) from termites and which he placed in the same genus, but from his descriptions of their nuclei it does not seem to be a close one and the whole group is plainly in need of further investigation.

Entamoeba thomsoni Lucas

This is a *histolytica*-like amoeba (Fig. 23), usually 15 to 25 μ in diameter when rounded, and so recognizably much smaller than *Endamoeba blattae*. According to Lucas (1927), infections are common—she gives no figures—but not very heavy. The animal has a habit of attaching itself by one end, on which it twists and turns, with endoplasmic streaming towards the free end (Fig. 24). The nucleus is about 6 μ in diameter, with a central karyosome and peripheral granules. Cysts are quadrinucleate and 11 to 16 μ in diameter; more information is needed about the occurrence of a race with smaller cysts (8 μ) mentioned by Lucas; no chromatoid bodies have been described.

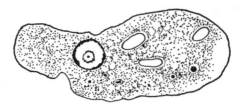

FIG. 23. *Entamoeba thomsoni*. Stained amoeba.
× 1,100. (Modified after Lucas.)

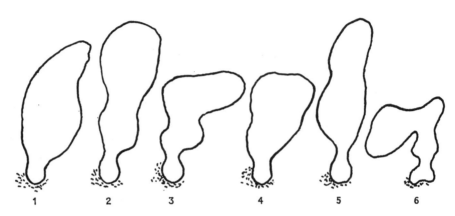

FIG. 24. *Entamoeba thomsoni*. Series of six outline drawings of a living amoeba, made at intervals of 30 seconds. They show the characteristic attitudes assumed by this species when attached to the substratum by its 'foot'. (Slightly modified after Lucas.)

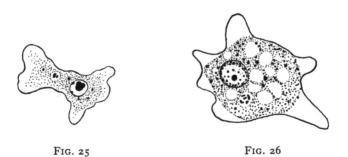

FIG. 25   FIG. 26

FIG. 25. *Endolimax blattae*. × 1,500. (After Lucas.)
FIG. 26. *Hartmannella blattae*. (Modified after Ivanić.)

Endolimax blattae Lucas

Like other members of the genus, *E. blattae* (Fig. 25) is small, rarely more than 22 μ in diameter when rounded up. It occurred in about half of Lucas's specimens of *Blatta orientalis* and was 'fairly frequent' in *Periplaneta americana*. The pseudopodia tend to be long, hyaline, and finger-like. The nucleus is 2 to 3 μ in diameter with a relatively large, sometimes irregularly shaped, karyosome. The cysts (7 to 10 μ) vary from round to oval in shape and are quadrinucleate when mature.

Hartmannella blattae Ivanić

This (small?) amoeba (Fig. 26) lives off bacteria in the hind-gut of *Blatta orientalis* and is one of the forms said by Ivanić to develop a temporary cytostome when feeding (see p. 19). The nucleus has a prominent, central or eccentric, karyosome (which appears to behave like a nucleolus during division) and scattered siderophile granules. The cysts contain up to 29 nuclei and the contents, at least in those with fewer nuclei, divide into as many amoebulae before excystation. No sizes are given for trophic amoebae or cysts (see Ivanić, 1937).

Permanent preparations

Smears of undiluted gut contents should be fixed in B or S+A and stained in H.H. The nuclei of *Endamoeba blattae*, especially in cysts, need slow and careful differentiation or the details will be lost.

ORDER TESTACEA

The Testacea include amoeboid rhizopods with monolocular shells; most of them occur in fresh water. The shell may consist only of a pseudo-chitinous base (*Arcella*, p. 44) or this organic matrix may be reinforced with foreign material such as sand grains, mud particles, or other debris (*Difflugia*, p. 46); *Euglypha* (p. 47) secretes a test of siliceous platelets. The test has a single large aperture through which emerge the pseudopodia and, when formed, the products of division. The pseudopods may be long, flexible lobopodia, consisting wholly, or nearly so, of hyaline ectoplasm, but some species have filopodia (*Euglypha*) and these, when branching and anastomosing, achieve the state more typical of Foraminifera; such a form as *Gromia* is monolocular like a testacean but in other respects is a typical foraminiferan (see p. 49). Like many other freshwater animals, the Testacea often form cysts. Reproduction is typically asexual, by binary fission, but there are reports of sexual processes.

The order links the Amoebina and the Foraminifera, with each of which, as the Amoeba Testacea or Foraminifera Monothalamia, it has been joined in one classification or another. A few species are marine; a number have taken to life in damp soil, among wet terrestrial vegetation, especially mosses, and the ecology of these species, which are easily collected, has been studied by Volz (1929) and Hoogenraad (1935); most are freshwater animals and their shells are familiar objects to the naturalist. Lists of species from various types of habitat are given by Penard (1909), Grospietsch (1958), and Chardez (1958).

Arcella vulgaris Ehrenberg

Various species of *Arcella* occur in water similar to that inhabited by freshwater amoebae and may be collected in the same way. *A. vulgaris* is usually found on submerged plants or on the floor of stagnant waters rather rich in organic matter. *A. gibbosa* tends to occur in somewhat purer water, *A. catinus* in damp moss, *A. arenaria* more especially in tree mosses or lichens. Suitable material should be collected, placed in water from the source, and examined later with binoculars. Most species have brown or yellowish shells and are easily picked out with a pipette. Mount several specimens—some shells will almost certainly be empty—and support the coverslips to avoid crushing. For identification consult Penard (1902), Cash and Hopkinson (1905), or, best, Deflandre (1928); Leidy (1879), though describing only a few species, has some beautiful plates.

The living organism

The shell of *A. vulgaris* (Fig. 27) is roughly a flattened sphere, 100 to 150 μ in diameter, of a brown or yellow-brown keratin-like material. The underside is concave, and in the centre of it is a single circular aperture with inflected margins. The surface is smooth with a fine hexagonal patterning.

Since the shell persists for long after the animal is dead, empty ones are common. The first clue to a living specimen may be a slight to-and-fro tilting of the shell, and closer observation shows a few, clear, blunt pseudopodia, projecting from below the rim. These originate from the aperture on the under side, and by their agency *Arcella* staggers slowly along and entraps its food, mainly green and colourless flagellates. The pseudopodia are extended one after the other and attach themselves to the glass by their tips; then they contract and, in doing so, drag the body forward. The cytoplasm in the shell is more fluid and more granular, and is suspended from the walls by filamentous strands. It contains 2 similar nuclei, situated at opposite ends of a diameter but liable to move about in the endoplasmic streaming. There are 2 contractile vacuoles. In some species there are also gas-filled bubbles, said to contain oxygen.

The paired individuals, often of different depths of colour, which occur are the results of binary fission. In this the 2 nuclei divide by a process recalling promitosis (Ivanić, 1936b) and then a binucleate daughter emerges from the shell aperture. It invests itself with a new shell, at first pale yellow, but later darker; the two individuals then separate. Asexual reproduction by binary fission is the only means of reproduction known with any certainty. There is no doubt that multinucleate stages occur in the life-history

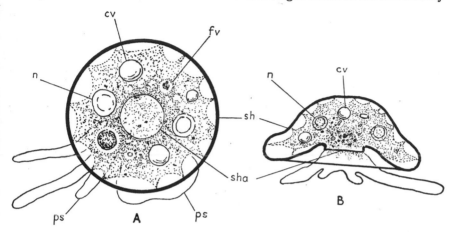

FIG. 27. *Arcella*. A, from above; B, from the side. Both specimens are drawn as transparencies. × 300. (Original: D. L. M.)

cv, contractile vacuole; *fv*, food vacuole; *n*, nucleus; *ps*, pseudopodium; *sh*, shell; *sha*, shell aperture.

(Ivanić, 1934), but their significance remains uncertain. Whether the small amoebulae sometimes seen in cultures of *Arcella* are really reproductive bodies or stages of some associated *limax* amoebae is not clear (see Bělař, 1926a; Cavallini, 1926; Reynolds, 1926); accounts of sexual processes in *Arcella* are as yet insufficiently supported.

Arcella apparently encysts within its own shell, but not enough is known of the properties of development of the cysts.

Permanent preparations

If material is scanty, fix and stain by irrigation (p. 428); but if it is plentiful, as often in mosses or good cultures, disturb the culture or shake out the moss well in water, and strew the bottom of the vessel with coverslips. Leave for some hours to allow the rhizopods to grip the slips, which should then be gently removed with fine forceps and dropped face downwards on to fixative. Fix in S+A; stain in D.H. or H.H.

A note on 'chromidia'. Staining will reveal the presence of numerous fine granules, which, in various patterns, occur in many Testacea and have been a source of confusion. These granules, or 'chromidia', are basophile and so stain with Haematoxylin like much of the nuclear content; the chromidia thus came to be regarded as extra-nuclear chromatin, and it was supposed that from time to time the primary nuclei degenerated and were replaced by new nuclei organized from the chromidia. But it appears that at periods when the primary nuclei were thought to have disappeared they were in fact merely masked by dense accumulations of deeply staining chromidia and could be revealed by suitable methods (Bělař, 1926*a*) and, further, Reichenow (in Doflein and Reichenow, 1952–3) found the chromidia to be F—. While the real nature of chromidia, a term which has probably been applied to a variety of substances, remains unsettled, there is no longer any reason to believe that they play any part in the development of the nucleus.

Difflugia Leclerc

This very common shelled rhizopod (Fig. 28) may occur along with *Arcella* and is sometimes abundant on the muddy floors of stagnant ponds.

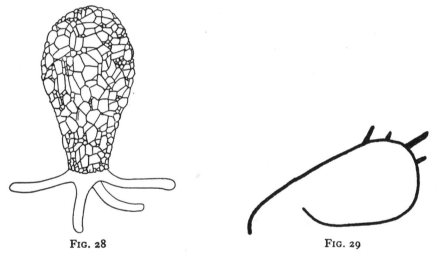

FIG. 28   FIG. 29

FIG. 28. *Difflugia* sp. × 120. (Original: D. L. M.)

FIG. 29. *Centropyxis*. Sagittal section of shell to show position of foramen. Coating of foreign bodies omitted. (Modified after Doflein.)

The shell is vase-, pear-, or balloon-shaped, with a single large aperture almost always symmetrical about its long axis, sometimes with thorn-like projections at the summit, and showing great variety in its proportions among the numerous different species. *Difflugia* forms its shell by cementing foreign particles such as sand grains or diatom cases on to an organic base, and the opacity of the result, especially in adults, makes it almost impossible to see anything of the living animal, except for the very long, hyaline pseudopodia which are protruded through the aperture. In binary fission one of the daughters forms a new shell before losing touch with the old one (Pateff, 1926) and young specimens have more transparent shells.

For identification, see Penard (1902), Cash and Hopkinson (1908), and Cash, Wailes, and Hopkinson (1919), and for locomotion, Mast (1931).

Centropyxis Stein

Centropyxis, though perhaps more dependent on a good algal growth, often occurs in stagnant waters along with *Difflugia*; many species are common in damp moss. The shell (Fig. 29) is bilaterally symmetrical and hood-shaped. It resembles a shell of *Arcella* that, so to speak, has been pulled out of shape upwards and backwards from the aperture, which usually lies towards the shallower end, but in a minority of species, constituting the sub-genus *Cyclopyxis*, is central. The shell is more or less covered with inorganic particles and may bear spiny projections. Its deeper end contains the nucleus and 'chromidia'; mitosis has been described by Schaudinn (see Bělař, 1926a, p. 73). The pseudopodia are lobose and hyaline, like those of *Arcella*, to which the genus is related. For identification, see Deflandre (1929).

Nebela Leidy

Sphagnum moss is probably the best source for a number of species of this elegant little rhizopod. The *Sphagnum* should be kept closely packed in large, deep glass vessels, damp, not flooded, and away from direct sunlight. The lower, brownish parts of the moss are the most thickly populated. Squeeze the moss dry, and filter the fluid obtained through four thicknesses of cheese-cloth. Allow to stand until a slight brownish deposit has appeared: this contains the *Nebela*. Gently pour off the supernatant liquid while it is still cloudy, before the bottom deposit becomes too dense. According to MacKinley (1936), very large numbers of *N. collaris* may thus be obtained, which, though only about 110 to 130 μ in size, are visible to the naked eye.

The shell (Fig. 30) is balloon-shaped or compressed; the single aperture may have two horn-like processes. The colour is yellowish or greyish. The whole shell is commonly invested with tiny plates of silica. *N. collaris*, studied by MacKinley, obtains these plates from ingested specimens of *Euglypha*, which are provided with siliceous skeletons of their own. *Nebela* digests the protein matrix of the shell it has captured, thus liberating the siliceous plates, which, together with the reserve plates accumulated by the prey, contribute to the captor's skeleton. In this way, the shell of *N. collaris* may come to consist of some five different types of plate.

In binary fission, a considerable amount of cytoplasm is extruded from the shell mouth, and a daughter shell is constructed face to face with the parent; into this most of the cytoplasm flows and in it nuclear division takes place, one product being returned to the parent before separation. The daughter shell, which contains most of the cytoplasm, is always the larger.

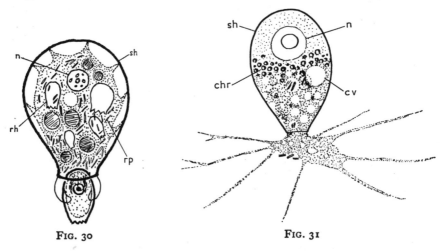

FIG. 30   FIG. 31

FIG. 30. *Nebela collaris*: capturing another small rhizopod. ×250. (Modified after MacKinley.)

n, nucleus; *rh*, shells of digested prey; *rp*, reserves of silica plates; *sh*, shell: the superficial investment of silica plates is not shown.

FIG. 31. *Chlamydophrys*: the living organism. × 1750. (After Bělař.)

chr, 'chromidia'; *cv*, contractile vacuole; *n*, nucleus; *sh*, shell.

Chlamydophrys Cienkowski

This tiny rhizopod (Fig. 31), commonly measuring some $20 \times 14\,\mu$, is easily obtained from horse-dung, or the faeces of rabbits, poultry, or frogs, which have been moistened and left covered for some days. It is also widely distributed in manured soils, along with *limax* amoebae. It should be sought with the use of No. o cover slips and an oil immersion lens.

The body lies within a very delicate, transparent shell of organic material, approximately pear-shaped, and so thin as to be easily overlooked, but it may be demonstrated by mounting in cane-sugar solution, when, after plasmolysis, the cytoplasm shrinks away from the shell. The nucleus lies near the broader end, in a region of hyaline cytoplasm. The 'chromidia', which are difficult to see without fixation and staining, lie nearer the shell aperture, and nearer still is a region of coarsely vacuolated cytoplasm, containing food, excretory and reserve materials, and 2 or 3 contractile, vacuoles. The pseudopodia are delicate, filose, branching strands, connected together at their bases by a cytoplasmic film lying about the aperture. The whole forms an effective apparatus for sweeping up bacteria and the small amoebae on which *Chlamydophrys* feeds.

Chlamydophrys forms uninucleate dissemination-cysts with thick, irregular, yellowish-brown walls; the organism which hatches from these has no shell at first and from this circumstance and its movement may easily be taken for a small amoeba.

For more detailed information and for methods of division, see the beautifully illustrated paper by Bělař (1921*a*).

Permanent preparations and culture

Fix in S+A; stain in H.H. or D.H.+Eosin. For culture, see p. 402.

ORDER FORAMINIFERA

Almost all the members of this order are marine, with calcareous, polythalamous shells (Figs. 32, 34) pierced with numerous minute pores through which the ectoplasm of the animal is extruded; this layer produces a mass of fine, anastomosing pseudopodia, which form a feeding net. A few species are monothalamous and some of these may be freshwater, but their life-histories are typically foraminiferan, and they are better classed here than with the Testacea (e.g. *Gromia*, see Arnold, 1955). The shells are very various (Fig. 32, and see the discussion in Thompson, 1942) and those of pelagic Foraminifera may form oozes contributing to the formation of limestone.

The life-histories of relatively few Foraminifera are known in detail; but there is a general alternation of sexual and asexual generations (gamonts and agamonts) and sometimes these may be distinguished by a morphological dimorphism. In *Elphidium*, the best-known example, a small zygote, formed from flagellated gametes, lays down the first chamber (proloculum) of the agamont, which is called microspheric (Fig. 36); the asexual reproductive bodies that this stage liberates are amoebulae and they lay down a conspicuously larger proloculum to the shell of the gamont, which is called megalospheric (Fig. 35). In many forms the gametes are amoeboid, and they form prolocula no smaller than those laid down about the agametes, so there is no prolocular dimorphism, though commonly agamonts are rather larger than gamonts. Even where the life-history is very like that of *Elphidium*, there may be no dimorphism. For example, in some species of *Discorbis*, the gamonts associate, so that fertilization by means of flagellated gametes occurs in a restricted space, the zygote feeds on the unsuccessful gametes, and it grows before laying down a proloculum no smaller than that of the parent (Myers, 1940). It appears that the only reason why

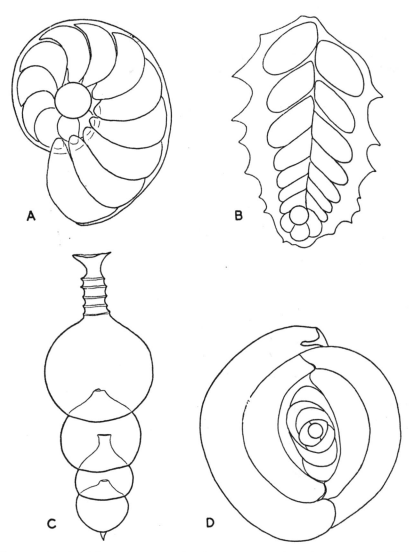

FIG. 32. Shells of Foraminifera. A, *Rotalia*. ×215. B, *Spiroplecta*. ×60. C, *Nodo-saria*. ×90. D, *Miliola*. ×135. (Original: D. L. M.)

sexually-produced shells of *Elphidium* are microspheric is that the zygote is formed in the open sea and does not feed or grow before producing its proloculum.* A summary of earlier knowledge of life-histories is given by Myers (1938).

Distinctions of deeper biological significance between the generations are known. In 1950 Le Calvez discovered that in *Patellina corrugata* the gamonts were haploid and the agamonts diploid, and *Patellina* was thus the first animal in which such an alternation of haploidy and diploidy was known. In a series of beautiful studies of Foraminifera in culture, Grell (1954, 1957, 1958 *a, b, c*) has shown that the same is true of *Rotaliella* spp., *Rubratella intermedia*, and *Glabratella sulcata*, in all of which meiosis occurs at the end of the life of the agamont. Grell has further discovered, also in these species, a type of nuclear dimorphism confined to the agamont (Fig. 33). After fertilization a number of mitoses supplies the young agamont with several nuclei, of which one increases in size and acquires a nucleolus and the rest remain compact; the former is the so-called somatic nucleus (*s*) and the latter are generative (*n*); *Glabratella* has several somatic nuclei. At the time when the generative nuclei undergo meiosis to provide nuclei of the agametes, the somatic nucleus begins to divide, but its chromosomes do not pair, and it fails and dies. According to Grell, the dimorphism is functional as well as morphological. In *Rotaliella roscoffensis* it happens that some nuclei may early degenerate and the young agamont be left with only a single nucleus. This is always a somatic nucleus and it is held that without it growth is impossible, though, as it cannot divide, the generation is frustrated, for only the generative nuclei can reproduce.

Elphidium crispum (L.) (= *Polystomella crispa*)

This common rhizopod creeps about on seaweeds in the littoral zone down to about 300 fathoms and for study is usually bought from marine biological stations. Specimens should be placed in aerated sea water in rectangular-sided vessels and by next day some will have climbed the walls and will afford good views through binocular dissecting microscopes.

The living organism

The calcareous shell is about 1 mm in diameter and pale yellow or deeper in colour. It is polythalamous and all the chambers are occupied

---

* The use of microspheric and megalospheric as synonyms for asexual and sexual respectively without regard to the size of the proloculum is misleading and should be abandoned; it is especially absurd in forms like *Spirillina vivipara* where the proloculum of the agamont (corresponding to the microsphere) is slightly larger than that of the gamont (Myers, 1936).

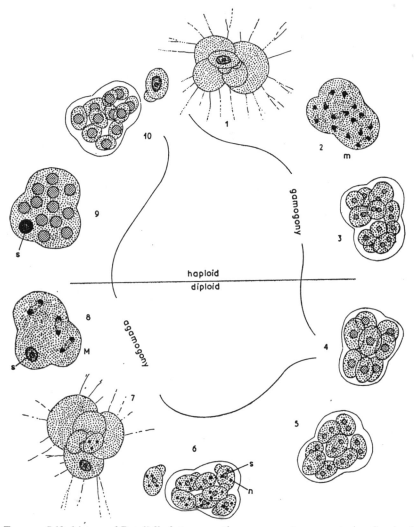

FIG. 33. Life-history of *Rotaliella heterocaryotica*. 1, gamont; 2, gametogenetic mitosis; 3, autogamous fertilization; 4, zygotes; 5, binucleate agamonts within parent shell; 6, quadrinucleate agamonts ready for dispersal: 1 nucleus (*s*) in each is somatic and the other 3 (*n*) are generative; 7, grown agamont: the somatic nucleus lives in a young chamber, generative nuclei remain in the proloculum; 8, meiosis; 9, degeneration of somatic nucleus; 10, agametes (= young gamonts). (After Grell.)

M, meiosis; *m*, mitosis; *n*, generative nucleus; *s*, somatic nucleus.

by cytoplasm (cf. Figs. 34, 35, 36). The chambers are laid down serially in the line of a flat logarithmic spiral, the largest being the most recently formed, and larger ones bestride those belonging to older whorls of the spiral and partially overlap them so that they are hidden from view; the

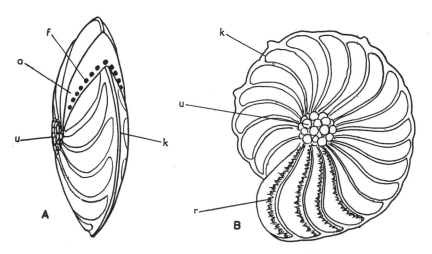

FIG. 34. *Elphidium*: the shell. A, end on, and B, lateral views. Detail shown on last 4 chambers only. × 80. (Original: D. L. M.)

a, alar process; *f*, foramen in exposed face of terminal chamber; *k*, keel; *r*, retral process, with minute foramina between adjacent processes; *u*, umbo.

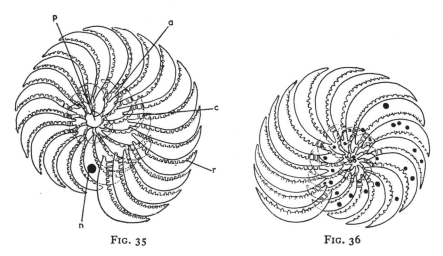

FIG. 35   FIG. 36

FIG. 35. *Elphidium*. Megalospheric specimen decalcified and stained with Borax Carmine. × 45. (Original: D. L. M.)

a, alar process equitant upon contents of the inner whorl of chambers; *c*, cytoplasmic connective between adjacent chambers; *n*, nucleus; *p*, proloculum; *r*, retral process.

FIG. 36. *Elphidium*. Microspheric specimen. Cf. Fig. 35, which it resembles except that microspheres have several small central chambers and numerous nuclei. (Original: D. L. M.)

overlapping portions are the alar processes (*a*) and they are said to be equitant upon the parts of the shell they enfold. Along the posterior, concave border of each chamber are retral processes (*r*) which in life are filled with protoplasm, and between the retral processes lie the minute pores through which most of the cytoplasm emerges, though some comes through the larger pores on the last-formed face of the last chamber (*f*). All the chambers are ridged with a continuous keel (*k*) about the periphery of the shell and the centre or umbo (*u*) is concealed by a secondary calcareous deposit.

A thin layer of cytoplasm invests the living shell and from this arise the thread-like, branching and anastomosing pseudopodia by means of which the animal drags its shell along, at a rate of as much as 4 to 6 mm per hr, and by which, also, it collects the diatoms on which it mostly or entirely feeds. Although the threads which have a firmer axis and more fluid cortex are sometimes no more than 1 μ in diameter, granules attached to opposite sides of them may move in opposite directions. For further discussion of foraminiferan pseudopodia, see Sandon (1934). According to Jepps (1942), who has written a lively description of the living animal, 'the pseudopodia may be shot out a short distance into the water like little rockets, and with the granules chasing up and down, wave about like minute feelers, bending, undulating, quivering and putting out side branches which meet and fuse and so establish the reticulum. This spreads, often in the form of a cone based on the shell, until in half an hour or so bundles of pseudopodia may lie more or less all round the shell reaching out for rather more than its diameter on every side, or for two or three times as far in one direction.' Food is dragged towards the shell and digested externally, and an actively feeding specimen may be plastered with patches of the diatom cases it has collected.

Permanent preparations

For a study of the body, fix specimens in 6-per cent mercuric chloride in sea water plus 5 per cent acetic acid at 60°–65° C for 1 hour. If, as is likely, decalcification is incomplete, transfer through 30 per cent and 50 per cent alcohol to 70 per cent alcohol tinged with a few drops of iodine for 2–3 hours, and then leave overnight in 70 per cent alcohol plus 3 per cent nitric acid to complete decalcification. Wash in clean 70 per cent alcohol. (2 to 3 changes in 1 hour) and stain in Borax Carmine or Picrocarmine. Dehydrate, clear, and mount with care to avoid crushing. (The fixed material supplied by marine biological stations is rarely suitable for making good preparations unless directions for fixation are given when ordering.)

The decalcified *Elphidium* (Figs. 35, 36) is a protoplasmic cast of the shell and shows clearly the chamber contents, each shaped rather like a 'section' of an orange that has been split lengthwise for a short distance at one end to give the two alar processes with which it bestrides the chambers in the preceding whorl. The retral processes, which end blindly, show as a double series of little knobs along the posterior, concave side of each 'section'. The delicate cytoplasmic connexions (c) that set the contents of successive chambers in communication with one another lie in the region of the alar processes: in the complete animal they are contained in the canalicular system of the shell, near the axial umbo.

The microspheric, asexual form or agamont is easily distinguished in this genus from the megalospheric gamont. In the former nuclear division begins early and the stage is multinucleate for most of its life. Only about 1 in 30 of the shells collected are microspheric, possibly because, if fertilization takes place in the sea between pelagic flagellated gametes, the chances of success are less than those in asexual reproduction. According to Jepps, the entire cycle of sexual and asexual stages takes about 2 years.

Culture

Methods of maintaining *Elphidium* ar.d for keeping individuals under continuous observation for several days are given by Jepps (1942).

ORDER HELIOZOA

The 'sun animalcules' are so named because their long, relatively stiff, unbranched axopodia radiate in every direction from their spherical bodies, like the rays in conventional pictures of the sun (Figs. 37, 39). They occur in fresh water and the sea, usually in shallow places, not near the surface. The majority float free, drifting with the current but to some extent manœuvring along by means of their axopodia, by which also they seize their prey, generally other Protozoa, rotifers, and desmids. A few (*Wagnerella*) are attached to the substratum by means of a non-contractile stalk. The best known are naked except when encysted, but some have an exoskeleton of gelatinous material encrusted with foreign bodies such as sand grains and diatom shells; others secrete a siliceous skeleton, either as a continuous lattice (*Clathrulina*) or as separate spicules (*Acanthocystis*) laid tangentially to the sphere or projecting from it between the axopodia.

The cytoplasm tends to be sharply divided into 2 zones—an outer, coarsely vacuolated ectoplasm and an inner, denser endoplasm where digestion takes place and which contains the nucleus. Some species have zoochlorellae in the endoplasm.

Asexual multiplication is by binary fission or budding and in the latter case biflagellate swarmers may be formed. Where sexual reproduction has been investigated, it is a peculiar form of autogamy (pp. 58–59, 61) associated with encystation.

·For identification and taxonomy, see Penard (1904), Cash, Wailes, and Hopkinson (1921), Roskin (1929), and Valkanov (1940).

Actinosphaerium eichhorni Ehrenberg

This large heliozoan lives in ponds and slowly moving streams, generally in well-oxygenated water and, though usually commoner in spring, it may persist in some habitats during the winter, even under ice; its rather sporadic occurrence much depends on the abundance of suitable living, animal food. *Actinosphaerium* is about a millimetre in diameter and easily seen with the naked eye as a white spot floating in water. It needs a good oxygen supply and should be transferred to shallow Petri dishes soon after collection.

The living organism

The slightest pressure causes the pseudopodia to withdraw and specimens should at first be examined by the low power in hollow ground slides without a cover slip. By transmitted light *Actinosphaerium* (Fig. 37) looks greyish, with a clear ectoplasmic cortex and a denser, more granular endoplasm; the line of demarcation between the two is quite evident. From all over the surface radiate the needle-like axopodia. Between them, on the periphery, appear a few bulging contractile vacuoles, which burst and swell up again at regular intervals. The endoplasm contains numerous and sometimes very large food masses in vacuoles. In feeding, the organism appears to paralyse, at least partially, passing ciliates and rotifers that come into contact with and stick to the axopodia, which contract and draw the food down into the body. Each axopodium shows an axis of firmer, more hyaline protoplasm, which is birefringent under polarized light, stains intensely with Iron Haematoxylin, and has a finely fibrillar structure (Roskin, 1925) which can be demonstrated by silver impregnation or staining after correct cytological fixation (Rumjantzew and Wermel, 1925); the axis passes down into the sphere to end just within the line of junction between cortex and medulla* (Fig. 37B). On this axis is a coating of more fluid, slightly granular cytoplasm continuous with a thin layer covering the body as a whole. Several axopodia co-operate in catching prey and their axes shorten until it is embedded in this surface layer, while the covering layer is distributed in irregular thickenings. For 5 or 10 minutes after it has been engulfed, a ciliate may continue to show movement, and a rotifer may keep going for some hours within its vacuole. The use of pH indicators injected into the food-vacuoles has shown that the digestive juice is acid

* In a closely related species, *A. nucleofilum*, described from North America, the axial filaments arise from some peripheral nuclei, a condition approaching that found in *Actinophrys* (Barrett, 1958, and p. 60).

(Howland, 1928*b*): the acidity diminishes as digestion goes on, but there is no evidence that an alkaline fluid is then secreted.

The very numerous circular nuclei lie in the endoplasm. They may be made more distinct by running a drop of Bouin's fixative or Methyl Green (p. 424) under the cover slip. In the centre of each lies a karyosome. The nuclei divide mitotically, and the whole organism from time to time

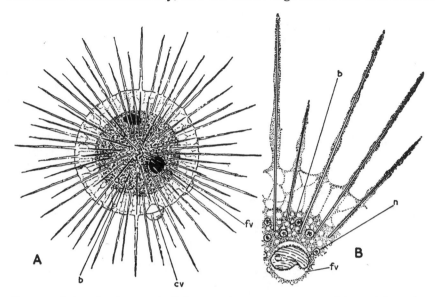

FIG. 37. *Actinosphaerium.* A. the living organism. × 300. B, part of the periphery seen in optical section. × 650. (Original: D. L. M.)

b, boundary between ectoplasm and endoplasm; *cv*, contractile vacuole: *fv*, food vacuole; *n*, nucleus.

divides, by constriction, into two daughter spheres, each containing a quota of nuclei.

Sometimes the bodies of 2 or more individuals fuse together. The meaning of this 'plastogamy' is not known (cf. *Actinophrys sol*, p. 61). It has nothing to do with the sexual phase, which is passed within cysts.

Encystment tends to occur in overcrowded cultures, and may be associated with a lowering of the pH of the water, perhaps induced by the accumulation of the animals' excretory products, or with starvation and cold. To induce encystment, take a few specimens from a crowded culture, deprive them of food for some days, and, if this does not have the desired effect, keep them in a refrigerator. Keep in sterilized salt-cellar watch-glasses with filtered water from their culture; cover with a glass lid.

Some of the animals will probably die when they have used up the contents of their food-vacuoles: remove the dead bodies at once. But others encyst, and these are entering on the sexual phase, which is autogamous (Hertwig, 1898). The external features of this can quite easily be followed if the watch-glass is kept on the microscope stage under a low power, and drawings made at intervals of a few hours (Fig. 38). The organism sinks to

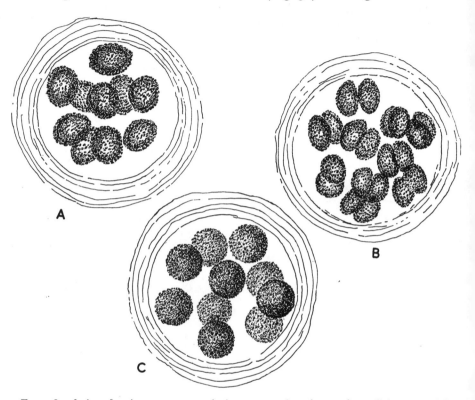

FIG. 38. *Actinosphaerium*: autogamy during encystation drawn from living material. ×440. A, gelatinous mother cyst containing 10 primary cysts; B, the primary cysts have divided into secondary cysts, the contents of which, after reduction, are gametes; C, the thick-walled copulation cysts: they are encysted zygotes formed from the fusion of the secondary cysts. (Original: D. L. M.)

the bottom of the watch-glass and withdraws its pseudopodia; the distinction between cortex and medulla disappears: the protoplasm looks uniformly greyish and opaque, and a mucus envelope is secreted which adheres to the glass. It is safe now to pour off the water gently and add a fresh supply from time to time. Within the gelatinous envelope, the protoplasm of this so-called mother-cyst absorbs some 90 per cent of its nuclei and proceeds now to divide into a number (on the average, 10) of uninucleate, elliptical 'primary cysts' (A), each measuring about $55 \times 48 \mu$. These become coated with tiny siliceous spicules, pigment is deposited, and they become opaque: under low power they look like a group of small black dots set in a yellowish jelly. Each primary cyst then divides into two, each measuring $48 \times 27 \mu$ on the average, and these, the secondary cysts (B), having prepared their nuclei by forming 2 polar (reduction) bodies, fuse in pairs to give spherical copulation cysts (C), with a diameter of about 48μ. The whole process takes about 9 hours after the mother-cyst has begun to divide. The accompanying nuclear changes can be seen only in stained sections. Within the very resistant copulation cyst each daughter will remain quiescent until external conditions are 'favourable' for emergence of a single uninucleate young, which feeds and grows and assumes the adult multinucleate form.

Permanent preparations

Actinosphaerium is too fragile to stand centrifuging and cannot be stained by mass methods. Allow specimens to expand on clean slips, and when they have gripped, invert and drop on to fixative. Fix in B or S+A; stain in D.H. and Eosin or, for filaments of axopodia, H.H. When mounting in Canada Balsam take the pressure off by inserting wax feet or twisting a hair in the medium.

The dividing nuclei have broad, blunt-ended mitotic figures, numerous chromosomes, and no centrosomes. It appears to be impossible to preserve the cytoplasmic features in a natural state, as contraction and shrinkage are very rapid.

The encysted stages are sticky and as they can be induced to form on cover slips as easily as in watch-glasses it is not difficult to obtain preparations of them; their walls are relatively thick and staining and fixation take about twice as long as for the trophic animals. Whole mounts of cysts do not show nuclei, and for these, sections must be cut.

Culture

Actinosphaerium may be maintained, somewhat uncertainly, in a mixture of tap- and pond-water, just above pH = 7, liberally supplied with *Stentor*, *Paramecium*, and other large ciliates as food. Knop's solution is better (p. 404). Keep away from strong light. Sub-culture weekly if encystation is to be avoided.

Actinophrys sol Ehrenberg

Actinophrys is usually most abundant in spring and summer in moorland waters and shallow pools elsewhere. It is omnivorous, but since it flourishes on green flagellates and algae generally, a good growth of these may be an index to its whereabouts. It sometimes appears in cultures of *Amoeba proteus* that have been left standing in light strong enough to encourage algal growth. It is commoner than *Actinosphaerium* but smaller and more difficult to handle.

The living organism

The body is about 50 μ in diameter with a coarsely alveolated ectoplasm; just within this is a zone containing granules of reserve material (Fig. 39).

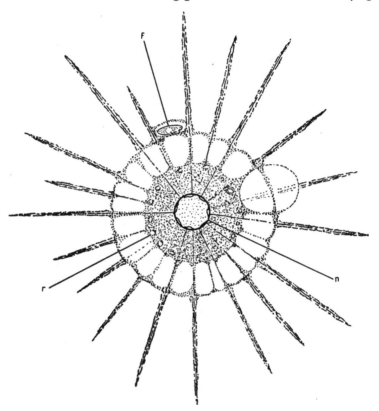

FIG. 39. *Actinophrys sol*: in optical section. × 800. (Modified, after Bělař.)

f, food about to be engulfed at surface; *n*, nucleus; *r*, reserve material in peripheral layer of endoplasm.

The endoplasm is closely vacuolated and dense, and the axes of the axo-podia pass through it to end on a layer of more homogeneous cytoplasm surrounding the single, central nucleus. By means of its axopodia, *Actino-phrys*, like *Actinosphaerium*, can slowly traverse some distance unaided by water currents. The nucleus is spherical and measures 10 to 15 μ. It is limited by a membrane, just within which lie some peripheral granules.

The method of feeding is best studied in a hanging drop containing about half a dozen specimens of *Actinophrys* and appropriate food, and inverted over a glass or polythene ring sealed with vaseline. *Actinophrys* is practically omnivorous—flagellates, ciliates, desmids, yeasts are all suitable food, and it is well to add a variety of material to the drop as the method of feeding varies with the size of the organism attacked. Ingestion is by means of special, always hyaline, pseudopodia (Looper, 1928). If the object is very small and relatively inactive, a small straight pseudopod is extended which, on coming into contact with the food, spreads out into a cup and envelops it: if the object is large and motionless, a wide hyaline outgrowth advances towards the prey, and, when near it or in contact with it, expands laterally in all directions, closing in on it when the contact is intimate: if the food is active, large sack-like pseudopods are sent out, and the palisade of axopodia helps to cut off a way of escape. If the prey is very large and active, for example, a rotifer, several individuals may jointly engage in ingestion, their cytoplasm fusing and separating after sharing the meal. According to Sondheim (1915), *A. oculata* differs from *A. sol* in that these feeding aggregates are formed, not by the coalescence of independent individuals, but by the incomplete fission of a single specimen while attacking large prey.

Besides binary fission, which takes from 40 to 90 minutes, the animal reproduces by autogamy when encysted. Encystation is induced by overfeeding with green flagellates such as *Gonium*, when *Actinophrys* gorges itself and encysts after 10 to 15 days. The specimens sink to the bottom, with their pseudopodia, become dark and opaque, and secrete about themselves a double envelope, membranous within and gelatinous without. Such a cyst may be detached with a needle and lifted into a depression slide with a drop of culture liquid which must be changed from time to time. The external features of the sexual phase, which lasts about 20 hours, may be followed (Fig. 40). The cyst contents divide into 2 about 12 hours after encystation (*a*). Each daughter ejects 2 polar (reduction) bodies and then fuses with its fellow to form a copulation cyst with a diameter of about 40 μ (*b–f*); this stage takes another 8 hours. According to Bělař (1923) one daughter throws out a pseudopodium towards the other to initiate the sexual fusion (*b, c*). The reorganized, uninucleate animal may be hatched by washing in sterile water, leaving in the refrigerator for about a week, and then transferring to room temperature (20–25° C); about 24 hours later the contents of the old copulation cysts emerge.

Permanent preparations

Put well-cleaned cover slips at the bottom of a rich culture and leave until specimens have settled and attached themselves. (For a refinement of the adhesion method, see Bělař, 1923). Fix in B by dropping the inverted slips on to the fixative. Stain with Meyer's Acid Haemalum; a few minutes in stain will suffice but longer will not overstain. Sharpen the picture by washing for 15–30 sec in 1 per cent aqueous Iron Alum, blue, and counter stain, if desired, in Orange G. The cysts may be fixed and stained singly

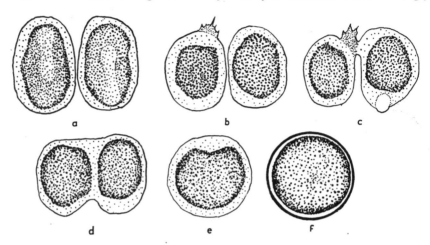

FIG. 40. *Actinophrys.* The living rhizopod encysted. (The outer, mucilaginous envelope is omitted.) Stages in the sexual phase. ×625. (Simplified, after Bělař.)

a. The encysted *Actinophrys* has divided into 2 potential gametes, which are shown at the end of the first reduction division of their nuclei.
b. One of the gametes throwing out a pseudopodium towards its partner.
c. The pseudopodium effecting contact and fusion of the gametes.
d. Ectoplasmic fusion completed.
e. Endoplasmic regions also joined.
f. The spherical, resistant copulation cyst.

by the irrigation method, or in bulk; longer times in all reagents are needed as the cyst walls are relatively impermeable. The celebrated figures by Bělař (1923) are based on sections.

ORDER RADIOLARIA

The Radiolaria are all marine and nearly all pelagic; though some occur at considerable depths most are planktonic. There is typically a skeleton, which is of silica, and the skeletons of dead radiolarians form oozes which ultimately have given rise to such deposits as Barbadoes Earth.

The distinctive character of the order is the central capsule, an organic membrane between the ectoplasm and endoplasm, which communicate through the capsular pores (Figs. 42, 43). There may be a single pore (Monopylaria), 3 pores (Tripylaria), or many pores distributed over the surface of the capsule (Peripylaria). Within the capsule, the endoplasm lodges various inclusions, such as pigment granules, crystals, and oil droplets. Just outside the capsules, the ectoplasm is somewhat fluid and contains the captured food in various stages of digestion. Over the whole outer surface, a similar fluid layer of ectoplasm is spread and from this radiate filiform pseudopodia, which tend to branch into a reticulum; they are not axopodia. Between these inner and outer ectoplasmic zones is the calymma, a thick, bubbly coat of gelatinous material, forming a stiff froth. The calymma is a flotation device; when it collapses, the organism sinks; as the bubbles re-form, it rises. 'Zooxanthellae' are very commonly present and they are lodged in the calymma, not, as in the Acantharia, in the endoplasm; they are of dinoflagellate origin (Hollande, 1953; Hovasse and Brown, 1953). The luminescent Radiolaria are remarkable for their capacity to shine in the absence of oxygen (Harvey, 1952).

The life-cycles of the Radiolaria have been the subject of much controversy, only now beginning to be clarified. Without going into details, it is now possible to state (1) that some Radiolaria without skeletons or with discontinuous skeletons multiply at times by fission (e.g. *Sphaerozoum* and some Tripylaria); (2) that at times the contents of the central capsule are converted into masses of isospores (Fig. 41), which are not spores at all in the ordinary sense, but flagellated swarmers, usually (but not always, even in the same brood) containing one or two crystalloid bodies; they are the 'crystal spores' of the authors, and their development is unknown; and (3) that the so-called anisospores, which in the past have been regarded as radiolarian gametes are, in fact, as brilliantly suggested years ago by Chatton, stages in the life-history of parasitic syndinian dinoflagellates. For a clear presentation of the whole problem, see Hovasse and Brown (1953). The form of the radiolarian skeleton is the subject of a celebrated discussion by Thompson (1942, pp. 694–702 and 706–40).

SUBORDER PERIPYLARIA (SPUMULARIA)

The suborder, characterized by the numerous pores in the central capsule, is conventionally divided into 3 groups: the Collodaria, solitary (monocyttarian) species (*Thallasophysa*), the Polycyttaria, colonial forms (*Sphaerozoum*), both with a rudimentary skeleton or none at all, and the Sphaerellaria, including the great majority of the Radiolaria, with a well-developed skeleton, usually spherical, often elaborated in concentric layers. But the distinction between the first 2 groups is insecure, and as more information about life-histories emerges, some polycyttarian and monocyttarian genera appear as stages in the development of single species (see especially Hollande and Enjumet, 1953).

Sphaerozoum Meyen

Colonies may be procured from biological stations, such as that at Naples, with access to warm seas.

Examine an entire colony under the hand-lens or binocular dissecting microscope. The hollow, gelatinous sphere (3 to 4 mm in *S. punctatum*)

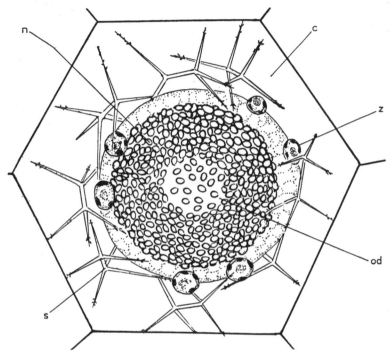

Fig. 41. *Sphaerozoum.* Individual member of a colony: in isosporogenesis. ×450. (Original: D. L. M.)

c, calymma; *n*, nuclei of isospores; *od*, position of oil drop; *s*, spicule; *z*, zooxanthella.

shows a wall composed of a single layer of adpressed peripylarian individuals, each with the symmetry of a sphere; the central capsules appear as dark dots at regular intervals in the common calymma, now collapsed.

Cut out small portions of the colony. Stain D.H., dehydrate, clear, and mount. The boundaries between the members of the colony (Fig. 41) appear as lines between the originally spherical bodies which, under pressure, assume hexagonal outlines in optical section. Note the delicate capsule. Within it the oil drop is now dissolved. The extracapsular cytoplasm (ectoplasm) contains the zooxanthellae and the skeleton; this is composed of separate spicules of silica, from each end of which come off rays, usually 3 at angles of 120° to each other; the tips are slightly thorny.

The allied polycyttarian genus *Collozoum*, often used in class work, has no skeleton.

Both *Sphaerozoum* and *Collozoum* are regarded as colonial stages in the life-history of species of *Thallasophysa* by Hollande and Enjumet (1953).

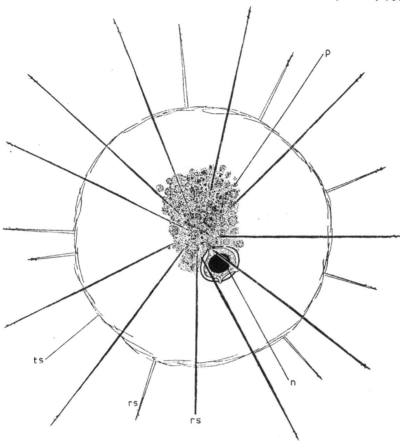

FIG. 42. *Aulacantha*: optical section drawn from stained specimen. × 100. (Original: D. L. M.)

n, nucleus within central capsule; *p*, phaeodium; *rs*, radial spicule; *ts*, tangential spicule.

SUBORDER TRIPYLARIA (PHAEODARIA)

The members of this order are distinguished by the phaeodium, the characteristic arrangement of the 3 pores of the central capsule (see below), and by the fact that the skeleton is nearly always hollow. They live at lower levels of the sea than other Radiolarians, and they have no zooxanthellae.

Aulacantha Haeckel

The body is spherical (Fig. 42). The skeleton is made up of separate needle-like spicules. Long, hollow needles with slightly thorny tips radiate from the centre and serve as a scaffolding. Minute, curved spicules are arranged tangentially in a layer near the surface.

The central capsule (Fig. 43) is bilaterally symmetrical, double-walled, and contains one large nucleus and an oil drop. It has 3 apertures—a larger one (astropyle) at the summit of a slight eminence, and 2 smaller parapyles on tiny conical projections on the side opposite the astropyle. The capsule lies somewhat out of centre with its astropyle directed against a mass of brown and greenish pigment, the phaeodium, which seems to consist of excretory matter and food-particles (Fig. 42). The gigantic nucleus is

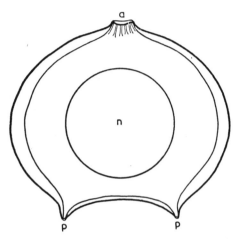

FIG. 43. *Aulacantha*: central capsule. (Original: D. L. M.)
a, astropyle; *n*, nucleus; *p*, parapyle.

remarkable for the number of its chromosomes, of which there are some 1,500 (see illustrations in Bělař, 1926*a*, and the excellent photographs in Grell, 1953*a*). This remarkable structure, according to Grell, is really poly-energid and is formed by repeated polyploidization, and its apparent chromosomes correspond to complete genomes or subnuclei, that is, they contain complete sets of genes, and are distributed singly only when swarmers are formed. (Cf. the ciliate meganucleus discussed on pp. 228f.)

ORDER ACANTHARIA

The members of this group were for long included among the Radiolaria from which, however, they differ sufficiently to merit separation in a position possibly nearer to the Heliozoa. In many, including all the primitive species, there is no central capsule, and, when present, it is a delicate, elastic secretion of the ectoplasm, by which it is surrounded on each side; it is not perforated, except for the transmission of the 20 spicules. Besides the fine, reticulated pseudopodia found also in Radiolaria, there are axopodia. Finally, the zooxanthellae are not of dinoflagellate origin and they occur in the endoplasm, as well as sometimes in the ectoplasm. Like the capsule,

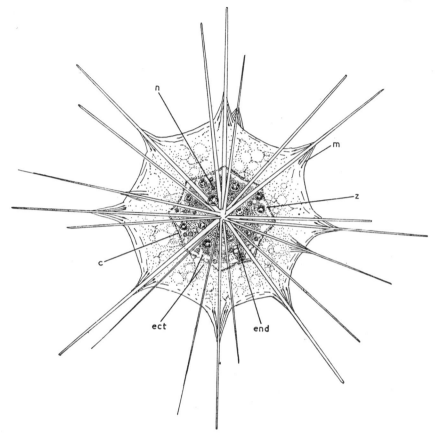

FIG. 44. *Acanthometra*: Fixed and stained specimen. × 200. (Original: D. L. M.)
c, central capsule; *ect*, ectoplasm; *end*, endoplasm; *m*, myoneme (myophrisk); *n*, nucleus; *z*, zooxanthella.

they thus differ in origin and position from their equivalents in the Radiolaria.

The spicules of Acantharia are said to consist of strontium sulphate, but the fact is doubtful. More certain is their arrangement, which follows Müller's Law, that is, if an equator, and 2 tropical and 2 polar circles be inscribed on a sphere about the organism, the spicules radiate from its centre so that 4 pass through the equator, 8 through the tropical and 8 through the polar circles.

Little is known of the life-history. There are many nuclei, so obscured by zooxanthellae, food, and parasites and other endoplasmic inclusions as to be very difficult to see except in section. Binary fission occurs in the simpler, but is unknown in the more advanced forms. In sexual reproduction, biflagellate gametes are produced which in structure and development resemble those of the Foraminifera (Le Calvez, 1938, p. 300).

For structure, biology, and taxonomy, see the magnificently illustrated memoir of Schewiakoff (1926).

Acanthometra Müller

This small acantharian (Fig. 44) occurs frequently in plankton round British coasts and can usually be obtained from marine biological laboratories.

In preserved material, the body, commonly about 250 μ in diameter, will be collapsed and the pseudopodia withdrawn, but it may be possible to observe the arrangement of the spicules in unmounted and uncrushed specimens. Stain lightly in D.H. Note the endoplasmic contents with numerous nuclei and zooxanthellae, and the curved sweep of the central capsule running between the spicules, about which it is caught up and pulled outwards. At the bases of the spicules, where they leave the body, it should be possible to observe the characteristic myonemes (myophrisks); they are powerfully contractile and, anchored to the stable scaffolding of the spicules, regulate the extension of the ectoderm.

II

CLASS MASTIGOPHORA

THE Mastigophora, or flagellates, probably exhibit a more interesting range of structural and physiological diversity than any other class of Protozoa. They include very simple forms such as *Bodo* and *Leptomonas* (*q.v.*) on the one hand, and on the other, among the trichomonad and diplomonad parasites and especially among the Hypermastigina, some of the most beautifully complicated cells ever described (Figs. 75, 76, 79, 83). It is worth noting that here as in the ciliates, the highest degree of structural differentiation has been achieved by entozoic forms and, as Pitelka said of *Trichonympha*, 'The functional significance of this lavishly complex anatomy remains in many respects a mystery.' Yet in spite of their elaborate variety, the flagellates form a natural group and they are always easily recognized; all of them have flagella, and all exhibit a method of binary fission, described below, which is characteristic of the class.

A typical flagellum, seen under the light microscope, is a long, flexible, and, as the name implies, whip-like organelle, used in locomotion and sometimes in feeding. The fine structure revealed by the electron microscope is more complicated. The length of the flagellum consists of a ring of 9 parallel fibrillae surrounding a central strand of 2 fibrillae; the members of the ring are double, the central fibrillae single (Fig. 45E). All lie in a matrix of about the same density as the surrounding cytoplasm and they are enclosed within a sheath. The 2 central fibrillae stop at the cell surface, but the 9 (or 18) peripheral ones penetrate the ectoplasm and end in it, forming a hollow tube; this is the structure which, in preparations made for light microscopy, appears as a solid, densely staining body generally known as the basal granule or blepharoplast (Fig. 45 and cf. Fig. 112, and see Manton, 1952, 1953, 1956; Pitelka, 1949, 1956; Pitelka and Schooley, 1955, 1958; Anderson, Saxe, and Beams, 1956). Now the structure described is precisely that of the cilium of a metazoan cell (Fawcett and Porter, 1954; Bradfield, 1955) or of a ciliate (p. 215) and in fact there is no real distinction between a cilium and a flagellum; the basal granule of the latter is really a kinetosome. Generally, a flagellum is long and a cilium is short; most ciliates have a more or less continuous covering of very numerous cilia, while flagella are few, usually 1 or 2, or sometimes up to 20 or so. But the Hypermastigina may possess thousands of short flagella, while some ciliates have few and long cilia (Figs. 83, 171). It is a matter of convenience to use the word flagellum for the ordinarily long organelle of the Mastigophora and cilium for the short one of ciliates; in doubtful cases, such as the Opalinata (p. 149), it does not matter which word is used, and the doubt about the name expresses a real doubt about the interpretation of the facts. Physiologically, there is a distinction; some flagella, like cilia, have a paddling, or rather breast, stroke, but usually, when a flagellum beats, a wave is initiated proximally and passes towards the tip, increasing in velocity and amplitude as it goes, and the rapid succession of such waves involves different levels of the whole organelle simultaneously. The means by which flagellar movement imparts motion to the organism is discussed for a simple case on

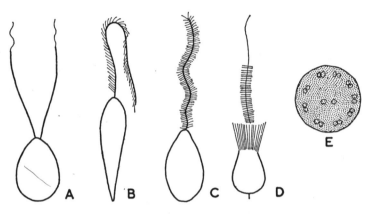

FIG. 45. Flagella. A, acronematic; B, stichonematic; C, pantonematic; D, pantacronematic; E, diagram of the arrangement of the 9 double, peripheral and 2 single, central fibrillae within the sheath of a flagellum or cilium. (A–C after Vlk; D, after Petersen.)

p. 76; it may be very effective, and *Monas stigmatica*, for example, is said to cover 40 times its own length per second when swimming freely. Not all flagella are locomotory: that of *Peranema* (p. 83) is very likely a sensory organelle; the flagella of sedentary forms such as the choanoflagellates are used for feeding (see Lowndes, 1936, 1941a, b, 1943, 1944, 1945).

By means of the ordinary light microscope, two main types of flagellum have been distinguished, the lash-flagellum, in which the main filament is prolonged by means of a finer end-piece (Fig. 45A), and the *Flimmergeissel* (Fig. 45 B, C), in which the axis bears fine, flexible lateral processes, or mastigonemata, constituting the so-called *Flimmer*. A photograph of *Flimmer* was published by Mainx in 1928, and since then it has been described by Petersen (1929), Deflandre (1934), and by Vlk (1938), who demonstrated it in living specimens of *Mallomonas acaroides*; it appears in some electron-microscope photographs of flagella (for discussion see Deflandre, 1950). Nevertheless, the existence of natural *Flimmer* has been denied, notably by Owen (1947, 1949), who regarded it as an artefact. Deflandre's classification of flagella (1934) is as follows (Fig. 45 A–D):

A. *Acronematic*: with a single endpiece or terminal mastigoneme (Phytomonadina, some Zoomastigina).
B. *Stichonematic*: with a single row of lateral mastigonemes (*Euglena*).
C. *Pantonematic*: with a double row of mastigonemes(Chrysomonadina).
D. *Pantacronematic*: with both terminal and lateral mastigonemes (Craspedomonadea).
E. *Simple*: apparently without mastigonemes (*Trypanosoma*).

The Mastigophora comprise the most primitive of Protozoa and must have included the ancestors of the other classes. The relatively primitive level of some existing forms is reflected in the variety and plasticity of their nutritional physiology. Most of the Phytomastigina have chlorophyll, are holophytic, and can, at least in theory, synthesize their food from carbon dioxide, water, and mineral salts; they are autotrophs. Some differ only in that, instead of nitrates, they require ammonium salts for their sources of nitrogen, and these are called mesotrophs; others, the metatrophs, require organic growth factors, such as amino acids. All three conditions may be found within a single genus, e.g. *Euglena*. All of the Zoomastigina, and some of the Phytomastigina, are heterotrophic, that is, dependent on organic food, which they cannot synthesize for themselves, and these feed on particular material (phagotrophic or holozoic feeding) or on food in solution (osmotrophic or saprozoic). One species may not be limited to a single means of nutrition.

Asexual reproduction is universal, typically by means of a process of binary fission which contrasts sharply with that seen in ciliates. The basal granule (blepharoplast or kinetosome) of the flagellum divides, and it frequently acts as a centriole. The old flagellum remains with one of the daughter granules and the other develops a new flagellum. The nucleus divides. Division of the body begins anteriorly and its cleavage plane is longitudinal, so that the daughters are symmetrical from the start (Figs. 49, 73, *d*). Fission of this kind is said to be symmetrigenic; it is seen at its simplest among the trypanosomids but the more complex figures of, for example, *Trichomonas* (Fig. 76 E, F) are essentially of the same kind. Flagellates may at times, as in the life-histories of some trypanosomes, divide by multiple fission. They also reproduce sexually, though the capacity for sexual reproduction appears to have been lost over wide taxonomic areas, so to speak, and its occasional retention in unexpected places is not easily explained. For example, as far as we know, no euglenids can reproduce sexually, except a single genus, *Scytomonas* (*Copromonas*), and this does not appear to be a primitive, but a very specialized form. Likewise, on the animal side, sex is very rare in the more primitive orders (e.g. Protomonadina) but it appears in the highly evolved Hypermastigina, not among the simpler lophomonads, but in the very specialized symbionts of wood-eating insects (see p. 141), among which the sexual phase appears to be evoked by hormones secreted by the host.

Flagellates occur in all known habitats, free-living in the sea, fresh water, and the soil. Many are, in the broad sense, parasitic; some, notably among the Trypanosomidae, are pathogens of the greatest importance; of the Zoomastigina, only one order, the Protomonadina, contains any free-living forms (unless the choanoflagellates be counted separately), all others are completely entozoic.

SUBCLASS PHYTOMASTIGINA

There is no single character on which members of this subclass can be diagnosed. The occurrence of chlorophyll by itself is no help. Some phytoflagellates, like *Chlamydomonas*, which have chlorophyll and a wall of cellulose or hemicellulose, are, in effect, plants. *Euglena* normally has chloroplasts and is holophytic, but their loss can be induced experimentally by treatment with streptomycin in *Euglena gracilis* (Provasoli, Hutner, and Schatz, 1948) or by prolonged culture in the dark in *E. mesnili* (or, more correctly, *E. deses*) (Lwoff and Dusi, 1935) and in these cases the chloroplasts are not re-formed after return to the light. Further, some clones of *E. gracilis*, in circumstances which are not understood, give rise to colourless (apochlorotic) strains without either chlorophyll or eye-spots and these have been found to be identical with a flagellate previously known as *Astasia longa* (Pringsheim and Hovasse, 1948, 1950; Fig. 48B). Such examples make it easy to understand how irreversibly apochlorotic species have become well established, and their affinities and taxonomic positions are then determined by their remaining structural characters; thus *Peranema* shares with the green Euglenoidina the distinctive and specialized organization of the anterior end (p. 74), and in spite of the fact that it is always colourless there is no doubt about its affinities. This instability of some phytoflagellates, however it may stand in the way of making simple diagnostic definitions, is in itself of the greatest interest, and the taxonomic difficulties encountered truly reflect the biological plasticity of the material. We are, then, still constrained to define the subclass as consisting of flagellates with photosynthetic pigments and their colourless relatives.

Most of the Phytomastigina (but not the Dinoflagellata, q.v.) have a vesicular nucleus, and usually only 1 or 2 flagella. Asexual reproduction by longitudinal binary fission is usual (Fig. 49) and may be the only means of propagation known; failure of the daughter cells to separate may produce colonies. Sexual reproduction is common and has been widely studied in the Phytomonadina, and also occurs in a few members of groups otherwise, so far as is known, exclusively asexual, for example, in *Noctiluca* among the free-living Dinoflagellata and in *Scytomonas pusilla* (= *Copromonas subtilis*) in the Euglenoidina. Encystation is common. Phytoflagellates occur in the sea, fresh water, and soil, and some of the Dinoflagellata have a well-developed parasitic habit.

The subclass may be divided into 6 orders, as follows:

Order 1. **Chrysomonadina**—yellow, brown, orange, or colourless. Often without a definite cell wall and able to form pseudopodia. Cysts characteristic, with a siliceous wall and a collared aperture closed by a plug. (*Ochromonas.*)

2. **Cryptomonadina**—yellow, brown, red, green, or colourless. With a definite body form. Flattened, with a vestibule and vestibular groove on the ventral surface, into which opens the contractile vacuole. (*Chilomonas.*)

3. **Phytomonadina**—usually green, sometimes colourless. With a definite body form and wall of cellulose (or hemicellulose). Usually biflagellate. (*Chlamydomonas, Volvox.*)

4. **Euglenoidina**—green or colourless, usually elongated. With a reservoir, which contains the roots of the flagella and receives the contents of the contractile vacuole and opens anteriorly to the exterior. (*Euglena, Peranema.*)

5. **Chloromonadina**—rare and little known; usually green, flattened, with 2 flagella, often 1 trailing. (*Goniostomum.*)

6. **Dinoflagellata**—with 2 flagella, 1 beating transversely and 1 posteriorly, each in a groove; often with a cellulose envelope which may be divided into plates. (*Ceratium, Noctiluca.*)

A representative treatment of the subclass, which forms the subject matter of many botanical studies, such as those on freshwater algae by West and Fritsch (1927) and Smith (1950), lies outside the scope of this book, which offers no more than a guide to some members of the Euglenoidea and Dinoflagellata, groups which traditionally find places in zoological syllabuses.

ORDER EUGLENOIDINA

The body of a euglenid flagellate is usually elongated and is covered by a firm pellicle, capable of some degree of deformation, as during metaboly or euglenoid movement (Fig. 47). Most members of the order are green and contain chlorophyll *a* and *b* in plastids whose shape and arrangement are useful in taxonomy, but many have lost their photosynthetic pigment and, with it, usually, the eye-spot or stigma, and these apochlorotic species are osmo- or phago-trophic. The reserve substance paramylum, found only in this order, is closely related to starch, but gives no colour reaction with iodine; it occurs throughout the endoplasm but more particularly in pyrenoids, which are associated with the plastids (Fig. 48c).

The anterior end of a euglenid is characteristic (Figs. 45 A, B; 53 B, C). Opening to the exterior slightly to one side of the apex of the organism is an invaginated pocket, the reservoir,* into which the contractile vacuole empties. The opposite wall of the reservoir bears the eye-spot, when this is present. There is generally a single obvious flagellum, inserted on the floor of the reservoir and emerging through its aperture; it bears near its base a lenticular thickening thought to play a part in photo-reception (p. 78). In the earlier accounts of the order and especially in textbook descriptions of *Euglena*, the flagellum is often described as possessing a bifurcated root, but, apart from the fact that it is very difficult to see how such a structure could have arisen, there are powerful reasons for supposing that the so-called roots are in fact 2 flagella, one the obvious organ which comes free of the body, and the other greatly reduced and lying entirely within the reservoir and only secondarily associated with its more conspicuous partner (Pringsheim, 1948, 1956). In the first place, many euglenids have 2 distinct flagella (*Eutreptia* in the Euglenidae, all Peranemidae, and some Petalo-monidae such as *Entosiphon*); in some of these, one flagellum is notably shorter than another and it may, as in *Distigma*, show no more externally than a stump; it is easy to see that a little more shortening will provide one long flagellum and another so short as to be contained entirely within the reservoir, a condition realized in *Euglena deses* (= *E. mutabilis*) (see Hollande, 1942) and sometimes seen in preparations of other species (Fig. 48B). If the tip of the short flagellum in this last case were to rest against the axis of the long one the apparent bifurcation of a root as generally portrayed for *Euglena* would be exhibited. Each so-called root does in fact arise from its own blepharoplast, and in longitudinal fission the blepharo-plasts divide in the usual way and the daughters give rise to two long and two short flagella (Fig. 49). Finally, the lenticular thickening on the larger root may occur above or below the junction with the smaller, which is difficult to explain if we are dealing with an organized morphological system, but it is easy to understand if there is no more than an adventitious coherence of two organelles either above or below the thickening on one of them. There is a third flagellum in the parasitic genus *Euglenamorpha*; it seems likely that in some species of *Astasia* and *Menoidium* the short flagellum is completely lost.

The nucleus is large, with a karyosome that persists and divides in mitosis; both karyosome and nuclear membrane are usually extremely

---

* The reservoir is sometimes called the gullet: it has nothing to do with feeding and the term should be abandoned. In phagotrophic forms like *Peranema* (p. 83) the cyto-stome exists side by side with the reservoir (Fig. 53A).

difficult if not impossible to detect in the living organism. Propagation is typically asexual by binary fission (Fig. 49). In the green, but not the colourless species, mitosis occurs only in the dark and begins an hour or two after the onset of darkness. This rhythm may be overcome by providing the flagellates with a rich organic medium, when mitosis becomes continuous, and Leedale (1959) suggested that the facts might be explained by the different modes and rates of nutrition obtaining under different conditions of light and dark with various media. Sexual reproduction has been reported in a single species, the organism known to Dobell (1908) as *Copromonas subtilis* and sometimes identified with *Scytomonas pusilla* (see Gatenby and Smyth, 1940). Encystation is common.

The Euglenoidina are abundant in fresh water, but they also occur in the sea (Pringsheim, 1953); some are coprophilous (*Scytomonas*) and a few even parasitic.* They frequently appear in mixed infusions.

A general account of the order, with a bibliography, was given by Jahn (1946).

The presence of paramylum and the organization of the anterior end are unique and distinctive characters of the Euglenoidina, which is a natural order. It is not easy to subdivide. In the older systems, 3 families were recognized, the Euglenidae, which were green, the Astasiidae, which were colourless osmotrophs, and the Peranemidae, which were colourless phagotrophs usually characterized by 'cytopharyngeal' rods (pp. 84, 86). That this arrangement is artificial is shown by a comparison between *Astasia* and *Euglena*: the former consists of apochlorotic counterparts of the latter, though not in all cases determined (Pringsheim, 1942, 1956); similarly, the euglenid genus *Phacus* has its apochlorotic counterpart in *Hyalophacus* (Pringsheim, 1936; Pochmann 1942). In the circumstances, it seems best to adopt provisionally a scheme proposed by Hollande in 1942, in which here, however, the suborders have been given no more than family rank.

Fam. Euglenidae—autotrophic and osmotrophic; metabolic; the flagella directed anteriorly and usually 2 with one much reduced. *Euglena, Astasia, Phacus.*

* The parasites are not well known and a study of their distribution, life-cycles, and host-parasite relations would be rewarding. Most infect freshwater invertebrates such as gastrotrichs, rotifers, and turbellarians; they have also been reported from the large ciliates *Stentor* and *Spirostomum* (Howland, 1928a) and from the eggs of a nudibranch (Zerling, 1933). One species at least, *Astasia chaetogastris* in the body-cavity of an oligochaete, appears to be highly pathogenic (Codreanu and Codreanu, 1928), but most are probably harmless and even casual in their parasitism. After the loss of their pigment and eye-spot, which often occurs, the maintenance of euglenoid movement gives them a deceptive resemblance to some acephaline gregarines and one species was for a time caught up in the genus *Monocystis*; Alexeieff (1912) has discussed the possible origin of the Sporozoa from the Euglenoidina. In addition to the references already given the following, though not exhaustive, will be found helpful—Haswell (1907), Beauchamp (1910), Nieschultz (1922), Wenrich (1924), Hall (1931), and, for the fullest account so far issued of the life-cycle of a parasitic euglenid, Johnson (1934).

Fam. Peranemidae—colourless, usually phagotrophic; metabolic with 2 flagella, one trailing; with a distinctive rod apparatus used in feeding. *Peranema, Heteronema.*

Fam. Petalomonidae—colourless, compressed; not metabolic; with a single flagellum or with 2, one then trailing. *Scytomonas, Entosiphon.*

Euglena gracilis Klebs

E. gracilis (Fig. 48) occurs in nature in standing water, such as duckponds, pools in meadows and pastures, especially those containing a certain amount of decaying weeds or other organic debris; it is generally accompanied by other species of the genus. It must be kept in moderate light, towards which it swims. If it is important that only a single species be present, cultures should be obtained from an appropriate institution. The taxonomy of *Euglena* is well covered by Johnson (1944), Gojdics (1953), and especially Pringsheim (1956). *E. gracilis* is the pigmented counterpart of the apochlorotic *Astasia longa* (Pringsheim and Hovasse, 1948, 1950). For E.M. studies see Wolken and Palade (1953).

The living organism

While it is swimming freely, in a drop of water, *E. gracilis* is a green, fusiform, sometimes almost cylindrical, organism, about 50 to 60 μ long, tapering posteriorly; the anterior end is obliquely truncated, with the reservoir opening on its slanting face (Fig. 48A). There is a red eye-spot or stigma. The flagellum is about three-quarters of the length of the body; the small flagellum contained within the reservoir is extremely difficult to see in the living animal.

The description given by Lowndes (1941*b*, 1943) of the movement of *E. viridis* is equally true of *E. gracilis* (Brown, 1945). The flagellate must be mounted without pressure, as in a hanging drop or on a depression slide (Fig. 46). The flagellum, swung back posteriorly, generates a wave from base to tip about 12 times per second. The body rotates about once a second, and as it does so it also gyrates about the line A. It is the gyration of the body acting on the principle of the moving inclined plane or screw which forces it along in the direction of the arrow. In *Euglena*, where the flagellum is pointed backwards during locomotion, the flagellum may itself contribute a little to the forward thrust, but this is not necessary; in the related *Rhabdomonas* (= *Menoidium*) studied by Lowndes, the flagellum is pointed more laterally (Fig. 52) and can add nothing to the impetus. Lowndes's *Euglena*, 52 to 64 μ long, travelled at 168 μ per second.

From time to time *Euglena* settles on the slide, the flagellum is withdrawn or vibrates ineffectively, and the whole organism sinuously writhes, contractions passing along it in reversible peristaltic waves (Fig. 47). This so-called metaboly or euglenoid movement may lead to a limited locomotion, and it is extremely important in soil-dwelling forms such as *E. deses* which commonly discard the flagellum and move by wriggling among earth particles; on the other hand, *E. acus* shows almost no metaboly, and the related genus *Phacus* (p. 82) is practically rigid.

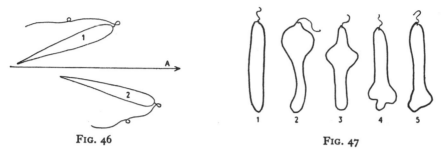

FIG. 46   FIG. 47

FIG. 46. *Euglena viridis.* To illustrate locomotion: for explanation see text. (After Lowndes.)

FIG. 47. Five successive stages of euglenoid movement. (Original: D. L. M.)

Living and fixed material

The structure of the anterior end can be understood only by means of a comparison of well-fixed and living material (Fig. 48). The reservoir opens just to the side of the anterior tip and into it the contractile vacuole discharges and re-forms from a circle of contributory vacuoles (Chadefaud, 1937; Hyman, 1937, 1938). The 2 flagella, each with its own blepharoplast, arise from the floor of the reservoir; normally they unite near the photoreceptor and so give the bifurcated impression illustrated in most of the books, but occasionally they remain separate and then their independence is clear (Fig. 48B, and see Pringsheim and Hovasse, 1950). The free part of the flagellum is, as in many euglenids, ribbon-like. Its contained portion bears, near the point of coalescence with its small partner, a swelling, considered to be a photo-receptor. Related to this and lying on the wall of the reservoir (conventionally called the dorsal wall) is an aggregate of oily droplets containing a carotenoid pigment and staining blue with iodine: this is the stigma or eye-spot.

It has long been supposed that the photo-receptor and stigma act together to control the orientation of *Euglena* in light. They are both present in all green, that is, light dependent, euglenids; when the eye-spot disappears under experimental conditions, so does the photo-receptor; colourless forms usually lack both the stigma and the light reactions seen in their coloured relatives. The optimal sensitivity is to the blue part of the spectrum, which is absorbed by the stigma. After experimental destruction of the stigma by ultraviolet light, the light reactions disappear (Tchakotine, 1936).

Coloured forms of *Euglena* are always photosensitive, moving towards moderate and away from bright light. They orientate in a beam either towards or away from the source, and they adjust their movements to the direction of incident light. As explained by Mast (1938*b*), when the moving

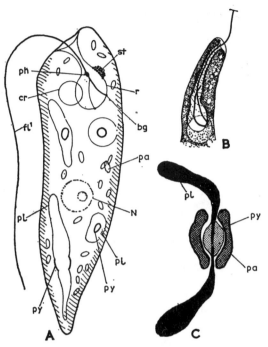

FIG. 48. A, *Euglena gracilis*: diagrammatic (× 1,500); B, *E. gracilis*, achlorotic strain (= *Astasia longa*): anterior end, showing the short flagellum free from the long one and crossing it (Flemming; H.H.); C, diagram to show the relations of a pyrenoid. (A and B original; C after Hollande.)

bg, basal granule; *cv*, contractile vacuole; *fl*^{I}., main flagellum; N, nucleus; *pa*, paramylum; *ph*, thickening on flagellum (photoreceptor); *pl*, chloroplast; *py*, pyrenoid; *r*, reservoir; *st*, stigma.

body rotates, the stigma acts as a screen, and, when light falls from the side, the photo-receptor is alternately exposed and shielded; the organism adjusts its position until the receptor is continuously exposed, and, as a glance at Fig. 48 A will show, this happens only when the source of light is straight in front of or behind the flagellate.

The chlorophyll of *E. gracilis* is contained in normally about a dozen chloroplasts, circular, ovoid, shield-shaped, or polygonal in outline; the plastids are not always as plainly individualized as in *E. gracilis*, and then the term plastidome is applied to their whole aggregate (*E. viridis*). The pyrenoids are the main centres for the accumulation of paramylum, though it also occurs independently in the cytoplasm in species that have no pyrenoids naturally or have been deprived of them experimentally, e.g. 'Astasia longa' (Pringsheim and Hovasse, 1948). The number varies greatly with the condition of the culture (Baker, 1933). Pyrenoids (Fig. 48c) are double disks with a thin layer of plastid clamped between each proteinaceous moiety and the whole surmounted by a cap of paramylum; they are further discussed by Pringsheim (1956). A short summary of information about other cytoplasmic inclusions is given by Jahn (1946) and more details will be found in papers by Brown (1930b), Baker (1933), Hollande (1942), and Hovasse in Pringsheim and Hovasse (1948).

The nucleus is spherical, and at or just behind the centre of the organism, except when dividing. In life it is a vesicle so transparent that it rarely shows any structure at all. By phase contrast microscopy or in fixed material, there is seen to be a karyosome and F+ granules of DNA which, as seen in squashes, are really linked in minute filaments.

Like all euglenids, E. gracilis reproduces by binary fission (Fig. 49). The nucleus migrates anteriorly till it lies very close to the reservoir and the karyosome elongates slightly in the transverse line. The filamentous structure of the chromatin becomes more apparent in prophase; this change is usually interpreted as the appearance of the chromosomes for the first time, but according to Leedale these structures maintain their individuality during interphase and merely become more recognizable in the looser prophase arrangement. During succeeding stages the karyosome elongates further, becomes dumb-bell shaped and finally severs into 2 portions at the end of anaphase. Meanwhile the chromatin threads have become orientated parallel to the elongated karyosome, and in a narrow circle about it; they are at first double and then single, that is, the chromatids are separated. They move in anaphase towards the poles, not synchronously, but in a staggered migration. There is neither metaphase nor anaphase plate. Nor is there a spindle. In spite of the topographical propinquity of nucleus and blepharoplasts, the latter play no part in mitosis and never act as division centres. In cell division, the external part of the flagellum is lost and the reservoir and stigma divide. Each blepharoplast divides and the new, short flagella for a time beat independently, so that in this respect the dividing individual passes through a stage resembling the adult of E. deses. The final stages of separation are actively assisted by the beat of the fully developed flagella. It is by no means clear how the chromatids are separated and dispatched to opposite poles during this peculiar mitosis; the explanations proposed (Tschenzoff, 1916; Baker, 1926; S. R. Hall, 1931; Gojdics, 1934; R. P. Hall,1937; Krichenbauer, 1937; Hollande, 1942) are summarized and criticized by Leedale (1958) in a beautifully illustrated paper (and see Fig. 49 F–G).

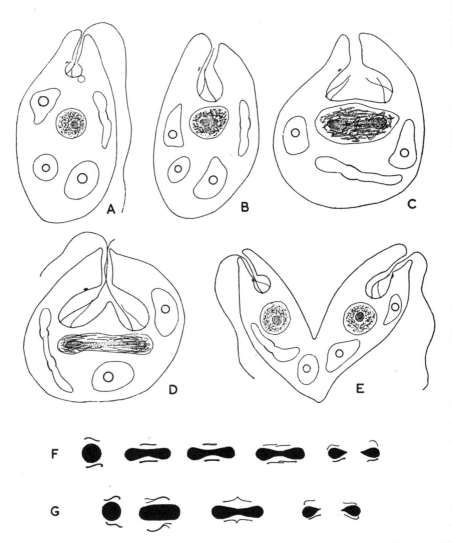

FIG. 49. *Euglena*: binary fission. A–E, fission: semi-diagrammatic. Duplication of chromosomes, here shown at C (metaphase) is in some species first detectable earlier (at B, prophase) or later (at D, anaphase). F and G illustrate alternative theories of chromosome duplication and separation of chromatids. In F the chromosomes are split and their products slide one on the other towards opposite poles. In G, the chromatids are thought of as stripping apart in a widening V. (A–E combined after various authors; F and G, adapted from Leedale.)

Various types of cysts have been described (Günther, 1928; Jahn, 1946): in the opinion of Krichenbauer (1937) they are all—whether called temporary or resistant or multiplication cysts—stages in the production (which may never be finally achieved) of a palmella stage. An individual of *E. gracilis* may withdraw its flagellum, round off, and surround itself with a gelatinous envelope. After a time the free-swimming form may emerge from what, in that event, corresponds to Günther's temporary cyst. Or the cyst may grow, its contents dividing to form the palmella stage (Fig. 50); in old cultures, these stages cling to the bottoms and walls of the container or may produce a surface scum. Within the gelatinous mass the organisms

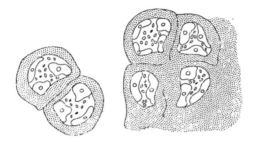

FIG. 50. *Euglena gracilis*. Stages in the growth of the palmella phase. (After Krichenbauer.)

divide to form up to 32 or 64 immobile individuals which, after growing flagella, break free. These and other encysted stages may play a very important part in the life-histories of euglenids and may even become the dominant stage (Johnson, 1934; Steinecke, 1932). They may withstand a certain amount of water-loss, but not prolonged desiccation; perhaps more importantly they provide some protection against strong and harmful light intensities.

Permanent preparations

Good general results are obtained by spinning down cultures, fixing *en masse* in Flemming or Champy, and staining in H.H. after attaching to the slide by the celloidin method (p. 429). Acetocarmine squashes are good for nuclei, especially in division.

Culture

E. gracilis tolerates a wide range of pH from 4·5 to 8·5 and is easy to maintain. A culture was kept for over 20 years at King's College, London, in 3 in. × 1 in. open tubes of tap-water containing 12–15 wheat grains. Three or four boiled wheat grains were replaced once a fortnight and the

flagellates sub-cultured when the medium began to look dirty or congested.*
For more refined methods, see p. 403.

Phacus Dujardin

Members of the genus are often large (100 μ or more), striking, and
easily recognized. They usually occur in small numbers among other
euglenids but may form concentrations of their own. They are typically
freshwater flagellates, found in organically rich waters; a few occur in the

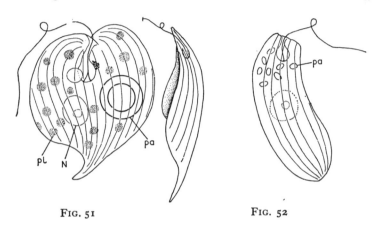

FIG. 51   FIG. 52

FIG. 51. *Phacus pleuronectes.* × 500. A, from above; B, from the side. (Redrawn from
various authors.)

N, nucleus; *pa*, paramylum body; *pl*, chloroplast.

FIG. 52. *Rhabdomonas incurva.* × 2,000. (After Hall.) *Abbr. as above.*

sea and *P. pleuronectes*, naturally confined to fresh water, can be adapted to
sea water (Finley, 1930). *Phacus* is a far easier object of study than
Euglena.

The body (Fig. 51) is flat, asymmetrical, with more or less of a tail; a
firm pellicle maintains a constant, almost rigid shape, which is basically
heart-like, or like an elm-leaf; the tail in *P. longicauda* is drawn out; *P.
tortus* is far more strongly twisted than *P. pleuronectes*. The pellicle is
marked with longitudinal striations, very slightly spiral in *P. pleuronectes*,
more so in *P. longicauda*, and very strongly spiral in *P. tortus*. The anterior
apparatus of reservoir with flagellum, stigma, and contractile vacuole
is complete; the vacuole functions as in *Euglena* (Hyman, 1938); there still
seems to be some doubt whether there is a second small flagellum associated
with the large one (cf. Hall and Jahn, 1929; and Haye, 1930); the flagellar

* Personal communication from Mr. Charles Biddolph.

roots are, as usual, indistinguishable in the living organism. The chloro-plastids are almost always numerous small plates scattered in the endo-plasm; pyrenoids are only exceptionally present and the reserves are normally contained in a few large paramylum bodies, the shape, size, and number of which are important in taxonomy. The genus has an apo-chlorotic counterpart in *Hyalophacus* (Pringsheim, 1936). For morphology and taxonomy see Skvortzow (1928), Pochmann (1942), or Allegre and Jahn (1943); division was described by Krichenbauer (1937).

Culture and permanent preparations

As for *Euglena*.

Rhabdomonas incurva Fresenius

R. incurva (= *Menoidium incurvum*) is a small euglenid, about 15 to 25 μ long. It is colourless, osmotrophic, and banana-shaped, and it commonly occurs in company with *Euglena* in mixed infusions, where it is con-spicuous by its curved, firm outline and well-marked pellicular ridges (Fig. 52). Though gyrating rapidly, it swims rather more slowly than *Euglena*; and the flagellum, generally held at right angles to the body, is easier to see. There are no chloroplasts, but paramylum bodies are present, usually grouped near the anterior end. The reservoir is obvious, but there is no stigma, and the detailed structure of the anterior has never been de-scribed. Division was reported by Hall (1923), who also gives some account of the morphology. The status of the genus *Rhabdomonas* in relation to the similar but flattened *Menoidium* is discussed by Pringsheim (1942). For cytology, see Smyth (1945b).

Peranema trichophorum (Ehrenberg)

*Peranema** lives in ponds rich in organic matter, a typical euglenid habitat where it is often accompanied by other species. Its occurrence is not predictable and it is never abundant, but it is large, easy to recognize and culture, and it is certainly more suitable for introductory studies than the small euglenids of the textbooks. An excellent description by Chen (1950) has been largely confirmed and extended by the E.M. studies of Roth (1959).

The living organism

Peranema (Fig. 53) is easily distinguished by its slow, steady progression and its habit of stopping from time to time and spasmodically distorting its

* Apart from *P. granulifera*, which was described by Penard in 1890 and apparently never seen again, *P. trichophorum* seems to be the only species (see Pitelka, 1945).

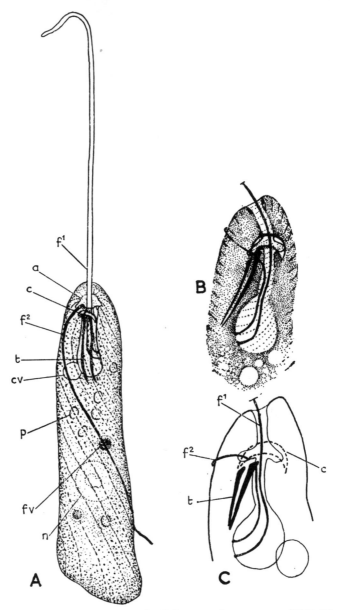

FIG. 53. *Peranema trichophorum.* A, the living organism. ×1,450. (N.B. The adherent flagellum can be seen only by dark-field or phase-contrast microscopy.) B, Anterior end, detail; fixed Champy, stained Heidenhain. ×2,650. C, the same; diagrammatic. The reservoir, receiving the contractile vacuole, communicates with the exterior by a duct which has a principal aperture transmitting the free flagellum; at about the level of the cytostome (broken line) the duct expands and here also communicates with the exterior to release the smaller attached flagellum; it is uncertain whether this expansion of the reservoir duct is confluent with the cytostome; note cytostome, with crescentic lips usually prominent in stained preparations (see B), the lower lip supported by the trichites. The deeply stained peripheral rods are protrichocysts or muciferous bodies in B; the pronounced basophil ring about the main aperture of the reservoir is always conspicuous and is not understood. (A after Hall and Powell with additions from Chen; B and C, original.)

a, main aperture of reservoir duct; *c,* cytostome; *cv,* contractile vacuole; f^1, free flagellum; f^2 adherent flagellum; *fv,* food vacuole; *n,* nucleus; *p,* paramylum; *t,* trichite.

body. It has no chlorophyll but its granular cytoplasm has a yellowish-grey tinge. The hind end is blunter than the front and looks truncated or even invaginated; it is an area of defecation. The pellicle is lightly striated and the striae mark the distribution of tiny, refringent bodies, best seen after vital staining in Neutral Red or Cresyl Blue or by dark-ground or phase-contrast microscopy; these are the protrichocysts of Chadefaud (1937) or muciferous bodies of Hollande (1942), though it is uncertain whether in fact they have anything to do with production of the mucus undoubtedly secreted by this species (see Jahn, 1946).

There are 2 flagella, each arising from its own basal granule in the reservoir (Lackey, 1933). One extends spirally and backwards about the body, adhering to the pellicle; it can be seen only with dark-ground or phase-contrast microscopy; its function is unknown. The other is free, about as long as the body, thick and very obvious; its function is uncertain; if it is sensory, the fact has not been clearly demonstrated.

Peranema moves in two ways, by swimming and gliding (Mast, 1912). Swimming follows the normal pattern described for other euglenids (p. 76, and see Lowndes, 1936, for photographs), but the commoner gliding has not been satisfactorily explained. It consists of a slow, forward progression, always on the same, that is, ventral side, with the posterior ends of the trichites pointing to the right, and it may take place on the bottom of a container or upside down on a surface film. The flagellum is held straight out in front and motionless except for the tip, which is turned back and moves to describe an ellipse. Progress is slow, about 15 μ per second on a solid substrate, about 20 μ on a surface film. There is no deformation of the body during gliding and it is very difficult to tell how it happens. Lowndes (1941b) pointed out that while it was true that a wave passing from base to tip of a flagellum held in the reverse position would impart a forward force, it was very doubtful that the magnitude of the force generated from so short a length of the flagellum (about a quarter at the most) would be enough to propel the organism even at its relatively low speeds. On the other hand, in the absence of the flagellum, and especially of its tip, gliding is impossible. If part or the whole of the flagellum is accidentally lost or experimentally removed, it regenerates and Chen (1950) found that true gliding does not reappear until almost the entire length has been restored. *Peranema* discharges mucus and sticks hard to its substrate, and it seems possible that this habit may in some way promote or assist gliding.

Euglenoid movement as shown in Fig. 47 does not occur in *Peranema* which is metabolic in rather a different way (Fig. 54). From time to time, often after the tip of the flagellum has touched some solid object, the organism settles, the body shortens and thickens and writhes, particularly at the hind end, which is very mobile and may even bend forward and engulf part of the anterior end like a collar. The movements are spasmodic, and

while they are continued waves of high amplitude run down the flagellum
from base to tip. After a time the organism extends its body, stretches out
its flagellum and glides off in a straight line.

Peranema feeds phagotrophically on a variety of plant and animal food,
to which it is led by a highly developed chemotaxis; it is capable of engulfing

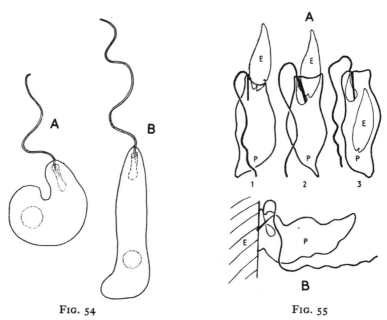

FIG. 54   FIG. 55

FIG. 54. *Peranema trichophorum*. ×625. A. The flagellate recoils and enters
on a 'metabolic' phase. B. Flagellum undulating while the organism returns
to its normal shape. (Both modified after Lowndes.)

FIG. 55. A. *Peranema* (P) swallowing an immobile *Euglena* (E). Three stages
in the process. Note the trichites and the very distensible mouth of the
predator, distinct from the vestibule whence springs the free flagellum.
B. *Peranema* (P) attacking with its trichites the side of a species of *Euglena*
(E) too large for it to swallow. It will suck out the protoplasm through the
slit it makes in the pellicle. (Both modified after Chen.)

prey almost as big as itself and of attacking organisms even larger. The
reservoir is a cul-de-sac receiving the contractile vacuole as in other euglenids (Hyman, 1938); from its floor originate the 2 flagella; there is no
stigma. The cytostome is much smaller, lying ventrally (Fig. 53 B+C);
associated with it are two hyaline rods, the trichites, forming the rod organ.
Feeding has been described by Chen (1950). The prey, say a specimen of
Euglena, is always attacked at its anterior end (Fig. 55 A+B). It is first
touched by *Peranema*, and then the rod organ is brought into contact with
it and somehow seizes a portion of its pellicle. While still held by the rod

organ, as much as possible of the prey is pushed into the now greatly distended cytostome, the rod organ then changes its grip and more is engulfed.
The whole flagellate may be swallowed in 2 to 15 minutes. Larger prey may
be attacked by several specimens, who suck the cytoplasm from punctures
that they make in the pellicle. For some account of digestion, see Chen.

The nucleus is nearly central with a large, sometimes irregular karyosome
or several karyosomes. Division has been described by Hall and Powell
(1928) and Leedale (1958): it follows essentially the same lines as in
Euglena (p. 79). For cytoplasmic inclusions see Hall (1929) and Hollande
(1942).

Permanent preparations

By far the best preparations are made by fixing in bulk with Flemming
or Champy, attaching to a slide with celloidin (p. 429), and staining in
Iron Haematoxylin. Or flagellates may be fixed while adhering of their own
accord to a cover slip.

Culture

Peranema grows well in tap-water with boiled wheat, peas, or rice, if
given small flagellates for food. For a more reliable method, see p. 408.

ORDER DINOFLAGELLATA

The members of this order are very easily recognized by their external
appearance and highly characteristic nucleus (Figs. 56, 57, 64). The body is
covered with a periplast* and is otherwise naked in the Gymnodinina or
protected in the Peridinina by an armour of closely fitting cellulose plates
(Mangin, 1907), the arrangement of which is important in taxonomy. There
are 2 flagella; one is usually ribbon-like and beats transversely in the manner of an undulating membrane; it lies in a groove, the girdle or cingulum,
which divides the body into an anterior epicone and posterior hypocone.
The second, longitudinal flagellum beats towards the posterior in its own
groove, the sulcus. Except for some of the larger species of *Ceratium*,
dinoflagellates usually travel in a spiral path at considerable speeds (125 to
500 μ per second at 18° to 20° C): for details, see Entz (1928) and Peters
(1929).

The plastids are usually brown, but may be yellow or green, and they
vary in size, number, and arrangement (Figs. 57 A, B; 64 A). Their colour
may be masked by that of cytoplasmic pigments, and apoplastic species
occur both in the sea and in fresh water. The free-living forms with plastids

* For the argentophyl reticulum, see Chatton and Hovasse (1934) and Biecheler
(1952).

form food reserves of starch, glycogen, fats, and oils, but it is uncertain how far their autotrophic habit suffices, for coloured as well as colourless species may be heterotrophic (pp. 92, 98, and see Biecheler, 1936 *a*, *b*). Some freshwater species have an eye-spot.

There are no contractile vacuoles, but one or two fluid-filled bladders, the pusules, often faintly pink in colour, and sometimes very large and conspicuous; they are connected to the exterior through a canal, or canals, opening by one of the flagellar pores (Fig. 57 A, B). They may change periodically in volume. Kofoid (1909) suggested that they might have something to do with nutrition, but in fact the function of the pusules is unknown.

The nucleus (Figs. 57B; 64 C, D), both in interphase and mitosis, is highly characteristic, and is known as the dinocaryon. Fundamentally it seems to be like that of euglenids. It is usually massive, filled with strongly F+ chromatic material in a filamentous arrangement which becomes more evident during prophase; the filaments are in fact the chromosomes, which appear to remain individualized and may be recognizable as such in the living organism, during interphase; there may be one or more karyosomes. The onset of mitosis is made the more curious by a display apparently unknown in other organisms, the so-called 'cyclose chromatique' described by Biecheler in 1935 and more fully in 1952, and in which the nuclear contents engage in a slow circulation within the membrane, either round and round or in a figure of eight, and lasting with occasional interruptions for several hours. There is no spindle, the chromosomes arrange themselves parallel to the axis of the dividing nucleus and their behaviour at anaphase poses the same problems as in euglenids (Fig. 49, F, G, and see Grell, 1952, for a discussion, and Grell and Wohlfarth-Bottermann, 1957, for a report of E.M. studies of, among other structures, the chromosomes).

Structures resembling the trichocysts of such flagellates as *Chilomonas* (Hollande, 1942) occur in some dinoflagellates and they are capable of discharging a considerable mucilaginous secretion (Fig. 58).

Except in the aberrant genus *Noctiluca*, reproduction is asexual and by binary fission, which is ordinarily nocturnal. Incomplete multiplication may lead to the production of longitudinal series in colonial form, with a common sulcus and a number of common nuclei (*Polykrikos*). Cysts (Fig. 64E) are common (Entz, 1925) and they may be reproductive.

Dinoflagellates occur, often in very large numbers, in fresh and brackish water and they are common in the neritic waters of the sea; but it is in the plankton of the open ocean that they reach their greatest importance, and together with diatoms and coccolithophorid flagellates, they must be among the most numerous of all marine organisms; their use as indicators of water movements is discussed by Wood (1954). Even under normal conditions, they may colour the water green or brown, and in certain circumstances,

they multiply excessively and produce the local phenomenon known as
'red tide' or 'red water'; in one such occurrence, Allen (1946) reported an
increase in the numbers of *Gonyaulax polyedra* from about 20 to over
1,000,000 per litre, when dinoflagellates practically replaced the diatom population. Red tide is typified by a diurnal discoloration (not always red) of
the sea, nocturnal phosphorescence, and sometimes by a very heavy mortality
of fish and Crustacea, while some animals such as molluscs, which may
survive, can accumulate toxin and become unfit for human food (Connell
and Cross, 1950). The 'zooxanthellae' of Radiolaria are dinoflagellates
(see p. 63), and it has been shown (Zahl and McLaughlin, 1957) that the
same is true of those in a nudibranch, a scyphozoan jelly-fish, and a sea-
anemone.

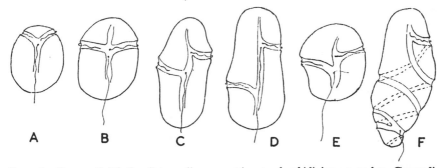

Fig. 56. Gymnodiniid flagellates: diagrammatic. A, *Amphidinium*; B and C, *Gymnodinium*; D and E, *Gyrodinium*; F, *Cochlodinium*. (A and D after Lebour; E and F after Kofoid
and Swezy. Simplified.)

For taxonomy, distribution, and notes on habits, &c., see Kofoid and
Swezy (1921), Lebour (1925), Entz (1927), Eddy (1930), Schiller (1933 and
1937, in Rabenhorst's *Kryptogamen-Flora*), Wailes (1934), Harris (1940),
Graham (1942), and Wood (1954). The parasitic dinoflagellates, of great
interest but outside the scope of this work, are excellently introduced by
Chatton in Grassé's *Traité* (I. i, 1952) and very fully treated in the same
author's paper dated 1920.

Apart from the parasitic and a few primitive forms, the Dinoflagellata
are easily divided into the naked Gymnodinina, including *Oxyrrhis*, the
more typical *Gyrodinium*, and the aberrant *Noctiluca* (all described below),
and the armoured Peridinina, such as *Ceratium* (p. 97).

Note. The determination of Gymnodiniid flagellates is difficult. Fig. 56
indicates the main differences between some common genera. *Amphidinium* (A) has the girdle at the anterior end and is symmetrical. *Gymnodinium*
(B, C) has a central girdle and the ends, if displaced at all, are not more than
one-fifth of the body length apart. In *Gyrodinium* (D, E) the girdle is displaced by more than a fifth, the sulcus is straight or, if twisted, then by less

than half the body diameter. *Cochlodinium* (F) shows marked torsion, the girdle with one and a half loops and widely displaced, the sulcus with at least half a loop. Within the genera, the main differences are in shape, size, colour, and presence or absence of periplastic striae. *Cochlodinium* is exclusively marine; the other genera have species in both fresh and brackish water as well as the sea.

Gyrodinium pavillardi Biecheler

G. pavillardi occurs on sandy bottoms or among algae in the brackish water of salt pans, including those diluted by freshwater inflows, and it is common, except from December to February. In the laboratory it tends to accumulate towards the light, and, in the evenings, on the bottom of its container. It was described by Biecheler first in 1934 and then more fully in 1952; there is an illustrated account of it in Grassé's *Traité*.

The living organism

The body is rounded, only slightly flattened, and measures 25–60 $\mu \times$ 25–45 μ (Fig. 57 A, B). The flagellar grooves are well marked. The girdle (cingulum) runs from the ventral surface in a descending sinistral spiral about the anterior end to rejoin the sulcus towards the antapex. The sulcus is rather narrow between the 2 ventral arms of the cingulum and widens posteriorly, where food is ingested. Anteriorly, it is continued forward as a delicate groove (the acrobase) winding about the apex to return to peter out close to the origin of the cingulum.

The lateral flagellum is flattened and undulating; the longitudinal one, circular in cross section, trails behind the body. As it moves, the organism rotates along a path that sways slightly from side to side.

Under very good optical conditions, tiny rod-like or spindle-shaped bodies, set just below the periplast, are visible. These are trichocysts and they are much more easily demonstrated by exploding them. As in the related *Gymnodinium*, different irritants produce different degrees of response (Fig. 58). In Methylene Blue the trichocysts are extruded immediately and coagulate to form an irregular continuous mass about the organism with a few protruding filaments. In osmium tetroxide vapour, the trichocysts also explode and they swell, but they do not fuse (cf. *Oxyrrhis marina*, p. 94). Though absent from some species, trichocysts occur among both naked and armoured dinoflagellates.

The pusule in this species is small, single, and opens by the anterior flagellar pore. It does not change significantly in size.

The chromatophores are numerous, yellowish green, and they radiate from a clear central area sometimes, on uncertain grounds, called the

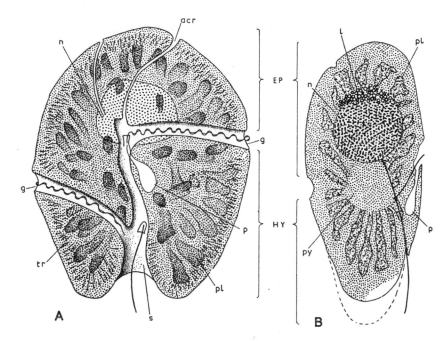

FIG. 57. *Gyrodinium pavillardi*. × 1,500. A, the entire organism; B, optical section. (After Biecheler.)

acr, acrobase; *EP*, epicone; *g*, girdle (cingulum); *HY*, hypocone; *l*, lipid globules; *n*, nucleus; *p*, pusule; *pl*, plastid; *py*, 'pyrenoid'; *s*, sulcus; *tr*, trichocyst.

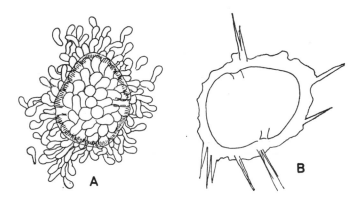

FIG. 58. *Gymnodinium* after discharge of the trichocysts: A, in osmium tetroxide; B, in Methylene Blue. (Redrawn after Biecheler.)

'pyrenoid'. Whether or not it is autotrophic, as one might suppose from the presence of the plastids, *G. pavillardi* is certainly phagotrophic, and is capable of attacking and ingesting prey practically as large as itself, such as the oligotrichous ciliate *Strombidium* (Fig. 59). According to Biecheler, if *Gyrodinium* touches with its anterior end a specimen of *Strombidium*, the two separate after a short pause and swim away without incident. But if contact is made by the posterior pole of the flagellate, the prey is at once somehow immobilized; it appears to be stunned and the curious

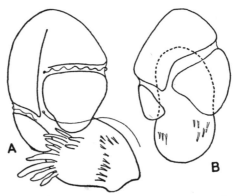

FIG. 59. *Gyrodinium pavillardi* capturing (A) and in-gesting (B) a specimen of *Strombidium*. The ciliate is held in the region of its frontal membranellae and ingested in the ventral part of the sulcus, the lips of which are distended. (After Biecheler.)

fact is that it does not discharge its own trichocysts although it is itself capable of attacking, among other Protozoa, species of the dinoflagellate *Peridinium*. At any rate, the ciliate is held in the region of the sulcus of its predator, and is there, more particularly at the posterior end, ingested, the lips of the groove gaping until the ciliate is finally engulfed, when the normal shape is regained. Ingestion takes about 10 minutes, digestion some 5 or 6 hours.

The nucleus is large, about 30 μ in diameter, rounded or slightly oval, and lies in the epicone. It has the characteristic appearance of the dino-caryon (p. 88 and Fig. 57 A, B) and in mitosis it exhibits the chromatic circulation already described.

Division usually occurs while swimming, exceptionally in the cyst. Cleavage passes from the hind end of the sulcus forwards, obliquely, so that the left moiety of the dividing flagellate lies in front of the right.

G. pavillardi can form gelatinous cysts but they are relatively rare in this species. Elsewhere, cysts are common and may become very large and sometimes crescent-shaped but still easily identifiable as the contained dinoflagellate usually retains its characteristic shape.

Culture

G. *pavillardi* has not yet been successfully cultured. Dinoflagellates are difficult subjects and a medium suitable for one species may fail with a closely related one. For methods, see p. 403.

Unless present in large numbers, *Gyrodinium* is not suitable for staining (but see examples following); it should be fixed in Duboscq-Brasil's Fluid and stained in Meyer's Haemalum by centrifugation.

Oxyrrhis marina Dujardin

This naked dinoflagellate is widely distributed in coastal and brackish waters and may appear in quantity in the greenish-brown encrustation or surface scum of sea-water aquaria. Barker (1935) found that it could be obtained by placing small pieces of *Ulva* in sea-water; after some weeks, *Oxyrrhis* might appear in great numbers.

The living organism

Oxyrrhis (Fig. 60) is colourless, transparent, very active, and asymmetrical, measuring 25–35 $\mu \times$ 10–25 μ, with occasional giants 45 μ long.

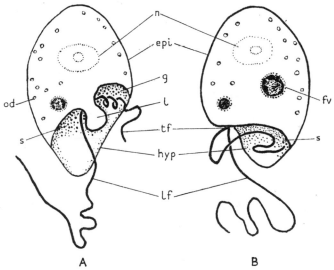

Fig. 60. *Oxyrrhis marina*. Diagrammatic sketch of living flagellate, A, ventral view. B, dorsal view. × 1,150. D. L. M. (After Hall.)

epi, epicone; *fv*, food-vacuole; *g*, girdle; *hyp*, hypocone; *l*, lobe; *lf*, longitudinal flagellum; *n*, nucleus; *od*, oil drop; *s*, sulcus; *tf*, transverse flagellum.

It moves with a lurching rotation in a spiral path. The body is an elongated oval, slightly compressed dorso-ventrally. The flagellar grooves are shallow concavities, far less sharply defined than in *Gyrodinium* or other typical dinoflagellates. The sulcus is a wide excavation, separated ventrally by a lobe from an ill-defined girdle. The longitudinal flagellum may be twice the length of the transverse one, which is ribbon-like, both are acronematic (Dragesco, 1952).

The very transparent cytoplasm makes it easy to see the conspicuous nucleus, with a large (F—) karyosome, and the food bodies. There is no pusule. *Oxyrrhis* is heterotrophic and the food, mainly bacteria and diatoms, tends to accumulate in the hypocone, where it is ingested. Other inclusions are oil drops and, at times, small, clear, non-contractile vacuoles; Biecheler (1952) further recognized small rod-shaped bodies, lying near the nucleus and resembling mitochondria except that they did not stain with Janus Green.

The trichocysts of *Oxyrrhis* are not visible in the untreated organism, but in Janus Green a faint subpellicular striation appears and this represents the rows of trichocysts, a few of which may be discharged. To observe the full effect, run a drop of iodized hydriodic acid under the cover slip of a fresh mount; organisms which come into contact with the acid eject numerous long, fine filaments, so like the well-known trichocysts of ciliates that their nature was suspected by Senn as long ago as 1911.

Division and cysts have been described by Hall (1925a). For E.M. studies, especially of trichocysts, see Dragesco (1952).

Culture and permanent preparations

Oxyrrhis can be maintained in 'sea water containing small amounts of dried hay' (Hall, 1925a). For a better method, see p. 407.

Noctiluca miliaris Suriray*

This aberrant dinoflagellate lives in the surface waters of neritic seas all over the world and the luminescence of shallow water, intensifying to flashes and sparkles at the stroke of an oar, is largely due to the phosphorescence of *Noctiluca*. It travels well in sea-water containers and may be cultured in the laboratory.

The living organism

Noctiluca attains a diameter of 1·5 mm and must be examined undistorted in a depression slide. The body (Fig. 61A) is shaped like a peach, covered with a thick pellicle, and indented by a groove, held uppermost in

---

* The name is sometimes given as *Noctiluca scintillans* (Macartney), as in Kofoid and Swezy (1921), who offer a discussion of the synonymy.

floating and marking the morphological ventral side. Towards this, normally upper, pole most of the cytoplasm is concentrated and the surface is strengthened by a rod-like pellicular thickening (*r*). Close by are grouped the nucleus, flagellar apparatus, mouth (cytostome), and various other organellae, and the whole complex is called the polar mass (Fig. 61B).

Branching and anastomosing threads of cytoplasm stretch from the polar mass across the interior of the sphere, and they exhibit streaming movements. Prominent among the particles which they convey are oil droplets;

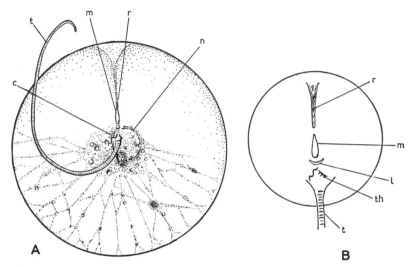

Fig. 61. *Noctiluca*. A, the living organism from the oral pole; the upper half in superficial view, the lower in optical section. × 500. B, diagram to show the relations of the polar mass. D. L. M. (A combined after various authors; B after Delage and Hérouard.)

c, cilium; *l*, lip; *m*, mouth; *n*, nucleus; *r*, rod; *t*, tentade; *th*, tooth.

these may aid in flotation and their oxidation may be either in brief flashes or in a longer glow, and it is evoked by mechanical or other stimuli (Harvey, 1952; Nicol, 1958). Between the threads is a semi-fluid cell sap, which is extremely acid (pH = *c*. 3); the sap has a lower density than sea water and this is said to be due to the retention in the acid medium of light ammonium salts. On mechanical or other stimulation the cell loses acid and sinks to lower levels, where it may remain for some hours before rising: see Gross (1934), Krogh (1939), and Gross and Zeuthen (1948). Mitochondria have been described by Causey (1926).

From the upper end of the groove, which leads to the mouth, springs a thick tentacle, cross-striated, and about as long as the body axis; its slow beat, about 4 to 8 times per minute, rotates the whole organism. Between the base of the tentacle and the mouth are crowded 3 structures of uncertain function. These are a tiny flagellum, here usually called the 'cilium', which flickers with an intermittent undulating movement, a soft, cleft flap, inappropriately called the tooth, and, just behind the cilium, the lip. *Noctiluca* can engulf almost any planktonic animal up to the size of a copepod larva, and the tentacle is the active organ in feeding (Pratje, 1921*a*; Gross, 1934). As it swings it comes into contact with food, which adheres to its sticky surface, and eventually the accumulation of organisms is sucked in by the

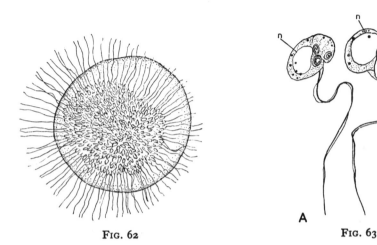

FIG. 62 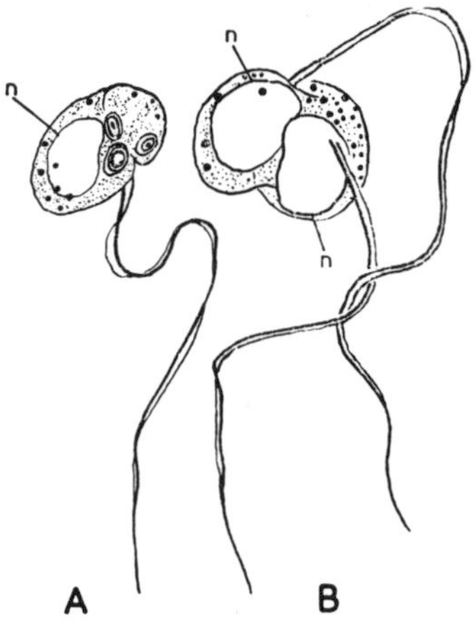   FIG. 63

A   B

FIG. 62. *Noctiluca*: gametogenesis. × 75. The relative size of the 'swarmers' at the oral pole is exaggerated. D. L. M. (Simplified, after Pratje.)

FIG. 63. *Noctiluca*: living 'swarmers'. × 650. D. L. M. (After Gross.)

A, single gamete; B, syngamy; *n*, nucleus.

mouth, to which it may be directed by the lip and the tooth. Defecation also takes place through the mouth. The function of the 'cilium' is unknown; it alternates long periods of inactivity with phases of rapid undulation; possibly it clears the area about the mouth of faecal debris.

Asexual reproduction by binary fission is preceded by a de-differentiation of the organellae, which are regenerated by the daughter cells; the whole process takes from 12 to 24 hours.

At times *Noctiluca* produces swarmers from its polar mass, and there they lie like a cap (Fig. 62) until they develop flagella and break away, when the parent body dies. Each swarmer (Fig. 63) measures 12–23 μ × 12–14 μ, and is bilaterally symmetrical; the anterior region is separated by a constriction from the posterior, which it overhangs, and from the constriction, or girdle, arises a single, narrow, ribbon-like flagellum, nearly 4 times as long as the body. By raising the pH of his culture medium Gross was able to follow the development of these swarmers and found that they were in fact isogametes (Fig. 63B). *Noctiluca* is, as far as we know, the only dino-flagellate to reproduce sexually.

After being classed first with the Coelenterata and then the Rhizopoda, *Noctiluca* was for long grouped with a few related genera to form the independent order Cystoflagellata; the dinoflagellate affinities are discussed by Kofoid (1920) and Pratje (1921*b*). The nucleus both in interphase and mitosis strikingly recalls the dinocaryon (Ishikawa, 1899; Chatton, 1920) and the gametes are like dinospores that have lost the transverse flagellum. The adult tentacle is found elsewhere among dinoflagellates (*Gymnodinium pseudonoctiluca, Pavillardia tentaculifera*). Kofoid considered that the groove leading to the mouth represented the sulcus, the normal site of ingestion in dinoflagellates, and that a trough near the base of the 'cilium' and plainer in young than in old specimens was the girdle; the 'cilium' was thought to be the longitudinal flagellum and the tooth, which sometimes has the appearance of an undulating membrane, a vestige of the transverse flagellum. It is, of course, possible to accept the general affinity of *Noctiluca* with the Dinoflagellata without insisting on such a proposed list of homologies for its parts.

Permanent preparations

Most fixatives cause shrinkage and produce poor results. Hofker (1930) recommends the following: glacial acetic acid, 1 part; trichloracetic acid, 1 part; absolute alcohol, 8 parts. Stain in D.H. or H.H. When mounting support the cover slip till the balsam has set on splinters of glass or slips of matchbox wood.

Culture

Newly captured specimens may live without difficulty in sea water, but they will not eat, and when their contained food is exhausted, they die. For Gross's method, see p. 406.

Ceratium hirundinella Müller

This large Peridinian (armoured) dinoflagellate occurs all over the world in permanent ponds, lakes, and streams of fair size; sometimes, especially in summer, in dense local populations (List, 1913); it is hauled with a plankton net. It is the best known of the relatively few freshwater species of *Ceratium* and its structure, especially that of the skeleton, has been thoroughly described by Entz (1927).

The living organism

C. hirundinella may reach an overall length of 400 μ, though specimens between 250 μ and 300 μ are commoner. The body (Fig. 64A) is flattened dorso-ventrally and drawn out into 3 conspicuous horns, 1 apical on the epicone, and 2 posterior, of which the left is always the larger, on the hypocone; the species is a very variable one, and specimens with a third antapical horn outside the long left one are common and, at times, dominant.

The body is clad in a cellulose armour of articulated plates, leaving a more flexible area (actually containing a few lighter plates not included in the list below) on the ventral surface bordering the sulcus. The anatomy of the ectoskeleton becomes plainer if a drop of 1 per cent Methylene Blue or Toluidine is added to a fresh mount. The plates are arranged in a series of 4 rings; in front and behind the girdle lie 5 pre-equatorial or post-cingular ($1'''-5'''$) plates; in front of the pre-cingulars are 4, or 3, apical ($1'-4'$), and posteriorly, clothing the left horn, are 1 or 2 antapical ($1''''$) plates. The plates are numbered round the body starting from the sulcus and working to the left, and the transverse row to which the plate belongs is indicated by the number of strokes behind the arabic numeral: thus, $4'''$ is the fourth plate to the left of the sulcus in the third (or post-cingular) row. The arrangement of plates, or tabulation, which is of great importance in taxonomy, can be expressed for any peridinian by a formula; that for the genus *Ceratium* is $4' 5'' 5''' 2''''$, sometimes with fusions of apical and antapical plates, and the arrangement is fairly constant (Kofoid, 1907).

All the plates are sculptured with a reticulate pattern and fenestrated by very numerous pores. The tip of the apical horn is open to the exterior. The whole skeleton is internally invested with a cytoplasmic lining (Fig. 64 B).

The flagella are easier to see than in most dinoflagellates and both are circular in cross section. In movement, the longitudinal flagellum describes a cone which at once propels and, doubtless with a contribution from the transverse flagellum, rotates the organism. According to Entz, the rotation and the path pursued are always clockwise.

C. hirundinella is reddish-brown to grey-green in colour, owing to the presence of rod-shaped chromatophores, which are generally distributed in 5 more or less distinct groups, one at the base of each horn and one at each (ventral) end of the girdle (Fig. 64D). There are reserves of starch, glycogen, fat droplets, and other substances. The cytoplasm also contains foreign bodies such as bacteria, small dinoflagellates, and other phytoflagellates (*Chlamydomonas*) and diatoms, and *Ceratium* is capable of capturing food of considerable size. It feeds by two methods. Cytoplasm may be extruded through the pores of the test generally and also through the apical pore to cover the body with a coat from which a feeding net of fine anastomosing threads is spun to entangle the prey; this is partially digested until it is reduced to a state in which, with the cytoplasmic reticulum, it can be withdrawn into the body. Large prey, on the other hand, is engulfed by a single capacious pseudopodium which emerges and retracts through the sulcus, taking with it the solid food for internal digestion. Feeding has so far been reported (by Hofeneder, 1930) in colourless individuals only of

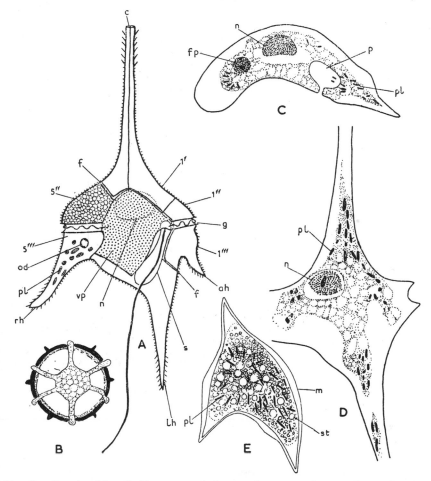

FIG. 64. *Ceratium hirundinella*. A, ventral view: surface patterning on 5th pre-cingular plate only. ×500; B, TS apical horn; C, TS mid-region. ×900; D, LS. ×900; E, cyst. ×900. (After Entz.)

ah, accessory horn; *c*, corona; *f*, fission line; *fp*, food (?) inclusion; *g*, girdle (cingulum); *lh*, left horn; *m*, cyst membrane; *n*, nucleus; *od*, oil droplet; *p*, pusule; *pl*, plastid; *rh*, right horn; *s*, saccule; *st*, st archy inclusion; *vp*, ventral plate; *1'*, first apical plate; *1"* and *5"*, first and fifth pre-cingular plates; *1"'* and *5"'*, first and fifth post-cingular plates.

C. hirundinella but from illustrations found in the literature inclusions which appear to be food occur side by side with chromatophores and it seems likely that coloured specimens do not rely entirely on photosynthesis as a means of nutrition.

There is a single, colourless pusule (Fig. 64 B, C) about the same size as the nucleus and opening at the sulcus. The nucleus lies near the girdle and is ovoid, elongated in the transverse axis of the body. The chromatin granules tend to the regular linear arrangement typical of the dinocaryon. There are 1 to 4 karyosomes. Mitosis has been described by Entz (1921), Hall (1925*b*), and Skoczylas (1958). Division is oblique and follows a constant fission line (indicated on Fig. 64A) running on the right side between pre-cingulars and apicals and on the left between post-cingulars and antapicals and, of course, crossing the girdle dorsally and ventrally.

The cyst (E) resembles a three-cornered cushion, with a cellulose wall, food reserves, chloroplasts, and a nucleus (Entz, 1925). Hall (1925*b*) observed cysts with 2 nuclei and considered that they might be reproductive.

Permanent preparations and culture

Fresh material should be fixed in S+A and stained in D.H.+Eosin or H.H. and prepared by centrifugation.

No method of culturing *Ceratium* is known.

SUBCLASS ZOOMASTIGINA

The members of this subclass are distinguished from their phytomastigine relatives by the following characters: they have no chloroplasts and they are not apochlorotic counterparts or close relatives of species which have, their flagellar apparatus tends to become more elaborate than in any of the coloured orders and there is often an undulating membrane, the kinetoplast and parabasal apparatus are developed only here, and there is a marked and widespread tendency towards parasitism. The simpler flagellates constituting the Protomonadida, with 1 or 2 flagella, include both free-living, coprophilous, and entozoic species. The polymastigote forms with more than 3, usually less than 20, flagella (Trichomonadida and related groups) are almost without exception entozoic, and all the Hypermastigida are obligate commensals or symbionts.

The flagella arise from a blepharoplast, usually at the anterior end of the animal. In the simpler flagellates this is no more than the basal granule (kinetosome) of the single flagellum or the double one of a pair (Figs. 66–68). But in the more complex forms, the blepharoplast is compound and consists of a number of granules ordinarily so close-set as to be indistinguishable, and to these are attached not only the flagella, but other organellae such as the axostyle, costa, parabasal body, and so on (Figs. 75–77). In division the granules tend to separate, and their relations become more evident; one granule divides, behaving like a centriole, and its daughters, at opposite poles of the mitotic nucleus, characteristically remain attached to each other by a lengthening thread, the centrodesmus, a conspicuous feature in preparations of this stage (Fig. 76 E, F).

Closely associated with the blepharoplast lies a structure of variable constitution, which appears in the literature under a perplexing variety of names, such as kinetonucleus, kinetoplast, parabasal body, parasome, and so on. This diversity of usage has promoted an extent of confusion to which no summary can do justice, and no more is now attempted than to explain a terminology recommended by Hoare (1938, 1940, 1954) and adopted here. The term kinetonucleus preserves a discarded view of the nuclear constitution of trypanosomes and ought to be abandoned. Terms like parasome and parabasome are based on distinctions that cannot always be drawn and are, at any rate in introductory studies, best avoided. The remaining 2 terms, kinetoplast and parabasal body, are needed, and the distinction between them is as follows. In the Trypanosomidae and some other protomonads (Figs. 66–74), there is a body lying near the blepharoplast which has the following characteristics: it is generally well preserved by acetic acid fixatives like Bouin; it is F+; it is self-perpetuating, divides when the blepharoplast divides, and one of its daughters goes to each product of fission. In this last respect it behaves like a plastid, and to it the name kinetoplast is applied. It further resembles other plastids in that once it is lost it cannot be regained; *Trypanosoma equinum*, which has no kinetoplast, has probably arisen from *T. evansi* after the irrevocable loss of the kinetoplast (Hoare, 1940, 1954). The term parabasal body (unfortunately applied at times to the structure just defined as a kinetoplast) is here reserved for an organelle best seen in the Trichomonadida (p. 123). It is more complex than the kinetoplast, usually compound, F—, and rarely if ever completely preserved except by 'cytological' fixatives. It is not self-reproducing; at division it disappears, or, if any portion of it remains, this passes entirely into one daughter cell (Kirby, 1944), and the other daughter develops a parabasal apparatus of its own *de novo*. The functions of these structures are uncertain; there is some suggestion that part at least of the parabasal apparatus may be concerned with secretion; for further discussion, see especially Lwoff and Lwoff (1931a) and Duboscq and Grassé (1933).

In many zooflagellates one flagellum, instead of beating freely, trails loosely behind the organism (Figs. 66, 77A, 86 D, E) and it is possible that it was by the attachment of this for some of its length to the pellicle of the body that the undulating membrane of many species arose in evolution, though it is not the means by which it develops in ontogeny (see Fig. 76F, where the new membrane is seen in contact with the ectoplasm as it grows). Certainly the membrane has arisen independently in various groups and in one, the Trypanosomidae (Fig. 69), it has nothing to do with a trailing flagellum (p. 110). Wherever it occurs, it consists of an axoneme, which arises from the blepharoplast and runs over the body in a more or less winding course, marking the edge of a cytoplasmic web, which is raised in a flickering membrane as the axoneme beats; distally the axoneme may leave the body to continue as a free flagellum (Figs. 73–77). Elsewhere, the trailing flagellum may be attached to the pellicular surface without the formation of a true undulating membrane (Fig. 67).

No complete and satisfactory classification of zooflagellates has yet been established, but the following will serve as a guide through the variety of the subclass, though it admittedly fails to account for a number of polymastigote genera left outside the Trichomonadida.* A discussion of more comprehensive classifications will be found in Hall's *Protozoology*.

Order 1. **Protomonadida**: with 1 or 2 flagella (*Bodo*, *Trypanosoma*).

       2. **Trichomonadida**: with 3 to 20 flagella (usually not more than 6) and well developed parabasal apparatus (*Trichomonas*, *Monocercomonas*).

       3. **Diplomonadida**: with duplicated organellae (*Hexamita*, *Giardia*).

       4. **Hypermastigida**: with very numerous flagella (*Lophomonas*, *Trichonympha*).

ORDER PROTOMONADIDA

The protomonads† are small zooflagellates with 1 or 2 flagella. Nearly all the free-living forms are included here, but many members are entozoic. Nutrition is phagotrophic, usually with a cytostome, or osmotrophic, as in most of the entozoic species. Reproduction is almost always by longitudinal binary fission and the few cases of sexual reproduction noted in the literature are doubtful.

Bodo (Ehrenberg)

These small colourless flagellates are common and sometimes extremely numerous in the surface film of infusions of hay, lettuce, horse- or cow-dung, or the bodies of earthworms or leeches. Munro Fox (1921) obtained *B. sulcatus* by allowing grass cuttings to stand for 6 days in tap water. In all such infusions, *Bodo* will be accompanied by and eventually overgrown by other flagellates and by ciliates.

Several species of *Bodo*, all small and difficult to distinguish, may occur in infusions (Alexeieff, 1911 *a*, *b*; Hollande, 1942). *B. caudatus* has an elongated, flattened body (8–18 $\mu \times$ 4–8 μ) with the posterior flagellum somewhat longer than the anterior. *B. edax* (Fig. 66B) is rather smaller

---

* Some brief notes on a few of the polymastigote flagellates of termites are on pp. 146 f; and see Fig. 86.

† The small group of choanoflagellates, or Craspedomonadea, is sometimes included within this order.

(6–12 μ × 4–8 μ) with the curved side more strongly convex. *B. saltans* has
a slim body (6–10 μ × 3–5 μ) and the trailing flagellum at least twice as long
as the anterior one. *B. minimus* is very similar but smaller (4–5 μ × 2–3 μ).
B. perforans is ectoparasitic on the colourless cryptomonad, *Chilomonas
paramecium*, which itself is likely to appear in infusions prepared for the
collection of *Bodo* (Hollande, 1938).

The living organism

Bodo forms spontaneous aggregates the shape of which is regulated by the
oxygen concentration in different parts of its environment (Fox, 1921, and
Fig. 65). This is easily demonstrated if a loop from the surface film of an
infusion is mounted below a coverslip supported at the edges on fragments

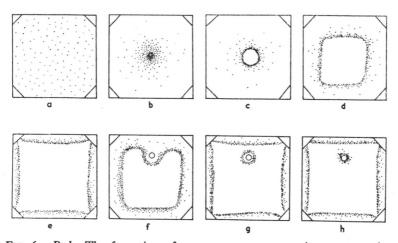

FIG. 65. *Bodo*. The formation of spontaneous aggregates in mounts under
square coverslips. The triangles at the corners are supports separating slips and
slides. *a–e*, the normal course of concentration; *f–h*, the effect of introducing
an air bubble. See text. (After Fox.)

of broken slips and examined under low power by reduced light. The
optimum concentration of oxygen for *Bodo* is below the saturation point
of water in free contact with air. At first the flagellates are uniformly
scattered but after a very variable interval (2 to 120 minutes) they collect
near the centre of the mount (*a–b*). As the concentration of organisms uses
oxygen, a space appears in its centre about which the flagellates form a
circle, gradually widening towards the edges of the slip (*c, d*). As it nears the
edge, the circle changes to a square, if a square slip is used (*e*). It never
reaches the edge, where oxygen from the atmosphere supplies a concentration above the optimum, and the distance from the edge at which the band
is halted is determined by the height of the slip above the slide, that is,

by the surface available for accepting oxygen. Similar concentrations will form in relation to air bubbles (f–h).

The body of *Bodo* (Fig. 66) is more or less elongated according to the species, and with one surface more convex than the other. There are 2 flagella, one directed anteriorly and the other, always longer, trailing

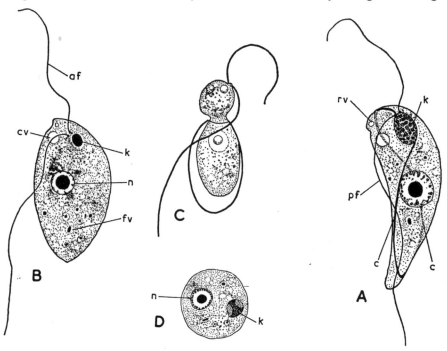

FIG. 66. *Bodo.* A, general structure; B, *B. edax*; C, excystation of *B. edax*; D, cyst of *B. caudatus.* All × 3,500. (B after Alexeieff; C after Kühn; D after Hollande.)

af, anterior flagellum; *c,* costa; *cv,* contractile vacuole; *fv,* food vacuole; *k,* kinetoplast; *n,* nucleus; *pf,* posterior flagellum; *rv,* rostral vacuole.

posteriorly but not attached to the pellicle. Towards the anterior, a small beak or rostrum may project over the flatter side; it overhangs the point at which food is ingested, but it is difficult to establish that there is any permanent cytostome. *Bodo* is certainly phagotrophic and contains food vacuoles, plainly brought out by mounting in Neutral Red. There is also a minute rostral vacuole and, near it, a more conspicuous contractile vacuole.

Permanent preparations

Fix in Flemming or Champy. Stain in H.H.

The flagella arise from basal granules (kinetosomes) lying near to a large kinetoplast. After fixation in fluids containing acetic acid, this structure usually stains as a homogeneous basophil mass, but cytological fixation shows it to consist of a basophil cortex with clear pale contents in which some deeply staining granules are scattered. It is F+(Robertson, 1927; Jírovec, 1927). Duboscq and Grassé (1933) believe that, as suggested many years ago by Klebs (1893) in a most lively paper, and also by Alexeieff (1917 a, b; 1928), the kinetoplast is connected with glycogen production, and drops of glycogen may be seen at its periphery after mounting in Lugol's Iodine Solution. The kinetoplast and rostral vacuole are connected by a thread, or costa, running in a figure 8, and of unknown significance; it is conspicuous in B. saltans, less so in other species.

The nucleus is spherical with a conspicuous karyosome and peripheral chromatin. Reproduction is by binary fission (Hollande, 1942).

Bodo forms very small, round or oval cysts (diameter = 4 μ) in which the nucleus and kinetoplast remain visible (Fig. 66D). According to Kühn (1915) the flagella are retained and the organism emerges by the anterior end (c). Both Kühn and Klebs report division within the cyst.

Culture

Bodo grows well in the infusions given above, or on Musgrave and Clegg's (p. 405) and other media (see Bishop, 1931).

Cryptobia helicis Leidy

These trypanoplasms are common in the spermathecae of many species of snails. According to Matthey (1923), 50 to 75 per cent of Helix pomatia, H. nemoralis, and H. aspersa may be infected, especially in places where the snails are common. There are no cysts; infection occurs during sexual congress. Immature snails are 'clean'. The name trypanoplasm is from Trypanoplasma, a discarded synonym of Cryptobia, and refers to a superficial resemblance to Trypanosoma, though the two genera are not closely related. Cryptobia is commonest in the blood of fishes, but the species in snails is more accessible; a good description of it was published by Kozloff in 1948.

The living organism

Remove the shell from a partly narcotized snail and slit open the body wall at the level of the second spiral. Gently separate the albuminous from the digestive gland, and against the brown of the latter the spermatheca shows as a rose-orange sphere. Remove it and express some of the contents on to a slide, add a drop of 0·75 per cent NaCl, cover with a No. 0 slip, seal, and examine with the oil-immersion lens.

The body of C. helicis (Fig. 67) is highly polymorphic, twisting and untwisting, lengthening and contracting, usually flat, but sometimes circular in section. When extended it measures some 15–25 $\mu \times$ 1·5–3 μ. Of the 2 flagella, one is free and anterior, as in *Bodo*, but the second not only trails behind but is attached along the length of the body and then continued posteriorly for some distance as a free flagellum; it is most doubtful that there is a true undulating membrane, though its appearance may some-

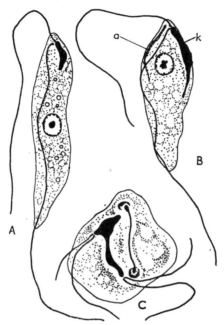

FIG. 67. *Cryptobia helicis.* A and B, trophic flagellates; C, fission, showing the nucleus in early telophase, with the karyosome daughters still connected, the kineto-plast still dividing, and with 2 pairs of flagella. × 2,150. (After Kozloff.)

a, aciculum; *k*, kinetoplast.

times be simulated during the animal's writhing movements. The nucleus is just visible in the living organism. There are no food vacuoles: *Cryptobia* is an osmotroph. There are 2 types of inclusions, spherical and ovoid, both minute, staining with Neutral Red and Janus Green respectively. To observe the kinetoplast, mount in Janus Green (1 : 10,000), leave uncovered in a moist chamber for 10 minutes, cover and examine. Without exposure to oxygen, the stain fails to take (Duboscq and Grassé, 1933).

Permanent preparations

Fix undiluted smears in Flemming, Champy, or S+A. Stain in H.H. The 2 basal granules of the flagella lie close to the kinetoplast; the latter is variable, usually bluntly rounded anteriorly and often drawn out into a fine process at the other end; as in *Bodo*, it is F+. Opposite the kinetoplast Iron Haematoxylin stains a long slender structure, discovered by Kozloff and named by him the aciculum (Fig. 67B); its function and homologies are unknown.

The nucleus contains a single conspicuous karyosome, persistent during mitosis (Bělař, 1926*a*), and peripheral F+ granules. Though reports of sexual processes exist, the only authenticated means of reproduction is binary fission (c).

Culture

Schindera (1922) maintained *C. helicis* in physiological saline containing 2 drops of egg albumen to 1 ml, sub-culturing every 5 days. No good method is known.

Proteromonas lacertae-viridis Grassi

This flagellate occurs all over the world in the rectum of lizards, including *Lacerta viridis*, *L. agilis*, and *L. muralis*. A form from amphibians and having a longer flagellum is considered a separate species, *P. longifila*; it is common in *Salamandra maculosa* in Europe, and in America (California) occurs in *Diemyctylus torosus*, *Plethodon oregonensis*, and *Batrachoseps attenuatus*. The structure and life-history have been fully treated by Grassé (1926). In both reptiles and amphibians *Proteromonas* is likely to be accompanied by a variety of other flagellates (*Trichomonas*, *Monocercomonas*, *Chilomastix*, *Retortomonas*, *Hexamita*) as well as other Protozoa.

The living organism

Proteromonas is found especially in the upper parts of the rectum, often very abundant in the mucus overlying the epithelium. It is absent from faecal contents that are dry or contain soil particles. Mount drops of rectal fluid and tease into it fragments of epithelium. Seal under a No. 0 slip.

The slim, long body (Fig. 68 A, B) bears 2 long flagella, of which the posterior usually trails inertly behind. Apart from a spiral torsion, usually slight (c), the shape is maintained, except when squeezing elastically among obstacles. In swimming, the anterior flagellum undulates in a wide spiral and the body rotates about its axis. At other times, the anterior flagellum is held stiffly in front and only the tip turns, as in *Peranema* (p. 83), while the posterior flagellum is wrapped about the body like the whip of a top. The cytoplasm contains vacuoles and granules staining with Neutral Red. There are no food inclusions. There is no cytostome. The outline of nucleus and kinetoplast may be distinguished in the anterior third.

Proteromonas divides by binary fission, and division stages may be found.

It also reproduces in pseudocysts. The organism becomes sluggish, loses its flagella, rounds up, and secretes a thick, elastic, gelatinous wall, to which bacteria and other debris adhere. The pseudocysts are found in the mucus

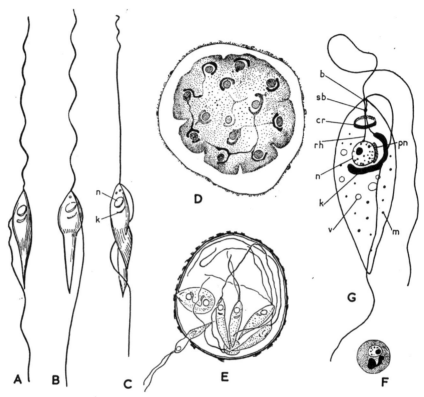

FIG. 68. *Proteromonas.* A–C, living flagellates. × 2,000. D, developing pseudocyst, fixed and stained: the nuclei have divided and separated, kinetoplasts still connected: note bacteria attached to gelatinous wall. × 2,000. E, living pseudocyst after nearly all the contents have escaped. × 1,500. F. Resistant cyst, fixed and stained, with single nucleus and kinetoplast. × 2,500. G, diagram to show cytology of the flagellate: the basal and sub-blepharoplastic granules and the rhizoplast between them are shown in a state of pre-division. (After Grassé.)

b, blepharoplast; *cr*, chromatic ring; *k*, kinetoplast; *m*, granule staining with Neutral Red (mito-chondrium?); *n*, nucleus; *pn*, paranuclear rod; *rh*, rhizoplast; *sb*, sub-blepharoplastic granules; *v*, vacuole.

covering the rectal epithelium, to which they stick closely. Young cysts are spherical or ovoid, only 6 to 8 μ in diameter. Some give rise to only a few individuals, but others grow greatly in diameter (100 μ). Within the cytoplasm, nucleus and kinetoplast divide repeatedly, the products of the latter remaining for a time connected so as to appear as serpentine coils among the peripherally placed nuclei (Fig. 68D); the organellae for 32 individuals may be laid down. After segmentation, the separate flagellates are extremely active, and escape at any point on the wall (E).

The resistant cysts are very different (Fig. 68F). They are small, only 3·5 μ in diameter, uninucleate, with a kinetoplast; presumably they are the infective stages of the life-history.

Permanent preparations

Material well fixed in osmic vapour, Champy, or Flemming is essential as much of the structure is destroyed by acetic acid. Stain in H.H.

The morphology is complicated (Fig. 68G). Each flagellum arises from a basal granule, and from the latter a rhizoplast is said to run to a centriole lying in contact with the nuclear membrane. Behind the blepharoplast, the fibril bears a sub-blepharoplastic granule, and, posterior to this, is surrounded by a siderophile ring (paracentrosome) of uncertain homology. The kinetoplast is a conspicuous basophil mass curving about the nucleus and lying for the most part behind it. A further structure, the paranuclear rod, lies against the nucleus; its significance is unknown. The nucleus is anterior and contains a karyosome and chromatin granules between it and the membrane. Mitosis was described by Bělař (1921b: under the name of *Bodo lacertae*); the karyosome disappears and it reconstitutes later and is apparently a nucleolus.

Culture

No method is known.

Family Trypanosomidae

The family constitutes a natural group of related organisms some of which are of very great medical and veterinary importance and, on this account, the subjects of extensive study, so that their life-histories, and their relations to one another and to their hosts are now well known; the same cannot be said for their cytology. All are entozoic, and although the best known are those pathogenic in man and his domestic animals, the great majority of trypanosomids are harmless commensals in their natural hosts, which are usually arthropods, or vertebrates with arthropods or leeches as their vectors.

There is a single flagellum, arising from a basal granule with which is associated a disk-shaped kinetoplast, which is, of course, rod-shaped in side view, as it is commonly seen in preparations. There is no cytostome. Ordinarily the body is a slim, long blade of cytoplasm with the flagellum freely projecting from the anterior end (Figs. 70–74), but all species show a tendency to shorten and thicken and become attached by their flagella to a host epithelium. Finally, they lose their flagella, round off, and remain recognizable only by their nuclei and kinetoplasts. They then resemble the first discovered (and for long the only known) stage of the kala azar and oriental sore parasites of the genus *Leishmania* and hence they are known as the leishmanial stages of the life-history in which they occur.

The relations of the kinetoplast vary and are of taxonomic importance (Fig. 69). Primitively, it lies close to the anterior end with a short internal

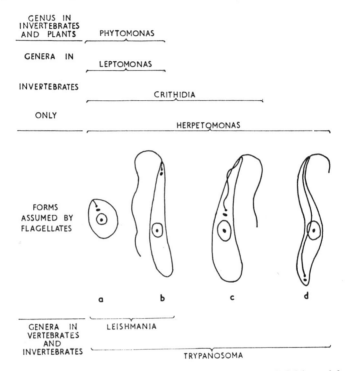

FIG. 69. Generic characters of Trypanosomidae. *a–d*, leishmanial, leptomonad, crithidial, and trypanosomid stages seen in the life-cycles. (Compiled after various authors.)

course, as in the fully developed forms of *Leptomonas*, *Leishmania*, and *Phytomonas*, all of which have both leptomonad and leishmanial stages; they differ in that *Leptomonas* (p. 112) is confined to invertebrate hosts, *Phytomonas* has both invertebrate and plant hosts, and *Leishmania* has both invertebrate and vertebrate hosts in its cycle. In *Crithidia*, confined to invertebrates, the kinetoplast is displaced at some stages so that it lies just in front of or to the side of the nucleus. *Herpetomonas*, also in invertebrates only, has leishmanial, leptomonad, and crithidial stages, but when fully developed the kinetoplast lies behind the nucleus so that the axoneme runs a long course through the body before the flagellum emerges freely. The genus *Trypanosoma* (p. 117) is morphologically like *Herpetomonas* but has both vertebrate and invertebrate hosts in its cycle; further, the axoneme runs along the margin of an undulating membrane, which is thrown into flickering folds by the flagellar beat.*

The evolution of the digenetic from the monogenetic habit has occurred independently of these morphological developments and more than once. Thus *Leishmania* is the digenetic derivative of *Leptomonas*, and both are morphologically simple and identical. At a more complicated level *Trypanosoma* is indistinguishable from *Herpetomonas* except that the former is digenetic. Further, an adaptive change has followed the adoption of the digenetic habit and has profoundly modified the life-cycles of the parasites affected. In monogenetic trypanosomids, the host is nearly always an arthropod, the infective forms occur in the rectum (posterior station), and are passed with the faeces; infection is contaminative† (Fig. 70A). Some of the more primitive digenetic types retain this habit; they develop in the posterior station of the invertebrate and contaminate the vertebrate, e.g. *Trypanosoma cruzi*, *T. lewisi* (p. 122). But more advanced digenetic species develop their infective phases in the fore-gut or salivary glands of their invertebrate and are inoculated into the vertebrate host, as in *Leishmania donovani*, *Trypanosoma brucei* (p. 120). One species is exceptional: *T. equiperdum* passes directly *in coitu* from one horse to another.

The cytoplasm of trypanosomids may be marked by longitudinal striae, either gross or visible by the light microscope (Lwoff and Lwoff, 1931*b*) or very fine and seen only in electron micrographs (Kranevald, Houwink, and Keidel, 1951); no function has been demonstrated for such striae, but they may be contractile. The nucleus, generally central, is vesicular, with a karyosome and peripheral F+ material. The details of mitosis are not entirely clear, but some accounts will be found in Robertson (1927), Lwoff and Lwoff (1931*a*), Noble, McRary, and Beaver (1953), and Sorouri (1955). Reproduction is asexual, by binary, occasionally multiple, fission, and the division of the nucleus is preceded by that of the kinetoplast. Reports of sexual processes in trypanosomids are in need of stronger

* In the interests of precision the taxonomic names of animals are conventionally printed in italics with capital initials for generic but not for trivial names; the nouns or adjectives from such names, when without taxonomic import, should be in ordinary type. Thus, 'a *Leishmania* stage' means a stage in the life-history of a parasite belonging to the genus *Leishmania*; 'a leishmania (better, leishmanial) stage' means a stage morphologically like one of *Leishmania* occurring in any life-history.

† The infective stages are called cysts, though it is exceedingly difficult to determine whether these minute leishmanial stages really develop cyst walls. They are certainly resistant, for Wenyon (1913*b*) obtained cultures of flagellates from thin faecal smears dried for 24 hours, though the comparable stages of *Leishmania* itself from the spleen of kala azar cases were not similarly resistant. It is worth noting that such fragile flagellates as *Monocercomonoides* spp. and *Trichomonas augusta* form no cysts but nevertheless can infect desert lizards by contamination, though unfortunately the details of the process are unknown (Amrein, 1953).

support before they can be accepted (Noble, 1955); such reports have never been directly confirmed and there is some indirect evidence that genetical recombination, which ought to result from sexual reproduction, fails to occur, at any rate in mammalian blood. For example, if 2 strains of *T. rhodesiense* separately conditioned to resist different drugs are mixed in the bloodstream of mice no cross-transference of resistance such as would be expected after syngamy or conjugation results (Amrein and Fulton, 1959).

An excellent account of the family is given in Wenyon (1926) and a stimulating discussion of their evolution and present relationships has been written by Hoare (1949).

Leptomonas jaculum (Leger)

Almost all the hosts of species of *Leptomonas* are insects, especially Diptera and Hemiptera. Among the latter, *Nepa cinerea*, the water scorpion, provides suitable material for the study of living and fixed material. *L. jaculum* was first reported by Leger (1902) and the life-history was described by Porter in 1909; both authors used the name *Herpetomonas* but the flagellate has only leishmanial and leptomonad stages and so falls within the limits of the genus *Leptomonas* as now understood (Woodcock, 1914). In its monogenetic cycle in an insect, production of flagellated stages in the mid-gut and numerous attached leishmanial stages farther back, and in the passage of resistant infective bodies (cysts) with the faeces and the oral entry of infection, it is typical of its genus. Its cytology has never received careful attention but there is no reason to suppose that it differs significantly from other members of its genus.

The living organism

Nepa cinerea is a dull, flat bug, relatively common in shallow stagnant water containing a good deal of vegetation. It is most abundant near the edge of a pool, inconspicuously clinging to the stems or leaves of aquatic plants or buried in the mud. To dissect it, remove the dorsum, clean away as much as possible of the fat body, examine the gut (Fig. 70C) and remove it whole into a drop of 0·75 per cent saline solution. A full description is given by Hamilton (1931). Divide the gut into three lengths of fore-, mid-, and hind-gut with rectum, and tease these separately in the saline on a slide, cover with a No. 0 slip and examine under an oil immersion lens.

The organism occurs in 2 forms, (*a*) the flagellates, abundant in the mid-gut, but also found in lesser numbers both anteriorly and posteriorly, where they are accompanied by (*b*) the leishmanial forms, which are post-flagellate in the rectum, where they give rise to cysts, and pre-flagellate in the fore-gut, where they have hatched from cysts. When fully developed, leishmanial stages usually lie free in the lumen of the gut, though the forms leading to them are mostly attached by their flagella. Both stages may be seen in division, and intermediate forms occur.

The leptomonad (Fig. 70 A) has a slim, long body, 15–30 $\mu \times$ 1·5 μ, rather blunt anteriorly and tapering behind, with a central oval nucleus and a single flagellum. It swims jerkily, the flagellum lashing and thrown into coils, and the body rotating about its axis. It can reverse at a reduced speed with the flagellum trailing behind. The flagellates tend to attach themselves in groups to epithelial cells and debris and form rosettes of numerous, attached, swaying and rotating organisms (Fig. 70B). Dividing forms (A, *b–e*) are common. As the new flagellum grows forward in close association with the old it may give the misleading impression that the latter splits longitudinally from its base.

In the hind-gut and rectum, the post-flagellate stages are for some time fixed; they might otherwise be swept out of the body, and, though they may survive for some hours in water, they are presumably less viable than the cysts formed from them. The post-flagellates (*h–k*) are small, ovoid, with short or no flagella, and they divide to produce minute stages (2·5–4·5 $\mu \times$ 1·5–2·5 μ) which, according to Porter, secrete a gelatinous envelope which hardens about them; these are the resistant cysts passed with the faeces (see footnote on p. 111).

Nepa cinerea lays its eggs in late March or April and places them on the decayed stems of water plants. The emerging young climb or float to the surface, where they cling to weeds, upon which the adults defecate. Nymphs have been seen to swallow faeces in nature, and when examined immediately afterwards they contained cysts in the crop. A habit of cannibalism may help in spreading the infections. The pre-flagellate forms in the crop at first resemble the leishmanial stages from the rectum; they are accompanied by all the growth stages leading to the leptomonads (*l–o* and *a*).

Permanent preparations

For dry methods, fix rapidly in osmic vapour for 15 sec and stain in Giemsa or fix and stain in Leishman (p. 443). For wet methods, fix in S+A or Flemming, stain in H.H.

The kinetoplast is described as rod-shaped; more probably it is a disk which looks like a rod when seen from the side. In division it becomes dumb-bell shaped and then constricts. It is anterior in the flagellate stages, but tends to lie near the nucleus in leishmanial forms and the cysts. The pre-flagellate stages show the development of the axoneme and flagellum. The nuclear structure is imperfectly known. In the related *L. ctenocephali* the chromatin is peripheral and there is a karyosome which persists in division (Lwoff and Lwoff, 1931*a*). Below the periplast longitudinal striations are sometimes stained; they have been thought to be myonemes.

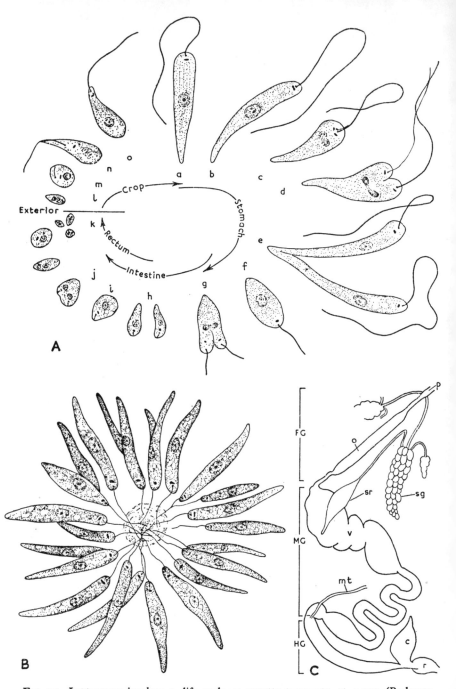

FIG. 70. *Leptomonas jaculum*. A, life-cycle; B, rosette aggregate. × 1,250. (Redrawn after Porter.)

a, trophic leptomonad; *b-e*, dividing leptomonad; *f–h*, post-flagellate stages, leading to *i*, attached leishmania stage; *j*, dividing leishmania; *k*, cysts; *l–o*, pre-flagellate stages, leading to *a*.

c, alimentary canal of *Nepa cinerea*. (Simplified after Hamilton.)

FG, MG, HG, fore-, mid-, and hind-gut; *c*, caecum; *mt*, Malpighian tubule; *o*, oesophagus; *p*, pharynx; *r*, rectum; *sg*, salivary gland; *sr*, salivary reservoir; *v*, ventriculus.

Culture

There is no record of the culture of *L. jaculum*, but related species have been maintained on N.N.N. medium after inoculation with faeces containing cysts (p. 420).

Herpetomonas muscarum (Leidy)

This appears to be the correct name of a herpetomonad which is common in house-flies (*Musca domestica*), bluebottles (*Calliphora*), and greenbottles (*Lucilia*) all over the world (Hoare, 1924). By means of cross-infection experiments, Becker (1923b) and Drbohlav (1925a) have shown that it infects other Diptera, mainly muscids, and it is likely that herpetomonads described under various names from other hosts belong to this species. There is, however, some degree of host-specificity; for example, flies will not accept *H. ctenocephali* from the dog-flea. In structure and life-history (Wenyon, 1913a, 1926; Becker, 1923a), *H. muscarum* closely resembles *Leptomonas* (p. 112), except that it includes crithidial and trypanosomid stages in its cycle. The flagellates are probably more easily obtained from bluebottles* or greenbottles than from house-flies. The first two are easily attracted by exposing high meat or parts of animals left over from dissections, and they may be more often infected than house-flies; thus Dunkerly (1911) could not find *H. muscarum* in *Musca domestica* in England, but 76 per cent of the greenbottles in this country (Strickland, 1911) and 83 per cent in North America (Drbohlav, 1926) were infected, and in Scotland Mackinnon (1910) found that about 60 per cent of the flies feeding on dung (*Scatophaga lutaria* and *Homalomyia*) carried a flagellate indistinguishable from our species.

Living and fixed material

A trapped fly is placed in a 2 in. × 1 in. bottle, which is inverted over a cover slip on which has been placed a tiny drop of sugar water. The fly sips and a minute later it defecates. The slip is at once inverted on a slide and examined for *Herpetomonas*. Clean flies are discarded and infected ones set aside for dissection.

Immobilize the fly with a whiff of chloroform or ether. Decapitate it at the front of the thorax. Posteriorly make two converging cuts in a V pointing towards the anterior end. Withdraw the gut and straighten it in a drop of

* The herpetomonad from the bluebottle was originally described as *H. calliphorae* by Swingle (1911) from *Calliphora coloradensis* and it happens that this host has never been shown experimentally to accept *H. muscarum*, though *Calliphora erythrocephala* certainly does. A similar herpetomonad occurs in *C. vomitoria*. For present purposes these flagellates are regarded as all one.

0·6 per cent saline. Tease portions of fore-, mid-, and hind-gut separately on No. o slips and either fix for staining or examine alive in saline. Fix and stain as for *Leptomonas* (p. 113).

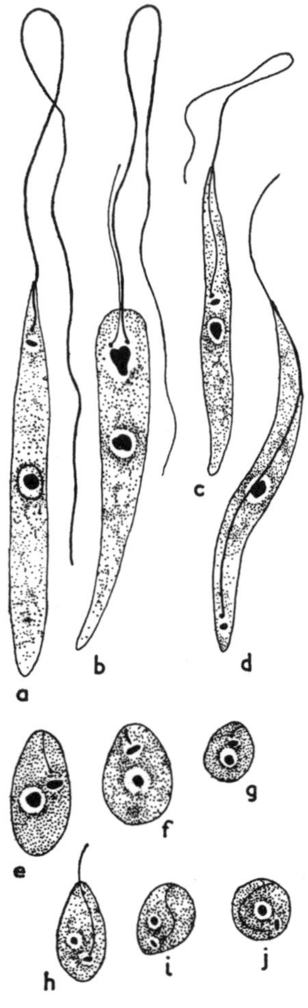

The commonest stage in the fore- and mid-gut and intestine is the leptomonad, up to 30×2–$3\ \mu$, and with a flagellum which may be 3 times as long (Fig. 71, *a*); the nucleus is more or less central, the kinetoplast anterior. The earliest indication of division is separation of the blepharoplast into 2 daughter granules, one of which retains the old flagellum while from the other the new flagellum begins its growth. This phase is evidently prolonged, for it is so common that it was long supposed that the natural state of *Herpetomonas* was biflagellate. Careful examination will show that one, the younger, flagellum is thinner than the other. As the basal granules draw apart the kinetoplast divides, beginning at the anterior margin, so that it is for a time heart-shaped (Fig. 71, *b*).

The trypanosomal stages are usually found at the posterior end of the hind-gut or in the Malpighian tubules or rectum. The kinetoplast lies behind the nucleus and the axoneme runs the length of the body to emerge anteriorly as a short, free flagellum. All intermediate stages, including crithidial, are found between the two extremes (*c*, *d*). Both the leptomonad and the trypanosomal forms produce leishmanial forms and cysts, and the products differ according to their origin (Fig. 71, *e–g* and *h–i*). The leptomonad contracts to an ovoid or globular body, and the cyst so formed has a nucleus, kinetoplast, and short straight axoneme. The trypanosomal forms produce cysts of a similar shape, either by contraction or by bending into a U followed by fusion of the apposed sides; in either case, the body accommodates, besides the nucleus and kinetoplast, a longer axoneme which curls within its restricted space. In their final forms the cysts may

FIG. 71. *Herpetomonas muscarum.* ×1,650. *a*, leptomonad; *b*, early division stage of *a*—the blepharoplast has divided into 2 basal granules and that on the left is growing a new flagellum: the kinetoplast is beginning to divide; *c*, crithidial and *d*, trypanosome stages; *e–g*, encystation of leptomonad stage; *h–j*, encystation of trypanosome stage. (*a*, *b*, *f*, *g*, *i*, *j* after Wenyon; *c*, *d*, *e*, *h* after Dunkerly.)

lose all trace of the axoneme. The post-flagellate stages are, as in *Leptomonas*, attached for a time. Though flagellated stages can give rise to infections experimentally induced (Becker, 1923*a*), their viability outside the host has not been tested and there is no reason to think that they play any part in nature in the distribution of the parasite; this, presumably, is the function of the 'encysted' leishmanial forms produced in the posterior part of the gut.*

Culture

H. muscarum has been cultured by Drbohlav (1925*b*, 1926) in a modification of N.N.N. medium (p. 421). The first trypanosomid to be cultivated in a synthetic medium was a herpetomonad, *H. culicidarum* (Cowperthwaite, Weber, Packer, and Hutner, 1953).

Trypanosoma Gruby

Flagellates of the genus *Trypanosoma* exhibit in the course of their life-cycles all possible positions of the kinetoplast from that seen in leishmania to that of trypanosome phases, and in the latter they commonly develop an undulating membrane. They are distinguished from *Herpetomonas* by having, with the secondary exception of *T. equiperdum*, both vertebrate and invertebrate hosts. Development in the latter may lead to the production of small, infective forms, known as 'metacyclic' trypanosomes, in either the posterior (*T. lewisi* and *T. cruzi*) or anterior stations (*brucei* group) with respectively contaminative and inoculative methods of infecting the vertebrate host. *T. rangeli* from man, dogs, opossums, and monkeys in Central and South America is of interest in that it can develop in both stations and employ either mode of infection.

Many trypanosomes form patently good species recognizable on morphological grounds, and a good deal is now known of the course of speciation in some ranges of the genus (see Hoare, 1949, 1954, 1956*b*, 1957*a*). Others are structurally identical but differ in various biological characters. In the *brucei* sub-group, for example, *T. gambiense* and *T. rhodesiense* are morphologically indistinguishable in man but are distributed by different tse-tse flies; *T. rhodesiense* and *T. brucei* are indistinguishable in their flies, which are the same, but infect man and domestic animals respectively. The taxonomic status of the various biological races produced in this unstable genus is discussed by Hoare (1943, 1952*c*).

To most students—and not only at first—all trypanosomes are apt to

* Wallace and Clark (1959) consider that the attached and 'encysted' stages have nothing to do with *H. muscarum* but belong to the life-history of a different trypanosomid parasite, *Crithidia luciliae*. But Wenyon (1913*a*) observed the formation of 'cysts' from both leptomonad and herpetomonad stages and the latter at least cannot have belonged to any species of *Crithidia*.

look alike, and it will be helpful if at the start the main points by which species are distinguished are grasped; the organisms should be examined in stained preparations, bearing the following in mind. On a basis of their morphology as seen in the blood and also on some of their biological characters, the trypanosomes of mammals may be arranged in 2 sections, containing 4 groups (Fig. 72). The classification is rational and reflects phylogeny (Hoare, 1957*b*).

Section A

Kinetoplast large, not terminal. Free flagellum always present. Posterior and pointed. Division in leishmania, crithidia, or trypanosome stage. Metacyclic trypanosomes in posterior station and transmission contaminative (except *T. rangeli*, see above). Only slightly pathogenic or harmless.

I. *LEWISI* GROUP. Characters of the section. The members are distinguished among themselves by the nature of the multiplicative phase, e.g. *T. cruzi* divides by binary fission in the leishmania stage (Fig. 72, *a*, *b*), *T. lewisi* by multiple fission in the crithidial stage (Fig. 74), while *T. rangeli* again approaches the next section in that it divides by binary fission in the trypanosome stage (Fig. 72, *c*, *d*).

Section B

Kinetoplast terminal or sub-terminal. Free flagellum absent or present. Posterior end blunt. Division in trypanosome stage. Metacyclic trypanosomes in anterior station (except *evansi* subgroup) and transmission inoculative (except *T. equiperdum*). Pathogenic.

II. *VIVAX* GROUP. Kinetoplast large, terminal. Free flagellum present. Undulating membrane inconspicuous. Monomorphic. *T. vivax* is long and *T. uniforme* short (Fig. 72, *e*, *f*).

III. *CONGOLENSE* GROUP. Kinetoplast medium, marginal. Free flagellum present or absent. Undulating membrane usually inconspicuous. Monomorphic or polymorphic.* *T. congolense* (Fig. 72, *g*) is monomorphic, short, with free flagellum short or absent, undulating membrane inconspicuous.

IV. *BRUCEI* GROUP. Kinetoplast small, sub-terminal (absent in *T. equinum*). Free flagellum present or absent. Undulating membrane conspicuous. *T. suis* is monomorphic,* stout, with short flagellum (Fig. 72, *h*). The members of the *brucei* subgroup (*T. brucei*, *T. rhodesiense*, and *T. gambiense*) are polymorphic,* with slender, stumpy and

---

* N.B. The term 'polymorphic' refers not to the well-known production during the life-cycle of several distinct forms such as leishmania, leptomonad, and so on, but to the

intermediate forms (Fig. 72, *i–k*). The members of the *evansi* subgroup resemble the *brucei* trypanosomes except that the stumpy forms are rare

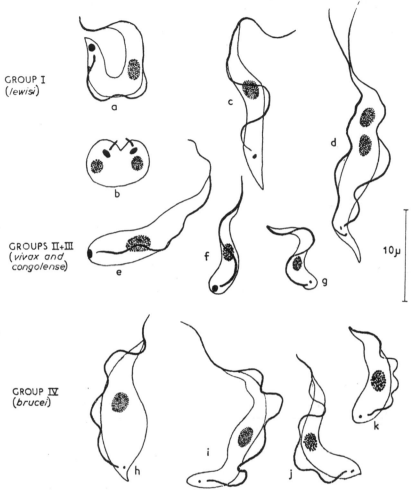

FIG. 72. Mammalian trypanosomes. *a* and *b*, *T. cruzi*; *c* and *d*, *T. rangeli*; *e*, *T. vivax*; *f*, *T. uniforme*; *g*, *T. congolense*; *h*, *T. suis*; *i, j*, and *k*, blood forms of *brucei* group (i.e. *T. brucei*, *T. gambiense*, and *T. rhodesiense*). *T. evansi* is like *h–k* but the short forms (*k*) are uncommon. *T. equinum* is like *T. evansi* but akinetoplastic. (After Hoare.)

and sporadic; they have no intermediate hosts but are transmitted mechanically by insects (*T. evansi* and *T. equinum*), or venereally (*T. equiperdum*).

display of various different forms assumed by the trypanosome stage itself in the bloodstream, as in the *brucei* subgroup. The monomorphic trypanosomes conform to a single pattern in the blood.

A clear introduction to the human trypanosomes will be found in Hoare (1949) and a more extended account of the genus in Wenyon's *Protozoology* (vol. i). No attempt is here made to describe the study of a trypanosome throughout its life-cycle. The observation of *T. brucei* in the mouse is easy and in some ways useful, but it is also misleading, and should be supplemented if possible by reference to *T. lewisi*, which can be followed through its cycle in a natural vertebrate host.

Trypanosoma brucei Plimmer and Bradford

The trypanosomes of the *brucei* subgroup are all pathogenic in man or his domestic animals; they are polymorphic in the bloodstream and are distributed by tse-tse flies, in which they develop in the anterior station. At all stages they are morphologically indistinguishable, and differ only in such biological characters as host-parasite relations, vector specificity, and sensitivity to various drugs.

T. brucei lives naturally as a harmless commensal of wild game in Africa, and it also infects horses, cattle, and other domestic animals, in which it causes a fatal wasting disease, nagana; it is one of the most virulent trypanosomes known. In the blood, it produces trypanosomes of three types: (i) long, slender forms, with a long free flagellum, (ii) short, stumpy forms, with no free flagellum or a very short one, and (iii) forms intermediate between the two foregoing ones (Fig. 72, *i–k*).

T. brucei readily infects laboratory mammals and is conveniently observed alive in the blood of the mouse; it must be borne in mind that this is an artificial situation, that the mouse is not a natural host, and what is most important, that, after repeated passage through laboratory animals, the *brucei* trypanosomes lose their characteristic polymorphism, the stumpy forms disappearing from the cycle; what is seen in the mouse, then, is not typical of the species, or of the group, in nature.

The living organism

Infected mice may be obtained from appropriate research institutes; it is essential to state when the mouse is to be used, as infected animals do not survive for more than about a week. Snip off the tip of the tail with very sharp scissors, 'milk' it if necessary to express a drop of blood on to a warmed slide, cover with a warm No. o slip, seal, and examine under oil immersion. Enormous numbers of flagellates may be present and they move too rapidly to observe in any detail; as they cool, they slow down and this is the time, before they become distorted and moribund, to study them. Trypanosomes are among the most graceful of all animals and are ideal subjects for phase microscopy.

Only the slender forms (Fig. 73, *a*) will be present in strains maintained for any length of time in laboratories. Each trypanosome is elongated, slim, flattened, flexible, and it curves with great elegance while in motion; the ordinary length is about 30 μ, but larger forms also occur. The axoneme of the undulating membrane, which ripples in well-formed but not very frilly folds, and the free flagellum can be seen plainly. The cytoplasm is generally clear, but may contain granules, perhaps of volutin. The nucleus is central.

Dividing forms should be studied side by side with stained preparations (Fig. 73, *b–d*). Multiplication of the *brucei* group is confined to the trypanosome stage in the blood and is always by binary fission (cf. *T. lewisi*, p. 122).

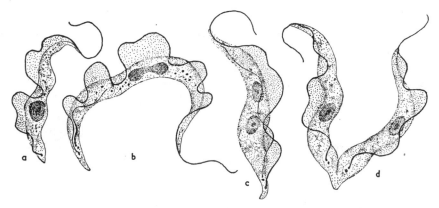

FIG. 73. *Trypanosoma brucei*. Longitudinal fission of slender forms in the blood of the mouse. The nuclear structure is not revealed by Romanovsky techniques and is shown semi-diagrammatically. × 1,500 (Redrawn after various authors.)

The kinetoplast and basal granule divide first, one daughter granule taking the old flagellum with it, and a new flagellum growing from the other. The nucleus divides as the axoneme of the new flagellum grows, and by the time that 2 sets of organelles are present, cytokinesis occurs from the anterior end backwards.

Permanent preparations

Excellent material for practising the Romanovsky staining techniques is offered by infected mice, and blood-films should be prepared and stained (see p. 441).

Culture

The pathogenic trypanosomes are difficult subjects; see Hoare (1949) for Razgha's medium, and Weinman (1946, 1953).

Trypanosoma lewisi (Kent)

This species develops in the posterior station of the rat flea (*Ceratophyllus fasciatus*) and infects rats by contamination. Rats snap at the fleas which bite them and they lick their bites and so may swallow fleas or the dejecta containing metacyclic trypanosomes. The parasite is cosmopolitan and in nature is harmless, though virulent strains may be experimentally built up by rapid passage in the multiplicative phase through the rodent hosts.

The living organism and stained preparations

The cycle in the rat occurs in 2 stages: one, early and temporary, is multiplicative; it lasts for about 10 days and leads to a trophic stage in which the trypanosomes are monomorphic and non-reproductive and these constitute a definitive infection lasting for some months. To study the cycle it is necessary to have control of it from the start, as wild infections are almost always in the second stage. Wild rats are examined till an infected animal is found; the rat's tail is withdrawn from the cage, milked towards the tip and punctured with a fine needle driven obliquely under the skin. The drop of blood is examined, and, if infected, a large drop is inoculated intraperitoneally into a clean, that is, uninfected, laboratory rat. The trypanosomes appear in the blood-stream after 4 to 6 days and remain in the first stage for some days; after the eighth or ninth day, dividing forms are rare and are soon replaced entirely by the characteristic monomorphic forms. Blood must be examined, then, on the sixth and seventh days and the films compared with those on the tenth or subsequent days. Living and stained preparations should be studied as for *T. brucei* (p. 120).

Conspicuous in the blood-films of the first stage are large broad flagellates (36 μ or more long) which divide in the crithidial phase (Fig. 74, *a–c*). The basal granule and kinetoplast divide first and from one daughter granule a new flagellum grows and develops a short undulating membrane. Such a daughter may separate (*f*) from its parent, or, more usually, repeated division of the organellae in advance of the cytoplasm leads to multiple fission (*d*, *e*). The daughters may themselves divide by binary (*f*, *g*) or multiple fission. The picture of this early stage in the infection is thus composed of a great variety of forms with many division stages. In dried films these stages will reveal nothing about the mitotic process; according to Wolcott (1952), who worked with wet films, *T. lewisi* has 3 chromosomes.

About the tenth day the division products have all grown into monomorphic trypanosomes which uniformly display the features characteristic of the species. They are about 25 μ long and they no longer increase in size, that is, within narrow limits they are subject to remarkably little variation until they have passed through the invertebrate host (Taliaferro,

1921 *a, b,* 1923, 1926); these stable forms are sometimes spoken of as 'adults'. They are slim, elongated, pointed at the posterior end, and usually curved in an arc (*h, i*). The kinetoplast lies behind the nucleus some distance from the hind end. The undulating membrane is only slightly developed and the axoneme runs a sinuous but not very wavy course. In this

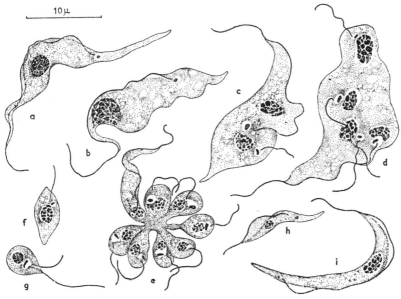

FIG. 74. *Trypanosoma lewisi.* ×2,000. *a–g,* multiplicative phase; *h–i,* trophic phase. (After Wenyon.)

a, b, large multiplicative trypanosomes; *c,* binary; *d, e,* types of multiple fission; *f,* crithidial daughter; *g,* the same in binary fission; *h,* young; and *i,* fully grown 'adult' in the definitive phase of the infection.

definitive form the flagellates are extremely active, in contrast with the slower multiplicative stages.

For an account of the cycle in the flea, see Wenyon's *Protozoology* (vol. i) or the monograph by Minchin and Thomson (1915).

Culture

T. lewisi can be maintained on blood-agar media (N.N.N.) and is easier to grow than the pathogenic trypanosomes (see p. 419).

ORDER TRICHOMONADIDA

The members of this order typically have 4 or 6 flagella (polymastigote) of which 1 trails backwards, either freely (*Monocercomonas = Eutrichomastix*) or, more commonly, attached to the body as the axoneme of an undulating membrane (*Trichomonas*, Fig. 77 A–C), with a more or less central, flexible skeletal rod, the axostyle, and a parabasal body (p. 101). The principal organellae, except the nucleus, are all related to a blepharoplast which divides at mitosis, when its daughters act as centrioles connected by a centrodesmus (Fig. 76 E, F).

Most members of the order are small, and the genus *Trichomonas*, considered below, is typical. *Trichomonas* itself (Fig. 75) is a remarkably complicated animal, but some of the Devescovinid flagellates from termites are even more elaborate (Kirby, 1941, 1942 *a, b,* 1945*b,* 1949). Others from the same hosts are polymonad, that is, the structural unit (mastigont) seen singly in *Trichomonas* is repeatedly multiplied until the organism may come to have hundreds of sets of nuclei, flagella, and parabasals (*Coronympha*), or, secondarily, the number of nuclei may be reduced (*Calonympha, Snyderella*) (Kirby, 1929, 1939). The more advanced members of the order together with the Hypermastigida well illustrate the fact that it is the entozoic flagellates which have evolved the highest degree of morphological complexity.

All trichomonads reproduce asexually by binary fission and in addition, according to Cleveland (1950 *a, b, c*), some species reproduce sexually under the influence of the host's moulting hormone.

Trichomonads are very widely distributed in the alimentary canals of vertebrates and invertebrates, more rarely in the urino-genital tract. They were previously thrown together with a heterogeneous collection of other entozoic flagellates to compose the awkwardly diverse order Polymastigina, but were separated into the present order by Kirby (1947), and we now see them as a natural group especially characterized by the parabasal body.

Trichomonas Donné

In Fig. 75 there are set out, together with the terminology used to describe them, all or almost all of the structures differentiated by members of this genus, which rarely exceed 20 μ and may be no more than 3 μ in length.

The body is mobile and flexible, usually elongated in repose, with one side, conventionally called dorsal, more convexly arched than the other and emphasized by the rippling of the undulating membrane. The oval nucleus is anterior and varies in content (Figs. 76, 77).* Just in front of it lies the

---

* By a curious slip, Kirby (1947) in his valuable paper instituting the order stated that it was characterized by a 'nuclear structure in which the chromatic material, distributed or organised in persisting chromosomes, fills much or all of the interior'. But vesicular nuclei are not uncommon in the Trichomonadida; see, for example, *T. augusta* in Fig. 77, or the interphase nucleus of *T. vaginalis* (Hawes, 1947); and I have examined many hundreds of trophic individuals of *T. sanguisugae* every one of which had a nucleus with palely staining homogeneous contents in which the only differentiated structure was a small, single karyosome. R. S. J. H.

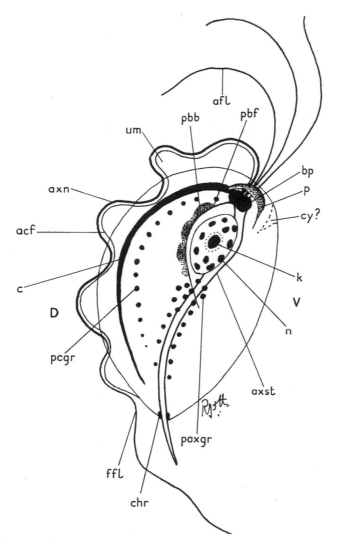

FIG. 75. *Trichomonas*: diagrammatic, from the right side, to show the fully developed structure. The pelta and accessory filament are ordinarily seen only after Ag impregnation; all other organellae are visible in cytologically fixed smears stained with H.H. (Original.)

acf, accessory filament of undulating membrane; *afl*, one of 3 anterior flagella; *axn*, axoneme of undulating membrane; *axst*, axostyle; *bp*, blepharoplast; *c*, costa; *chr*, chromatic ring of axostyle; *cy?*, cytostome?; D, dorsal; *ffl*, free flagellum from undulating membrane; *k*, .karyosome; *n*, nucleus; *p*, pelta; *paxgr*, paraxostylar granule; *pbb*, parabasal body (chromophobe substance); *pbf*, parabasal fibre (chromophile substance); *pcgr*, paracostal granule; *um*, undulating membrane; v, ventral.

blepharoplast, generally seen as a homogeneous siderophile mass; in over-differentiated specimens or at the beginning of division its compound nature is evident. From the blepharoplast originate the anterior flagella, the posterior flagellum (axoneme), the costa, axostyle, and parabasal body.

There are 3 to 5 anterior flagella, arising from different constituents of the blepharoplast and accordingly parted at division (Fig. 76 E, F). On the basis of their number the genus *Trichomonas* is by some authorities sub-divided into *Tritrichomonas*, *Trichomonas* (not *Tetratrichomonas* because *Trichomonas*, the type species, has 4 flagella), and *Pentatrichomonas*. The rippling axoneme of the undulating membrane may travel nearly the whole length of the dorsal curve of the body (*T. hominis*) or be confined to an anterior segment of it (*T. vaginalis*, *T. tenax*); in the last 2 species the axoneme stops short at the end of the membrane, but more usually it continues posteriorly as a free flagellum (Figs. 75–77); along its attached length it is usually paralleled by an accessory filament which is not pro-duced beyond the membrane. The membrane itself is supported by a curved, flexible skeletal rod, the costa, which varies in thickness from a very fine fibril in *T. vaginalis* to the stout, deeply staining organ of *T. hominis*.

The parabasal body, of variable structure, lies between the costa and the nucleus. In *T. vaginalis*, where it is well developed, it consists of a fibre, easily stained after most common fixatives, and a rather irregular mass of chromophobe substance, preserved only after 'cytological' fixation; the apparatus is that illustrated in Fig. 75. In some species the parabasal is double (*T. batrachorum*, Fig. 77 B). It impregnates clearly, though capriciously, with silver. Its function is unknown, but the variations in the quantity and appearance of the chromophobe component have suggested that it is secretory.

The axostyle runs down the centre of the body to protrude as a shorter or longer rod at the hind end. It may be slim, siderophile, and fibrillar (*T. vaginalis*), a long tapering rod (*T. hominis*, *T. batrachorum*), or a thick blunt structure resisting staining except at the edges (*T. muris*); in some species it is surrounded by a basophil ring where it leaves the body (cf. Figs. 76 and 77).

The body, or cytosome, of *Trichomonas* often contains a number of deeply basophil spherical granules, which tend to form groups alongside the costa and axostyle. Their nature is not understood; in *T. vaginalis* they have many of the properties of mitochondria.

Close to the blepharoplast, on its right and somewhat anterior to it, lies a curved organ called the pelta by Kirby (1945a) who discovered it. It may occasionally be seen by dark-ground or phase-contrast microscopy, but it is most surely revealed by silver impregnation.

On the antero-ventral border of the body there is sometimes to be seen a clear area of cytoplasm which has often been called the cytostome. It is usually very evident in *T. muris* (Fig. 76 A, B). It is certainly absent in *T. vaginalis*. Not much is known about feeding in *Trichomonas*; some species are osmotrophic; even where feeding is known to be phagotrophic the so-called cytostome has never been seen to function as such and it is present in some species known to ingest their particulate food posteriorly (see p. 131).

Species of *Trichomonas* are found all over the world almost always living harmlessly in the alimentary tracts of invertebrates* and vertebrates. It is doubtful if true cysts are ever formed and little is known about transmission (p. 128). A few species have invaded the urino-genital tracts of vertebrates, where they may be pathogenic (*T. foetus*, in cattle; *T. vaginalis*, in man); infection certainly (*T. foetus*) or probably (*T. vaginalis*) occurs during coitus. *T. vaginalis*, which forms no cysts, occurs in 3 to 5 per cent of symptomless women in Great Britain and the United States (Feo, 1956; Whittington, 1957), and in the male urethra, where it is harder to detect than in the vagina, it is much commoner than at one time supposed (Feo, Varano, and Fetter, 1956); but formal proof that the vaginitis sometimes caused by this organism is venereal is still lacking, though it is sometimes assumed (Coutts *et al.*, 1955). A free-living species from pond-water has been described by Bishop (1935, 1936, 1939).

Trichomonas muris (Grassi)

This accessible species is found in the caecum and to a lesser extent the large intestine of wild and laboratory mice in different parts of the world. In this country Elton *et al.* (1931) found it in two-thirds of the long-tailed mice (*Apodemus sylvaticus*) examined; nearly all short-tailed field mice, *Microtus agrestis* (*M. hirtus*), had heavy infections, but those in bank voles, *Clethriomys* (*Evotomys*) *glareolus*, were few and light.† In North America, Wenrich (1921) found that about a third of his white mice, but fewer wild mice (*Mus musculus* and *Peromyscus leucopus*), were infected. The parasite occurs in other rodents, e.g. ground squirrels, *Citellus* spp. in USSR (Sassuchin, 1931) and North America (Kirby and Honigberg, 1949), and it has been experimentally transferred to rats and hamsters (Saxe, 1954). The morphology is given by Wenrich (1921) and Kirby and Honigberg (1949); for E.M. studies of ultra-thin sections see Anderson (1955) and Anderson and Beams (1959).

In its natural hosts, *T. muris* may be accompanied by a smaller species, *T. microti*, originally described by Wenrich and Saxe (1950) from *Microtus pennsylvanicus*. *T. microti* (Fig. 76 G) is on the average 5 to 7 μ long, has

---

* For a brief note on trichomonads of termites see p. 148.
† Miss Margaret Ring kindly informs me *in litt.* that all of the 31 *C. glareolus* she examined were infected with *T. muris*: there is evidently some local variation.

4 flagella, and a slim tapering axostyle without a siderophile ring; it is much rarer than *T. muris*.

The living organism

Diluted smears of caecal contents are examined as for *Entamoeba muris* (p. 38). *T. muris* remains active for some time at room temperatures and is not difficult to observe under the oil-immersion lens.

The animal (Fig. 76 A, B) is spindle-shaped, some $10-20 \mu \times 5-15 \mu$, with a flexible, elastic body. The cytoplasm is delicately vacuolated and granular. From time to time the animal settles by its posterior end on cellular and other debris, when the motion of the granules in the fluid endoplasm is easily seen as it bends and rotates its body. There are 3 equal, free flagella. The undulating membrane is frilly and conspicuous, its axoneme extended posteriorly as a free flagellum. The course of the costa is marked by a row of paracostal granules. The only other structure likely to be seen before staining is the stout, hyaline, flexible axostyle.

It is uncertain how *T. muris* feeds. A clear, antero-ventral patch of cytoplasm was interpreted by Wenrich as a cytostome. But contained bacteria are rarely seen in the body, and though a stream of them may be directed by the undulating membrane, this leads, not to the position of the hypothetical cytostome, but towards the side of the body lower down. It is possible that *T. muris* is ordinarily osmotrophic but retains some capacity for phagotrophic feeding; or collected bacteria may be digested extracellularly. The point deserves further attention.

The means of transmission is equally uncertain. In the rectum and faeces of infected animals rounded trichomonads are often found, sometimes in great numbers, each with a complete (?) set of organellae curved to fit the spherical form (Fig. 76D); but no cyst wall is demonstrable. Wenyon (1907) found that these bodies were still viable after a week at room temperature. This does not necessarily imply the presence of a protective wall, for *T. vaginalis*, which certainly has none, is also tolerant of low temperatures for short periods (Whittington, 1951b). Mayer (1920) maintained that he had seen a cyst wall in *T. muris*, but it does not appear in his figures, his statement that it was soluble in water discourages belief in it, and his description of hatching suggests the recovery of a dormant organism rather than a process of excystation. Wenrich (1921) regarded the bodies as 'preparing to encyst' but he did not pursue their development. It seems likely that *T. muris* does not form cysts but is viable in a quiescent and rounded form for some time outside its host.

Permanent preparations

The best results are obtained by fixing in Champy or Flemming and staining by Heidenhain's long method.

In well-fixed material the cytoplasmic organellae stand out more clearly than the nucleus. Most obvious is the strong axoneme of the undulating membrane, thrown in 6 to 8 waves; it is a heavy structure and it seems to

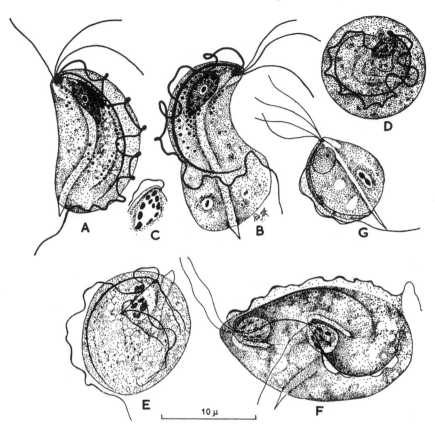

FIG. 76. Trichomonads of mice. A–F, *Trichomonas muris*. A and B, trophic flagellates: in A, the parabasal body may be seen between the nucleus and the costa, with its fibre running to the blepharoplast (Flemming; H.H.); C, nucleus, orientated as in B (Duboscq-Brasil; Feulgen); D, rounded individual or 'pseudocyst' from the rectum (Duboscq-Brasil; H. H.); E, early division stage, with the nucleus in prophase: the blepharoplast has divided, 2 flagella and the old undulating membrane and its costa remain at one pole, one flagellum has gone to the other pole, and a new membrane and costa are growing from it, the axostyle is degenerating; F, telophase: new axostyles are growing from each pole, the centrodesmus has lengthened; G, *Trichomonas microti*. (A–D original; E after Wenrich, modified; F, after Kuczynski; G after Wenrich and Saxe.)

be only loosely attached to the body (see figures by Anderson, 1955) so that it often breaks free, when its relations are those of the trailing flagellum of *Monocercomonas*; there is not the slightest evidence that this is ever anything more than accidental or that, as once supposed, a stage with a free trailing flagellum is natural to the life-history. Also clearly stained are the paracostal granules, costa, and blepharoplast. This last gives rise to the 3 anterior flagella, which stain weakly. The axostyle is a thick, pale rod, with slightly siderophile edges; its short free projection is bluntly pointed and where it leaves the body it is marked with a basophil ring. The parabasal body depends from the blepharoplast by a filament, usually revealed only by silver impregnation, and it curves round the nucleus as a sausage-shaped organ of loose texture up to about half the length of the whole animal.

In haematoxylin preparations the nucleus may be obscured by some of the paraxostylar granules. It lies anteriorly, is oval, with a membrane and a karyosome and a number of basophil granules. There are about 12 of them in the interphase nucleus, and, unlike the karyosome, they are F+ (Fig. 75C).

Division (Fig. 76 E, F) has been described by Kuczynski (1914, 1918) and Wenrich (1921). In the nucleus the chromosomes (6 according to Wenrich, 8 to Kuczynski) are formed early, in prophase, and they split almost at once into 2 moieties which remain associated until anaphase. The karyosome behaves like a nucleolus and disappears by the end of prophase. Of the cytoplasmic organellae, only the blepharoplast divides, and the flagella are distributed by its daughters each of which later develops its full complement of flagella. The daughter blepharoplasts migrate as centrioles to opposite poles of the nucleus where they remain connected until late telophase by a basophil thread, the centrodesmus. The new costa and undulating membrane, at first only slightly sinuous, appear early in prophase. The axostyle is disconnected from the blepharoplast and disappears; 2 replacements grow out from the daughter blepharoplast at telophase. The origin of the new parabasal bodies is uncertain; the original does not divide. The result of all these processes is, at telophase, a large, still active and undivided trichomonad, with 2 blepharoplasts, from each of which extend a well-developed costa and membrane, a number of flagella, and a short axostyle (F). The blepharoplasts draw apart taking with them their associated nuclei and sets of organellae, and cytoplasmic fission follows.

Culture

No method is known; the techniques for other trichomonads fail for this species.

Trichomonas batrachorum Party

This common parasite of the posterior gut of many species of frogs and toads was probably seen about 250 years ago by Anthony van Leeuwenhoek (Dobell, 1909, 1932). It has been shown experimentally that the flagellate from *Rana temporaria* can infect *Bufo vulgaris* and *Salamandra maculosa* (Bishop, 1934), and an indistinguishable organism from snakes can infect toad tadpoles (Whittington, 1951a). Honigberg (1953) has published a long list of frogs, toads, salamanders, snakes, and lizards from which a similar flagellate has under one name or another been recorded. But it by no means follows that all such trichomonads from Amphibia and Reptilia can be summarily equated; for example, Bishop could not infect frog or toad tadpoles with a flagellate (*T. lacertae?*) from *Lacerta viridis*.

   T. batrachorum is often accompanied by 2 other trichomonads, *Monocercomonas* (= *Eutrichomastix*) *batrachorum* and *T. augusta*; the latter does not occur in *Rana temporaria* but is present in the European *R. esculenta* and North American species of *Rana, Diemyctelus,* and *Hyla*. *Monocercomonas batrachorum* (Fig. 77A) has 3 anterior flagella and 1 trailing flagellum; there is no undulating membrane or costa (Dobell, 1909). *T. augusta* is larger than *T. batrachorum* and is readily distinguishable by its stouter axostyle with a chromatic ring and blunt point and conspicuous axostylar granules (see Fig. 77C and Kofoid and Swezy (1915), and Samuels (1941)).

The living organism and permanent preparations

   Dissect the frog dry, remove the intestine and rectum to a Petri dish, moisten with 0·7 per cent saline or Frog Ringer's Solution. Mount small portions of diluted gut contents, seal, and examine. Fix undiluted smears in S+A, Flemming, or Champy and stain in H.H. Structure and division have been reported in Bishop (1931), Whittington (1951a), Honigberg (1953), and in more detail by Samuels (1957) who also offered an account of feeding.

   T. batrachorum (Fig. 77B) is very active, jerky in motion, but often settling for long periods, bending or twisting on its axostyle. The undistorted body is oval or pyriform in outline, some 8–12 $\mu \times$ 4–8 μ, with 3 anterior flagella, generally of unequal length. The animal ingests bacteria and, in culture, much larger objects, such as starch grains and other trichomonads. Yet it is very doubtful if the organ called the cytostome is used in feeding. Samuels has described the use of pseudopodia for taking food, and Honigberg (1951) 'never noted any food intake at the anterior end of the cytosome* in either *T. prowazeki* or *Tritrichomonas batrachorum*'. The former species is also phagotrophic and is known to capture food by the rapid extension and withdrawal of fine filamentous pseudopods from the posterior end of the body.

   The undulating membrane is boldly convoluted with an axoneme which trails freely behind as the posterior flagellum. The costa is slender, often accompanied by an arc of granules. The axostyle tapers and is slimmer

---

* The body. The resemblance of the word to 'cytostome' is fortuitous,

than in *T. muris*. The parabasal is particularly difficult to demonstrate except by silver impregnation; there are 2 filaments depending from the blepharoplast in an inverted V about each arm of which is collected a variable amount of parabasal material. Finally, overlying the blepharoplast, and again seen usually after silver impregnation, is a crescentic pelta. The nucleus is oval, anterior, with a karyosome which is F—.

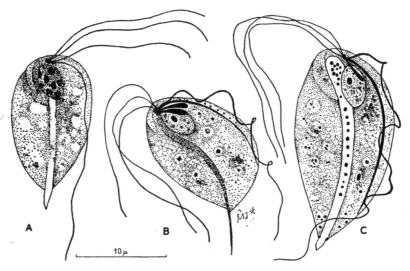

Fig. 77. Trichomonad parasites of frogs and toads. A, *Monocercomonas* (= *Eutrichomastix*) *batrachorum*; B, *Trichomonas batrachorum*; C, *Trichomonas augusta*. (A after Dobell; B original; C after Samuels.)

At division, according to Whittington (1951a), the flagella, undulating membrane, and costa are distributed in the usual way, the axostyle dedifferentiates, and each prospective daughter develops rudiments of the missing organellae before cytokinesis.

T. batrachorum does not form cysts. The flagellates can survive for some months in rain-water in the absence of oxygen according to Bishop, who used the flagellate stage for her transfer experiments mentioned above. Infection in nature is presumably by contamination with free flagellates.

Culture

T. batrachorum is easily maintained, once isolated from accompanying Protozoa, on HSre+S or HShs (using 1 part inactivated horse serum in 9 parts 0·5 per cent NaCl) or even in this dilute serum alone, though Bishop found that cultures could not be initiated on it. Whittington kept her cultures for years in 5 per cent horse serum in 0·6 per cent NaCl. Honigberg grew his flagellates on Balamuth and Sandza's medium (p. 413).

ORDER DIPLOMONADIDA

These polymastigote flagellates have a bilateral symmetry produced by the duplication of their flagella, nuclei, and other organellae. Some are free-living, especially in fresh water contaminated with organic refuse; most, or, at any rate, most of the accessible forms, are entozoic, usually in the intestinal tract, whence they may invade other sites, such as the blood-stream; there is evidently a wide tolerance, and even those in homoio-thermic hosts (e.g. *Hexamita muris*) may be recovered in the active phase from faeces of infected hosts diluted with tap water. Cysts are common. Reproduction in the free or encysted stage is by binary fission.

Hexamita intestinalis Dujardin

The name was proposed in 1841 by Dujardin for an organism from stag-nant water and also parasitic in frogs and newts, and which he believed to have 6 flagella; in fact, it had 8, but the misnomer has priority and may stand: it is the animal described by Dobell (1909) under the name *Octomitus dujardini*. It is very common in many Amphibia where it is usually accom-panied by other flagellates, from which it may be distinguished by its small size and its slim, elongated, highly flexible body.

The living organism

H. intestinalis is the commonest flagellate of frogs, occurring in the large intestine, rectum, and cloaca, where it is apparently harmless; infections may be extremely heavy. A little of the gut content is diluted on the slide with 0·7 per cent saline or Frog Ringer's Solution, sealed, and examined with the oil-immersion lens. The organism (Fig. 78) is about 10 μ long, though very much smaller forms only some 2 or 3 μ long may occur; it is slim, with a rounded anterior end tapering a little towards the posterior, which is slightly bifid. Swimming is very rapid, always head first, and for some time after mounting the flagellates cross the field so fast that observa-tion is impossible, but as they slow down the flagella can be counted. Of these, 3 pairs emerge anteriorly and 1 posteriorly; the former lash in loco-motion, the latter trail limply behind. From time to time the animal settles by its posterior end, turns from side to side or bends back on itself, stretch-ing, contracting, and twisting with great vigour and flexibility.

Permanent preparations

Smears are best fixed in Flemming or Champy, though S. or B. will give good results. Harden for 48 hours or more in 96 per cent alcohol. Stain in H.H.

The diplomonad structure is very striking (Fig. 78 A, B). The nuclei are oval, each with a heavily staining mass occupying nearly all of the space within the membrane. Between and slightly anterior to the nuclei are the paired blepharoplasts; their differentiation cannot be visually controlled

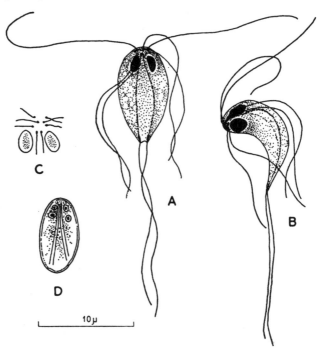

FIG. 78. *Hexamita intestinalis*. A and B, trophic forms: B.; H.H.; C, the arrangement of blepharoplasts as seen in films fixed in osmic vapour and dried; D, cyst, after division of organellae. (A and B original; C and D after Wenyon.)

and accordingly they are rarely distinguishable except by chance; there are, in fact, 4 pairs of basal granules (Fig. 78 c). From the anterior 3 arise the first 6 flagella; from the last pair run 2 parallel, basophil fibrils, which end in the points of the bifurcated 'tail' whence emerge the 2 posterior and trailing flagella. These fibrils are sometimes regarded as axostyles, sometimes as the internal courses, or axonemes, of the trailing flagella.*

Hexamita undoubtedly reproduces by binary fission, but accounts of the details vary (see, for example, Swezy, 1915, and Bishop, 1933).

* The point is hard to settle on so small an organism as *H. intestinalis*; in the somewhat larger *H. gigas* from the horse-leech *Haemopis sanguisugae* the posterior flagella were reported by Bishop (1933) as applied but not attached to the body, i.e. the fibrils referred to were independent for their whole lengths of the flagella and cannot have been axonemes.

The cysts (Fig. 78 D) are oval, up to about 6 μ long, and a single mitosis provides them with 4 nuclei.

Other species of **Hexamita**

Flagellates apparently identical with *H. intestinalis* occur in many Amphibia and also in fishes, e.g. trout (Schmidt, 1920). *H. muris* is very commonly found in mice in company with *Trichomonas muris*.

An apparently free-living form, perhaps really the type species, *H. inflata*, may be very reliably obtained as follows. A small quantity of the microdrilous oligochaete *Tubifex* is kept in a shallow bowl under a very slow running or dripping tap. After a time some of the worms become unhealthy; they are pale and tend to separate from the clump of their fellows. Gently dry such an animal and tease its flesh with needles on a slide in a drop of water. A rich supply of *Hexamita* is very often revealed. *H. inflata* is an inhabitant of stagnant water and might well be attracted by the decomposing organic material of the dying oligochaetes. Ryckeghem (1928) also records *Hexamita* from *Tubifex*, but he regards the flagellate as truly entozoic and a new species, *H. tubificis*: but in the experience of one of us (D. L. M.) the flagellate is first found in the coelom, an improbable site for an entozoic species of *Hexamita* but intelligible enough on the assumption that the flagellates are invaders of tissue already putrefying from other causes; if they do occur in the gut it is only when that too has begun to decay. The examination of thousands of healthy worms failed to reveal a single infection.

Culture

Hexamita is so easily obtained there is scarcely any need to cultivate it for class purposes. Bishop (1933) grew *H. gigas* on *HShs* (see p. 414) or in the liquid component plus starch (*hs+S*), the *hs* used being 1 part inactivated horse serum to 10 parts 0·5 per cent NaCl. The richer cultures were obtained in the diphasic medium at room temperatures. They should be sub-cultured weekly.

Giardia* muris (Grassi)

The flagellates may be found in large numbers in the small intestine of laboratory mice, especially in the duodenum, but sometimes in the caecum

---

* *Giardia* is fairly common in the intestinal tract of vertebrates; one species is the only protozoan to occur in the small intestine of man (see Hoare, 1949); one has been recorded from a parasitic nematode (Thomson, 1925). The taxonomy of the genus is difficult; many species have been named on alleged biometrical differences of doubtful reliability or on the even more fallible grounds of host specificity; progress is hindered by lack of a culture method. Nevertheless, there seem to be two good species in mice, *G. muris*,

and elsewhere. Cysts are formed lower down the gut and are passed with the faeces. Kofoid and Christiansen (1915) found that 22 per cent. of their animals were infected.

The living organism

Examine as for *Entamoeba muris*, but search the small instead of the large intestine. *G. muris* will remain alive for some time at room temperatures in sealed preparations.

The flagellate (Fig. 79 A, B) is about 10 μ long and in outline shaped rather like a child's tailed kite, the more pointed end being posterior.

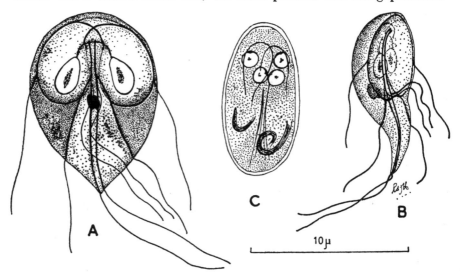

FIG. 79. *Giardia*. A, *G. muris*; B, the same, seen obliquely from the side (both fixed B., stained H.H.); C, cyst of *G. intestinalis*. (A and B original; C after Wenyon.)

Dobell and O'Connor aptly compare the shape of *Giardia* to a pear from which a large longitudinal slice has been cut obliquely at the thicker, anterior end. The 'cut' surface is slightly concave and seems to act as a sucker by which the organism attaches itself to the surface of the intestinal epithelium. The body is flexible but kept in shape by the pellicle. There are 2 vesicular nuclei and the flagella are in 4 pairs. There is no mouth. The cytoplasm is very clear.

with small round median bodies, and another species, with crescentic median bodies, and indistinguishable from the human form (*G. intestinalis*): the subject has been discussed by Filice (1952), who provides many references. Besides the taxonomy, the structure, development, and host–parasite relations of the genus all need more study. The accompanying description of *G. muris* is admittedly based to a large extent on inference from what is known of other species.

Giardia progresses by up and down skipping movements, with flexures of the tail; as it turns over the concave sucker can be seen plainly. The animal frequently becomes attached, with the flagella still vigorously fluttering, and then is the time to count them. One pair (anterior) comes free of the body where it is broadest; one (ventral) arises between the nuclei; a third (lateral) emerges well behind the sucker; the 2 posterior or caudal flagella leave the tip of the tail. In such a stationary animal it may also be possible to see the outline of the sucker and, within it, the 2 nuclei, placed like eyes in a face.

The animal multiplies by binary fission in the free and encysted states; the accounts of this extremely complicated process disagree; one for *G. duodenalis*, in rats, is given by Filice (1952).

The cysts (Fig. 79C) are oval, thin-walled, averaging $13 \times 7 \mu$. There is a tendency for the soft, contained body to withdraw from the wall, especially at the poles. When mounted in iodine the outlines of the nuclei, remains of skeletal fibres and median bodies become visible. In some cysts there are 4 nuclei, usually crowded at one pole, and the cytoplasmic organellae are also duplicated, or, rather, reduplicated; according to Hegner (1927) the organism hatches as a whole and cytokinesis follows.

Permanent preparations

Fix smears with warmed S+A; stain in H.H. The differentiation is tricky, for unless stopped at the correct point, the flagella will have disappeared. Watch for the karyosomes to appear in the nuclei and then remove at once from iron alum to water. The encysted forms require longer fixation, staining, and differentiation.

In the trophic forms, the following may be observed: the 2 nuclei, each with an F+ karyosome; the sucker outlined by its fibrillar border; the 8 flagella, the origins of which are difficult to ascertain; the 2 long siderophile fibrils (axonemes?) running between the nuclei to the end of the tail. Crossing these fibrils below the sucker are 2 basophil structures sometimes unfortunately called parabasal bodies; they differ from the latter in that they are well preserved by fixatives containing ascetic acid, they do not impregnate with silver, and they are apparently self-perpetuating (Filice, 1952); as their homologies are unknown the non-committal name 'median bodies' is here used. In a proportion of the specimens, they are absent.

Stained cysts have the structure shown in Fig. 79C.

Culture

No method is known for any species of *Giardia*.

ORDER HYPERMASTIGIDA

The members of this order have, as the name implies, very numerous flagella; in the simpler forms about 50 of them are grouped at the anterior end, but in others a more or less continuous coat of many thousands of flagella invests most of the body. All species are entozoic in blattid Orthoptera or Isoptera. As is well known, those from xylophagous hosts have developed with them a remarkable partnership in which the insect obtains and the Protozoa digest the wood on which all feed, and their relationship is probably the most completely studied symbiosis known to zoologists. Set rather apart from these, simpler in structure and in their life-histories, are the lophomonad flagellates of cockroaches, sometimes grouped into a suborder of their own, distinguished by the fact that their flagella and associated organellae, which are grouped together anteriorly, are resorbed during division.

Lophomonas blattarum Stein

Of the simpler hypermastigote flagellates, 2 species, *L. blattarum* and *L. striata* (p. 140) are fairly common, often side by side, in the hind-gut of the same hosts, cockroaches of the genera *Blatta*, *Blattella*, and *Periplaneta*.* They are cosmopolitan. From 10 to 30 per cent of the adults, especially females and in the summer, are infected. The flagellates have been studied by, among others, Janicki (1910, 1911) and Kudo (1926 a, b); an excellent account of division is to be found in Bělař (1926 a, pp. 36 ff.).

The living organism

The flagellates are most abundant behind the openings of the Malpighian tubules. Tease this region of the hind-gut in a drop of 0·8–0·9 per cent saline on a slide, seal under a No. 0 slip, and examine with high power and oil-immersion lenses.

L. blattarum (Figs. 80, 81) is usually between 15 and 30 μ long. The colourless body is spherical to pyriform, soft, and easily deformed as it pushes between obstacles; there is a tendency for the anterior end, with flagella and nucleus, to be torn away from the rest, which is often left behind to perish; or the posterior end, anchored to some particle, may be drawn out into a thread. There are 50 to 60 flagella, set closely in an anterior tuft. Their blepharoplasts form an incomplete circle and opposite the gap in it the flagella are longer than elsewhere. Just behind them a glistening area marks the position of the nucleus, calyx, and collar described below, and through the centre of the body runs a slim rod (axostyle?) which sometimes

* For a list of Protozoa entozoic in cockroaches, see index, under *host-list*.

protrudes posteriorly. There is no cytostome and solid food (bacteria) is ingested at any point on the soft, posterior surface; food inclusions may be abundant, in distinction from the related *L. striata*.

The cysts are spherical, 12 to 20 μ in diameter, and found at any time of the year in the hind-gut or faeces; they contain 2, 4, or 8 nuclei and the surface is often marked with wavy lines (Fig. 80 C, D). Encysting flagellates

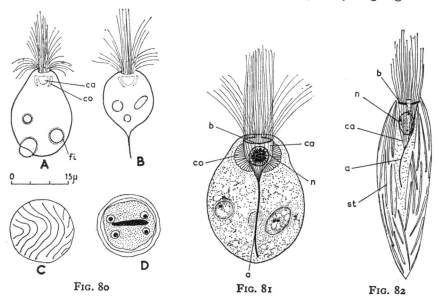

FIG. 80. *Lophomonas blattarum.* A and B, the living flagellate (A ingesting food); C, the living cyst; D, the same, fixed and stained. (A, B, and D modified after Kudo; C after Janicki.)

ca, calyx; *co*, collar; *fi*, food inclusion.

FIG. 81. *Lophomonas blattarum.* Somewhat schematic. × 1,500. (After Kudo.)

a, axial rod (axostyle?); *b*, blepharoplasts; *ca*, calyx; *co*, collar; *n*, nucleus.

FIG. 82. *Lophomonas striata.* Stained Iron Haematoxylin. × 1,500. (After Kudo.)

st, striation on pellicle; other abbreviations as in Fig. 81.

become sluggish and vacuolated, stop feeding and resorb first the calyx, then the axial rod, and finally the flagella. The nucleus divides two or three times. Excystation has not been reported.

Permanent preparations

Fix in warm S+A or B. Stain in D.H. or H.H.; counterstain with Eosin or Orange G. Differentiation needs care as the flagella may easily become invisible before the nuclei and other structures begin to stand out. It may be best to differentiate some smears for nuclei and others for cytoplasmic organellae.

The nucleus (Fig. 81) has a central mass containing deeply staining granules almost filling it. Anteriorly lies the incomplete circlet of basal granules. Each of these is slightly elongated and through each the flagellar root is continued to form with its fellows the calyx, enclosing the nucleus, below which the fibrillae of the calyx unite to form the axial rod. From the calyx radiate a compact series of small rods composing an enigmatic organelle sometimes called a parabasal body; it is absent from the related *L. striata*, is resistant to acetic acid, and is possibly best regarded as a structure *sui generis* and called by Janicki's non-committal name for it, the collar.

In division, the nucleus migrates from the calyx, which with the collar, blepharoplasts, flagella, and axial rod are eventually lost and replaced in the daughters by newly differentiated structures. The centrioles are said by Bělař to persist and in mitosis they are connected, as in trichomonads, by a centrodesmus.

Stained cysts (Fig. 80D) show a fairly thick wall, usually 4, sometimes 8, nuclei, and the centrodesmus of the first division persists, staining more and more feebly with age.

Lophomonas striata Bütschli

The body of this species (Fig. 82) is club-shaped and moves blunt end foremost. It is between 30 and 40 μ long, larger than *L. blattarum* and far less flexible. The surface is covered with slim, needle-like striations between 5 and 25 μ long, more or less parallel to the long axis. Most observers have regarded these striae as cuticular differentiations, but Grassé (1926) considers them to be symbiotic Schizophyta, which he named *Fusiformis lophomonadis*; they resemble similarly interpreted structures in the pellicle of *Polymastix*; so far, however, none of these supposed symbionts has been cultured and Grassé's hypothesis awaits proof.

The flagella are shorter than those of *L. blattarum* and less vigorous in action. The axial rod never protrudes posteriorly; if its function is indeed skeletal then its slighter development here may be correlated with the firmer pellicle. The calyx is longer and narrower, surrounded by a layer of somewhat granulated endoplasm, but without a collar. There are no food inclusions, and *L. striata* appears to be osmotrophic. The cysts are usually 15 μ in diameter, subspherical and binucleate; the contained organism retains at least some of its ectoplasmic striae. For more information see Janicki (1910) and Kudo (1926 b).

Culture

According to Kudo (1954, *Protozoology*, 4th edn.), the white of one egg in 100 ml Ringer's Solution, sterile, with a little added yeast cake, is an excellent medium for both species. Incubate at room temperature and sub-culture every 4 to 6 days.

The flagellates of termites and wood-eating roaches

Members of 4 out of 5 families of termites, that is, all except the Termitidae (the family which, however, contains the majority of species) eat wood and all are infected with flagellates, most of which are hypermastigotes. These Protozoa are so numerous as to pack the hind-gut almost solid, and estimates of their mass range from one-seventh to one-third of the total weight of the insect (Hungate, 1939; Katzin and Kirby, 1939). Some at least of the hypermastigote and polymastigote flagellates are dependent on cellulose for their carbon which, as far as is known, they cannot accept from any other source, and they secrete a cellulase (Trager, 1932, 1934a). If all the Protozoa are eradicated, the host continues to eat wood, but it cannot digest it and it dies. If the fauna is destroyed by parts, it is found that not all the flagellates are necessary, e.g. in *Zootermopsis*, the polymastigotes *Tricercomitus* and *Hexamastix* play little or no part in the host's physiological economy and their presence makes no difference to its survival; with *Trichomonas termopsidis* (p. 148) the termites can live some three times longer than with no Protozoa; but the essential genus is *Trichonympha* (p. 142) in the presence of which *Zootermopsis* can live indefinitely on a diet in which apparently the only effective ingredient is cellulose (Cleveland, 1925 a–d, 1928).

It follows that all wood-eating termites, which are unable to secrete their own cellulase, must be infected with their symbiotic flagellates, and this is so. There are no cysts and the infection is lost at each moult, but the means of reinfection is uncertain (Andrew, 1930); it always takes place in the presence of other and infected termites; if newly hatched larvae are isolated from infected adults they never acquire any Protozoa, they cannot digest cellulose, and they die.

The wood-eating roach, *Cryptocercus punctulatus*, maintains in its hind-gut no fewer than 25 species of flagellates; here the infection is permanent and the Hypermastigida form cysts, but only at ecdysis. Like the termites, the roach does not produce any enzyme capable of attacking wood, but the flagellates contain a cellulase and cellobiase which *in vitro* produce dextrose from cellulose, and it seems likely that *in vivo* they pass some of the dextrose to their hosts and convert the rest into glycogen which they retain for their own use. The entire subject is dealt with in a magnificently illustrated monograph by Cleveland and his colleagues (1934) which should be known to all students of protozoology.

All the flagellates of *Cryptocercus* reproduce asexually, but according to Cleveland some of them exhibit a sexual phase at ecdysis and he believes that this is evoked by the moulting hormone of the host. The cycle is inhibited by transfer to non-moulting hosts, or by removal of the pars intercerebralis, thought to initiate moulting, from the cerebral ganglia (Cleveland and Nutting, 1955; Nutting and Cleveland 1958). Summary accounts of this phenomenon are given in Cleveland (1947, 1957, 1958 *a*, *b*) and Wenrich (1954), and the details are described in a series of papers by Cleveland (1949 onwards) issued under the general title 'Hormone-induced sexual cycles in flagellates'.

Trichonympha campanula Kofoid and Swezy

T. campanula, originally studied by Kofoid and Swezy (1919*b*), occurs in the hind-gut of all 3 species of *Zootermopsis* from California and Arizona and is always accompanied by a number of other flagellates (p. 146); these include, in *Zootermopsis angusticollis* and *Z. nevadensis*, 2 other species of *Trichonympha* (Fig. 85); in *Zootermopsis laticeps*, *T. campanula* is the only representative of its genus. Very good accounts of *Trichonympha* spp. have been given by Kirby (1932), whose results have been confirmed and augmented by the fine E.M. studies of Pitelka and Schooley (1958).

The living organism

Termites pickled for years in alcohol will yield recognizable specimens of *Trichonympha* but only a study of living material can give a just impression of the extent and vigour of the flagellate fauna. All hosts are infected, except at the moult. A living termite is placed in a drop of 0·6 per cent NaCl on a slide and transected just behind the thorax; it will immediately leak flagellates among which the trichonymphids are visible to the naked eye; the drop is covered and sealed for examination.

T. campanula (Figs. 83, 84) is a large, handsome flagellate ranging from 150 to 315 μ long and 55 to 145 μ broad; Kirby gives a mean of 217 × 87 μ. The body is divided into three regions: (1) a rostrum, bearing longish flagella of equal length, and surmounted by a cap without any flagella, (2) a middle region, broadening backwards and with flagella lengthening towards the posterior end, and (3) a soft, naked, rounded posterior region, which is the site of ingestion and always contains fragments of wood in various stages of digestion. The rostrum is separated from the middle region by a deep cleft in the ectoplasm cutting it off behind, but this is not usually visible except when the animal bends to one side and exposes the cleft in the convexity. More obvious is the sharp difference between the length of the rostral and body flagella; the former are some 30 to 60 μ long; immediately behind the rostrum they are only 20 to 25 μ long and they increase in length very little down the sides of the body until towards the end of the middle region they lengthen greatly up to 150 μ.

On withdrawal from the host some specimens remain quite still, others remain active and some regain their activity soon. *Trichonympha* is an extremely vigorous organism. It moves forward, usually rotating, bending its rostrum from side to side or twisting it back on its body. The flagella emerge from the body pointing posteriorly and are usually so held for most of their length, so that waves passing from base to tip drive the animal along. Flagellar activity is less co-ordinated than that of ciliates. The rostral flagella are the most active, the shorter ones of the middle region move less, and the long posterior ones trail limply behind. The twisting movements of the flexible body are apparently effected by the pressure of the flagella on the external medium; *Trichonympha* has no myonemes, and as the rostrum bends to one side it does so against a flagellar 'push' from the other side, and the reverse as it turns back.

Behind the flagellated region the posterior is soft and apparently sticky; small wood particles adhere to it and are ingested at local and temporary invaginations of the surface. At times the hind end of the animal may be drawn up into a shallow concavity and it is then that the organism assumes the shape of a bell.

Much of the complex detail of the structure is visible in the living animal. Under high power, the whole surface of the flagellated body is seen to be marked by longitudinal ridges, between which the flagella emerge; the ridges are about twice as numerous behind the rostrum as on it (Fig. 83). Below them, and alternating with them so that they correspond with the rows of flagella are flat, plate-like structures sunk into the ectoplasm. The basal granules mark the inner limit of the deep ectoplasm; they are set obliquely and run a spiral course about the body (Fig. 84). Between these outer and inner ectoplasmic layers lies a middle region containing the flagellar roots which run irregularly between the lines of plates and the rows of blepharoplasts (Figs. 83, 84). Thus in focusing downwards from the pellicle one sees first the longitudinal grooves, then the plates, then a middle ectoplasmic layer containing the disorderly mass of flagellar roots, and finally the basal granules, so regularly disposed as to form longitudinal, transverse, and diagonal rows. The outer layer of *T. campanula* is clear and contains only the plates; in *T. collaris* it also contains numerous peripheral granules, visible in the living animal (Fig. 85), and they provide perhaps the easiest distinction between the 2 species. Behind the middle region, the complex wide band of ectoplasm is reduced to a thin undifferentiated layer.

The endoplasm is finely granular and the granules, which may well be glycogen, stain yellow with Lugol's Iodine Solution. A slim core of endoplasm within the rostrum is the only connexion between this part of the body and the middle region; anteriorly it is surmounted by a refringent hemispherical granule. For other endoplasmic inclusions, see Kirby's account.

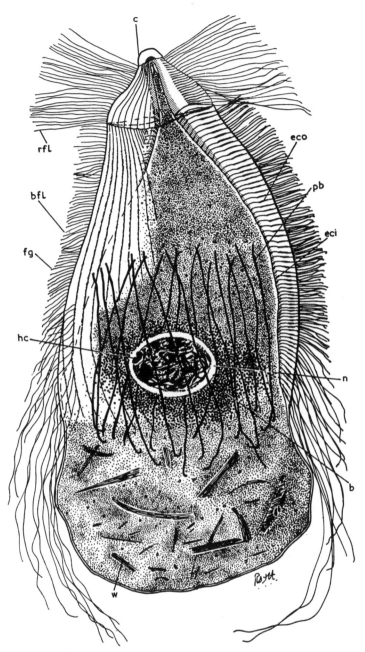

FIG. 83. *Trichonympha campanula*. The surface of the organism bearing longitudinal flagellated grooves is in focus to the left of the drawing and the right and posterior are seen in optical section. ×650. (Original.)

b, commensal bacteria; *bfl*, flagella of middle region; *c*, cap; *eci*, inner layer of ectoplasm; *eco*, outer layer of ectoplasm containing platelets; *fg*, longitudinal groove: some of the flagella emerging from it are seen posteriorly; *hc*, 'heterochromosome'; *n*, nucleus; *pb*, parabasal cord; *rfl*, last rostral flagellum; *w*, wood particle in endoplasm of posterior region.

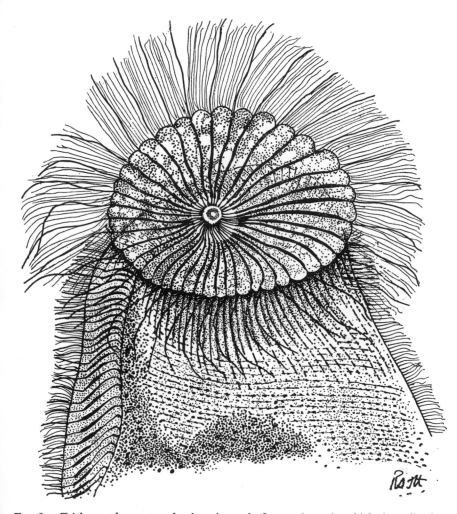

FIG. 84. *Trichonympha campanula.* Anterior end of a specimen in which the collar has become partly detached and then flattened in mounting, to show details of flagellar insertions. The flagella of the rostrum are plainly seen leaving their grooves, which are more widely spaced at the top of the drawing owing to the spread of the collar. Below the collar, the top of the body is seen in surface view, with longitudinal grooves, more numerous than on the collar; in slightly deeper focus, the longitudinal lines give way to transverse or spiral fibrillae connecting the blepharoplasts; posteriorly, in still deeper focus, are the endoplasm, and, to the left, the ectoplasm, showing the outer layer with platelets, middle layer with flagellar roots leading to the rod-shaped blepharoplasts of the inner layer.

Flagella out of focus are lightly drawn. Flemming; H.H. × 1,200. (Original.)

The nucleus is large, spherical (19 to 33 μ) or ellipsoidal, and lies in the middle of the body. The chromatin is coiled in threads surrounded by a clear space within the membrane. The 'heterochromosome' is described below.

The parabasal apparatus consists of a number of slender threads surrounding the nucleus like a cylindrical rope curtain or sleeve. Some at least touch the nucleus in passing, and the sinuous cords are usually bent forwards like hooks at their posterior ends; anteriorly they form the inner wall of the rostral tube but the fact is apparent only in electron micrographs.

Trichonympha like other flagellates of termites is peculiarly susceptible of infection by hyperparasitic micro-organisms, of which a considerable number have been described (Kirby, 1937). Conspicuous among these in *T. campanula* is a bacilliform or filamentous parasite which is invariably present, confined to the perinuclear endoplasm, where it often forms a thick and obvious mass.

Permanent preparations

Fix smears in S+A, B or, best, Champy. Stain in H.H. with or without Orange G. *Trichonympha* is a large flagellate and there are marked differences between the time taken to differentiate specimens spread thinly on the slide and those retaining their normal thickness. Over- and under-stained individuals are rewarding as well as the good specimens between extremes, and with cytological fixation very fine results are possible.

Most of the structures seen in the living animal are made plainer by staining, especially the nucleus. In this the so-called 'heterochromosome', characteristic of this species, is seen as a coiled, curved, or bent rod lying in a small space among the other chromatic elements of the nucleus. The parabasal apparatus is preserved by cytological fixatives (e.g. Champy) and staining shows that each cord consists of a chromophile thread with a smooth line of chromophobe substance running along its length.

Other flagellates of *Zootermopsis*

The two Californian termites, *Z. angusticollis* and *Z. nevadensis* harbour the same flagellates and a gregarine: the flagellates are *Trichonympha campanula*, *T. collaris*, *T. sphaerica*, and the following 4 polymastigotes, *Trichomonas termopsidis*, *Streblomastix strix*, *Tricercomitus termopsidis*, and *Hexamastix termopsidis*. The Arizonan termite, *Z. laticeps*, has the same flagellates, except that there is only 1 trichonymphid, which is *Trichonympha campanula*, and *Hexamastix termopsidis* is replaced by *H. laticeps*, i.e. there are 5 flagellates in all (Figs. 85, 86). It should be borne in mind

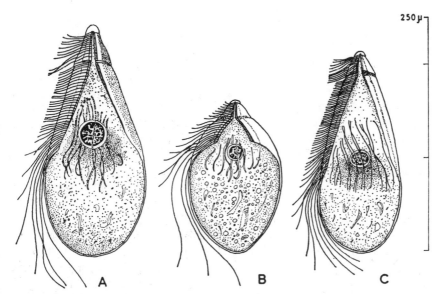

250 μ

FIG. 85. *Trichonympha* from *Zootermopsis angusticollis*. Diagram to show typical forms and average sizes. ×250. A, *Trichonympha collaris*; B, *T. sphaerica*; C, *T. campanula*. (After Kirby.)

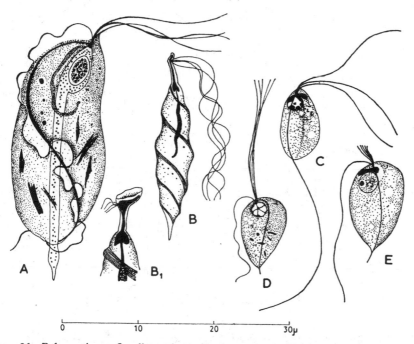

0   10   20   30μ

FIG. 86. Polymastigote flagellates from *Zootermopsis*. A, *Trichomonas termopsidis*; B, *Streblomastix strix*, and B₁, diagram to show the anterior end of the same; C, *Tricercomitus termopsidis*; D, *Hexamastix termopsidis*; E, *H. laticeps*. (A, C–E modified after Kirby; B, B₁ after Kidder.)

that slides differentiated for trichonymphids are unlikely to show the other and much smaller flagellates very clearly.

Trichonympha collaris Kirby (Fig. 85A) is slightly larger and stouter than *T. campanula*, and averages 247×114 μ, with a noticeably shorter flagellated region. Peripheral granules, rod-shaped, rounded, or slightly elongated, are always present in the outer layer of ectoplasm and distinguish the species at once. The parabasal cords, as they pass the nucleus, bend inwards and come close to it and they are collected into strands of several cords each. The nucleus is larger and lies more anteriorly and has no 'heterochromosome'. See Kirby (1932). It is found in *Z. angusticollis* and *Z. nevadensis*.

Trichonympha sphaerica Kofoid and Swezy (Fig. 85B) is easily distinguished from both the preceding species. It is smaller (165×89 μ) and much rounded, though certainly not spherical, with a shorter rostrum and flagellated region. The nucleus lies far forwards with only a short broad cone of endoplasm in front of it. The flagella on the rostrum are not longer than those behind it. According to Cleveland (1925d) and Lund (1930), this species (which is their *Leidyopsis sphaerica*) is rare, but Kirby (1932, q.v. for a full account) found that all 3 trichonymphids usually occurred in about equal numbers. It is found in *Z. angusticollis* and *Z. nevadensis*.

Trichomonas termopsidis Cleveland (Fig. 86A), usually abundant in all species, is large for a trichomonad, from 10 to 85 μ long, with a mean of rather over 40 μ. When relaxed the axostyle is more or less straight, the costa and undulating membrane run in a broad spiral about the elongated body; when contracted, the body is rounded, the costa C-shaped, and the membrane almost completely encircles the body. There are 4 flagella, often as long as the body. The axostyle is conspicuous, stout, containing endaxostylar granules, abruptly tapering, with a large spoon-shaped capitulum on the left-hand side of the nucleus. The parabasal body is very long, more or less flattened and coiled and contains a row of granules staining with Delafield's but not with Iron Haematoxylin. The nucleus has numerous deeply staining granules. For details see Andrews (1925), or better, Kirby (1931). It is found in all species of *Zootermopsis*.

Trichomonas termopsidis is xylophagous and its cytoplasm contains pieces of wood. The axostyle and more especially the endaxostylar granules stain with Lugol's Iodine Solution and contain glycogen or some similar substance. The flagellate cannot survive without a supply of cellulose and produces its own cellulase (Trager, 1932, 1934). For culture see p. 418.

Streblomastix strix Kofoid and Swezy (Fig. 86 B, B$_1$) is a curious polymastigote flagellate occurring in nearly 100 per cent of the termites examined by Kidder (1929), who gave an account of its structure and division. It is confined to the anterior part of the hind-gut and is especially abundant near the wall, to which it often attaches itself by its hold-fast organ. The animal is slim and spindle-shaped in its contracted state (15 to

50 μ long) but may extend into a finely elongated, whip-like form up to 300 μ or more long. There is an anterior rostellum bearing at its tip a cup-shaped sucker or hold-fast and containing the greater part of the blepharoplast. The 4 flagella (not 6, as Kofoid and Swezy, 1919a, supposed) come off just behind the hold-fast and trail backwards in attached forms. The greater part of the body is spirally ridged and the ridges are marked by bands of fibrillae said to be myonemes. The nucleus is itself elongated and attached to the blepharoplast by a rhizoplast. According to Kidder, binary fission is transverse, which in a flagellate is remarkable. *Streblomastix* is apparently an osmotroph and has nothing to do with the digestion of cellulose. It is found in all species of *Zootermopsis*.

Tricercomitus termopsidis Kirby (Fig. 86c) is usually common and especially so in newly moulted hosts which have not been reinfected with their larger Protozoa. The body is pyriform or elongated oval, 4–12 $\mu \times$ 2–3 μ, with usually 4 flagella, of which 3 are equal and free and the fourth very long (up to 65 μ) and attached along the greater part of the length of the body. There is perhaps an axostyle. The blepharoplast is relatively large. The parabasal is variable, up to the length of the nucleus. Giants and elongated whip forms may occur. The endoplasm may contain wood. For further information, see Kirby (1930) and for culture (p. 419) and resistant stages, Trager (1934b). It is found in all species of *Zootermopsis*.

Hexamastix termopsidis Kirby (Fig. 86D) is 5 to 11 μ long. It moves rapidly and jerkily without making much progress, in contrast to *Tricercomitus*, which can cover some distance in spasmodic stages. There are 6 or fewer flagella, 1 trailing, the rest turned anteriorly; they and the axostyle and parabasal body are all attached to an anterior blepharoplast. The axostyle is slender, usually projecting. The parabasal is 'trumpet-shaped', longer than and curved round the nucleus opposite the axostyle. There is a cytostome and the animal ingests bacteria and wood fragments. For details see Kirby (1930). It is found in *Z. angusticollis* and *Z. nevadensis*.

H. laticeps (Fig. 86E) Kirby is like the foregoing but somewhat larger (up to 14 μ long) and with a deeply staining bar stretching in from the blepharoplast in front of the nucleus. It is found in *Z. laticeps*.

INCERTAE SEDIS: ORDER OPALINATA

The opalinid Protozoa constitute a natural group of entozoic organisms which, although morphologically rather monotonous, have for the parasitologist the interest of their life-histories, and for the taxonomist the merit of possessing cilia but none of the other characters of ciliates and so compelling him to answer the question, is the possession of cilia the truly distinctive character of the Class Ciliophora? A brief sketch of an answer to this question is offered below (p. 154) after some study of the opalinids.

Almost all known species live in the lower part of the alimentary canal of frogs and toads, but there is some reason to suspect that they may be commoner among fishes and other poikilothermic animals than is yet fully grasped (Sandon, 1949). All have a uniform coat of longish 'cilia'*; there is no mouth; there are two to over a hundred nuclei in the endoplasm and they are all alike; they reproduce asexually during most of the year, but form cysts during the host's breeding season, and these, hatching in the new generation of hosts, produce anisogametes and thence zygotes.

The taxonomy and distribution of the Opalinata have been extensively treated by Metcalf (1923, 1940); he recognized 4 genera—*Protoopalina*, circular, and *Zelleriella*, flattened in transverse section, and both with only 2 nuclei; *Cepedea*, circular, and *Opalina*, flattened in section, and both with numerous nuclei.

Opalina ranarum (Ehrenberg)

This large and convenient species is common in *Rana temporaria* and infections of it are retained longer in captivity than of many accompanying Protozoa. *R. esculenta*, the edible frog, often used by parasitologists for class work, harbours the related *Cepedea dimidiata*, which does not differ essentially from *Opalina* except in the shape of its section. It is unfortunate that there does not exist any single, complete, and generally accepted version of either the life-history or the structure of any member of the genus *Opalina*, and the following account, admittedly leaning towards simplicity, may be treated with some reservations. Among others, Metcalf (1909), Brumpt (1915), and Konsuloff (1922) have studied the life-history of *O. ranarum*, ten Kate (1927), van Overbeek de Meyer (1929), and Chatton and Brachon (1936) its structure; Chen (1936 *a, b*, 1948) showed that opalinids are ordinarily diploid, with monomorphic nuclei which undergo a normal mitosis. Cosgrove (1947) gave an account of the fibrillar pattern of *Opalina obtrigonoidea* from *Rana pipiens* in North America, and the same species was used for a valuable E.M. study of ectoplasmic structures by Pitelka (1956). For mitochondria (in *Protoopalina*?) see Horning (1925).

The living organism

Remove the rectum from a freshly killed frog, dissected dry, and keep it moistened with Frog Ringer's Solution or 0·7 per cent saline in a Petri dish. The opalinids are especially common in the upper part of the rectum, often near the wall, and are usually accompanied by other Protozoa.†
Mount a little of the rectal contents, including some material scraped from the wall; dilute, but only if necessary, with a very little of the moistening fluid; cover and seal.

---

  * To anticipate what is said below, the locomotory organs of opalinids may indifferently be called flagella or cilia; the usual name is retained here.
  † See index, under *host-list*.

Under low power, *Opalina* is seen to be a much flattened, leaf-shaped organism, with a distinctly paler ectoplasmic border and darker interior (Fig. 87 A). The apical margin is more pointed; the abapical is rounded or truncate. The size varies with the age since the last division but lengths of 600 to 700 μ are not uncommon. The entire body is covered by a coat of uniform cilia (holotrichous) arranged in oblique lines, and their successive waves are easily observed as the animal drives along in the rather viscous medium. It usually swims on a flat side, but may rotate in a spiral course, first in one direction and then, after a hesitation, in the other. The very numerous nuclei are plainly seen as small, hyaline spheres.

Under high power, the nuclei are clearer, and so too are smaller endoplasmic inclusions, the so-called endospheres (Fig. 87B) which have been supposed to represent, *inter alia*, a Golgi apparatus, stored food, and even nuclear components; their nature is still doubtful.

Dividing organisms may be seen and it is important to note the direction of fission; this is always more or less longitudinal or rather oblique in relation to the apex, in that the cleavage line passes between and not across the ciliated lines.

Trophic forms, such as the foregoing, and those reproducing asexually, are found throughout the year, and, except in early spring, they are the only forms present. In February, however, or earlier, as spawning approaches, the opalinids divide more rapidly and produce numerous smaller daughters, which themselves divide and eventually encyst. The infection cysts so formed (E–G) are transparent, spherical to ovoid, and the contained organism is rounded and folded to fit the confined space; the number of nuclei remaining to the organisms when they encyst varies—2 to 6 are common, a single nucleus less so, though it is usually possible to find one without much difficulty. The cysts pass into the water and infect tadpoles. They hatch within a few hours and there is no doubt that some, if not all, of the excysted organisms are gametocytes; it is possible that some grow at once into adults; however that may be, slightly anisogamous gametes (H, I) are eventually produced which form zygotes by syngamy. The zygotes are said to encyst, or else they grow and some of their descendants encyst, while others remain to continue the infection; the encysted small forms resulting from zygotes are then supposed to enter the water and infect a second batch of tadpoles. It is plain that we need to know more about gametogenesis, fertilization, the development and fate of zygotes and their relation to the encysted and infective stages. The production of infective bodies at the same time as a new generation of host animals becomes available is of obvious adaptive importance (cf. *Gonospora varia*, p. 181); the sexual cycles of host and commensal are causally linked so that the approach of one evokes the onset of the other. Recently, El Mofty and Smyth (1960) have shown that the active agents are probably gonadal

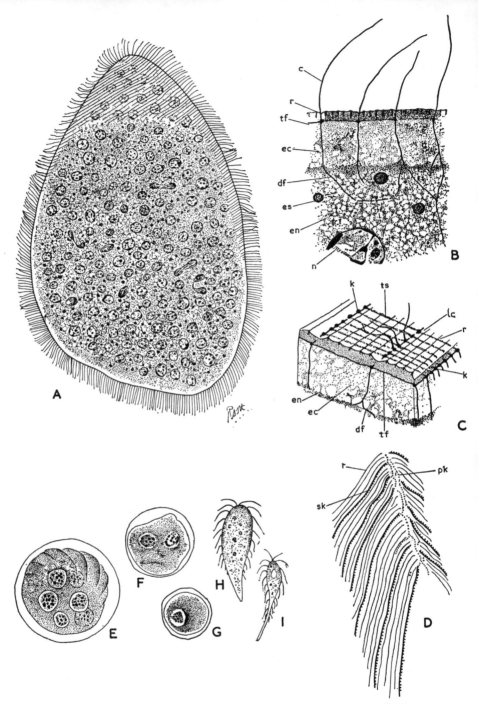

Fig. 87. *Opalina ranarum*. A, adult. ×125; B, VS body wall. ×3,000; C, fibrillar system: diagrammatic; D, anterior margin with falx; E–G, infection cysts. ×825; H–I, gametes. ×825. (A–C, E–G original; D after Chatton and Brachon; H–I after Konsuloff.)

c, cilium; *df*, deep fibril; *ec*, ectoplasm; *en*, endoplasm; *es*, endosphere; *k*, kinetosome; *lc*, longitudinal connective; *n*, nucleus; *pk*, primary kinety; *r*, ridge; *sk*, secondary kinety; *tf*, transverse fibril; *ts*, transverse stria.

rather than gonadotrophic hormones of the host. Thus, testosterone induced sexuality (as indicated by cyst production) in the opalinids at any time of the year, but gonadotrophins only just before the host's breeding season. Whether the effect on the Protozoa is produced directly by the hormones or, as seems more likely, through some consequential product of their own or the host's metabolism is not yet known.

Permanent preparations

Smears made in spring must be compared with those from any other time of the year. Sections are indispensable to the study of fine structure and its bearing on the taxonomic status of opalinids.

For whole mounts smear undiluted rectal contents with heavy infections on No. 0 slips; fix in B or S+A; stain for 12 to 24 hours in dilute D.H. ($\frac{1}{2}$ to $\frac{1}{3}$ strength) and differentiate very slowly until nuclear detail stands out. Counterstain some preparations lightly with Eosin or Chromotrope 2R. *Opalina* has rather dense endoplasm and the fault to be avoided is to leave the cytoplasm so opaque as to obscure the nuclei. If *Opalina* is accompanied by such ciliates as *Nyctotherus* and *Balantidium*, disregard them and concentrate on the opalinids only; the ciliates may look well in the end, but it is useless to aim for a preparation in which all the organisms will be shown at their best.

For sections, fix a heavily infected rectum whole in B, cut at $10\,\mu$, and stain in H.H. or Masson's Triple Stain. Such methods give good results; better ones are obtained by means of the refinements given on p. 426.

The general distribution of cilia in lines running obliquely across the broad surface of the body may be seen in whole mounts. Far more detail is found in sections cut tangentially to the flat surface to include an area of the pellicle with a thin slice of the underlying ectoplasm. From such, and from transverse sections (Fig. 87 B, C) a composite picture of the ciliature may be constructed. Like all cilia and flagella those of *Opalina* arise from kinetosomes (basal granules), and the obliquely set lines in which they are arranged underlie corresponding pellicular grooves. The lines arise from free rows of basal granules on the anterior margin, constituting the falx (growth zone, area of generative kinetics) and from them new ciliated lines grow out after division of the organism (Fig. 87D: and see Chatton and Brachon, 1936). The lines on either side of the falx are said to be asymmetrical (Mohr, 1940) but this is not obvious in *O. ranarum*. The longitudinal connectives (*lc*) seen in good preparations between adjacent kinetosomes are not quite like the kinetodesmata of typical holotrichous ciliates (p. 217). As Pitelka (1956) has shown, each kinetosome of *Opalina* transmits 2 fibres anteriorly; they join each other and presumably reach the next kinetosome anteriorly. There are no long overlapping fibres constituting a multiple link of many successive kinetosomes as in ciliates. The transverse and deep fibrillae shown in Fig. 87 B, C (*tf*, *df*) are not understood: they are evidently not part of the infraciliature. Between the pellicular grooves run ridges (*r*) which in section have the appearance of being strengthened by underlying thickenings of ectoplasm; such longitudinal thickenings may fortify the pellicle while leaving thin areas between of undiminished permeability. Transversely between the ridges run striae (*ts*) of uncertain nature and function.

Sections also show the distribution of nuclei and that they are monomorphic and divide asynchronously. Each is vesicular with an F— nucleolus: the F+ material forms granules and clumps.

The status of the Opalinata

This question, as already suggested, is of importance to the solution of more than one taxonomic problem. Here only an outline of a reasonable answer is offered; for a considered account of the matter see Corliss (1955).

There are two distinct propositions: first, that Opalinids are ciliates, and, second, that they are primitive ciliates, called Protociliata by Metcalf (1918 *a*, *b*) and still so in many textbooks. Support for the latter view was mainly based on misunderstandings about the nuclei and attempts to interpret them, sometimes together with the endospheres, as equivalent in some primitive way to the mega- and micronuclei of 'Euciliata'; in fact all the nuclei are alike. The absence of a mouth is not primitive; it is found in other entozoic groups, notably the Astomatida. Opalinids are more correctly regarded as a specialized stock of restricted distribution; the question is, are they specialized ciliates?

The obvious ciliate character of the group is the possession of cilia. But this loses its force when it is remembered that cilia or flagella of fundamentally identical structure occur among Protozoa, Algae, Metazoa, and in, for example, the sperm tails of mammals. As explained elsewhere (p. 68), the distinction between flagella and cilia is conventional and it breaks down completely when we compare the ectoplasmic processes of, say, *Trichonympha* with those of *Opalina*. The former is an undoubted flagellate and its flagella are at least as numerous as, and many of them are no longer than, the 'cilia' of *Opalina*. It is not yet possible to know whether to attach much significance (in this discussion) to the differences between the kinetodesmata of ciliates and the connecting fibres (interkinetosomal bodies) of opalinids, for it is not clear how far we may generalize from the few cases of the former that have been well described.

If we abandon the number and length of the locomotor organellae as evidence of affinity, we are left with an organism in which most, but not all, of the characters are those of flagellates. In all true ciliates the nuclei are dimorphic and sexual reproduction is by the complicated and unique method of conjugation or its derivative, autogamy, and there are neither gametes nor syngamy; these are fundamental characters. In *Opalina* all the nuclei are monomorphic; sexual reproduction is by syngamy. Further, during binary fission, ciliates divide so that the two daughters are produced by a fission line which typically cuts across the kineties, which thus have a genetic continuity between one generation and the next. In *Opalina*, the daughters are produced by a fission line passing between the rows of cilia and during growth new kineties are supplied from the primary kineties* (Fig. 87D).

Opalinids have no centrioles and this has been called a ciliate character. But they are absent from some Mastigophora (*Euglena*) and perhaps the most that can be made of the point is that division centres are never lacking in the more advanced flagellates and, whatever the origin of the opalinids may be, it is unlikely to be among the simpler Mastigophora.

On their own showing, the Opalinata ought to be removed from the ciliates, and doing so has the additional advantage that it reveals the more plainly the true character of the Ciliata as a natural class. But it remains hard to see where to place the opalinids firmly among the Mastigophora, and for this reason we leave these remarkable animals in an uncertain position.

* See p. 214 for the contrast between homothetigenic and symmetrigenic division.

III

CLASS SPOROZOA

ALL Sporozoa are entozoic and are incapable of active life outside their hosts and their normal and primitive means of distribution is the resistant spore or sporocyst, containing the sporozoites which constitute the infective phase of the life-cycle. The process of sporogony or spore formation, in the Telosporidia (that is, the great majority of Sporozoa), begins only after growth is completed; it is initiated by the zygote so that sexual reproduction leads to the development of spores. In addition, many Sporozoa have developed a means of asexual fission, or schizogony, which spreads the infection within the host, and this too precedes sporogony. In monogenetic species, that is with a single host, the entire life-history may be observed in one individual, or, more especially in the Coccidia of homoiothermic hosts, immature spores are passed which complete their development in the soil or in water. In the digenetic species, the asexual cycle commonly occurs within one host species and the sexual cycle, with sporogony, in the other. The most highly evolved digenetic forms are found in the order Haemosporidia (not considered here), where the sporozoites are always developed in a blood-sucking invertebrate which injects them directly into the blood of the vertebrate host in which schizogony occurs, and the sporocyst is no longer developed.

A few gregarines are said to be capable of some phagotrophic feeding but the great majority of Sporozoa are probably osmotrophs obtaining their food from their immediate environment. There is never a mouth. In general, only the liberated sporozoites and the merozoites (products of schizogony) are motile; the very peculiar movements of translation performed by cephaline gregarines (p. 185) are not well understood; they certainly have nothing to do with feeding.

Sporozoa may parasitize a cavity (coelozoic) or a tissue (histozoic), and even when most of the life-history is coelozoic, there is generally some stage in which the organism attaches itself to, or penetrates, a host cell. This phase may be so brief that the effect is negligible (gregarines); but where the intracellular part of the cycle is prolonged and widespread by the repeated occurrence of schizogony, as in the Coccidia, the destruction of tissue may be extensive and highly pathological, and some Sporozoa are of great medical or veterinary importance (see *Eimeria tenella*, p. 195 and under Cnidosporidia). Yet many hosts have undoubtedly developed a high degree of tolerance for even the histozoic Sporozoa and it seems likely that the best-known species, which are the causal organisms of disease in man or domestic and food animals, are those for which host–parasite relations are unusual in their imperfect adaptation.

The origin of the Sporozoa is unknown but speculation seems to lead towards a tentative belief in their affinity with flagellates; the topic is examined by Grassé (1. ii, p. 546).

In older classifications, the Sporozoa were divided into 2 subclasses, the Telosporidia, a large natural taxonomic unit the members of which are easily seen to be related, and the Neosporidia, a heterogeneous collection of parasites of doubtful affinities and with so little in common that the group is almost impossible to define: of its components, only one, the Cnidosporidia, regarded as an independent subclass, is here retained for treatment.

SUBCLASS TELOSPORIDIA

These are the typical Sporozoa including such well-known forms as *Monocystis*, *Eimeria*, and *Plasmodium*, which clearly exhibit the characters of the class as outlined above. They differ from the Cnidosporidia in that (i) the organism always completes its growth before sporogony, so that the trophozoites, i.e. the feeding and growing individuals, the reproductive and spore-forming phases are all represented by distinctive stages in the life-cycle, (ii) the young infective body that emerges from the spore is typically a slim, elongated gregarinula, never amoeboid, and (iii) the spore lacks the peculiar polar capsules of the Cnidosporidia. Although the point has been disputed, there seems now to be good reason to believe that throughout the subclass the first post-zygotic divisions constitute meiosis, so that the Telosporidia are haploid organisms; the facts have been established both for gregarines (Dobell and Jameson, 1915; Jameson, 1920; Valkanov, 1935; Weschenfelder, 1938; Noble, 1938; Sprague, 1941; Grell, 1940; Phillips and Mackinnon, 1946) and coccidians (Dobell and Jameson, 1915; Reichenow, 1921; Dobell, 1925; Bělař, 1926b; Wedekind, 1927).

The subclass is easily subdivided into 3 orders, the Gregarinida, the Coccidia, and the Haemosporidia; the last, containing the highly specialized blood parasites of vertebrates and blood-sucking invertebrates, such as *Plasmodium*, is not treated in this book and we are left with the two related but interestingly contrasted orders of gregarines and coccidians.

ORDER GREGARINIDA

Gregarines are essentially parasites of invertebrates, common in annelids, arthropods, especially insects, and in echinoderms; they also occur in ascidians; they are unknown in vertebrates. The characteristic life-cycle, illustrated diagrammatically in Fig. 88, shows numerous distinctions from that of the Coccidia.

The young organism (sporozoite) emerges from the spore, enters or attaches itself to a host cell from which, as it grows, it eventually comes free (a–c). Thus, as the intracellular life of the parasite is short and schizogony is exceptional, infections tend to be light and to cause very little damage to tissue. The feeding organisms may grow to a considerable, i.e. macroscopic, size, and often develop very great variety of form. The storage substance which they accumulate is paraglycogen, characteristic of the order, and closely related to starch; it turns reddish brown in iodine, is insoluble in alcohol, but soluble in strong mineral acids; it is stored in the form of spherical or ovoid capsules and it is their presence which gives many gregarine trophozoites their grey, opaque appearance. The fully grown adults are the sexual forms or gametocytes and they associate in pairs and secrete a gametocyst (e, f); gametocytes are always of approximately equal size and similar appearance and such sexual differences as may be detected between them are slight.* The gametes are produced superficially, leaving a residual mass of cytoplasm; they are generally said to be isogamous or only slightly anisogamous, and even if, as seems likely, careful cytological studies should reveal that minor differences between the sexes are commoner than usually stated, it remains true that the marked anisogamy of Coccidia is never seen in gregarines; in relation to their approximate equality of function they are produced in equal numbers. It is a diagnostic character of the order that each zygote encysts and produces within its sporocyst a number of sporozoites, which is nearly always 8—that is to say, one zygote gives rise to a single spore (h–j).

While this type of life-history is found in almost all gregarines (all Eugregarines), it is not, according to Grassé (Traité, I. ii), to be regarded as primitive. Schizogony occurs in a small number of parasites from the intestinal tract of polychaetes, and also in some gregarines from the fat bodies, haemocoele, or intestine of insects. It has been the custom hitherto to group all these asexually reproducing forms together and call them Schizogregarines, but Grassé maintains, with some reason, that they ought to be divided. In the small group from marine invertebrates, represented by Selenidium (p. 161), the schizogony is supposed to be primitive. It has been lost by the great majority (Eugregarines) and then secondarily regained by a number of specialized forms in insects, which in fact do exhibit diverse types of asexual reproduction, and which morphologically do not show much in common with the Selenidiids. We have, then, three suborders, of which the last is not treated here.

* They may differ in size, cytoplasmic inclusions, or staining reactions; see Léger and Duboscq (1909) and Göhre (1943).

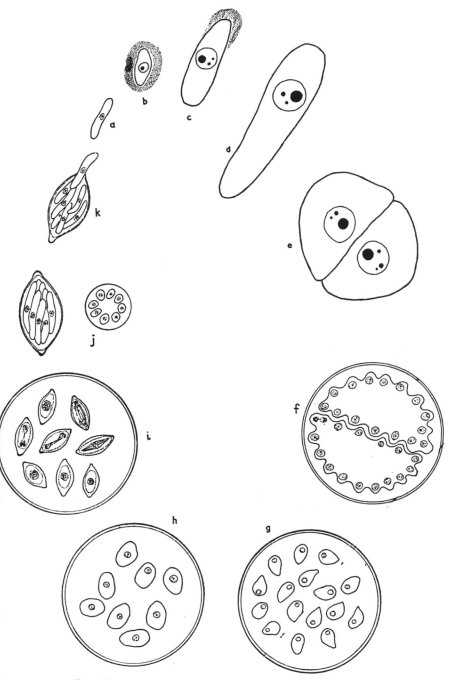

FIG. 88. Eugregarine life-history. Diagrammatic. (Original.)

a, the liberated sporozoite enters a host-cell, *b*, which it outgrows, *c*; *d*, trophozoite; *e*, gametocytes in association; *f*, gametocyst: the gametocytes produce gametes at the periphery; *g*, gametes; *h*, zygotes; *i*, each zygote encysts and begins to divide; *j*, sporocyst containing 8 sporozoites, and, on the right, in TS; *k*, liberation of sporozoites.

Suborder i. *Archigregarina*—gregarines which retain a complete life-cycle with schizogony in its supposedly primitive form. The number of sporozoites varies. Parasitic in the intestinal tracts of marine invertebrates, especially Polychaeta. (*Selenidium.*)

Suborder ii. *Eugregarina*—the best-known and typical gregarines, in which schizogony has been lost from the life-cycle. With 8 sporozoites. (*Monocystis, Gregarina.*)

Suborder iii. *Neogregarina*—gregarines which have regained a secondary schizogonic phase. With 8 sporozoites. Parasitic in insects. (*Ophryocystis, Mattesia.*)

SUBORDER ARCHIGREGARINA

Members of this group (Selenidiids, from the typical genus, *Selenidium*) are very common and easily accessible parasites, especially of polychaete worms, in which they may occur in great numbers. A few infect ascidians, Enteropneusta, and Sipunculoidea. Characteristically, the body of the fully grown trophozoite (Figs. 90, 91), in its free, extracellular, stage, is elongated, vermiform, like a nematode, or flattened and foliacious, or both; the same organism may be watched while transforming, by means of a powerfully developed system of myonemes, from one form to the other (Fig. 90D). The pellicle is grooved above the myonemes, and the longitudinal striation produced is an easily recognizable feature of Selenidiids. In the complete life-history (Fig. 89), a sporozoite enters an epithelial cell, grows to a large size and becomes a schizont (A). This divides into several hundred merozoites (B–D), which escape and infect other cells, and there, perhaps without any repetition of schizogony, they outgrow their cells, and move into the gut lumen to live as gametocytes (G, H). After pairing and production of a gametocyst, which is soft and flexible, sporogony leads to the formation of cysts containing a variable number of sporozoites, usually less than 8 (I). The feature which marks off the group is, of course, the asexual phase in the development, and this, as in Coccidia, seems to be associated with prolongation of the intracellular phase, which is certainly much more important than it is in Eugregarines. It must be said at once that, while this type of life-history is amply confirmed for some species, such as *Selenidium caulleryi* (Brasil, 1907; Ray, 1930a) and *S. mesnili* (p. 161), in the majority of the species, schizogony has never been observed. It is true that in many cases it has never been seriously sought; but sometimes it has, and the results are striking: Ray, for example, sectioned and searched 300 specimens of *Scololepis fuliginosa*, of which 97 per cent were infected with *Selenidium*, and found no trace of schizogony. Either it is very rare in some cases, or, as seems more likely, the primitive type of schizogony which Grassé considers to have been abandoned by the Eugregarines, has already been lost within the genus *Selenidium*.

Some account is here offered of one species which is very easy to obtain and to this are added a few notes on some other readily accessible species from various Polychaeta; many others, both described and undescribed, occur in these hosts. For additional information, see Ray (1930a), who studied some of the species at Plymouth, Mackinnon and Ray (1933), for a very clear account of Selenidiids from *Potamilla reniformis*, Reichenow (1932), who gives a useful list (pp. 22–25); for myonemes, see Fowell (1936), and for microparasites of the gregarines, Caullery and Mesnil (1919).

Selenidium mesnili Brasil

This species occurs in 90 per cent of the tubicolous worm *Myxicola infundibulum* at Plymouth and is confined to the anterior half of the gut. The earliest stages of development are unknown, but intracellular forms grow to a considerable size and reproduce by schizogony; the merozoites eventually grow into gametocytes, which lie freely in the gut lumen and associate; the rest of sporogony takes place in the sea. The life-history as we know it is due to Brasil (1909) and Ray (1930a), except for the sporogony, which was reported by Reed in 1933. It will be understood that in smears only the gametocytes are seen or sometimes other stages which have been accidentally dislodged from their host cells; for schizonts, growing trophozoites, and merozoites, it is essential to examine sections.

The living organism

Smears are made by teasing small pieces of gut-wall on a slide and diluting very slightly with sea water. The trophozoites (Fig. 89 G, H) are easily picked out; they are elongated, tapering posteriorly, measuring usually some 50–90 μ × 20–30 μ, though larger sizes are reached. The anterior end is bluntly rounded and often drawn out into a slight nipple at the base of which occur some 6 to 8 deeply basophil bodies, which are refractile and easily visible in the living animal; they are said to be characteristic of the genus and they assume different forms in different species (Figs. 90, 91). *S. mesnili* possesses well-developed longitudinal myonemes and, as usual in this genus, they lie at the bases of 24 to 30 pellicular grooves, which are far more easily visible than the myonemes themselves, especially when the trophozoite contracts and the grooves are widened (Fig. 89, H and cf. F): when the body is stretched the grooves may be practically impossible to detect (G). A slight transverse striation is also visible in many individuals, and this seems to be due to the arrangement of cell inclusions, perhaps in relation to the contractions of circular myonemes (G). The nucleus is conspicuous, more or less central, spherical except when distorted by the movements of the body, and contains a refringent, vacuolated karyosome, and a few other small granules or droplets.

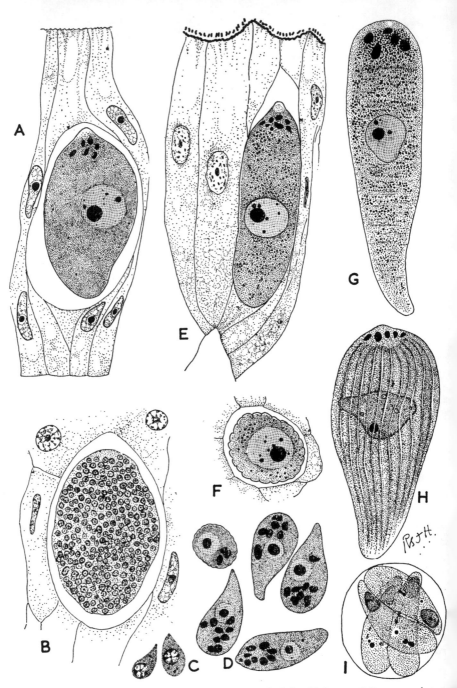

FIG. 89. *Selenidium mesnili* from the gut of *Myxicola infundibulum*, A, fully grown intra-cellular trophozoite (schizont?) in gut epithelium (Champy; H.H.); B, schizogony (from a preparation of Dr. Ray's); C, merozoites (× 5,500); D, later growth of merozoites (Champy, H.H.); E and F, LS and TS intracellular stage (gametocyte) with granular inclusions (Champy; H.H.); G, the same, in gut lumen; H, free trophozoite contracted showing deep longitudinal furrows and no granular cytoplasmic inclusions (Champy; H.H.); I, sporo-cyst with 4 sporozoites (× 2,500). All figures × 1,000 except where indicated. (A and E original; C after Ray; D–H original; I after Reed.)

The gametocytes associate by their posterior ends, broaden and round off, and secrete about themselves a gelatinous gametocyst, averaging about 50 μ in diameter. This is passed with the faeces and further development takes place in the sea. According to Reed, some stages in sporogony are always found in faeces collected daily from the hosts. She thought there was complete isogamy. The cysts (1) are smooth-walled and tetrazoic.

Permanent preparations

Smears and pieces of gut for sectioning may be fixed in B and then stained with H.H. and counterstained with Chromotrope 2R or Orange G. But far more faithful preparations may be obtained by fixing in Champy, either smears, or very small pieces of infected gut, and then prolonged staining, after 24 hours' washing in running water, in H.H.

The intracellular stages (Fig. 89 A–E) are found in sections of the gut. Here the young parasites grow, always recognizable by the conspicuous nucleus and the anterior basophil bodies which are present in all stages except for a time during sporogony. The schizonts (A, B) are ovoid, up to 200 μ long, and they produce some 200 or 300 nuclei, each of which comes to be accompanied by a small basophil granule; these are not derived from the large anterior bodies of the parent, for the latter persist. The merozoites produced by schizogony are pyriform with the nucleus usually anterior (C), and large aggregates of them may be found in restricted areas of gut epithelium while they are growing (D); for a time the number of basophil bodies they contain is greater than that found in adults, but it is not clear how the reduction in their quantity is effected. The trophozoites derived from the merozoites may grow up to about 100 μ long and many of these, in well-fixed preparations, contain, in addition to the large anterior bodies mentioned, very numerous small basophil granules distributed throughout the cytoplasm (E); by this time the longitudinal striae have already appeared on the pellicle (F) and the trophozoites are ready to emerge; they are apparently identical in structure with the extracellular forms seen in smears. It is to be noted that these, like the large intracellular forms, may or may not contain the small granular inclusions (cf. G and H), but the significance of the difference is not understood; possibly it is sexual. Such forms become gametocytes and pursue their development as already described.

Although *S. mesnili* is perhaps the most fully described of its group, it will be seen that much remains to be learnt of its life and structure. The early course of the infection, the frequency of schizogony, the interpretation of the differences in cytoplasmic characters, possible sexual distinctions, and the details of gametogenesis all require further investigation; and nothing is known about the history of the chromosomes in this or any other member of the genus.

Selenidium spionis (Kölliker)

The commoner of the 2 species in the gut of *Scololepis fuliginosa*, *Selenidium spionis*, is found, posteriorly, in 97 per cent of these worms at Plymouth. The full-grown trophozoite (Fig. 90A), up to 300 μ long, is an impressive animal and may occupy more than half the space offered by the gut lumen. The anterior end is broad, with a slight concavity to one side, and below it a number of chromatic threads about 12 μ long. A streak, hyaline in living, basophil in fixed, material, runs as an axis through the body, and within it lies the nucleus, with a conspicuous karyosome. The nature of the streak is uncertain: many sections show no or little internal differentiation; but Ray thought it was a canal or tube, and Fowell (1936) claimed that fibres radiated from it, which he considered to be skeletal, serving to anchor the myonemes and restrict their action to a small segment of the body. There are some 24 to 30 of these myonemes and they are responsible for the bending and straightening movements of trophozoites lying free in the lumen, and the habit of the attached animals swaying like a pendulum.

In interpreting stained specimens the following should be borne in mind. Myonemes are best revealed by Mallory's stain; in haematoxylin preparations they are difficult or impossible to trace, but their courses are indicated either by striae in the pellicle or by the distribution of cytoplasmic granules. For example, in Fig. 90A, the longitudinal lines are not myonemes but the pellicular striae above them; the transverse lines of dots are granules, not the morphonemes of Fowell mentioned above; likewise, in the section (B), the large subpellicular dots are not transversely cut myonemes but members of longitudinal rows of granules marking the courses of the myonemes.

Ray (1930a) searched sections of 290 infected hosts without finding schizogony. The gametocytes are 250 to 300 μ long and associate by their posterior ends. The cysts are about 60 × 100 μ, ovoid; they develop in the sea. The spores (C) are ovoid, smooth-walled, about 25 μ long, and contain 4 sporozoites.

Selenidium foliatum Ray

One of the loveliest and most delicate of Selenidiids, this species (Fig. 90D) accompanies the foregoing in about 70 per cent of the hosts at Plymouth. It has been variously described as flattened, leaf-like, or snake-like, but really the body is polymorphic. It grows to 250 μ long. At one extreme it is like a very active, transparent ribbon, deeply furrowed by some six or seven longitudinal grooves on each side of the flattened body; the grooves divide the ribbon into long strips and a few of the central

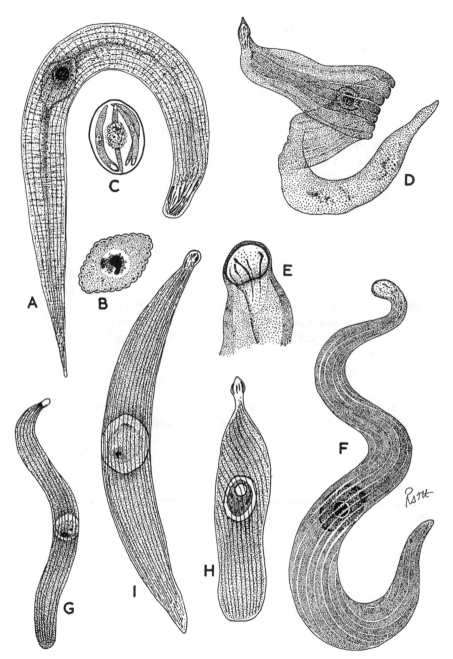

FIG. 90. *Selenidium* spp. from Polychaeta. A–C, *S. spionis* from *Scolelepis fuliginosa*: A, trophozoite (Champy; H.H.); B, TS same; C, sporocyst with 4 sporozoites (×800); D, *S. foliatum* from the same host, the free trophozoite, with the anterior part in the flattened and the posterior in the cylindrical phase (Champy; H.H.); E, the same, anterior end showing sucker (×3,000: Champy; H.H.); F, *S. branchiommatis* from *Branchiomma vesiculosum* (B; H.H.); G, *S. alleni* from same host; H, *S. sabellae* from *Sabella pavonina* (B; H.H.); I, *S. brasili* from *Pomatoceros triqueter*. All figures ×1,000 except where indicated. (A, B, D–F, H original; C, G, I after Ray.)

strips may project from the rest for about half the animal's length so that a thickened ledge stands out from one side. At the other extreme the organism is like a nematode, circular in section, with the pellicle much smoother. Most commonly the body, as in the figure, is ribbon-like in front, with a vermiform tail, which tends to change from one shape to the other. There is an anterior sucker, sometimes very clearly seen (Fig. 90E) and sometimes surmounted by a slight projection resembling a mucron; the walls of the sucker contain the basophil threads typical of the genus. The nucleus is elongated antero-posteriorly, with a karyosome at one end containing a single large vacuole; in the figure the nucleus has been stretched transversely to a rough square by the lateral expansion of the body.

Ray never found schizogony and considered the stages said by Caullery and Mesnil (1901) to be schizogonic to belong to the life-history of a different organism which he called *Dorisiella scolelepidis* (Ray, 1930 *a*, *b*). The gametocytes associate while still attached to the gut epithelium, or when free in its lumen, and are often of very different sizes; as gametogenesis had not been followed a possible sexual significance in this and other differences has not been investigated. The cysts are 68 to 70 μ in diameter; the sporocysts are oval, smooth-walled, 20–22 $\mu \times$ 18–20 μ, with 8 sporozoites.

Selenidium branchiommatis Ray

This long Selenidiid (Fig. 90F) is common in the anterior half of the alimentary canal of the tubicolous Sabellid, *Branchiomma vesiculosum*. The body is elongated, slim, vermiform, up to 600 μ long and only 20 μ broad. The anterior end bears a small, knob-like epimerite or mucron and below this is a vacuole to which some refringent, basophil strands are related. There are 25 to 35 longitudinal striations. The free trophozoite bends to and fro, twists spirally or throws itself into an S, straightens and repeats itself. The nucleus is oval with a spherical karyosome. The life-history is unknown.

Selenidium alleni Ray

This occurs in the same host as the last, but is less common, smaller, up to 120 × 15 μ, with only about 12 to 16 striae (Fig. 90G). The nucleus is oval but, in adults though not in the young, it is set at right angles to the length of the body. The anterior end is pointed with a chromatic ring. The life-history is unknown.

Selenidium sabellae (Lankester)

The body is spindle-shaped when young, but with a blunt posterior end, sometimes flattened, in older specimens, up to 120 × 60 μ, and with a conical organ of attachment anteriorly (Fig. 90H). The cone contains a vacuole with 4 to 6 refringent threads. The anterior end seems to be more mobile than the posterior, which may attach itself to the slide while the front part moves. There are up to 40 striae in fully grown animals. The parasite occurs in the posterior half of the gut of *Sabella pavonina* and its life-history is unknown.

Selenidium brasili Ray

Common in the gut of *Pomatoceros triqueter*, this form reaches up to 180×35 μ. The epimerite is knob-like with 6 to 8 refringent threads. The nucleus is spherical, situated rather towards the anterior end (Fig. 90I).

Selenidium terebellae (Kölliker)

This is a very handsome and striking animal (Fig. 91 A, B), found in the middle and posterior part of the gut of *Terebella lapidaria*. The body is spindle-shaped, up to 300 μ long, with 6 or 7 deep longitudinal grooves. The animal has a habit of twisting itself into a spiral, which is emphasized by the turning of the grooves seen both superficially and through the transparent body. An anterior conical projection contains refringent threads.

Selenidium spp. from Audouinia tentaculata

During examination of this host* for other Protozoa it is certain that striking infections with Selenidiids will be encountered, and, though little is known, something must be said, of these organisms (Fig. 91 C–H). They look very like nematode worms, for which they have been mistaken; they are slim, elongated, and the longitudinal ridges on the pellicle are less obvious than in many of the forms described above. The body, which reaches about 300 μ in length, is very commonly thrown into a curve, like a comma, or a C, or S-shaped and from such a curve the animal slowly relaxes, and then reforms it again.

It is almost certain that more than one species is present, and they were distinguished, but not named, by Caullery and Mesnil in 1899. The first (say, *Selenidium* A) has some twenty pellicular striae and a more or less spherical nucleus (C, D); that in the figure has its nucleus perhaps a trifle nearer the anterior end than is usual. There is certainly some anterior differentiation by which the organism attaches to the gut epithelium and this appears to be a weak sucker. The second species (*Selenidium* B) is most easily distinguished by the far more numerous and shallow striae (50–60)

* I am not aware of any differences between the Selenidiid parasites of this species and of *Cirratulus cirratus*. R. S. J. H. For the other Protozoa, see index, under *host-list*.

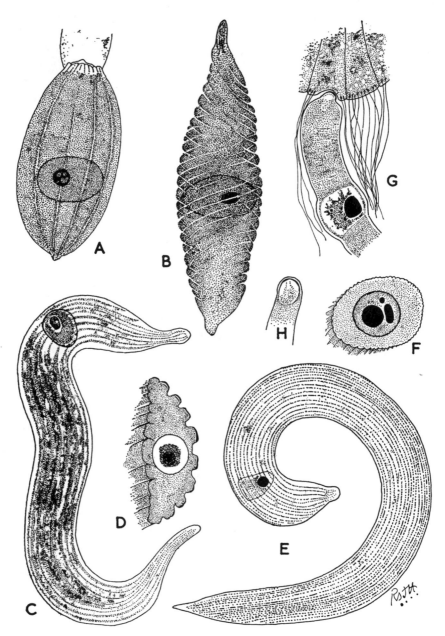

FIG. 91. More *Selenidium* spp. from Polychaeta. A and B, *S. terebellae* from *Terebella lapidaria*: A, attached phase (B; D.H.); B, free trophozoite showing spiral twisting (B.; H.H.); C and D, *Selenidium* A and E–H, *Selenidium* B, both from *Audouinia tentaculata*: C, trophozoite (Champy; H.H.); D, TS of the same (B; D.H. and Chromotrope 2R); E, trophozoite (Osmium tetroxide-da Fano-Chatton-Lwoff silver impregnation for pellicular pattern plus light Delafield staining for nucleus); F, TS trophozoite (B; H.H.); G, LS attached form (B; H.H.); H, anterior end of similar stage seen from below and showing sucker. H, × 1,200; all others, × 1,000. (Original.)

running the length of the body (E). The nucleus is always well forward and is compressed so that it is square (G), or oblong, or slightly triangular (E). There is a plain sucker (H), most easily seen in sections of smears containing an animal which has just relaxed its grip of the epithelium, and above the sucker there may point forward a slight anterior projection perhaps representing a mucron (G).

The life-history of these forms is obscure, though they have been known for many years; certainly before the date of Caullery and Mesnil's paper, which contains all, and, indeed, rather more than all, that we know about them. The infections are very common and so heavy that they strongly suggest the existence of a schizogonic phase.

Permanent preparations

The methods for *Selenidium mesnili* apply (see p. 163). Again, it should be mentioned that good cytological fixation (e.g. in Champy) of small pieces of gut followed by prolonged staining in H.H. will give the best pictures of many features, such as the anterior differentiations (mucra, suckers) of these parasites, which have never been carefully described.

It is often important to count the number of striae (sometimes mistaken for the myonemes themselves, and then so-called); in many species they are easily visible in living animals or haematoxylin preparations, but where they are shallow or very crowded and difficult to see, silver impregnation methods, as for ciliates, will be found easy and useful (see p. 443 and cf. Fig. 91E).

SUBORDER EUGREGARINA

These, the most numerous and widely distributed gregarines, depend entirely on sexual reproduction and sporogony, lack the schizogonic phase completely, and produce spores which always contain 8 sporozoites. They are divided naturally into two tribes, the Acephalina, which are predominantly coelozoic with the simple body undivided, and the Cephalina, which are gut parasites in which the body is typically divided into different regions, of which the anterior develops an organ of fixation called the epimerite.

TRIBE ACEPHALINA

The acephaline gregarines are essentially simpler in the structure of their trophozoites than the cephalines. The body is monocystid, that is, undivided by septa, and, although some of them are able to attach themselves to host cells by means of an anterior hold-fast organ, the mucron, this never develops into the true epimerite by means of which a cephaline maintains its position in the gut, and unlike epimerites, the hold-fast organs of Acephalina are not left behind when the trophozoite breaks free of its host cell to occupy more freely the lumen of its habitat.

Monocystidae of the seminal vesicles of earthworms

Monocystids are very common in earthworms, especially in the seminal vesicles, where almost all stages of their life-histories are at times to be found. A few can develop in the perivisceral cavity (e.g. *Monocystis herculea*) and these are sometimes noticed during dissections, at the hind end of the worm and lightly attached to a septum or nephridium. But the seminal vesicle is, so to speak, the *locus classicus* of monocystids; it is there that they are commonest and most easily accessible for study alive; further, the consistency of the vesicular fluid is such that material from it is particularly suitable for making smear preparations. The vesicles are, of course, divisions of the coelom, the typical site for acephaline gregarines.

Over 30 years ago Bhatia (1929) listed some 15 species of *Monocystis* itself, and 7 of related genera from the vesicles of a single species of common earthworm, *Lumbricus terrestris*; according to Meier (1956), 27 species have been recorded from *L. rubellus*. Even allowing that some of these are invalid, and that only some of the good species are likely to occur in any one specimen, it is obvious that mixed infections are common. This is evident from the variety of trophozoites and the very different sizes of cysts met with in the same smear. One consequence of this is that while we are able to distinguish between species from the characters of the trophozoites and also to recognize that cysts of different species are present, it is impossible with confidence to relate particular trophozoites to particular cysts. No clean hosts have ever been infected with single cysts, or the contents of single gametocysts; gregarines cannot be cultured. It follows that while we may give a general account of the life-history of '*Monocystis*', no detailed account of the complete cycle in any single species is offered. Only 3 common species are selected here for treatment—*Monocystis agilis* (p. 172), *Rhynchocystis pilosa* (p. 175), and *Nematocystis magna* (p. 176)— and the details given below under their names are only those which may be picked out and ascribed to them from smears made from mixed infections.

In general, the life-cycle of a monocystid from the seminal vesicles of an earthworm follows the pattern outlined in Fig. 88. It is presumed that infection is oral. Hesse (1909) introduced sporocysts into the gut of worms and noted that empty cysts were later passed in the faeces. On opening worms thus experimentally infected, he found that unhatched cysts were found in the oesophagus and crop, but empty ones in the intestine, where, in one case, he was able to follow the actual process of hatching (Fig. 92). The means by which the liberated sporozoites find their way from the gut to the seminal vesicles is quite unknown. Arrived there, the sporozoite begins its intracellular phase by penetrating a cytophore (the cytoplasmic mass about which the sperm are arranged during their development) or, in the case of *Nematocystis magna*, an epithelial cell of a ciliated funnel, or development may be entirely extracellular and take place in the cavity of the vesicle (e.g. *Rhynchocystis porrecta, Nematocystis elmassiani*: see Troisi, 1933 and 1940 respectively). Whatever the early history, the host cell is soon outgrown and the body of the parasite, now a young trophozoite, lies freely in the vesicle; *N. magna* remains anteriorly attached to,

though not strictly within, an epithelial cell. Of the free stages, it is these growing trophozoites that are most easily identified in smears.

Eventually the trophozoites associate in pairs as gametocytes, usually by their anterior ends, but in some species side by side, and they surround themselves with a double-walled gametocyst. The outer ectocyst is thicker than the endocyst, but neither assumes the thickness or complexity characteristic of cephalines such as *Gregarina* (Figs.

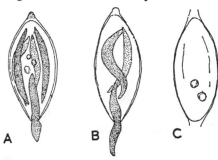

Fig. 92. *Monocystis* sp. Liberation of sporozoites. A and B, hatching of sporozoites in the intestine of a worm 1¼ hour after their injection into the pharynx; C, empty sporocyst passed in the faeces of a worm about 12 hours after complete cysts were fed to it. (After Hesse.)

102, 103) which sporulate in the external environment. Gametocytes in the 'bead' stage are sometimes seen and in whole mounts their endoplasm is dense and opaque as in the trophozoite while small transparent protoplasmic bodies are constricted off all over the surface of each; these are the gametes; they are far more clearly observed in sectioned material (Fig. 97D). The gametes are not amoeboid and have no flagella but they move about in a so-called 'dance of the gametes' before syngamy. Each zygote secretes a sporocyst, which is always biconical with a mucoid plug at each end, the shape implied by the name 'pseudonavicellae' sometimes given to the cysts. The 8 sporozoites can be counted only in sections (Fig. 97F[3], *x*).

The means by which the sporocysts find their way to the exterior are no more understood than the process of infection. Bhatia (1924) found a few sporocysts in the spermathecae of worms of the genus *Pheretima*, but the numbers were so small that he supposed that escape through the genital ducts into spermathecae could not be the principal means of dissemination; there is no evidence that more than a few odd spores ever reach this site, while the number produced is, of course, enormous. It is usually surmised that the spores escape when their hosts die and rot or when they are eaten;

it is known that spores can pass intact through the intestinal tract of various animals* (see Hesse, p. 213).

Hesse's fine monograph of 1909 remains the best source for identifying monocystids of earthworms; see also Berlin (1924) and Cognetti de Martiis (1925), Troisi (1933, 1940), and Meier (1956); Roskin and Levinson (1929) have described movement and the myoneme system and de Puytorac (1956b) the 'argyrome'; Loubatières (1955) has much biological and taxonomic information. Grassé (1. ii) gives a magnificent general account of the gregarines.

The living organisms

Freshly collected earthworms provide the best material and active trophozoites and associating and sporulating stages are said to be commoner in Northern Europe during late spring and early summer. The worms commonly used for dissection in this country are species of *Lumbricus* and *Allolobophora*; in the former the prostomium sends a mid-dorsal band back along the head to meet the peristomium (tanylobous) and in British species of the latter the band stops short of the peristomium (epilobous). A key to species is given by Černosvitov and Evans (1947).

Open the worm dry to expose the seminal vesicles, cut off the lateral tip of one of the horns of these, and smear a little of the white fluid exuded on a slide, dilute if necessary with invertebrate fluid (p. 426), cover and examine. If a good infection is found the worm should be used repeatedly and as many preparations as possible sealed. Sporulation takes a comparatively short time and the mature sporocysts remain thereafter unchanged within their gametocysts and accumulate; cysts are therefore much more common than active stages, and the latter, when found, should be exploited at once for study.†

Monocystis agilis Stein

The sporozoites invade sperm morulae and take up a position within the cytophore; they live and grow at the expense of this and they inhibit the development of the spermatogonia or spermatids, which never mature. The youngest stages found are usually rounded or ovoid, about 5 μ long, and as they grow they also elongate. There is a single, usually spherical nucleus, containing a large and conspicuous hyaline karyosome (Fig. 93F). As the parasite continues its growth the sexual cells of the morula divide

* And that is all that is known; there is no evidence that predators of earthworms play, in nature, anything like the important part as distributors of monocystids which is sometimes ascribed to them in the books. We only know that some of them could play some part.

† The following notes on a few species must be taken with the general account given above, without which they are incomplete (see pp. 170–172).

and become arranged with their nuclei towards the monocystid, which
may in time become invested with a sort of adventitious coat of aborted
spermatids and in this condition it bears some resemblance to *Rhynchocystis pilosa*. Eventually it breaks free and the discarded sexual cells die.
It is to be noted that only developing sexual cells in the lumen of the
vesicle are attacked and the testes themselves, from which the spermatogonia are continuously supplied, are unaffected.

The fully developed trophozoite (Fig. 93 A, B) may reach a size of
some 500 μ long by 40 μ broad. It is typically spindle-shaped and arched,

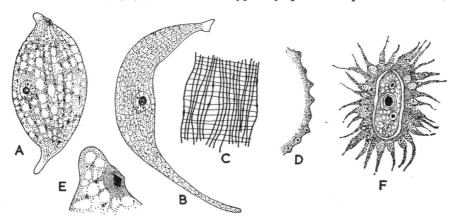

FIG. 93. *Monocystis agilis.* A and B, stout and slim forms of the trophozoite. ×200;
c, myonemes as seen in tangential section of the ectoplasm: the thicker lines are longitudinal; D, TS ectoplasm, showing pellicular ridges and below them longitudinal myonemes running in their canals; E, anterior end of trophozoite to show the mucron. ×650;
F, young parasite in cytophore. ×650. (A, B, E, F after Hesse; C, D after Roskin and
Levinson.)

tapering sharply to the posterior end, but bluntly truncate anteriorly; here,
to one side, it bears a short, transparent pellicular process, the mucron,
shaped like a rose-thorn (E); possibly it may be used for fixation at times,
though this species is typically free, and it is in the fixed forms such as
Rhynchocystis that it assumes more importance; it is not to be confused
with the more developed organ of fixation, the epimerite, found in cephalines. The pellicle is longitudinally striated and the lines seen in the living
animal are the longitudinal myonemes which run in the ectoplasm just
below the pellicle; the transverse myonemes, which are more delicate, are
less easily seen in untreated preparations; further, the longitudinal lines
are emphasized by the presence of ridges on the pellicle running above the
myonemes. The so-called 'argyrome', now known to occur in a number of
monocystids, is a system of lines encircling the body, of which 4 are closely
set about the mucron and the rest are more widely spaced (see de Puytorac,

1956*b*). The lines are visible in living animals but are more plainly demonstrated by silver impregnation (p. 443).

The myoneme pattern (Fig. 93 C, D,) is easily displayed as follows. A little 1–2 per cent acetic acid is lightly coloured with Acid Fuchsin and a drop of the mixture is added to a smear of *Monocystis* already diluted with invertebrate fluid or 0·7 per cent NaCl. The acid fixes the gregarines and the myonemes are stained by the Fuchsin within a few minutes. The longitudinal threads run the length of the body and then peter out at the ends;

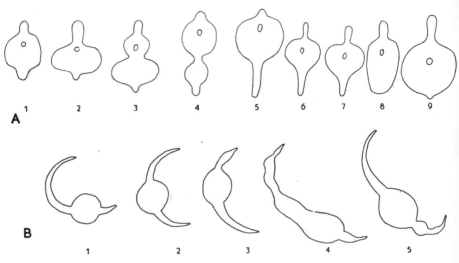

FIG. 94. *Monocystis agilis*. A and B, 2 types of movement seen in this species. In A 1–9, the euglenoid peristalsis takes the organism as a whole towards the top of the page. (After Roskin and Levinson.)

the transverse myonemes form closed rings lying in the ectoplasm. Further details are given by Roskin and Levinson (1929). The myonemes are responsible for the rhythmical contractions and relaxations which pass down the elastic body and recall to some extent the euglenoid movement of some flagellates. The two main types of peristaltic distortion seen are shown in Fig. 94 (and cf. Fig. 47); in each case the contractions begin and for some time are maintained while the gregarine remains stationary, but eventually they lead to movements of translation, which are quicker in the case of type B. The movement is very striking and is accompanied by a marked circulation of the endoplasmic contents, which are mainly circular or ovoid granules of paraglycogen (p. 158).

The nucleus is obvious as a clear patch in the anterior part of the body. It is vesicular with 1 large gleaming karyosome and 2 or 3 smaller ones. Under good optical conditions it may be seen that the large karyosome is not homogeneous, but vacuolated; the point is clearer after fixation and staining. There is evidence that the F+ material of the gregarine nucleus is concentrated during interphase in the karyosome, which contains at least two substances, one F+, in which are distributed the vacuoles or spherules mentioned, which are F— (see Fig. 99C, and Loubatières, 1955).

According to Meier, the cysts are 70 to 140 μ; the spores are 22·5–25 $\mu \times$ 8–10 μ.

Rhynchocystis pilosa (Cuènot)

The genus *Rhynchocystis* Hesse (Fig. 95) differs from *Monocystis* in having a well-developed, soft, transparent, cylindrical papilla at the anterior end; in *R. pilosa* it is used for attachment to host cells. *R. pilosa*, common in this country and North America, is plainly distinguishable by its coat of cuticular 'hairs' covering the body. It was treated at length by Hesse (1909) and again by Troisi (1933).

There is some disagreement about the habit of the earliest stages seen in the vesicles. According to Hesse, these are very small, $4 \times 3 \cdot 5$ μ, lack the 'hairs', and they completely invade a cytophore (Fig. 95A). Troisi maintains that this never happens and that the young are always extracellular; the smallest stages he saw were 12·5 μ long and had already developed 'hairs', and it is possible that he missed those reported by Hesse. Be that as it may, the smaller, growing trophozoites in the lumen apparently have the habit of attacking cytophores with their anterior ends and this they continue to do till they are some 100 μ in length. At this size they begin to develop reserves of paraglycogen and completely resemble the adults.

Fully grown trophozoites (B) are large, up to 500 μ in Europe, but only about 200 μ in North America. The form ranges from slim and elongated to short and thick, but, even during movements of translation, there is very little change in shape; transverse myonemes appear to be absent in this species. The entire body is longitudinally striped with fine, close-set ridges and from these emerge the cuticular hairs, thick at the base and then evenly fine for most of their length; they may be as much as 40 μ long. The attachment organ, or mucron, is a cylinder or papilla of finely granular cytoplasm, lying at the anterior tip and arising from a cavity, and it is to a large extent retractile. At this end the pellicle is marked by thick, wide ridges, not to be confused with the finer striae on the body. Towards the anterior tip the ridges are more marked and they are infolded to form the cavity; behind, they weaken and disappear. When the cavity is everted and the mucron extended, the whole structure is symmetrical and easily understood; when contracted, the ridges show considerable distortion (C, D).

The endoplasm is viscous and filled with oval paraglycogen granules. The nucleus is anterior, large, spherical, ovoid or irregular, with a large conspicuous karyosome.

Grown trophozoites have the habit of autotomizing some portion of the posterior part of the body and this is a preparation for association and encystation, which were seen and reported by Troisi. The smaller, precystic forms associate by their anterior ends, rotating about each other, and secreting a mucoid fluid which sets into a thin membrane. The finished

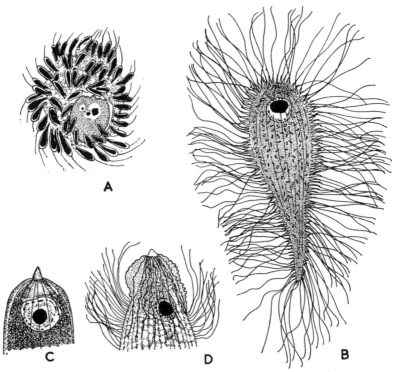

FIG. 95. *Rhynchocystis pilosa*. A, young parasite in cytophore. ×650; B, trophozoite. ×500; C, anterior end of trophozoite with mucron protruded. ×1,000; D, anterior end with mucron partially retracted. ×1,000. (A and B after Hesse; C and D after Troisi.)

gametocysts seen by Troisi in his smaller American form were ovoid, $95 \times 85 \mu$: in the European forms, according to Meier (1956), they are usually round and 90 to 180 μ in diameter. Within the cyst the gameto-cytes lose their hairs and the mucron is de-differentiated to a small clear area of cytoplasm. The process of encystation takes from 25 to 60 minutes. The spores are said to measure $13–16·5 \mu \times 5–6 \mu$.

Nematocystis magna (Schmidt)

This large form is less common than the foregoing and likely to be less numerous in any host, but it is easily found and at once recognized by its great size—up to 5 mm long, but very slender, usually less than 50 μ in diameter. By reflected light it is creamy white in colour, rather suggestive of a nematode, and hence the name of Hesse's genus.

The young animal is intracellular, occupying, not a cytophore, but one of the epithelial cells of the ciliated funnels of the vasa efferentia of the worm. Here it grows (Fig. 96A), the cell hypertrophies, but eventually the greater part of the parasite lies freely in the lumen of the vesicle; at all times the anterior end, slightly swollen, remains attached to, or rather embedded

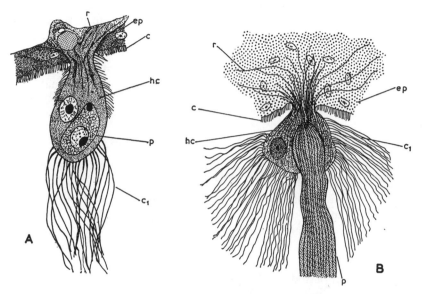

FIG. 96. *Nematocystis magna.* A, young parasite in hypertrophi-epithelial cell of seminal funnel. × 650. B, adult trophozoite depending from cup-shaped cavity in host cell. × 700. (After Hesse, modified.)

c, normal cilia; c_1, hypertrophied cilia of infected cell; *ep*, normal epithelium; *hc*, host cell; *p*, parasite; *r*, root-like process, in A, developed in host cell, in B, the processes are mixed, some from the head of the parasite and some proper to the host cell itself.

within, the excavated epithelial cell, into which root-like cytoplasmic extensions of the head are prolonged, where they mingle with similar fibrillae belonging to the host cell (B). When fully grown, the long, slim body depends far into the vesicle. The ectoplasm is longitudinally ridged, with well-developed myonemes, longitudinal and circular, and a third system of longitudinal fibrillae, non-contractile, wavy when relaxed, which Roskin and Levinson regard as skeletal. The flexible body is frequently distorted by strong waves of peristaltic contraction which disturb and mix the endoplasmic inclusions. The nucleus is large, ellipsoidal, but subject to deformation as the body contracts; there is a conspicuous karyosome. The cysts are round or slightly oval, 300 to 700 μ in diameter; the spores are 30–34·5 $\mu \times$ 12–13·5 μ (measurements given by Meier).

Permanent preparations

For general purposes fix thin even smears of undiluted seminal vesicle contents in B. and stain in D.H. alone or lightly counterstain with Eosin. Excellent preparations, showing myonemes clearly, are obtained by fixing in Champy or Flemming followed by Heidenhain's long method.

For all stages except trophozoites, fix infected vesicles in B. for 24 hours, wash in repeated changes of 70 per cent alcohol over several days, so that the material is both washed and hardened simultaneously. Embed. Cut at 8–10 μ. Stain in H.H., or Weigert's Haematoxylin with Orange G. For nuclear detail, Feulgen with Light Green is excellent. In good material all the stages shown in Fig. 97 may be found.

Some monocystid gregarines from *Eisenia foetida*

This charming worm, the Brandling, ringed with alternating bands of reddish brown and yellow, is common in some manure or compost heaps; it is a sort of living parasitological museum. From the seminal vesicles no fewer than 13 species of monocystids have been recorded and the gut is a useful source of astomate ciliates (p. 331). The monocystids include 6 species of *Monocystis*, 2 of *Rhynchocystis*, and 1 each of *Nematocystis* and *Zygocystis*; representatives of these genera (except the last, distinguished by the length of its association period, so that specimens are always found coupled) have already been considered. But *E. foetida* also contains 3 species of *Apolocystis* (Fig. 98), a genus far less common in large earthworms, and the following notes briefly introduce it. *Apolocystis*, when at rest, is usually spherical or ovoid and possesses no apparent polarity.

Apolocystis gigantea Troisi* (Fig. 98A) is usually spherical when undistorted by movement and may be as much as 800 μ in diameter; 300 to 500 μ is commoner. The pellicle is fine and covered with short 'hairs' (10 to 15 μ). The endoplasm is dense and the nucleus spherical with a karyosome, and sometimes with a smaller, accessory karyosome. The animal has myonemes and is very active. Two waves of contraction are set up at a point on the body and they pass over it in opposite directions to meet on the other side (A, 1–6); where they disappear, two other waves originate and reverse the paths of the first pair. Alternatively, a wave of contraction may pass round and round the organism. The movements may

*. *A. gigantea* was described from North America where it was found only from October to March; as far as I am aware it has not yet been recorded from the United Kingdom. R. S. J. H.

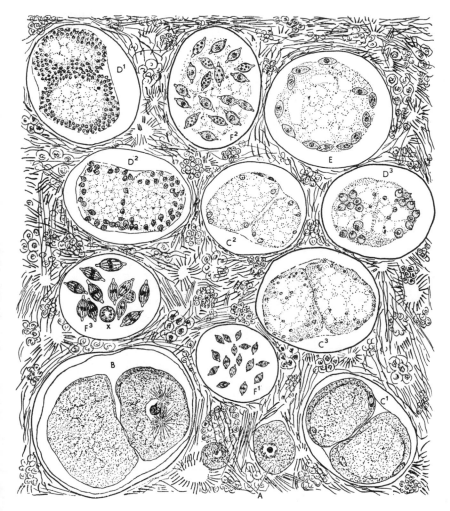

FIG. 97. Monocystidae. Composite drawing of several sections through heavily infected seminal vesicles of an earthworm. Stages in sporogony are set against a background diagrammatically representing spermatogenesis of the host. Dimensions of gametes and spores indicate the presence of at least 3 species of monocystids. Fixed B.; stained H.H. × 500. (Original: D. L. M.)

A, trophozoites; B–F, sections through gametocysts. B, gametocytes in gametocyst; note endo- and ectocyst; C^1–C^3, nuclei divide and become superficial; D^1–D^3, gametes at surface of cytoplasmic residuum, which may contain a few degenerating nuclei: note 3 sizes of gametes; E z gotes; F^1–F^3, sporogony (x, in F^3, marks an equatorial section through a sporocyst, showing 8 sporozoites): note 3 sizes of spores.

last for long periods, e.g. all night, but the organism scarcely shifts from its position during their performance. Early life is extracellular. The game-

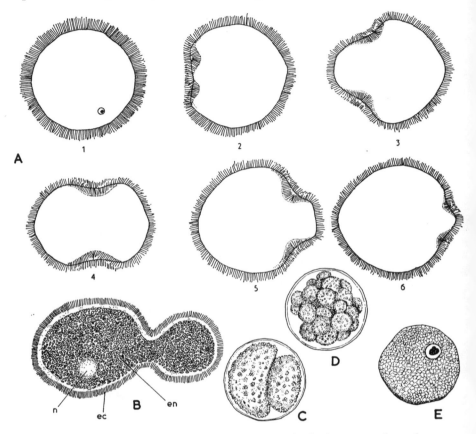

FIG. 98. *Apolocystis* spp. from *Eisenia foetida*. A, 1–6, *A. gigantea* to show the wave of peristaltic contraction: the nucleus is sketched in 1 only. × 50; B, *A. elongata*, living trophozoite. × 270; C, living gametocyst with associated gametocytes. × 50; D, the same at a later stage: the gametocytes have divided into spherules, each bearing gametes. × 50; E, *A. lumbrici-olidi*, trophozoite: very short ectoplasmic processes may invest the whole body or they may, as shown, be reduced to compact rodlets confined to one region. × 175. (A after Troisi; B–D after Phillips and Mackinnon; E after Hesse.)

ec, ectoplasmic processes; *en*, endoplasm with paraglycogen; *n*, nucleus.

tocytes lose their hairs after encystation. The cysts average 400 to 800 μ; the sporocysts $19 \times 8 \mu$. (Details in Troisi, 1933.)

Apolocystis elongata Phillips and Mackinnon (B–D) is smaller than the foregoing, also covered with short, stiff ectoplasmic hairs; it is rounded only when at rest and is usually very active, and sausage-shaped when extended ($220 \times 95 \mu$). The endoplasm is very dense and the nucleus not clearly seen in the living animal; it has one large karyosome and commonly two smaller ones. The gametocytes are usually unequal in size; in the cyst each becomes deeply lobed, the lobes constrict off as spheres, the surface of each of which produces very numerous transparent gametes. The gametocysts average 460 μ; the spores 16×8 μ. (See Phillips and Mackinnon, 1946, who reported the chromosome cycle.)

Apolocystis lumbrici-olidi (Schmidt), the smallest of the species known from this host, is spherical, ovoid or reniform, 90 to 100 μ in diameter (E). Very short 'hairs' either cover the body or are confined to a cap over part of the surface. The nucleus has one large and one small karyosome. According to Hesse (1909) the species is generally immobile but is subject to waves of distortion. The development is unknown and the species needs more investigation.

Gonospora varia Léger

Apart from the gregarines of the gut described above (p. 167), the Cirratulid polychaete *Audouinia tentaculata** is very commonly infected by a coelomic monocystid which is of some interest because its seasonal development is related to the sexual cycle of the host in such a way that the spores are produced in time to escape with the host's gametes (Hentschel, 1926).

The living organism

Living worms should be obtained from the Marine Biological Station at Plymouth during the periods given below as suitable for the various stages of the parasite's cycle. The worm is opened longitudinally and the flaps of skin turned back to expose the inner coelomic walls. The gregarines occur only in the segments of the worm containing gonads and if they stray outside the genital region they abort; the anterior sixth and posterior third of the host are free of normal specimens. When fully developed, *G. varia* may be as much as 2 mm long and is easily picked out as a thin, whitish thread. Smears may be diluted slightly with sea water.

During the autumn only young trophozoites are found, up to about 350 μ long. They grow throughout the winter and by February or March reach their maximum size, which is usually between 1 and 2 mm. The trophozoite (Fig. 99 A, B) is elongated, club-shaped, with the anterior end rounded or flattened, sometimes a little expanded; it may be loosely attached to the coelomic epithelium. The nucleus is prominent, clear, with a conspicuous, refringent, vacuolated karyosome which often has the appearance of consisting of two spheres, of unequal affinity for stains, closely and irregularly fitted together (Fig. 99c). Movement is very slight.

* See also index, under *host-list*.

During April, the trophozoites associate by their now expanded anterior ends as gametocytes (D); the gametocysts vary greatly in size from 300 to 800 μ. By May or June, the gametocysts usually contain only fully developed spores; this is the spawning season for *Audouinia tentaculata* at Plymouth

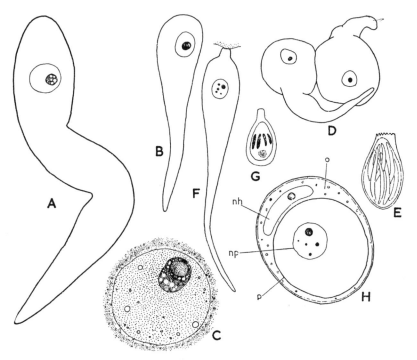

FIG. 99. *Gonospora.* A–E, *G. varia*: A and B, trophozoites. ×150; C, nucleus, showing vacuolated karyosome (fixed B.; stained D.H.). ×500; D, associating gametocytes. ×60; E, sporocyst. ×1,500; F–G, *G. arenicolae*: F, trophozoite attached to coelomic epithelium. ×500; G, sporocyst with 4 of the 8 sporozoites. ×1,000; H, *G. minchini*, trophozoite in ovum of host. ×250. (A–C original; D after Hentschel; E original; F–G after Cunningham; H after Goodrich and Goodrich.)

nh, nucleus of infected ovum; *np*, nucleus of gregarine; *o*, ovum; *p*, parasite.

and it is supposed that the spores escape through the genital ducts; the spent worms are apparently free of parasites for a time until new infections appear in the autumn. The sporocyst (E) is 18 to 20 μ long, ovoid, with a denticulated orifice at one pole.

Two other species of *Gonospora* may be obtained from another poly-chaete from Plymouth, *Arenicola ecaudata*. *Gonospora* (= *Kalpido-rhynchus*) *arenicolae* Cunningham is found in the coelom where it is more definitely attached by a fairly well-developed epimerite (or mucron) to the epithelium (Fig. 99F). Its spores (G) are bottle-shaped, with a smooth neck in contrast to that of *G. varia*; Cunningham (1907), who described the life-cycle, found that spores were most numerous in hosts containing large quantities of gametes and he thought they might escape together. Spawning occurs at intervals throughout the year and the Southwoods (1958) found cysts at all times, but they were most numerous in March and December. *Gonospora minchinii* (Goodrich and Pixell Goodrich, 1920) also occurs in the coelom of *Arenicola ecaudata*, where the young trophozoites attack and enter the developing ova (Fig. 99H).

TRIBE CEPHALINA

Cephaline gregarines inhabit the alimentary canal, mainly of insects, and are at once distinguishable from acephalines by the greater complexity of the body (Figs. 102, 104). In relation to the backward movement of the gut fluid, there is here, as in many metazoan gut parasites, an organ of fixation; the mucron sometimes found in acephalines is replaced by a more highly developed epimerite by means of which the organism is, for much of its period of growth, anchored to an epithelial cell of the host. The epimerite may be a simple knob, or it may be stalked, frilled, proboscis-like, with recurved cuticular hooks, or it may produce root-like processes which ramify within the host cell.

The sporozoite enters or becomes attached to an epithelial cell; if the former, it eventually outgrows the cell (Fig. 102C), and so achieves the latter condition, in which the growing trophozoite is attached by its epimerite to a cell with its body hanging into the gut lumen. In the great majority of cephalines, the body behind the epimerite is subdivided by a transverse septum so that altogether it consists of 3 regions: the epimerite, an anterior differentiation distinguished as to its posterior limit only by a difference in the appearance of its cytoplasm; the protomerite, between the epimerite and septum; and the posterior deutomerite, which is the largest region and contains the nucleus. Such gregarines are tricystid (Figs. 102, 103). In a few the septum never develops and the body remains dicystid (*Sycia*, Fig. 104). Such fully developed trophozoites are called cephalonts. Eventually they break away from their epimerites and live freely in the gut lumen as sporodins or sporonts, which will grow into gametocytes. Sporonts associate in syzygy, by their anterior or posterior ends, laterally, or head to tail; this last arrangement *in tandem*, which occurs in *Gregarina* (Fig. 102J), permits the formation of chains of individuals, or several small ones may become attached to a larger anterior partner; whatever the combination, the anterior member is called the primite, the posterior member(s) the satellite(s). (It was the observation of numerous individuals united in syzygy which suggested the name of the order, from *grex, gregis*, a flock.) Larger groups are sooner or later reduced to pairs of gametocytes which encyst. The polycystid body is simplified before gametogenesis. The gametocyst may be simple or very elaborate. Size, shape, and ornamentation of the sporocyst provide good taxonomic characters. There are always 8 sporozoites. For taxonomy, see Watson (1916) and Watson Kamm (1922).

Cephaline gregarines of meal-worms

Meal-worms are the larvae of the beetle *Tenebrio molitor*, and they harbour 4 species of cephalines. They are most simply obtained from pet shops, kept in tins with perforated lids, and fed on crushed oats. They burrow into their food and defecate and readily infect one another; their spores are certainly very resistant—for example, while exposure for 6 days to a temperature of 37·5° C kills all the trophic stages of the gregarines of meal-worms, the spores are still viable after 90 days at this heat and can survive 20 minutes at 69° to 70° C (MacDougall, 1942). Considering the properties of the spores and the habits of the hosts it is not surprising that infections may be found in as much as 95 per cent of some populations; yet incidence is variable and may be as low as 20 per cent.

The cephalines present (Fig. 102), all in the mid-gut, are:

> *Gregarina cuneata* Stein
> *G. polymorpha* (Hammerschmidt)
> *G. steini* Berndt
> *Steinina ovalis* Léger & Duboscq

and all are taxonomically valid, except perhaps *G. steini*, which is of dubious merit (see p. 184). The best accounts of the good species remain those of Léger and Duboscq (1904a) for the trophic stages, and Kuschakewitsch (1907) for the gametocyst, with additions on their biology by Mühl (1921) and Göhre (1943); for cytology, see Daniels (1938).

Some general account is here offered of what may be seen in preparations from mixed infections, followed by notes on the species to aid in identification.

The living organisms

Lightly anaesthetize the larva, cut off its head, posteriorly direct 2 oblique cuts through the body wall and pull away the hind end with the gut attached to it. Float this in Ringer's Solution or invertebrate fluid (p. 426) and remove any adherent fat. According to Göhre the species are not haphazardly distributed through the mid-gut, but *G. cuneata* occurs anteriorly, where the pH is lower, *G. polymorpha* posteriorly with a gap between the two, while *G. steini* is overlapping (Fig. 100). Remove the hind-gut and cut the mid-gut into two to separate roughly the first from the last 2 species. Tease the fragments in a drop of diluting fluid on a slide, seal under a No. 0 cover-slip.

The gregarines (Fig. 102) are conspicuous objects looking like elongated, short-necked ninepins, opaque and brownish-grey by transmitted light when fully grown, transparent when young. A few, torn from their moorings in the gut epithelium, may still retain the epimerite, which is a simple rounded knob in *Gregarina*. Most lie freely in the gut lumen and these will have lost their epimerites; the protomerite is separated from the much larger deutomerite by a hyaline septum, which is ectoplasmic. Under the oil-immersion lens the pellicle is seen to be longitudinally striated; it is, in fact, not thickened, but, as E.M. studies have shown, deeply folded

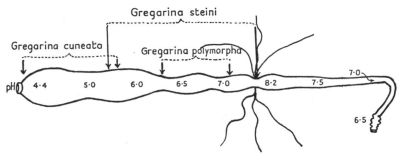

FIG. 100. Gut of larva of *Tenebrio molitor*, with pH regions indicated and distribution zones of the 3 commonest gregarine species. (After Göhre.)

in parallel grooves and ridges (Fig. 101A). Below the ectoplasm lie the myonemes; certainly circular myonemes occur; longitudinal ones have been described, but could not be demonstrated by any of the methods (phase-contrast and electron microscopy) used by Kümmel (1958) or by Beams and his colleagues (1959), who, however, have described a sub-pellicular fibrillar network which may be contractile. The endoplasm contains paraglycogen and other inclusions, all of which are less dense in young than in mature trophozoites. The nucleus is a clear vesicle containing a conspicuous karyosome and some smaller refringent material. There are never any vacuoles.

The gregarines of meal-worms exhibit a kind of movement that sets one of the unsolved problems of protozoology. This is a slow, steady progression accomplished without any apparent change in shape. Many authors have attempted to explain this phenomenon (see Fig. 101).* All agree that the pellicle is covered by a sticky substance which (almost) always flows backwards. Schewiakoff long ago suggested that this substance was exuded from a gelatinous layer through small pores in the pellicular grooves and, flowing to the posterior, set behind the animal into a hard trail which,

* See especially Schewiakoff (1894), Crawley (1902, 1905), Sokolow (1912), Dembowski (1913), Watson (1916), Prell (1921), Mühl (1921), Kümmel (1958), and Beams *et al.* (1959).

accumulating, pushed the body along in front of it (Fig. 101B). Against this it has been pointed out that the trail is not always continuous, but is sometimes left in a series of isolated splashes, though the steadiness of movement is unimpaired. The authors of E.M. studies of cephaline gregarines have inclined to the view that the mucus trail is the result and not the cause of locomotion which they thought was probably due to undetected

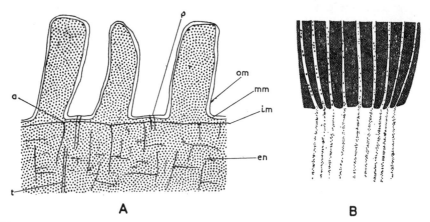

A   B

FIG. 101. Structure of the surface in *Gregarina* and the gliding movement. Diagrammatic. A, the structure as revealed by electron microscopy. The pellicle has three membranes, of which the outer and middle (*om* and *mm*) are thrown into longitudinal folds, here shown in T.S. The inner membrane (*im*) is not folded. Below it is a fibrillar network (*en*), which may be contractile; some of its elements are attached to *im*, as at *a*, and may transmit movements to the pellicle as a whole. Tubular structures (*t*) appear to find openings (*p*) between the ridges and may be mucus pores. The minute scale of this hypothetically contractile apparatus could account for gliding without any change of shape visible by the light microscope (based mainly on Beams *et al.*). B, the mucus trail (after Schewiakoff).

pellicular contractions (Kümmel, 1958; Beams *et al.*, 1959). It must be admitted that it is easier to find fault with any of these theories than it is to improve on them.

Syzygies *in tandem* generally consist of couples but sometimes a primite may be followed by two or more smaller attached satellites. Some are still attached for a time to the epithelium by the epimerite of the primite, and Göhre held that this, the member of the pair which remains longer attached, is typically the female gametocyte. Mühl (1921) claimed that differences in the reactions of primite and satellite to vital dyes were related to sex. But until more is known about the gametogenesis of these species it seems premature to refer to either member of a couple as male or female. However that may turn out, multiple associations, it seems, normally break down into pairs before encystation. For details of cysts, see below under species.

Gregarina cuneata Stein

The sporozoite partially penetrates an epithelial cell, its internal portion growing more rapidly than the part left lying extracellularly (Fig. 102C). The former region differentiates, while still within the cell, first an epimerite, and then behind it the septum which separates the protomerite from the deutomerite. Soon afterwards it acquires the definitive form of the trophozoite. In the cephalont (A), the epimerite is a simple knob, a generic character of *Gregarina*.

When fully grown the trophozoite of *G. cuneata* (B) may reach nearly 400 μ in length but it is commonly shorter. The protomerite is dilated anteriorly, or at least wider at its anterior than at its posterior margin. The deutomerite expands towards the posterior.

The early stages of association are found in the host, where the beginnings of the cyst are laid down. But this is completed after the parasites have been ejected with the host's faeces, which takes place before gametogenesis and sporogony. Younger and immature gametocysts, then, may be found in the hind-gut, older stages in the black faecal pellets of the meal-worms, which should be moistened with Ringer's Solution and then spread on a slide and covered. The ripe gametocysts (D) are early recognized. They are large and spherical, about 240 μ in diameter. The endocyst is extremely tough; the thick ectocyst is a many-layered mucoid secretion. At first the cyst is yellowish, then dark grey and so opaque that it must be crushed for examination of the contents. The spores escape through long, tubular sporoducts (E, F), which are everted from the endocyst through the ectocyst to the exterior; they may be seen in the completely mature cysts. The spores (G) emerge attached in chains. Each is barrel-shaped, 6×4 μ. The sporoducts are formed from the gametocystic residuum, which moves from the centre to the periphery, and thence sends towards the centrally disposed spores outgrowths like finger-stalls; these are evaginated by the shrinkage of the maturing gametocyst plus swelling of its contents.

Gregarina polymorpha (Hammerschmidt)

The epimerite is rather small (Fig. 102H). The rest of the body is roughly cylindrical, not expanding towards the hind end as in the preceding species. The protomerite is dome-shaped, the deutomerite either keeps the same diameter down its length or it narrows towards the posterior end (I, J). The whole organism measures up to 350 μ long. The cysts and spores have never been described. Léger and Duboscq (1904*a*) state that the development of this species does not differ significantly from that of the last, which they themselves described.

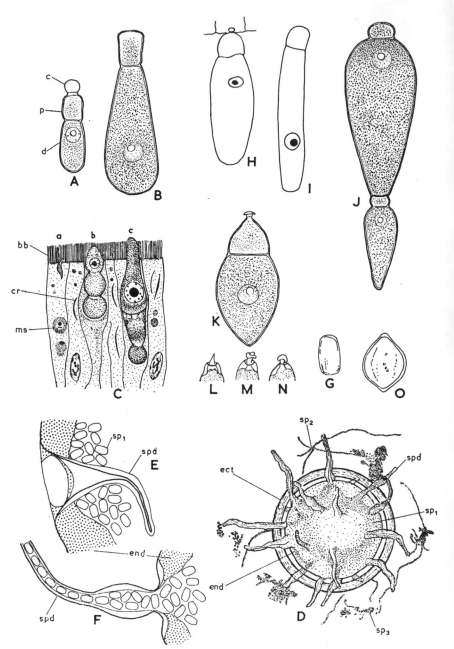

FIG. 102. Gregarines of the meal-worm. A–F, *Gregarina cuneata*: A, cephalont. × 125;
B, sporont. × 125; C, intracellular stages; *a*, sporozoite entering epithelial cell; *b* and *c*,
growth of cephalont. × 1,000; D, gametocyst. × 120; E, part of gametocyst wall, sporoduct
still invaginated; F, the same, with sporoduct everted; G, sporocyst of *Gregarina* (?*cuneata*).
× 1,750; H–J, *G. polymorpha*: H, attached cephalont. × 175; I, sporont. × 175; J, syzygy.
× 175; K–O, *Steinina ovalis*: K, cephalont. × 1,200; L, M, N, epimerites; O, sporocyst.
× 1,750. D.L.M. (A, B, G, H–J original; C, K–O after Léger and Duboscq; D–F after Kuschakewitsch.)

a, sporozoite; *b*, developing cephalont; *bb*, brush border of epithelial cell; *c*, older cephalont than
b; *cr*, crystalloid of host cell; *d*, deutomerite; *e*, epimerite; *ect*, gelatinous ectocyst; *end*, endocyst;
ms, mucoid spherule of host cell; *p*, protomerite; sp_1, sporocysts within the gametocyst; sp_2, chain
of sporocysts; sp_3, groups of sporocysts; *spd*, sporoduct.

Gregarina steini Berndt

Berndt (1902) separated this from the other 2 species on doubtful grounds. The sporodins measure up to 150 μ and are therefore smaller than in the other species. The protomerite is hemispherical, the deutomerite wide at the 'shoulder' and then tapering backwards to a small but well-rounded posterior end. The cysts are said to be ovoid, up to 100× 160 μ. The information given is not really of much taxonomic value unless it could be shown, by tracing the life-histories of all species, that the differences described are constant; especially, more investigation of sporogony is needed before any decision about the validity of this species can be final, and, plainly, a good deal depends on how polymorphic *G. polymorpha* really is.

Steinina ovalis (Stein) Léger and Duboscq

This genus belongs to the large family Actinocephalidae in which the epimerite varies from a complex to a most simple structure, but is always symmetrical about the long axis of the animal. Syzygy occurs late, so that most of the sporodins seen are solitary. The gametocysts have no ducts but dehisce by simple rupture. The sporocysts are biconical, tending to cylindrical or irregular, smooth or spiny.

S. ovalis (Fig. 102K) is plump, up to 100 μ long, solitary. The epimerite of the young cephalont is a flexible, digitiform process which becomes transformed with age into a mushroom-shaped or disk-like structure (L–N). The protomerite is cylindrical but terminates anteriorly in a large cone, the deutomerite is rounded to ovoid. The gametocysts are spherical to ovoid, 100 μ in diameter, dehiscing by rupture. The sporocysts (o) are very plump, almost, at times, spherical, though strictly biconical, 9×7·5 μ. Sporogony occurs outside the host, as in *Gregarina*.

The pellicle is longitudinally striated and the transverse myonemes are usually visible as well. Soon after loss of the epimerite the sporodins associate, glide over each other, become attached by their anterior ends, and proceed at once to formation of the gametocyst without the intervention of any prolonged syzygy.

Permanent preparations

Smears from well-infected gut should be made and fixed in B or S+A, stained in D.H. or H.H. Sections are best cut at 5 to 8 μ, and longitudinally, as the parasites are usually orientated with their heads towards the anterior end.

Gregarina blattarum v. Siebold

It was with this species that over 75 years ago Bütschli performed what were probably the first infection experiments with gregarines and he provided us with what is still one of the best descriptions of the gametocyst of a cephaline. The animal is cosmopolitan in the mid-gut of cockroaches, *Periplaneta americana*, *Blatta orientalis*, and *Blattella germanica*, all hosts widely used for parasitological demonstrations.* The incidence of infection seems to vary: Sprague (1941), who collected in Illinois, found light infections in about 5 per cent of his cockroaches between September and December, but during January and February 30 per cent were heavily infected, the mid-gut being packed with parasites and as many as 30 cysts being obtained from one hind-gut. Sprague's paper gives a list of previous authors; Bütschli (1881) remains indispensable.

The living organisms

The insect gut is laid out in 0·75 per cent NaCl and smears diluted with this fluid are mounted and sealed (p. 421). Not much is known about the attached stages and almost all the parasites seen will be free in the gut lumen.

The trophozoites are roughly cylindrical, often irregular in outline (Fig. 103A). They generally measure some 400 to 500 μ in length, when fully grown, but exceptionally large animals may occur, perhaps more commonly in light infections. The epimerite is a simple transparent knob. Soon after losing it, the animals associate in syzygy; the partners may be equal or the satellite smaller, sometimes much smaller, than the primite. The early association means, of course, that pairs of all sizes occur. The protomerite of the satellite is usually flattened and broadened compared with that of the primite. The nucleus is small and spherical and has up to half a dozen small inclusions, sometimes called karyosomes.

The process of encystation (B–H) cannot be completed in NaCl solution, but it may be followed if the associated gametocytes are mounted in egg albumen; it appears that the viscous substance may be needed to assist them in assuming their head to tail positions. They glide over each other, bending and folding the body, so that they tend to move round in a circle, the satellite pushing its hind end towards the front of the primite until they meet: it is here that the viscosity of the medium seems to help. Now joined laterally, and head to tail, the gametocytes continue to rotate and a sticky, gelatinous layer is formed (E) to which small foreign particles adhere. This layer, which constantly occurs in nature and will eventually develop extensively, is not always seen *in vitro*; possibly its construction depends on

* For other parasites of these hosts see index, under *host-list*.

material supplied by the host. Within it the true, resistant cyst wall appears (G). The cyst is at first spherical and may remain so, but some become ovoid. Within it, the septa between the protomerite and deutomerite disappear and the superficial ectoplasm produces a compact layer of gametes

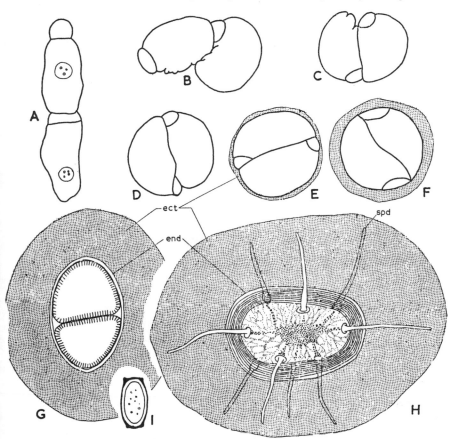

FIG. 103. *Gregarina blattarum.* A, syzygy. ×60; B–G, association of gametocytes and cyst formation. ×60; H, gametocyst. ×100; I, sporocyst. ×1,750. (A after Schneider; B–G after Sprague with additions after Bütschli; H after Bütschli; I after Sprague.)

ect, ectocyst; *end*, endocyst; *spd*, sporoduct.

which come to resemble an epithelium. The sporoducts are formed after fertilization and vary in number from 5 to 30 according to the size of the gametocyst. The latter measures from 200 to 800 or 900 μ in length, but most fall between 300 and 600 μ. During the 48 hours after the first appearance of the sporoducts the cyst becomes more transparent, possibly because the paraglycogen in the residual cytoplasmic mass is becoming used up.

Then, at the end of this time, the sporoducts are everted (H) and the spores discharged. The area of the gametocyst wall over the disk-like base of the inverted duct appears to weaken, and Sprague thought this might be due to the lytic action of an enzyme in the basal part of the sporoduct, which is more acid than the rest; the cyst membrane is elastic and its contents are kept at a relatively high pressure which, at the discharge, ruptures the weak areas and so permits eversion of the ducts. The spores are usually described as barrel-shaped (dolioform) with truncate ends, but Sprague reports them as broadly rounded at the ends, the truncate appearance being due to a mucoid membrane which surrounds them (1). They measure, on the average, $8\cdot5\ \mu\times4\cdot5\ \mu$ approximately. When first discharged, they emerge in long chains, up to nearly 9 mm long, each containing many thousands of spores.

Permanent preparations

As for gregarines of meal-worms (p. 189).

Sycia inopinata Léger

Although not extremely common, this dicystid cephaline is likely to be seen when its hosts, species of *Audouinia* and *Cirratulus*, are searched for other parasites;* and a brief account of it is here offered.

S. inopinata (? = *Ulivina elliptica* Mingazzini) occurs in the gut of *Audouinia tentaculata* and *A. filigera* and possibly in other Polychaeta (see Reichenow, 1932, p. 36). The young cephalonts are shown in Fig. 104 A, B, where the smaller is still attached to the intestinal epithelium. Both show the characteristic collar below the epimerite. Most of the organisms seen are sporonts (C) which have lost the epimerite and in which the only distinction between protomerite and deutomerite is in the texture of the endoplasm; there is no septum. The organism is now elliptical in outline, with a greatly thickened pellicle which usually shows at least two marked longitudinal folds on its surface. The life-history is unknown and until sporogony is clearly reported the taxonomy of this genus will remain obscure. The 2 species named by Ganapati (1946) from trophozoites are not well established and may only indicate a wide distribution of *S. inopinata* itself. For microparasites of *Sycia*, see Caullery and Mesnil (1919).

ORDER COCCIDIA

The type of life-history found in the Coccidia is undoubtedly derived from that already seen in the Gregarinida (cf. Figs. 88 and 105), but it

* See index, under *host-list*.

displays a number of alterations and additions of which the following are the most important. Much of the life-cycle is intracellular and there is always a prolific phase of asexual reproduction; these 2 factors combine in some cases to produce very heavy and destructive infections of great veterinary importance. The gametocytes are always distinguishable as males and females, and the gametes differ in size and number; commonly the anisogamy is very marked. There is an additional generation during sporogony, so that each zygote gives rise to a number of spores. Unlike gregarines, the Coccidia occur in both vertebrate and invertebrate hosts.

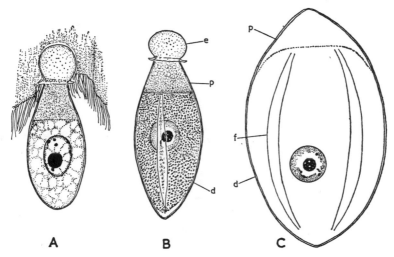

FIG. 104. *Sycia inopinata.* A, young cephalont anchored to epithelium. ×800; B, free cephalont. ×325; C, adult trophozoite (sporont). ×325. (Original: D. L. M.)

d, deutomerite; *e*, epimerite; *f*, pellicular fold; *p*, protomerite.

The young organism (Fig. 105, *a*) penetrates a host cell, usually in the intestinal epithelium, grows into a schizont (*c*), which produces by multiple fission a number of merozoites (*e*), which escape and set up new infections. The area of tissue eventually destroyed may be very extensive. After repeated cycles of asexual proliferation, some merozoites, for reasons not understood, become sexually distinguished and develop differently. The presumptive female enters a cell and grows, without any nuclear division, into a large gamete (*f–h*); the growing stage is generally called the macrogametocyte and the adult, ready for fertilization, the macrogamete. The male parasite (microgametocyte) grows within its host cell and produces very many flagellated microgametes (*i–l*). The zygote at once forms an oocyst and this generally develops a tough, resistant wall and persists as an important agency in dissemination, though in digenetic forms where cross-

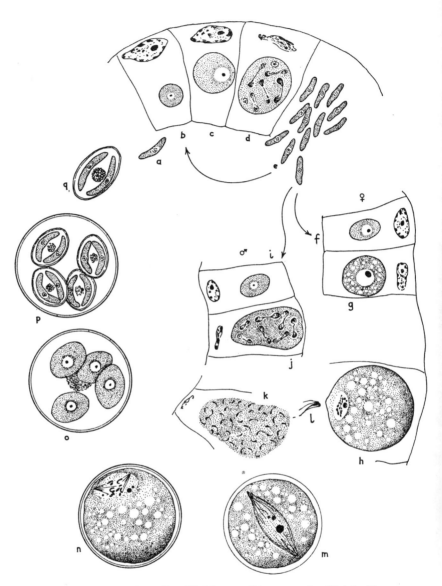

FIG. 105. Coccidian life-history. Diagrammatic. (Original.)

A sporozoite, *a*, enters a host cell and grows, *b*, into a schizont, *c*, which divides asexually, *d*, into a number of merozoites, *e*, which infect more cells and repeat the asexual cycle. Eventually some merozoites initiate the sexual cycle, *f–m*: without nuclear division, the female parasite (macrogametocyte) grows, *f–g*, into a macrogamete, *h*, while the nucleus of the microgametocyte divides repeatedly, *i–k*, and numerous biflagellate microgametes, *l*, are produced; after fertilization, *m*, a resistant wall is laid down about the zygote as the oocyst, and sporogony follows. The first zygotic division, *n*, is reductional, and within the oocyst a number of bodies, the sporoblasts, are produced, *o*, and each encysts within a sporocyst, *p*, within which each sporoblast produces the sporozoites, *p*; *q* is a sporocyst containing 2 sporozoites and a residual body.

infection is otherwise mediated (e.g. by food relations between hosts) the oocyst may be reduced to a more or less soft membrane. The zygote within the oocyst divides into a number of sporoblasts, often leaving a cytoplasmic residuum (*o*), and each sporoblast becomes surrounded by a protective envelope as a sporocyst, in which the sporoblast itself divides into sporozoites (*p*). Thus, in contrast to the gregarines, each coccidian zygote produces, not one spore, but a number of spores; the entire contents of the oocyst are the products of a single zygote. In spite of some variation among individuals, the number of spores in each oocyst and the numbers of sporozoites in each sporocyst are taxonomically useful characters and so, too, is the shape of the oocyst: oocysts are said to be monosporous, disporous, and so on, according to the number of spores they contain, and the spores themselves are called dizoic, trizoic, tetrazoic, &c., to indicate the number of contained sporozoites, and the division and arrangement of genera are determined by these numerical characters (Hoare, 1933, 1956*a*).

Some departures from the type of life-history outlined above, which is characteristic of the important Eimeriid group of Coccidia, occur. *Aggregata* has 2 hosts, with schizogony in one and sporogony in the other. In the Adeleid group, there is an early association or syzygy of the male and female parasites and the number of microgametes is reduced to 4. The most striking modifications are seen in the Haemogregarines, which are not gregarines at all, but Coccidia that spend part of their lives in the bloodstream of the vertebrate. Wenyon (1926) has excellent accounts of the specialized Coccidia. In this chapter only two of the more conservative species are considered. Of these *Eimeria tenella* is more typical in its habit as a gut parasite, and offers the advantage that it is readily studied in experimental, and therefore controlled and pure infections.

Eimeria tenella (Railliet and Lucet)

Some 8 species of *Eimeria* occur in domestic fowls (*Gallus gallus*) and they range in veterinary importance from *E. praecox*, which appears to be harmless, to such dangerous parasites as *E. necatrix* and *E. tenella*, which are commonly fatal in older and younger birds respectively. The greater part of what is known of the life-histories and pathology will be found in Tyzzer (1929) and Tyzzer, Theiler, and Jones (1932). Tyzzer (1932) gives a very clear account of the problems set to the parasitologist dealing with mixed infections and the means of their solution. Horton-Smith (1957) discusses the factors influencing the transmission of coccidiosis in fowls.

Young birds infected experimentally with *E. tenella* remain normal till the fourth day, when they eat less, are listless, and appear to feel cold. Autopsy at this stage shows that haemorrhage into the caeca has already begun. Next day bright red blood is discharged profusely and the feathers may be stained with it; the skin and mucous membranes are pale, and death may occur now or on the next day. Oocysts appear in the faeces on the seventh day and the parasite has now run its cycle. Birds which survive for so long may recover if kept warm, well-fed, and guarded against reinfections; but ill-kept and reinfected birds waste, their skeletal muscles atrophy, and they cannot stand and so become helpless. There is some degree of acquired immunity and older birds are less severely affected. Maximum sensitivity is at 4 weeks old.

The life-cycle is essentially like that shown diagrammatically in Fig. 105. The early stages all occur in the epithelial cells lining the deeper regions of the caecal glands, though later the large and the lower part of the small intestine may be involved. These are 2 generations of schizonts and merozoites, which are morphologically distinguishable, and there may be a negligible third generation. The sexual forms appear on the sixth day and the oocysts are discharged on the seventh. It is to be understood that the infection is a self-limiting one in which the life-history runs a predictable course, producing its various phases at known times and then, if the host is still alive, terminating with the production of oocysts and acquisition of some degree of immunity. The life-history is studied in two stages—(1) from sections of material fixed at intervals from the beginning of an experimental infection, (2) from observations on the discharged oocysts, which complete their sporogony outside their hosts. It is easier and more logical, therefore, to begin with the examination of permanent preparations and then pass to the study of the living oocysts.

Permanent preparations

Day-old chicks may be regarded as clean, i.e. uninfected. They are fed with heavy doses of oocysts obtained as described on p. 200 and killed at intervals to obtain the desired stages. The earliest of these are found at about 48 hours, but they are elusive, and good pictures of the important stages will be obtained from birds killed at 72, 120, 144, and 168 hours. Fix the caecum in B. Stain in H.H. with Chromotrope 2R as a counterstain if desired. Masson's Triple Stain gives good histo-pathological pictures.

Birds killed at:

60–72 hours show first-generation schizonts and merozoites
120 ,, ,, second ,, ,, ,,
144 ,, ,, the same plus stages of the sexual cycle.
168 ,, ,, oocysts and perhaps some late schizogony.

The earliest intracellular stages are found towards the end of the second day in epithelial cells near the bottom of the glands of the caecum. They are elongated, pointed at one end and blunt at the other, and towards the blunt end lies a globule which stains brightly with Eosin and black with Haemato-xylin (Fig. 106A). This trophozoite has developed by growth from a sporo-zoite and will in turn grow into a first generation schizont in which the nuclei repeatedly divide. Mitoses are not synchronized. The schizonts of this first generation (B, C) are distinguished as follows. Their nuclei (E) are small, tend to be peripheral, with an ill-defined vesicle containing a number of granules; among these one may be larger than the others and is perhaps a karyosome. The cytoplasm is often folded so that in section it gives a false impression of having divided by plasmotomy (C). The eosinophil globule persists. The host cell and its nucleus are hypertrophied and are eventually extruded into the lumen of the caecal gland.

The enormous number of up to 900 merozoites may be produced from a single first-generation schizont. They are very small and inconspicuous, $2-4\,\mu \times 1-1\cdot5\,\mu$, pointed at one end, which contains a terminal granule, and rounded at the other, which bears a number of granules in the cyto-plasm (D). A merozoite penetrates another deeply placed epithelial cell and usually comes to lie between the outer cell boundary and nucleus; it grows into a second generation schizont which differs from its predecessors. The cytoplasm stains more deeply, the body reaches a larger size (about $45\,\mu$ in diameter), the nuclei (F) are distributed throughout the body, not peri-pherally, and they have a distinct karyosome. The host reacts more severely to second-generation schizonts. The infected cells become very greatly enlarged, round off, lose their epithelial character, and may migrate deeply into the submucosa. The very great numbers of first-generation merozoites and their tendency to invade cells towards the bases of the glands leads to a picture in which extensive tracts of deeply situated epithelium may be heavily modified while normal cells continue to line the upper part of the gland walls and these unmodified epithelial cells may unite and cover over the damaged and infected tissue below.

By the time that the second-generation schizonts are ready to divide, extensive haemorrhage has already taken place and this, therefore, cannot be due to the liberation of the merozoites. Probably it is the result of pres-sures set up by the disproportionate growth of infected cells which interfere with the circulation. At any rate, the haemorrhage is severe and in 5 days most of the epithelium may be sloughed. At this point the second-genera-tion merozoites (G, H) are liberated. They are larger ($16 \times 2\,\mu$) than the first, and they move blunt end first with a pointed posterior. The number produced from a single schizont is variable but less than in the first genera-tion: Tyzzer suggests a figure of about 250.

The second-generation merozoites invade the epithelium wherever it persists and initiate the sexual part of the cycle. (A few produce third-generation schizonts, but these are small, not common, and bud off only some 4 to 30 merozoites, which are possibly the source of the oocysts

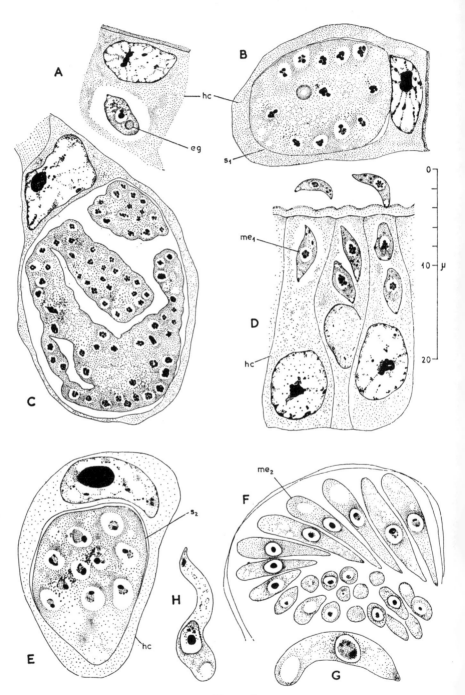

FIG. 106 a

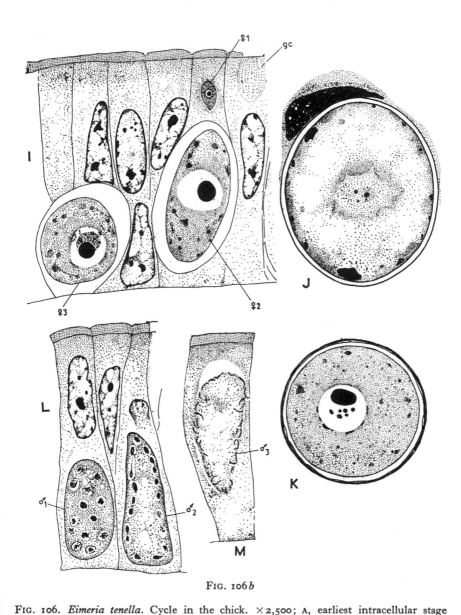

FIG. 106 *b*

FIG. 106. *Eimeria tenella.* Cycle in the chick. ×2,500; A, earliest intracellular stage
(46 hr. after infection); B, young 1st generation schizont in epithelial cell (52 hr.); C, more
advanced stage of the same in excavated and hypertrophied epithelial cell (72 hr.); D, 1st
generation merozoites: some have penetrated glandular epithelium (72 hr.); E, 2nd
generation schizont (120 hr.); F, 2nd generation merozoites still in cavity bounded by
remains of host cell (120 hr.); G, H, the same after release; I, strip of epithelium with successive stages (1, 2, 3) in development of macrogametocyte; ♀₁ is a very young stage cut
obliquely; J, L.S. oocyst in lumen of gut: the wall is single and the oocyst is still attached to
remains of its host cell (144 hr.); K, T.S. slightly later stage in development of oocyst (144 hr.);
L, M, epithelium with 3 stages in development of microgametocyte (144 hr.). (A–D after
Tyzzer; E–M original. All original figures from material fixed in B., stained H.H. and
Chromotrope 2R.)

eg, eosinophil globule; *gc*, goblet cell; *hc*, host cell; *me*₁, ₂, 1st and 2nd generation merozoites; *s*₁, ₂,
1st and 2nd generation schizonts; ♀₁₋₃, macrogametocytes; ♂₁₋₃, microgametocytes.

discharged after the main crops of the seventh and eighth days about to be described.) The host-cell reaction is slighter than that to previous invasions and the epithelium may persist in continuous strips of cells infested with sexual stages. The microgametocyte is oval, 5·5 to 18 μ long, and produces numerous small comma-shaped gametes (L, M). The macrogametocyte, or female parasite (I), is also oval, grows somewhat larger than the male, and eventually shows in its cytoplasm, especially near the periphery, irregular masses of basophil reserves, which possibly contribute to the formation of the oocyst wall. The details of fertilization are not known.* The appearance of a slight thickening of the pellicle, the beginning of the oocyst wall, pre- sumably indicates that fertilization has taken place. The wall, at first single, doubles into a thick outer and more delicate inner layer (J, K). The completed oocyst is oval, with little distinction between the poles, measures 20–26 $\mu \times$ 16·5–23 μ, and contains the zygote. This at first fills it, but later contracts from the wall. There is very little development in the host and cysts in the condition described are passed in enormous numbers on the seventh and eighth days of infection.

The living oocysts

Birds killed on the seventh or eighth day may show a white marbling of the distended caecal wall, and this is due to the accumulation below it of

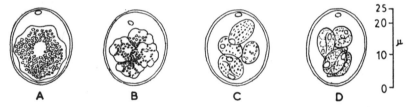

FIG. 107. *Eimeria tenella*: development of the oocyst. (After Tyzzer.)

A, the oocyst on discharge, containing the zygote; B, division into 4 sporoblasts; C, be- ginning of spore formation; D, development of sporocysts.

great masses of oocysts, which also occur in the caecal and, sometimes, the intestinal discharge. Material from the discharge or from the broken up caecum is spread in Petri dishes and mixed with 2·5 per cent aqueous solution of potassium bichromate. This checks the growth of bacteria and moulds but does not penetrate the cyst wall; the use of such a poison as a storage solution for living cysts is an indication of their powers of resistance. Cysts are withdrawn at intervals and examined.

Within 24 hours the zygote has divided into 4 cells, at first irregular, but later smoothly ovoid (Fig. 107). These are the sporoblasts, and each secretes

* The sexual stages and sporogony are much better understood in *E. stiedae*: see p. 202.

about itself a tough wall, the sporocyst, within which the contained sporoblast divides into 2 sporozoites. The species is thus tetrasporous and dizoic, and this is characteristic of the genus *Eimeria*. After division of the zygote there is no obvious residuum such as is seen in, for example, *E. magna* (Fig. 109), but there is a small and unexplained hyaline globule found not only in this species but in other Coccidia of the fowl.

Eimeria stiedae (Lindemann)

This species is well known as the cause of a severe hepatitis in rabbits and various species of hares, where it occurs in the epithelium of the bile ductules. It differs from *E. tenella* in that it tends to become chronic in survivors, especially in older animals, and that the asexual and sexual cycles of the parasite overlap, so that, in sections of material fixed at the right time, nearly all the endogenous stages of development may be displayed at once. It seems very probable that the oocysts of *E. stiedae* were observed as long ago as 1674, by Antony van Leeuwenhoek, and, if so, it was the first of the parasitic Protozoa, and one of the first of all Protozoa, to be observed and recorded, though its nature was not recognized (Dobell, 1922).

The course of the infection may be briefly outlined as follows. The oocysts are known to hatch under the action of trypsin and this event, *in vivo*, must take place near the opening of the pancreatic duct into the duodenum, a position some 40 cm from the exit of the bile duct, not allowing for folding of the mucosa: however, the sporozoites do not make use of this obvious route to the liver, but reach it through a factor of the portal system. The earliest lesions are found a week after infection in the small and medium branches of the intrahepatic biliary ductules, and infections may be experimentally established by injections of sporozoites into the mesenteric vein (Smetana, 1933 *b*, *c*). During the next week the infection extends by means of repeated schizogonies of unknown number and duration; there is a marked proliferation of the epithelial cells which swell and diminish the lumen of the ductules. From the fourteenth to eighteenth days of the infection sexual reproduction and schizogony go on side by side, the latter giving way to the former, so that within 3 weeks only the sexual forms are found.* By now the bile ducts are hypertrophied, the epithelium much folded, and nearly all its cells harbour parasites. The foci may be encapsulated in a fibrous, or, later, calcareous nodule, and these cream or white spots are conspicuous in the livers of dissected animals. Young hosts, after diarrhoea and polyuria, become pot-bellied from enlargement of the liver, and at this stage may die after experimental infection. But natural infections

---

* According to Perard (1925) the infection runs a shorter course and oocysts are passed on the sixth or seventh day.

may often be lighter; many animals, especially older ones, survive, and their nodules come to contain a pus-like substance, full of oocysts, or, after these foci have disappeared, oocysts may be found in the gall-bladder. Infection does not appear to confer any degree of immunity. The oocysts do not sporulate unless they are dropped with the faeces and reach the outside world. Doubtless the coprophagous habits of rabbits assist in maintaining infections.

The logical approach to the study of the life-cycle is to begin with stained sections of the endogenous stages and pass thence to the examination of sporogony *in vitro*, as in the case of *E. tenella*. Much of the life-cycle was reported by Reich (1912); sporogony has been studied by Perard (1924, 1925), excystation and the means of infection by Smetana (1913, *a–c*); a general account of coccidiosis in rabbits with information about other species will be found in Becker (1934). More references are given by Wenyon (1926).

Permanent preparations

For sectioning, cut from an infected liver the smaller and softer nodules, which emit fluid when pressed. Slice across the nodule to help penetration by reagents, fix in Zenker or ZFA for 24 hours (see p. 431 for procedure), cut at 10 μ. Stain in H.H. with Orange G or Chromotrope 2R as counter-stain if desired, and mount under a No. o cover slip. Material fixed at a suitable interval after infection (?14–16 days) will provide the following stages (Fig. 108).

The sporozoites, after hatching in the gut, reach the liver, as already explained, through a factor of the hepatic portal vein, and there they invade the epithelial cells of the biliary ductules. During development of the parasite, these host cells are stimulated to divide and they proliferate irregular trabeculae across the lumen of the ductule, while the cellular elements themselves become hypertrophied and finally suffer extensive destruction. The number and duration of schizogonies are uncertain but they must be many and frequent to provide the numerous schizonts seen and the extensive radius of infection. The smallest schizonts are spherical, with homogeneous cytoplasm and a nucleus appearing as an ill-defined vesicle containing a centre of chromatic material (Fig. 108, *a*); after growth (*b*, *c*), the nucleus divides (*d*) and the schizont gives rise to a number of slim elongated merozoites, which at first are arranged *en barillet*, i.e. like the staves of a barrel (*e*). The number of merozoites depends on the size attained by the schizont and figures from 16 to several hundred appear in the literature. Certainly, *E. stiedae* never produces the enormous number of schizonts seen in the early stages of infections with *E. tenella*. Eventually a generation of merozoites grows into the sexual members of the cycle.

The microgametocyte (*f*, *g*) is the largest stage in development, and pro-

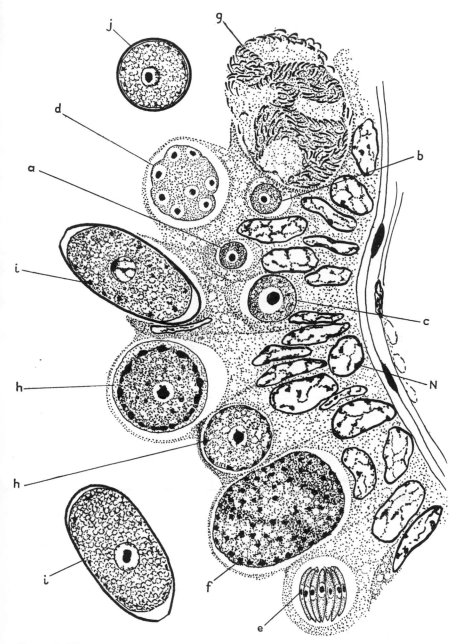

FIG. 108. *Eimeria stiedae*: composite drawing of section of infected biliary epithelium
of a rabbit. Stained Iron Haematoxylin. × 1,400. (Original: D. L. M.)

a, b, c, growth of schizont; *d,* schizogony; *e,* merozoites; *f,* microgametocyte during gametogenesis;
g, the same with gametes at the surface; *h,* macrogametocytes cut transversely; *i,* zygote in oocyst
cut longitudinally; *j,* the same, cut transversely; *N,* nucleus of host cell.

duces enormous numbers of minute nuclei, which are arranged superficially; these break away with some cytoplasm as biflagellate gametes which swim in the lumen of the duct in search of a macrogamete. The female parasites (*h*) are at first round, then oval, and are easily distinguished by their accumulations of basophil material, forming clumps or skeins in the cytoplasm; its function is not altogether clear: it may form a food reserve and it possibly contributes to the production of the oocyst wall. The latter appears after fertilization* (*i, j*), first as a delicate membrane, and later as a triple-walled structure. The middle wall is the obvious and conspicuous one and is interrupted only at the micropyle, where it is plugged by some material, which, as will be seen below, is proteinaceous. The outer, mucoid, and the inner membraneous walls are delicate, except where the former is thickened above the micropyle (see Fig. 109A). The zygote within the fully formed oocyst cannot develop further within the host and exogenous sporogony may be followed by the method given below.

The living oocysts

The oocyst when passed in the faeces is an ovoid, yellowish structure, flattened at the micropylar end. It is at first filled by the zygote within which a central clear spot, the nucleus, may be distinguished. In spite of the frequent assertion that this and comparable stages of other parasites are drought resistant, it is in fact killed by drying. Conceivably the diarrhoea and polyuria which characterize the disease contribute to its survival. Putrefaction is a more probable and therefore more serious danger than drying. On the other hand, oocysts can survive and complete their development in such unlikely substances as potassium permanganate, formalin, and hydrochloric and sulphuric acid solutions (Perard, 1925). Advantage of these properties is taken to encourage sporulation under healthy conditions.

Faecal pellets containing oocysts are ground in a mortar and the material covered, in a flask, with 1–2 per cent chromic acid. Oxygen is supplied either by bubbling it directly through the liquid in the flask or by distributing the cysts in Petri dishes, which must be watched to prevent evaporation. Sporulation at room temperature takes 3 days or more and material is withdrawn from time to time to observe its progress. The ovoid zygote contracts to a sphere within the oocyst and then becomes quadrangular; it divides into 4 separate bodies, the sporoblasts, each of which elongates to become enclosed within a sporocyst. After separation of the sporoblasts

---

* Some ambiguity on the part of Reich (1912), aggravated by a misleading diagram, has suggested to many that the oocyst wall forms first and that the macrogamete lies within it and is fertilized by a microgamete which swims in through the micropyle. This extraordinary misunderstanding is transmitted by some of the books, but, as Dr. C. A. Hoare has kindly pointed out to us, a careful reading of Reich's account shows that in its process of fertilization, *E. stiedae* is unexceptional among the Coccidia.

and formation of the sporocysts there is nothing left free in the oocyst in the nature of a residuum, though a few granules of material may be seen. Each sporoblast in its cyst divides into 2 sporozoites, which are elongated, pointed at one end, with a conspicuous spherical, refractile body occupying the opposite and rounded end. In each sporocyst there remains a distinct residuum (Fig. 109A).

At least 2 other species of *Eimeria* may occur in the intestine of rabbits and their oocysts must be distinguished from those of *E. stiedae*. The following information provides sufficient means; details of yet other species,

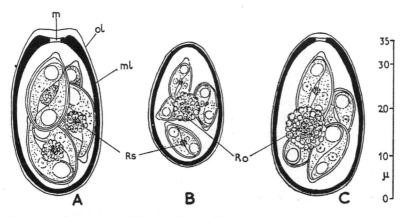

FIG. 109. Oocysts of rabbit Coccidia. A, *Eimeria stiedae*; B, *E. perforans*; C, *E. magna*. Each oocyst contains 4 sporocysts with 2 sporozoites. (Composite, after various authors.)

m, micropyle; *ml*, middle layer of oocyst wall; *ol*, outer layer; the inner layer is thin and closely applied to the inside of the middle layer: it is seen as the lower line across the micropyle; *Ro*, residual body in oocyst; *Rs*, residual body in sporocyst.

known so far only from the New World or from Russia, are given by Becker (1934).

Eimeria stiedae: oocysts 37·5 μ × 21·5 μ (mean) and mostly between 35 and 40 μ long. Usually orange/yellow. Without a residual body in the oocyst, but with a relatively large residuum (mean, 8 × 6 μ) in each sporocyst. Sporocysts 18 × 10 μ (Fig. 109A).

Eimeria perforans: oocysts 25 μ × 15·5 μ and mostly between 24 and 30 μ long. Usually not coloured. With a conspicuous residuum in the oocyst (4 × 8 μ) and only small sporocystic residua (1–3 μ). Sporocysts 8–15 μ × 5–8 μ. The oocyst is at once distinguished from that of *E. stiedae* by its smaller size and large oocystic residuum (Fig. 109B).

Eimeria magna: oocysts 28–40 μ × 20–26 μ. The cyst is very like that of *E. stiedae* in size and colour but is distinguished by its large oocystic residuum (Fig. 109 c).

Excystation in vitro

Smetana (1933a) has offered a technique for hatching oocysts, using trypsin (the active part of which is trypsin-kinase) to open the micropyle at 37° C and an optimum pH of 7 to 8. The procedure, which enables us to watch the emergence of the sporozoites under the oil-immersion lens, is as follows. It is to be realized that, in Smetana's words, 'the process of excystation is first induced by the passive destruction or removal of the protein substance closing the micropyle of oocysts; it is, however, completed only by the action of the sporozoites themselves.'

The sludge from the flask of oocysts in chromic acid is taken and washed in two changes of sterile distilled water. The best way of obtaining oocysts from the bottom deposit in the flask is to place some of it in a saturated solution of salt or cane-sugar and leave; the oocysts rise to the top and may be skimmed off. The washed cysts may be stored in the refrigerator. Only fully sporulated cysts can hatch. When ready, add 2 drops of the oocyst suspension to 2 ml of 5 per cent aqueous solution of a commercial trypsin preparation, adjust pH to 7 to 8 by adding drops of 1 per cent hydrochloric acid or sodium bicarbonate, incubate at 37° C, and examine in 5 to 7 hours.

When the micropyle has been opened the sporozoites in their sporocysts begin to rotate and eventually they squeeze out into the jelly-like substance contained in the oocyst, seemingly much as the sporozoites of *Monocystis* hatch from their sporocysts. The process takes 10 to 20 seconds in *Eimeria*. Within the oocyst the sporozoites swim about until they find the micropyle, through which they push their way into the surrounding medium, taking from 20 seconds to several minutes. In sealed smears, sporozoites may remain active for 24 hours. They are slim, crescent-shaped slips of cytoplasm, $12–14\,\mu \times 2–4\,\mu$; the anterior end is pointed and contains some refractile granules, while the posterior end and some of the middle is occupied by a large, homogeneous droplet or globule.

SUBCLASS CNIDOSPORIDIA

The members of this subclass form a recognizable and natural group distinguished by their spores (Fig. 111), which always contain one or more polar capsules; these on a small scale recall the nematocysts of Coelenterata, they are more or less pyriform and contain a long thread coiled spirally on the inner wall. Infection is oral and within the gut the thread is shot out and tethers the spore. The infective body, known as the sporoplasm, hatches in the form, not of a gregarinula as in Telosporidia, but as an amoebula, or a number of amoebulae, and migrates as a planont (the wanderer) to its definitive position in the host.

The planont settles and grows, as a trophozoite, but, again in contrast to what is found in the Telosporidia, there is no distinction between the trophic and reproductive phases and the feeding, growing organism simultaneously forms spores within its body (Fig. 110A). In spite of their interest and importance, much remains to be learned about the Cnidosporidia; the facts of their life-histories are uncertain and disputed. No attempt can be made here to do justice to the many hypotheses which fill the gaps in our knowledge. What is beyond question is that some stages of their development are cellular and it may be that their affinities are not with the Protozoa at all. Very clear introductory accounts will be found in Kudo's *Protozoology* (1954) and Grassé's *Traité* (I. ii). There are three orders:

Order Myxosporidia: with large, bivalve spores, and usually 2 polar capsules (*Myxobolus, Ceratomyxa*).

Order Microsporidia: with tiny spores (3–6 μ long) having a single valve and 1 capsule (*Nosema, Thelohania*).

Order Actinomyxidia: with large spores having 3 valves and 3 polar capsules (*Triactinomyxon*).

ORDER MYXOSPORIDIA

Myxosporidia are parasites of cold-blooded vertebrates, the great majority occurring in fishes, though a few are known from Amphibia and reptiles. The sporoplasm hatches in the gut as an amoebula, makes its way to a suitable site for development and there, while feeding, growing, and multiplying asexually, it sporulates. In general, the degree of injury to the host depends on the site of development. Almost all organs are liable to infection by one or another species, but none is known to develop in the gut lumen. The more primitive forms are coelozoic, occurring especially in the gall- or urinary bladder of fishes (*Ceratomyxa, Leptotheca, Myxoproteus*). It is the histozoic species, occurring in the musculature, gills, or connective tissues, which tend to become highly pathogenic. These so intricately infiltrate the tissues that it becomes difficult to dissociate the parasite from the host in the infected region. *Myxobolus pfeifferi* causes boil disease in cyprinid fishes such as barbel, carp, and tench, and relatively huge tumours, as large as a hen's egg, oozing blood, pus, and myriads of myxosporidian spores, burst from the surface of the dying fish (Fig. 110K). *Myxosoma cerebralis* attacks the cartilage, especially of the head, tail, and fins of salmonid fish, in which it produces spin or twist disease; the distorted and often abnormally pigmented host whirls spasmodically in circles, and, since the disease is almost always fatal, it is easy to understand how, under the crowded conditions of fish rearing, the disintegration of putrefying corpses laden with spores will start epidemics.

The growth of the young organism is accompanied by repeated nuclear division and the resulting plasmodium itself reproduces asexually to form uni- or multinucleate products which spread the infection. Such a plasmodium is syncytial and contains 2 types of nuclei, vegetative nuclei, said to divide amitotically, and reproductive nuclei, which divide mitotically, and are concerned in sporulation. Each of the reproductive nuclei becomes surrounded by its own mass of cytoplasm; the plasmodium is now cellular, having produced a number of internal or endogenous reproductive cells (Fig. 110A). The immediate development of these cells is disputed; it is claimed on the one hand that they give rise to spores directly, and, on the other hand, that they produce gametes, the zygotes from which produce the spores. However that may be, the general course of events in, for example, *Myxobolus pfeifferi*, appears to be as follows (Fig. 110, and see Keysselitz, 1908). A reproductive cell (*rc*) in the interior of the plasmodium divides into a larger and smaller cell and each divides again (A–D). The 2 small cells (*np*) form the wall of the pansporoblast, i.e. the cellular sporulating unit, and they contribute nothing further to the life-history; they are, so to speak, somatic cells, and they eventually die. The 2 large cells are sporoblastic, and each in this disporous species will form 1 spore. The nucleus of each divides into six (E, F). Two of these are cut off to form the spore valves (*vc*). Two form the polar capsules (*pc*), there being 2 of these to each spore. Two remain as those of a binucleate sporoplasm (*spl*), which is the infective body, or germ, contained within the spore (G). There seems to be very little doubt that, either before or after hatching, the 2 nuclei of the sporoplasm fuse; for a lucid account of the various interpretations of this and other (more or less hypothetical) sexual phenomena supposed to occur during the life-history, see Poisson, in Grassé's *Traité* (I. ii).

The mature spore is enclosed within a shell formed by 2 transparent, refringent valves, meeting in a suture which may be straight or curved in a long S (Figs. 110 H–J; 111 D–M). The valves are generally symmetrical and often produced into longer or shorter processes either in front or behind, and their surface may be marked with a pattern. There are usually 2 polar capsules, sometimes 1 or, in *Chloromyxum*, 4, and they are ordinarily placed at one end, called the anterior, of the spore. Freshly collected spores will shoot out their filaments with great rapidity if mixed with a concentrated solution of hydrogen peroxide (Kudo, 1918). The sporoplasm lies behind the capsules and generally fills the rest of the spore; in the Myxobolidae and their relatives it contains a conspicuous vacuole which stains deeply with iodine (Fig. 110 H–I, *iv*). The hardness of the spore* and regularity of its ornamentation make it taxonomically the most useful stage in the life-cycle. For much information, both biological and taxonomic,

---

* The chemical nature of the spore wall (valves) is uncertain. It is certainly very resistant. Kudo (1921) showed that the spore membrane of a microsporidian was 'composed of a substance similar to chitin' and that of a myxosporidian was 'less similar'.

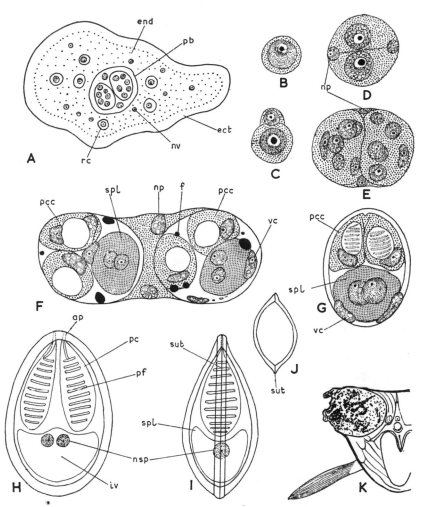

Fig. 110. Sporogony in a Myxosporidian, *Myxobolus pfeifferi*. A, diagram of the components of the growing plasmodium, with its own vegetative nuclei (*nv*), reproductive cells (*rc*), and a developing pansporoblast(*pb*); B, a reproductive (endogenous) cell, divides into 2 (C) and these divide again (D); the 2 smaller cells (*np*) are those of the pansporoblast itself and contribute nothing to the spores; each of the 2 larger cells divides into 6 (E); F, a pansporoblast: in each group of 6 cells, 2 form the valves (*vc*) and 2 the polar capsules (*pcc*) and the remaining 2 nuclei belong to the sporoplasm (*spl*); G, a single spore; H, diagram of fully developed myxosporidian spore (*Myxobolus* sp.); I, the same, from the side; J, T.S. spore; K, section through the body of an infected fish showing a tumour, or 'boil', caused by *Myxobolus pfeifferi*. B–G, ×c. 2,500; other drawings diagrammatic. (A modified after Poisson; B–G, J–K after Keysselitz; H and I after Kudo.)

ap, aperture through which polar filaments are discharged; *ect*, ectoplasm; *end*, endoplasm; *f*, fatty (?) inclusion; *iv*, iodophile vacuole; *np*, nucleus of pansporoblast; *nsp*, nucleus of sporoplasm; *nv*, vegetative nucleus of plasmodium; *pb*, pansporoblast; *pc*, polar capsule; *pcc*, capsulogenous cell; *pf*, polar filament; *rc*, reproductive (endogenous) cell; *spl*, sporoplasm; *sut*, valve suture; *vc*, nucleus of valve cell.

Thélohan's long paper published in 1895 remains a valuable source; see also a general review by Noble (1944) for life-cycles, and, for taxonomy, Kudo (1920, 1933).

Ceratomyxa arcuata Thélohan

Ceratomyxa is a coelozoic genus with some 70 species almost all of which occur in the gall-bladders of marine fishes. It is nearly always disporous (Fig. 111 C, 1), i.e. each parasite produces 2 spores in contrast to the many from each plasmodium of the polysporous *Myxobolus*. The spore valves are laterally drawn out into hollow tapering cones, which, in most cases, are only partly filled by the sporoplasm.

Only a few species have life-cycles that are known but, generalizing from these and from his own studies on *C. blennius*, from *Hypsoblennius gilberti*, Noble (1941) outlined a typical life-history as follows. On germination, the 2 nuclei of the sporoplasm fuse and the uninucleate zygote grows into a multinucleate body, which reproduces asexually by budding and spreads the infection. Sporogony is initiated by a pansporoblast, which may be derived either from a bud or directly from the zygote. This structure eventually comes to have 12 sporoblastic and one or two vegetative nuclei, of which the former divide into 2 groups of 6. The 6 nuclei behave as in *Myxobolus*, 2 forming the spore valves, 2 the polar capsules, and the remaining 2 are sporoblastic. These last are said to be produced by reduction, all other stages being diploid, with 4 chromosomes. Ripe spores are probably liberated through the bile duct into the intestine and thence to the exterior: certainly the spores of species from the bile duct were found in the intestine and faeces of their hosts by Thélohan as long ago as 1895.

C. arcuata is known at Plymouth from *Blennius ocellaris* (butterfly blenny), *Callionymus lyra* (dragonet), *Gadus merlangus* (whiting), *Arnoglossus laterna* (scaldfish), and *Morone labrax* (bass), as well as from fishes obtained off the coasts of France, Italy, and Monaco.*

The living organism

It is essential that freshly killed fish should be examined. The gall-bladder is exposed and the living parasites may be studied in drops of its contents. Infections may be extremely heavy, with thousands of trophozoites present, and from these the young forms, with 2 nuclei, the growing trophozoites, which are multinucleate, and the sporulating forms may be

---

* Thélohan (1895) gives *Onos tricirratus* (Roscoff), *Crenilabrus melops* (Roscoff, Concarneau), *Pagellus centrodontus* (Concarneau), *Scorpoena porcus* (Marseilles, Banyuls), *S. scrofa*; Parisi (1912) gives *Gobius paganellus*, *Chromis* (*Heliases*) *chromis*, and *Pagellus centrodontus*, all from Naples; Jameson (1913) gives *Ophidium vaselli* and *Chromis chromis* at Monaco; it is obviously worth examining these fishes from other waters.

picked out. The spores may be mounted in hydrogen peroxide to extrude the filaments.

The trophic forms are nearly always elongated, with one end much expanded and the other cylindrical or tapering (Fig. 111 A, B). The ectoplasm is hyaline and produces short, conical pseudopodia, always localized and almost always on the expanded surface of the animal; they are used in movement and for attachment to the biliary epithelium, but never for penetration, the parasite being strictly coelozoic in habit. By no means all the parasites are located on the epithelium and in sections of the gall-bladder many will be found occupying the centre of the lumen, in which they apparently swim with freedom. The endoplasm contains oil droplets and also larger globules (up to 2 μ in diameter) of unknown constitution; they are refringent, sometimes arranged with some regularity (B), and are not found in young or sporulating individuals; Thélohan (1895), to whom most of our knowledge of this species is due, thought they were possibly nutritive reserves used by the parasite during sporulation. The Myxosporidia are not phagotrophic and the endoplasm contains no food particles. The trophozoites reach a length of 35 to 40 μ and a breadth of 12 to 15 μ.

The spore (D) is shaped like a broad arc, with the convex side anterior, and the polar capsules lie on either side of the suture. The breadth varies with the degree of development of the lateral processes from 20 to 30 μ, and the length along the suture is 5 to 8 μ. The polar filament when discharged is 25 μ long.

The hosts of *C. arcuata* named above harbour in addition other Myxosporidia and infections of the gall-bladder may be mixed. At Plymouth, the following species of *Ceratomyxa* are recorded as well as *Myxidium*, *Leptotheca*, and *Coccomyxa*. They may be distinguished by their spores as follows (Fig. 111). In *Ceratomyxa* the valves are hollow and conical, attached at the suture by their broad ends and tapering away to the sides. *C. lata* (F): 19×7 μ, crescentic, rounded at the ends (*Microstomus kitt, Capros aper*). *C. truncata* (G): valves bluntly truncated, 25×5 μ, irregular spores with 3 or 4 valves common (*Sardinus pilchardus*). *C. dubia* (H): 17·5×8 μ, ends rounded, almost hemispherical (cf. *Leptotheca*, which this species approaches) (*Cottus bubalis*). *C. appendiculata* (I): 50 μ×5–7 μ, lateral prolongations well developed, the adult trophozoite with long processes extending from the body (*Lophius piscatorius*). *C. sphaerulosa* (J): with enormous spores, 90–100 μ×10–12 μ (*Limanda limanda*). *C. awerinzewi* (K): 26×10 μ, asymmetrical, one end rounded and the other more pointed, both ends bent backwards and bearing a long thread-like process (*Microstomus kitt*). Of the other genera, *Coccomyxa* is distinguished by the possession of only a single polar capsule (Georgevitch, 1926); in *Myxidium* (L) the spores are more or less fusiform; and *Leptotheca* (M) closely resembles *Ceratomyxa*, but has the valves hemispherical or at least very broadly

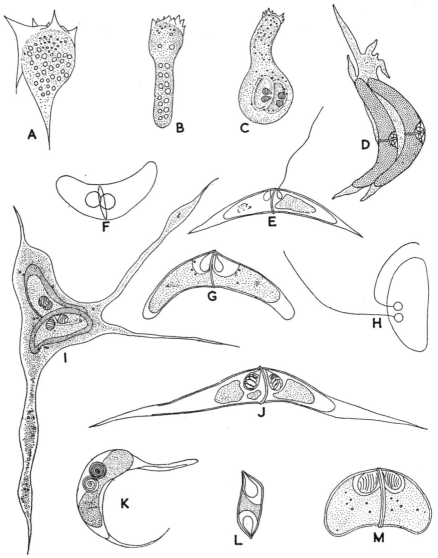

FIG. 111. Myxosporidia from some marine fishes. A–E, *Ceratomyxa arcuata*: A, B, tro-
phozoites; C, D, sporulating individuals; E, spore; F, *C. lata*; G, *C. truncata*; H, *C. dubia*; I,
C. appendiculata sporulating; J, *C. sphaerulosa*; K, *C. awerinzewi*; L, *Myxidium incurvatum*;
M, *Leptotheca informis*. All spores × 1,500 except J, which is × 1000.

(A–C, E, G, I, J, L after Thélohan; D after Parisi; F and H after Dunkerly; K after Reichenow; M after
Auerbach.)

rounded. Most of these species are described in Thélohan (1895), *C. lata* and *C. dubia* are briefly recorded in Dunkerly (1921), and the only description of *C. awerinzewi* is in Doflein and Reichenow, *Lehrbuch der Protozoenkunde* (5th or 6th edn.).

Permanent preparations

Fresh material is fixed in B and sectioned, or smears are fixed in B or S+ A; it is stained in H.H. Fully formed spores are almost impenetrable and the best results are obtained with stages still within the sporulating trophozoite.

IV

CLASS CILIATA

OF all the groups of Protozoa the Ciliata are the most clearly defined, with an underlying unity which is reflected as much in the physiology of their life-cycles as in their morphology; however diverse their structure—and it is beautifully diverse—they form a truly natural group. Further, from the study of their structure and development we can construct for the ciliates as for some metazoan groups a comparative anatomy such as, except in the most fragmentary way, eludes us elsewhere among the Protozoa, and upon it we may establish a classification believed to reflect phylogeny.

The fundamental characters of ciliates are as follows. (1) All possess cilia at some time during their life-histories. (2) There is always a system of subpellicular structures, the kinetosomes, from which the cilia arise, usually associated with cytoplasmic strands called kinetodesmata to form compound morphological units, the kineties. The whole system is the infraciliature and it persists even during stages devoid of superficial cilia. (3) At fission the organism divides to produce 2 daughters, an anterior proter and a posterior opisthe, and morphogenesis occurs in such a way that the daughters are duplicates of each other, but not, as in flagellates, mirror images. This type of division is called homothetigenic, as opposed to the symmetrigenic division of flagellates, and it is usually transverse. (4) There is a pronounced nuclear dimorphism, in which a large, usually single, meganucleus contrasts with one to many much smaller micronuclei, and the 2 types behave very differently during the life-history. (5) The sexual exchange which is the basis of genetic recombination occurs during conjugation and autogamy, and there is never any syngamy of independent gametes. Some of these features occur elsewhere (flagellates, for example, have kinetosomes) and some are not quite universal (a single species of ciliate is known to have monomorphic nuclei) but except in some purely formal sense their combination uniquely typifies the class.

Of all the characters, the cilia themselves are the least remarkable. But cilia are the ordinary organs of locomotion and feeding, and they are the organellae most apparent in the living animals, and they require consideration. Primitively, and still commonly, the ordinary cilia of the body form a complete coat of fine, short, cytoplasmic 'hairs', often emerging from more or less parallel longitudinal furrows which stripe the pellicle. This coat is the somatic ciliature, and when the cilia are all alike or nearly so, the condition is called holotrichous (e.g. Figs. 119, 131). The cilia of a row normally beat in metachronal rhythm, each acting a little behind its anterior neighbour, they are reversible, and in simple cases they assist in feeding as well as locomotion. Somatic cilia are completely lost in adult Suctorida, Chonotrichida, many Peritrichida, and the Entodiniomorphida, and they tend to be sparse and often specialized in the remaining Peritrichida, some Thigmotrichida, and most Spirotricha. It will be seen that not all Holotricha have a holotrichous ciliature and some Heterotrichida do (cf. Figs. 149 and 163).

All cilia arise from subpellicular bodies known as kinetosomes. Stained with Haematoxylin or impregnated with silver, as in most preparations, they appear as solid granules, and they are the 'basal granules' of many authors. In the great majority of ciliates the kinetosomes are arranged in longitudinal lines or meridians, and to the right of each meridian is found a faintly staining line, which does not impregnate with silver, called a kinetodesma or *km* fibre. A row of kinetosomes and its associated kinetodesma constitute a kinety (Fig. 112A and frontispiece). The knowledge that a kinety has a right and left side (the so-called rule of desmodexy pronounced by Chatton and Lwoff, 1935a) may be of practical use in determining the topography of a difficult case, e.g. of sections which cannot otherwise be orientated. The kinety is a useful morphological unit, commonly seen in preparations and in living ciliates, but it is not a necessary one; kinetosomes may occur freely in the cytoplasm in the absence of kinetodesmata or even of cilia (e.g. Suctorida), and the kinetosomes of complex organellae are not simply related to recognizable kinetodesmata. The entire complex of kinetosomes and, where they occur, the kinetodesmata compose the infraciliature.

E.M. studies have now revealed the fine structure of the infraciliature of a few genera, especially *Paramecium* (Metz, Pitelka, and Westphal, 1953; Metz and Westphal, 1954; Sedar and Porter, 1955; Ehrets and Powers, 1959) and a few Spirotricha, notably *Stentor* (Randall, 1956, 1957, 1958; Randall and Jackson, 1958). Both *Stentor* and *Paramecium* are very specialized ciliates and no primitive case has yet been investigated, but the results so far permit the following assertions (Fig. 112 and frontispiece). The free part of a cilium, the part external to the body, like that of a flagellum, consists of 9 peripheral pairs and 1 central pair of fibrillae. The central pair is arrested at the level of the pellicle, where there is a transverse partition (B, *tp*) across the cilium, but the peripheral fibrils extend across the cortex and fuse with each other or with some condensation of the matrix to form the wall of the kinetosome* (cf. C and D). This body, which is seen as a solid granule under the light microscope, is thus really a tube, open at its

---

* *Euplotes* is possibly exceptional in that the central as well as the peripheral fibrillae extend into the kinetosome (Roth, 1957).

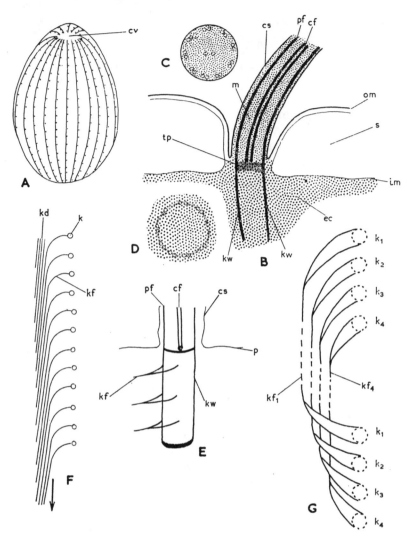

FIG. 112. Infraciliature (cf. frontispiece). A, diagram of simple ciliate, in ventral view, showing kineties, each consisting of a row of kinetosomes with a kinetodesma on its right; B, base of a cilium of *Paramecium*. × 37,500. The 9 peripheral pairs of fibrillae (*pf*) continue below the pellicle to form the wall of the kinetosome (*kw*), the central pair (*cf*) stop at a transverse partition (*tp*), the kinetosome is open at its base; C and D, T.S. cilium and kinetosome; E, kinetosome and proximal part of cilium of *Stentor*, showing mode of attachment of several fibrils (*kf*) from a kinetodesma to a single kinetosome: the base of the latter is closed; F, relations of fibrillae in *Paramecium*, where apparently single fibrils run from the kinetosome (*k*) to the kinetodesma (*kd*) and there overlap their fellows: the fibrillae probably run towards the anterior; G, hypothetical arrangement in *Stentor* of kinetosomes linked by compound fibrils (*kf*) to others below them in the same kinety: such a structure could provide a basis for contractility and a serial effect on the cilia.
(B after Sedar and Porter; E and G after Randall and Jackson.)

cf, central fibrillae; *cs*, ciliary sheath; *cy*, cytostome; *ec*, ectoplasm; *im*, inner pellicular membrane; *k*, kinetosome; *kd*, kinetodesma (or *km* fibre); *kf*, fibril from *k* to *kd* (or *km* fibril); *kw*, wall of kinetosome; *m*, matrix; *om*, outer pellicular membrane; *p*, pellicle; *pf*, peripheral fibrilla; *s*, space, in *Paramecium*, between outer and inner pellicular membranes; *tp*, transverse partition.

inner end (*Paramecium*, B) or closed by a membrane (*Stentor*, E): it does not essentially differ from the root of a flagellum (Pitelka and Schooley, 1958).

The kinetodesmata, which under the light microscope appear as single separate threads, are compound structures linked directly to their kinetosomes. In *Paramecium* (F), a fibril, the *km* fibril, leaves each kinetosome and turns to run longitudinally with its fellows, which together form the *kinetodesma* or *km* fibre. Each fibril runs a course of some 5 interkinetosomatic intervals, tapers and peters out, so that the kinetodesma consists of overlapping fibrils each of which springs from a kinetosome. Such a system could provide the basis for co-ordination if transmission occurred laterally between the fibrils. The latter have a striated appearance owing to the alternation along them of bands of greater and less density. In *Stentor* (see especially the fine description by Randall and Jackson, 1958) the number of *km* fibrils is greater at any level than in a kinetodesma of *Paramecium*, and they occur in sheets to which a kinetosome may contribute more than one fibril (E and G in Fig. 112 are purely diagrammatic; see frontispiece). The kinetodesmata may here be contractile agents. When *Stentor* contracts, the kinetosomes come closer together, and the kinetodesmata, which are visible under the light microscope in the living animal, thicken but remain straight, as if they were shortened. The facts are consistent with a contractile function which would, of course, require 2 points of attachment to be effective: so far the only known attached point of a *km* fibril is a single kinetosome. If the kinetosomatic attachments, seen at different levels, belonged, as suggested in the diagram G, to the same fibril, and if they were serially arranged, the basis for contraction and conduction with a periodic effect, such as is seen in a metachronal wave along a meridian, would be complete.*

Early in the history of ciliates, some of the cilia about the 'mouth', the oral cilia, tended to become specialized for feeding, and in advanced orders, especially where the somatic ciliature is reduced, the oral ciliature, now highly specialized, may recombine the old function of locomotion with that of feeding. The arrangement of the oral ciliature is a cardinal point in taxonomy, and, as it is functionally intelligible only in relation to the rest of the feeding apparatus, all oral structures are here considered together. The terminology to be employed is that expounded by Corliss (1959), which at once economizes in names and expresses homologies† (Fig. 113). The

---

* There are other structures, the *M* bands, in *Stentor*, which may be contractile, but if they are this does not take all contractile function away from the kinetodesmata (p. 348). *M* bands could not account for the periodic excitation of cilia.

† The literature provides a confusing diversity of terms like mouth, gullet, oesophagus, which have been very haphazardly used. When it is considered that some twenty names may be reduced in Corliss's system to five (cytostome, cytopharynx, vestibulum, buccal cavity, buccal overture) it will be seen that the practical reasons for adopting it are as strong as the theoretical one.

simplest existing condition is that seen in some of the rhabdophorine gymnostomes (A) where regularly disposed meridians of typical somatic cilia converge upon an apical cytostome which opens through an unciliated passage, the cytopharynx, to the endoplasm. The trichites of *Holophrya* presumably represent some slight degree of specialization but otherwise the simplicity here encountered is probably primitive. (The astomate, that is, mouthless, condition is always secondary in ciliates.) In the Gymnostomatida the cytostome is always superficial, though it need not be apical (B, and cf. Figs. 121, 122). Wherever it occurs, throughout the class, the cytostome is the true opening into the body, and it marks the limit of the ciliation; any passage beyond it is unciliated and is a cyto-pharynx.

The first complication is the depression of the cytostome to the base of a chamber or passage into which the somatic ciliature is extended without any or with only very slight modification. Such a cavity is called a vestibu-lum (C, D, F); it may lead directly to the cytostome (*Coelosomides*, Fig. 130) or there may be intervening complications (*Paramecium*, Figs. 140, 141). Its distinctive feature is the absence of any specialized oral cilia such as are found in a buccal cavity (see below). In the simplest cases the meridians of the somatic cilia converge upon and turn into the vestibulum without modification (*Coelosomides*), but elsewhere the vestibular cilia may have a distinctive arrangement (Chonotrichida, Figs. 128, 129). The vestibulum is the characteristic oral cavity of the Trichostomatida. A buccal cavity (Fig. 113 E–I) is a more highly evolved and efficient structure than a vestibu-lum, and it is far commoner. It is typified by the presence within it of a specialized oral ciliature, usually in the form of compound organellae. It may open directly to the exterior (*Tetrahymena*, Fig. 137) or from an inter-vening vestibulum (*Paramecium*), or it may be everted and, so to speak, spread out on the surface of the body so that much of the characteristic oral ciliature becomes superficial: the expression 'peristome' or 'peristomial field' is here confined to this type of everted buccal cavity, which is typical of the Spirotricha, though it may occur in some Holotricha (Figs. 113 G–I, 150, 153, 161–71). The opening of the buccal cavity, wherever it may occur, is called the buccal overture.

The ordinary specializations of the ciliature within the buccal cavity are the membranellae and the undulating membrane (UM) or derivatives of them. The UM is simply a line or arc of cilia, set closely in a single row, and more or less permanently coalesced into a membrane; it has nothing whatever to do with the structure of the same name in some Zoomastig na. The UM is set towards the right of the buccal cavity and is generally small (Figs. 137, 168), but in some genera it may be greatly enlarged (Fig. 145). Membranellae are composed of a few, usually 2 or 3, rows of cilia, adhering together like the damp hairs of a house-painter's brush drawn out to a

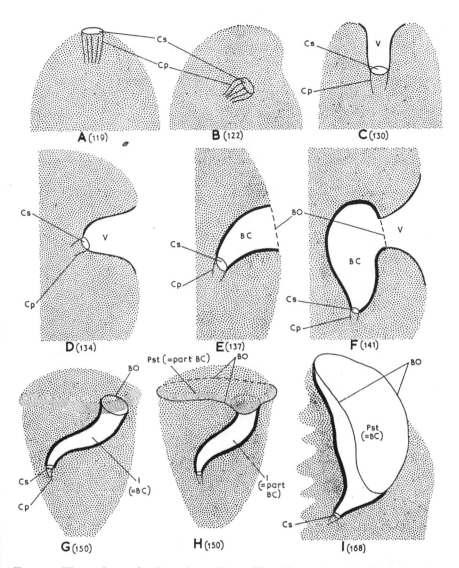

FIG. 113. The oral complex in various ciliates. The ciliature is omitted. The numbers in brackets refer to figures of actual species for comparison. A, B, rhabdophorine and cyrtophorine gymnostomes: the superficial cytostome leads to a cytopharynx; C, D, trichostomes: apical or lateral vestibulum, containing extensions of somatic ciliature, lead to cytostome; E, tetrahymenine hymenostome with buccal cavity, i.e. containing specialized oral cilia; F, peniculine hymenostome, combining vestibulum and buccal cavity; G, H, alternative interpretations of a peritrich (see text, p. 316); I, hypotrich with extensive buccal cavity or peristome. (After Corliss.)

Bc, buccal cavity; *Bo*, buccal overture; *Cp*, cytopharynx; *Cs*, cytostome; *I*, infundibulum; *Pst*, peristome; *V*, vestibulum.

point so that the whole organella beats as a paddle or flap (Fig. 114). They are always arranged in a series which typically, though by no means always, lies to the left of the buccal cavity and beats along a clockwise course towards the cytostome, and this series as a whole is known as the adoral zone of membranellae, usually abbreviated, in writing and in speech, to AZM. The AZM reaches its greatest elaboration in the Spirotricha, where it is consistently clockwise, always conspicuous, and may be the principal or only organ of locomotion as well as of feeding (Figs. 161–71). But it is now well established that a true AZM occurs among the Holotricha, though in this subclass it lacks the stability and never achieves the importance it has in the Spirotricha, but is, in comparison, poorly developed and tends in evolution to break up into specialized tracts or patches of cilia which are sometimes difficult to homologize. *Tetrahymena pyriformis* has what is probably the simplest type of complete buccal cavity among the Holotricha; it is a rather shallow chamber containing a UM on the right and a short AZM of 3 membranellae on the left curving clockwise towards the cytostome, which opens into a cytopharynx (Fig. 137): the buccal overture is superficial. But even within the same order there is great variation. In *Paramecium* the buccal cavity lies below a vestibulum, the membranellae are thought to be represented by the quadrulus and 2 peniculi, and the UM by the endoral membrane (Fig. 141). In *Cyclidium* on the other hand the UM is hypertelic and the AZM vestigial (Fig. 145). In the Thigmotrichida and Peritrichida the membranellae and UM no longer exist as such though there are strong reasons for regarding the oral ciliature of these groups as derived from the tetrahymenal complex (p. 325 f, and see Figs. 146–8, 151, 153, 155).

The structure of the membranellae is best known from the work of Bishop (1925), confirmed and extended by that of Roth (1957) and Randall and Jackson (1958) on the Spirotricha (Fig. 114). The external blade, or lamina (*la*) consists of usually three rows of cilia; apart from their large size they differ from ordinary cilia only in having a covering of minute lateral protuberances serving to hold them together to give coherence to the blade, which has no limiting membrane. The cilia end in rows of very closely set kinetosomes* forming a subpellicular basal plate. From each kinetosome depends a number of fibrillae (about 10 in *Stentor*, giving about 600 to 750 to each membranella) and they converge distally in the form of a fan-shaped lamella (*bl*) leading to a long end-thread, itself composed of continuations of the fibrillae. In section (c) the fibrillae are seen to be arranged very regularly in a hexagonal pattern and they are connected to their neighbours by slight lateral bridges. The end-threads are linked by a basal fibre (*bf*) into which the fibrillae are continued. The entire AZM is thus

---

* There seem to be no differences between kinetosomes of membranellae or simple cilia, except in Hypotrichida (see p. 375).

seen to have a structural continuity which reflects and presumably supports its integrated activity.

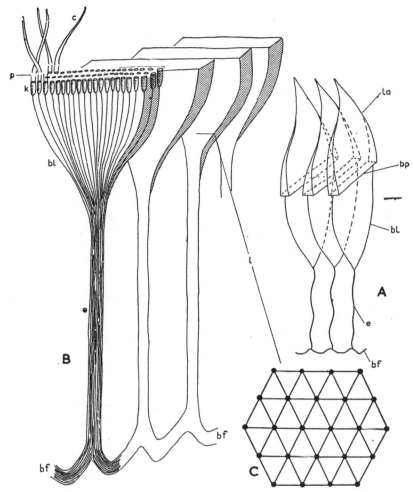

FIG. 114. Membranellae of Spirotricha; diagrammatic. A, 3 membranellae from the AZM of *Spirostomum*; B, part of AZM of *Stentor*, with details: each line from a kineto-some in the basal lamella represents about 10 fibrillae; only a few isolated cilia are shown; C, section through part of basal lamella at the level indicated by *l*. (A, after Bishop; B and C, after Randall and Jackson.)

bf, basal fibre; *bl*, basal lamella; *bp*, basal plate; *c*, cilium; *e*, end-thread; *k*, layer of kinetosomes (basal plate); *l*, level of section shown in C; *la*, lamina; *p*, level of pellicle.

The elements of the infraciliature have been known since the early years of this century, perhaps earlier (see Fig. 120, p. 238), but our realization of the great importance of the system for an understanding not only of structure but also of development and evolution in the ciliates depends from the work of the last 30 years, especially of the French protozoologists Chatton and Lwoff and their pupils (see the general summaries by Fauré-Fremiet, 1948a, and Lwoff, 1950; a preliminary sketch of the characters of the infraciliature was published by Chatton, Lwoff, and Lwoff, in 1929). It is a universal, permanent, autonomous, self-reproducing system. Put more concretely, this is to say that all ciliates have kinetosomes, always have them, and they arise only from pre-existing kinetosomes.* Thus the infraciliature, or more particularly the kinetosomes, form the basis of genetic continuity between the ciliary organellae of one generation and the next. The evidence for these generalizations is to be found in the facts that kinetosomes persist through all stages of the life-histories of ciliates which have been examined, even when all the superficial ciliature has been lost, that areas of proliferating kinetosomes are invariably found in close relation to pre-existing kinetosomes and they always produce orderly arrangements of kinetosomes wherever organellae are developing, and that in good preparations appearances sometimes suggest that kinetosomes are multiplying. It is to be noted that the structure of kinetosomes with attached cilia as seen in electron micrographs (Fig. 112B) does nothing to help us understand how they can divide, and it is unfortunate that as yet no studies have been published showing the composition of the free kinetosomes which participate in morphogenesis. Some applications of these theoretical points must now be considered.

At binary fission the parental structures may persist and be divided between the daughters: the oral structures then go to the anterior daughter, or proter, and new ones are developed for the posterior daughter, or opisthe. Alternatively, more or less extensive dedifferentiation of organellae may occur, when both daughters will need new sets. Similar dedifferentiation, especially of the mouth-parts, may occur at conjugation or during encystation. Although the study of morphogenesis is concerned, of course, with the development of all structures, only ciliary organellae and their derivatives are considered here. Formation of the oral equipment, or stomatogenesis, is of particular importance. In all sufficiently investigated cases the origin of the new ciliary structures for the 'mouth' is found in the infraciliature, and it can be detected very early, usually before any signs of nuclear division.† The pattern of events varies from group to group or

* It is possible but not certain that the curious genus *Cyathodinium* from the caecum of guinea-pigs (*Cavia* spp.) forms the only exception. The parent produces, in 2 internal pouches, the cilia for its daughters, and no free kinetosomes have been described for their early stages; but unfortunately the methods so far used to investigate *Cyathodinium* have not been those known to demonstrate free kinetosomes, if they were present (see Lucas, 1932 *a, b*; Nie, 1950).

† According to Mugard and Lorsignol (1957) stomatogenesis in the hymenostomes *Ophryoglena* and *Deltopylum* does not begin until the micronucleus has reached its anaphase.

within a group but it generally conforms to one of the following types*
(Fig. 115).

I. In very simple cases where the kineties symmetrically surround an
apical cytostome (*Prorodon*), they elongate, the kinetosomes multiply to
lengthen the meridians, and division is a simple transection across all the
kineties equatorially (perkinetally) and so transmits to the daughters the
essential somatic pattern of the infraciliature by dividing it equally between
them (Fig. 115 IA, and cf. IB). The parental mouth remains as that of the
proter and no special ciliary structures are required to equip the opisthe.
Such a straightforward type of morphogenesis is typical of primitive
gymnostomes, and it reappears secondarily, as a result of simplification,
among the Astomatida. Where the cytostome (or vestibulum) is no longer
apical, complicated migrations and reorientations of the rudiments, always
somatic in origin, or of the oral ciliature may be involved (Fig. 135).

II. As in the former class, the kineties elongate during growth, but formation of the new oral structures, whether for one or for both daughters,
depends entirely upon the activity of one or a few neighbouring kineties,
lying in the line of the parental oral apparatus, which they have previously
produced. Such stomatogenic kineties proliferate kinetosomes, which form
a field, at first disorderly but later displaying a regular arrangement (Fig.
115 IIA, IIB). By rearrangement of the kinetosomes within the field, migration, and growth, the stomatogenic field eventually lays the foundation for
the new oral organellae. The method occurs in widely separated groups
of ciliates, e.g. some Hymenostomatida (Fig. 137 E–H) and many Spirotricha (Fig. 163C–F, and, as an extension of the process involving many
ventral kineties, Fig. 162).

Essentially like the foregoing is the modification seen in *Ophryoglena*
(Mugard, 1948). A small number of kineties is interrupted behind the old
oral apparatus, which is resorbed (Fig. 115 IIc). The break extends across
their neighbours until about twenty lines are involved, and the kinetosomes
liberated by this dislocation are the source from which the stomatogenic
field is proliferated. There are in this instance two such fields, one behind
the other, and they provide the mouth-parts for both daughters.

III. Where the ciliature is suppressed in the adult, free or 'erratic'
kinetosomes always persist and it is they which supply the cilia for the
larval phase. In the naked, trophic stages, such kinetosomes are scattered
at random below the pellicle, and in preparation for budding they form a
local concentration within which they assume an orderly arrangement that
is transmitted to the bud (III, and Figs. 125, 126). In the aberrant thigmotrich, *Gargarius*, which also has no cilia in the adult, the kinetosomes persist, but retain throughout life an orderly arrangement. In neither example

* The special or exceptional cases, omitted for lack of space, do not infringe any
general principle here discussed.

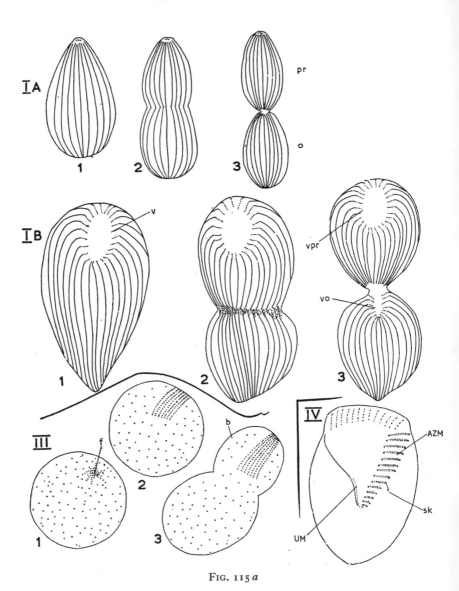

FIG. 115 a

FIG. 115. Types of morphogenesis in ciliates. Diagrammatic: most kineties are represented by single lines though all have the composition shown in IIA, 1. Simple perkinetal
division of kineties between the daughters: if there is a vestibulum (IB) its ciliature is an
extension from the somatic kineties; II, a field (*f*) of kinetosomes is proliferated from one
(IIA) or several (IIB) stomatogenic kineties and becomes organized to form the new buccal
apparatus: the parental buccal structures go to the proter in IIA (a hymenostome) and IIB
(a heterotrich), and in IIc (*Ophryoglena*) the parental structures regress (*pa*) and are replaced from *bpr*, while *bo* provides for the opisthe; II or IV, the parental buccal apparatus
regresses (*pa*) and reforms *in situ* for the proter; the *field* (*f*) migrates posteriorly along the
director meridian (*d*), which is not a kinety, and gives the buccal apparatus for the opisthe:
the condition appears to derive from Type II but in so far as the kinetosomes of *f* are proliferated from the UM in 1 stomatogenesis is autonomous as in Type IV; III, there are no
cilia or kineties in the adult, but a reserve of erratic kinetosomes which produce the field
(*f*) before budding and this is organized to provide the ciliature of the larva (2, 3) (Suctor-

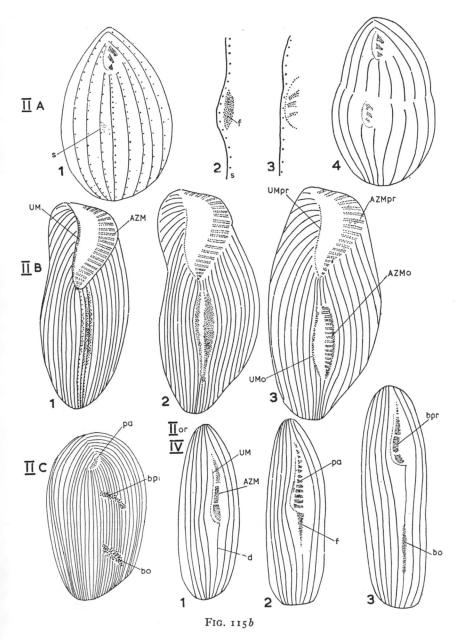

FIG. 115*b*

ida); IV, autonomous stomatogenesis; a single stomatogenic kinetosome (*sk*) produced from the border of the AZM proliferates the infraciliature of the new buccal apparatus (*Euplotes*). For further explanation see text. (Based on Chatton, Lwoff, Lwoff, and Monod; Villeneuve-Brachon; Mugard; Guilcher; Chatton and Séguéla.)

AZM, AZMpr, AZMo, adoral zone of membranellae of parent, proter, and opisthe; *b*, bud; *bo*, *bpr*, buccal apparatus of opisthe and proter; *d*, director meridian; *f*, kinetosomal field; *o*, opisthe; *pa*, parental buccal apparatus in regression; *pr*, proter; *s*, stomatogenic kinety; *sk*, stomatogenic kinetosome; *UM, UMpr, UMo*, undulating membrane of parent, proter, and opisthe; *v, vpr, vo*, vestibulum of pareet, proter, and opisthe.

is there any cytostome, and the neoformations are purely somatic. In the Chonotrichida, which have oral but no somatic cilia, there are nevertheless somatic free kinetosomes, and they contribute a supply to the bud (Fig. 128); the circumstances are very similar to those in Suctorida.

IV. In a number of groups stomatogenesis has independently developed an autonomous nature, the new oral structures being derived from kinetosomes directly provided from parental oral structures. This is obviously so in the Peritrichida, where the only available ciliature is oral (Fig. 154), and in some Spirotricha. In *Paramecium*, the new mouth-parts develop in continuity with the old, as if the oral ciliature had absorbed the functions of a stomatogenic kinety. The Hypotrichida provide some of the most specialized cases known and the entire oral complex of the opisthe may be derived from a single stomatogenic kinetosome arising from the border of the parental AZM (Fig. 170). It is possible that the exceptional and imperfectly understood type of stomatogenesis seen in some Hymenostomatida, such as *Philaster* and *Anophrys*, ought to be included here (Fig. 115, marked II or IV). Mugard (1948) has described how the new oral apparatus is developed from kinetosomes which appear just behind the old one, in close relation to the parental UM, and then differentiate in relation to an unciliated line, the director meridian, which may be a reminiscence of a stomatogenic kinety.

It will be seen from the foregoing that a single order may display several different types of morphogenetic pattern in respect of a single system (e.g. the oral apparatus) and further that the same type of stomatogenesis occurs in different orders. To some extent the classification is unnatural. The various autonomous processes flung together under IV are not strictly comparable or, if they appear to be, they are the end products of different lines of evolution. Yet some resemblances are suggestive. In both the Hymenostomatida and the Spirotricha the simplest type of development, governed by a single stomatogenic kinety, is seen in presumably primitive members (e.g. *Tetrahymena* as compared with *Paramecium*, or such heterotrichs as *Spirostomum* as compared with the Oligotrichida or Hypotrichida), and in both groups this elementary process gives way to one involving a greater number of kineties, or, eventually, the stomatogenic properties are lost from the kineties and incorporated into the oral infraciliature itself, which becomes autonomous. These facts fortify a presumption that there is an affinity between the hymenostomes and the spirotrichs. In more direct ways, morphogenesis may hold the indispensable clue to phylogeny: only during development can the affinities of the Suctorida, the steps leading to the evolution of the Peritrichida, or the position of such a misunderstood genus as *Balantidium*, be correctly apprehended (see pp. 248, 325–8, 264–5).

With the single exception noted below, all ciliates, as far as is known, have at least 2 nuclei; 2 is the usual number, but some species have several and a few have very numerous nuclei. As is well known, they are of 2 kinds, sharply contrasted in form and behaviour. The meganucleus is large, nearly always compact, it divides amitotically and plays no part in sexual processes; at conjugation and autogamy it regresses and is replaced from a product of the micronucleus. There is normally a single meganucleus. In a few forms such as the hypotrich *Stylonychia* there appear to be 2 meganuclei, but they unite before dividing at fission (Summers, 1935), and a similar unification occurs even in *Urostyla grandis*, also a hypotrich, where there are a hundred or so meganuclei or meganuclear components (Raabe, 1946, 1947). There is much variation in gross appearance. The nucleus may be round or oval, elongated and straight or bent within the body, or moniliform, that is, divided by constrictions into nodes (Figs. 126, 131, 132, 150, 158, 161). A particular form may characterize a group (e.g. Peritrichida) or there may be variety within even a genus (cf. A, B, and C, D in Fig. 163). The cytological character of the nucleus is, on the other hand, fairly constant, and in most groups it consists of a dense crowd of F+ granules among which are included F— nucleoli (Fig. 116D, which shows the composition of the nucleus in a young stage). Fauré-Fremiet (1957) has drawn attention to a different type of meganucleus occurring in some gymnostomes and the related Chonotrichida (Figs. 122, 129A); this, the so-called heteromerous nucleus, consists of an orthomere containing basophil granules and some nucleoli, and a pale paramere of karyolymph; both zones are F+, but the granules of the orthomere are much more strongly so than the karyolymph of the paramere. Such a nucleus usually contains a basophil karyosome, which may be F+ or —. The assumption is that deoxyribonucleic acid (DNA) is here distributed in granules, as it generally is in meganuclei, and also diffused in the nuclear sap. All ciliates with heteromerous nuclei are specialized and the condition is regarded as secondary.

Micronuclei are small, may be difficult to detect, and vary considerably in number even within a genus (e.g. *Paramecium*, Fig. 138). At fission they divide mitotically—and it is characteristic of ciliates, as opposed to flagellates, that their nuclei have no division centres (centrioles)—and after meiosis they provide the genetic pronuclei of all sexual processes. No ciliates are known which can survive without a meganucleus, but some are known to have amicronucleate strains that can be maintained for long periods in the laboratory and are fairly common in nature (*Tetrahymena*, p. 278). Obviously such strains can never reproduce sexually nor can they renew their meganuclei from micronuclear sources.

It is usual to ascribe to the micronucleus genetic and to the meganucleus trophic functions. This is a simple generalization and it conveys a simplification of the truth. As only micronuclei undergo meiosis only they can provide a basis for genetical recombination at sexual reproduction. But the partition of function is not clear-cut. The possibility of survival, reproduction, and morphogenesis without micronuclei which exists in some groups (Balamuth 1940; Weisz, 1954) demonstrates that sometimes the meganucleus is adequate for all but the sexual functions of the organism. For instance, in all heterotrichs so far tested, fragments can regenerate only if they contain a portion of the meganucleus, but they do not need a micronucleus. On the other hand, some hypotrichs require both and all amicronucleate fragments are inviable (Weisz, 1954), and this requirement confers on the micronucleus a function that is more than sexual. The meganucleus is known to be genetically active. In *Paramecium* it determines the phenotype; thus, it is possible experimentally to obtain organisms whose nuclei have contrasting genotypes and in these cases the characters are those proposed by the meganucleus (see p. 298). The similarities between the 2 nuclei may be as important as their differences and it must be remembered that the meganucleus originates as a sister of the micronucleus and it carries, at least in the beginning of its life, the same genetic message. According to Moses (1950), both nuclei in *Paramecium* have the same biochemical composition and even when fully differentiated contain the same proportions of DNA, RNA, and protein (about 1 : 2 : 20).

There are grounds for a belief that during its growth the meganucleus becomes a highly polyploid version of the micronucleus, and in doing so it sacrifices the means of organizing a single mitosis capable of controlling its division as a whole. During the budding of some ciliates small portions of the meganucleus are extruded, one to each bud (Figs. 116c; 125) and from these, as from fragments produced at other times, whole meganuclei can be developed. All such portions of meganuclei must be genetically competent, i.e. each must contain a sufficient set of genes to ensure the survival of the owner, and this implies the presence in the parent of as many complete sets of genes. Grell (1953a) has figured early stages in the development of the meganucleus in exconjugants of *Ephelota* and the young nuclei show thread-like bodies duplicating and reduplicating themselves; these are interpreted as the beginnings of polyploidization.

The organization within the nucleus of the many sets of genes it must contain is not easy to understand. There are two possibilities. Each meganucleus may contain very large numbers of genes related to elements which are mingled at random. If the numbers are large, then many different partitions of the nucleus may be imagined which would provide by chance a complete selection of genes to each daughter, though eventually divisions would occur giving defective sets and their products would be inviable. It has been suggested that this ultimate impoverishment of the meganucleus accounts for senescence in some ciliate stocks and for the periodic necessity for renewing the meganucleus from a micronucleus (see p. 300).

On the other hand, such a haphazard means of allocating whole sets of
genes to each daughter might seem insufficient to explain regular regeneration from small fragments, and even more, the cases where an entire
meganucleus is completely and repeatedly exhausted during budding. For
example, the free-living stage of *Tachyblaston ephelotensis*, which is a

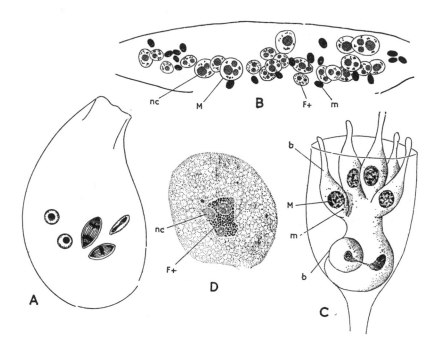

FIG. 116. Nuclei of ciliates. A, *Stephanopogon mesnili*: all the nuclei (usually about 16)
are alike and they divide by promitosis. × 1,250; B, *Trachelocerca margaritata*, with many
dimorphic nuclei; the micronuclei (*m*) are rich in DNA, the meganuclei (M) have nucleoli
(*nc*) rich in RNA and also DNA granules (F+): they do not divide but are replaced by
mitotic divisions of the micronuclei (endomixis). × 500; C, budding in *Tachyblaston
ephelotensis*: the entire parental nucleus is exhausted to give apparently equal nuclei to the
buds. × 1,300; D, the young meganucleus of *Tachyblaston ephelotensis* during growth.
× 1,000. (A after Lwoff; B after Raikov; C and D after Grell.)

b, bud; *F*+, Feulgen positive material; *M*, meganucleus; *m*, micronucleus; *nc*, nucleolus.

suctorian parasitic on another, does not feed or grow, but it buds daughters
(the infective stages of the life-cycle) until it uses up all its substance, including the entire meganucleus (Grell, 1950). It is most difficult to believe
that each small portion of a meganucleus provided to a bud always contains
a complete set of genes (or genome) grasped, so to speak, at random from a
mixed pool of genes in the parent nucleus. Further, the meganuclei of the
buds (Fig. 116c) are all of the same size and they appear to be cytological

equivalents. Again, in *Colpoda steinii*, the meganucleus at division displays regularly 8 small groups of F+ material which are shared by the daughters, and it has been suggested that the whole nucleus is octoploid and each identifiable patch of DNA represents a genome (Piekarski, 1939). In more highly polyploid forms, such as *Paramecium*, the genomes are no longer recognizable as such, but if they exist at all each amitotic division of the whole nucleus may be simply a means of distributing them. Such a supposition leaves unexplained the means by which, after the multiplication which must succeed each autogamy and conjugation, the sets of genes (or chromosomes?) are sorted into complete genomes, but once this is done, further duplication at fission is easier to understand; for example, it has been suggested that the peculiar process of reorganization seen before fission in the meganucleus of hypotrichs (see p. 375) is really a wave of successive mitoses of subnuclei (genomes) passing through the nuclei. The evidence is further discussed by Sonneborn (1947), Grell (1952), Fauré-Fremiet (1953*b*), and Gall (1959).

This remarkable nuclear dimorphism, with its puzzling corollaries, occurs only in ciliates, and the Russian protozoologist, I. B. Raikov (1958, 1959*a*), who has speculated on its origin, believes that it has arisen within the class. For many years it has been known that a single species of gymnostome, *Stephanopogon mesnili*, has only one type of nucleus (Lwoff, 1936). The young have two such nuclei and they divide to give up to 24, usually fewer, in the adult, and their division is promitotic, which is unknown elsewhere among ciliates (Fig. 116A). Raikov himself has described the nuclei of several species of *Trachelocerca*, which are gymnostomes from the interstitial fauna of sand. There are numerous nuclei of both kinds (Fig. 116B) but the meganuclei cannot divide. They possess no more DNA than the micronuclei, they cannot synthesize it or form chromosomes, and they do not multiply. At fission both sorts of nuclei are distributed, and between fissions the micronuclei divide and some of their products become meganuclei and so maintain the number; the provision of meganuclei by purely vegetative divisions of the micronucleus is known as endomixis (see p. 292, footnote) and it occurs in other gymnostomes (e.g. *Loxodes*, Fauré-Fremiet, 1954; Raikov, 1959*a*; *Geleia*, Raikov, 1959*b*). In the fully developed dimorphic condition seen in most ciliates the meganuclei can synthesize DNA and their chromosomes are assumed to divide by an endomitosis to multiply the genomes within the growing nucleus; when the meganucleus divides amitotically, as already suggested, it merely separates the genomes into 2 groups, one for each daughter. Raikov's views are professedly hypothetical. It is not easy to understand why one set of nuclei should first lose and then regain the capacity to synthesize DNA and divide, and the conditions in these gymnostomes might be interpreted as a less successful alternative to, rather than a step in the direction of, the type of dimorphism found in most ciliates, where all nuclei can divide. On the other hand, in their small holding of DNA, large quantity of RNA, and common habit of endomixis, all the nuclei of Raikov's genera, which are taxonomically fairly well separated, are remarkably similar, and his view that he is dealing here with a primitive condition commands respect as a serious attack on a difficult subject.*

The sexual processes of autogamy and conjugation, described below for *Paramecium* (pp. 293, 296), are highly distinctive, and are always followed by a reorganization during which the meganucleus is replaced by a product of the zygotic micronucleus (the syncaryon). No true gametes are produced by ciliates and only the sexual nuclei are exchanged; the highly specialized case of the entodiniid *Cyclopisthium*, which produces strikingly sperm-like bodies with tails as male pronuclei, and which enter their conjugating partners through the mouth, is surely secondary (Dogiel, 1925).

The system of classification adopted here (p. 234) is that proposed by Fauré-Fremiet(1950a) and expounded in a series of papers by Corliss(1956, 1957, 1959†); of these the first discusses the basis of the new arrangement and the last contains a complete key to it: both are indispensable guides. The system is based firmly on the characters of the infraciliature, which is rather more conservative than the ciliation, and takes into account the implications of studies in development, and it claims to sketch in outline, if not yet in detail, a faithful reflection of phylogeny. When it is compared with other systems, such as those very clearly summarized in Hall's *Protozoology* (1953), the principal differences from them are seen to be as follows. (1) The subclass Protociliata is excluded from the class (and the alternative subclass Euciliata automatically disappears) for the reasons discussed on pp. 154–5. (2) Only 2 subclasses, the Holotricha and the Spirotricha, are recognized. (3) The Suctorida, usually regarded in the past as an independent subclass, is reduced to an order among the Holotricha (p. 248). (4) The orders Peritrichida and Chonotrichida are removed from their old positions, which were usually adjacent and either within or very close to the Spirotricha, and they now occupy widely separated places within the Holotricha. The Chonotrichida, like the suctorians, are thought to have diverged early from the gymnostomes (p. 258) and the Peritrichida are seen at the end of a long line of evolution stemming originally from the Hymenostomatida (p. 325).

The grounds on which these and some slighter adjustments to previous

* Besides normal nuclei and the conditions mentioned above, the gymnostomes have the heteromerous nuclei referred to on p. 227, and the peculiar dispersed meganuclei of *Dileptus anser*, the hundred or more fragments of which divide separately (Hayes, 1938). The extreme case is *Centrophorella fistulosa*: it has numerous nuclei and none of them ever divides by any regular method but by fragmentation (Fauré-Fremiet, 1954).

† See also Corliss, J. O. (1961). *The ciliated Protozoa; characterization, classification, and guide to the literature.* London and New York.

systems have been decided are to some extent discussed in the following
pages of this chapter, but it may be helpful here, before introducing an
arrangement of some 5,000 species in 15 orders, to offer a preliminary and
admittedly crude outline of the main constellations seen within the class.
Three stand out, though their composition is not always clear in detail
(Fig. 117).

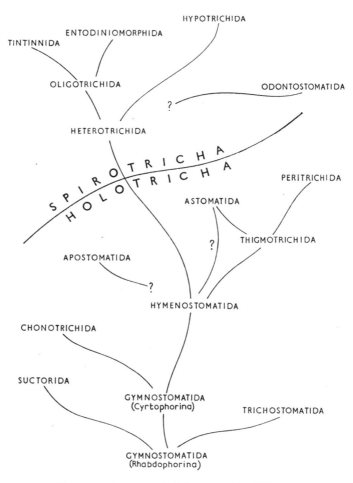

FIG. 117. A proposed phylogeny of the Ciliata.

1. The Gymnostomatida include the most primitive existing ciliates and
their simplicity of structure is shared by the related Trichostomatida,
which are a blind end in evolution. Many gymnostomes develop a set of
characters, which might be called the cyrtophorine facies, which is striking

and easily detected; the dorsal side becomes convex and devoid of cilia or nearly so; the ventral side is flattened and ciliated in a characteristic and asymmetrical pattern, very plainly seen in *Chilodonella* (Fig. 122); most of the kineties are parallel, but those of the right are better developed than those of the left and they turn in an arc in front of the 'mouth' and meet the left field in an oblique suture. None of the ciliates possessing this appearance has any oral apparatus more complex than a vestibulum, and the facies is encountered, not only in the Cyrtophorina, but also in many Chonotrichida and Suctorida and it very strongly suggests a common origin.

2. The rest of the Holotricha either possess a true buccal cavity, however reduced or otherwise modified it may be, or they have secondarily lost it. It seems likely that the tetrahymenal complex of an AZM with 3 membranellae and a small UM is nearest to the ancestral condition (Fig. 137). Within a large group of related orders this complex has undergone very far-reaching modifications and some of these are diagrammatically presented in Fig. 155. The affinities of the Apostomatida are doubtful but they may belong in this large group. It seems certain that the Astomatida do. The best-known members are the hymenostomes, thigmotrichs, and peritrichs.

3. Except for the elusive little order Odontostomatida, the Spirotricha form a natural group; they all show a well-developed AZM and a common tendency to reduce, specialize, or lose the somatic ciliature.

Between these 3 main groups there are existing links. The small organism called *Pseudomicrothorax dubius*, once regarded as a trichostome, is now known to possess a cytopharynx like that of a cyrtophorine gymnostome and at the same time a rudimentary tetrahymenal buccal apparatus, and it firmly ties the first 2 groups together (Corliss, 1958 a, b; Thompson and Corliss, 1958). And the possession of the AZM on the left and UM on the right of the buccal cavity by both the Tetrahymenina and the Spirotricha is thought to reflect, though perhaps rather faintly, an affinity between the two.

The class Ciliata,* then, with the characters defined at the beginning of this chapter, is divided into two unequal subclasses. The Holotricha, usually with a simple somatic and inconspicuous oral ciliature, contains a diverse selection of orders showing great plasticity in form. The Spirotricha is a more compact subclass typified by its dominating AZM contrasting with a somatic ciliature which is often sparse or absent.

* Some authorities (e.g. Corliss, 1956) allocate the class to a separate subphylum, called the Ciliophora, with the same characters as the Ciliata. The Protozoa are not here divided into subphyla.

SUBCLASS I. HOLOTRICHA

Order 1. Gymnostomatida

Suborder i. Rhabdophorina (*Holophrya*)
           ii. Cyrtophorina (*Chilodonella*)

2. Suctorida (*Ephelota, Discophrya*)
3. Chonotrichida (*Spirochona*)
4. Trichostomatida (*Coelosomides, Colpoda, Balantidium*)
5. Hymenostomatida

      i. Tetrahymenina (*Pseudomicrothorax, Tetrahymena*)
     ii. Peniculina (*Paramecium*)
    iii. Pleuronematina (*Pleuronema, Cyclidium*)

6. Thigmotrichida

      i. Arhynchodina (*Kidderia, Ancistrum*)
     ii. Rhynchodina (*Crebricoma, Gargarius*)

7. Peritrichida

      i. Sessilina (*Vorticella, Carchesium, Vaginicola*)
     ii. Mobilina (*Trichodina, Urceolaria*)

8. Astomatida (*Anoplophrya, Hoplitophrya*)
9. Apostomatida (*Gymnodinioides*)

SUBCLASS II. SPIROTRICHA

Order 1. Heterotrichida

Suborder i. Heterotrichina (*Stentor, Spirostomum*)
           ii. Licnophorina (*Licnophora*)

2. Oligotrichida (*Halteria*)
3. Tintinnida (*Tintinnidium*)
4. Entodiniomorphida (*Ophryoscolex, Epidinium*)
5. Hypotrichida (*Kerona, Stylonychia, Euplotes*)
6. Odontostomatida (*Epalxis*)

SUBCLASS HOLOTRICHA

When a fairly simple spirotrich such as *Stentor* (Fig. 161) is compared with a holotrich occupying a central position in the subclass, such as *Tetrahymena* (Fig. 137), the difference between them seems to be no more than one of degree. Both have a holotrichous ciliature in a simple arrangement; both have a buccal cavity, and an AZM. But in *Tetrahymena* the buccal cavity is small and the AZM so tiny that it is exceedingly difficult to observe, while in *Stentor* the cavity is immensely extended on to the oral surface to form a wide peristome and the AZM is the most striking feature of the animal. The Holotricha are correctly defined as ciliates with a small AZM, if any, and the Spirotricha as ciliates with a large AZM, but the definitions do not do justice to many less constant but significant differences. The holotrichs usually retain the somatic ciliature; they show a great variety of form; their oral structures, however developed, are never as elaborate as those of spirotrichs. Within these limits they explore a great number of habitats and assume a wide range of forms among which they break most of the rules that can be invented to confine them.

The main trends within the subclass have already been expressed (pp. 231 f. and Fig. 117). The Gymnostomatida produced in the Trichostomatida, Chonotrichida, and Suctorida specialized orders which have advanced no further, and in the Cyrtophorina a link with the Tetrahymenina. The last suborder stands very centrally within the class: from it there radiated short lines leading to the Peniculina and possibly the Apostomatida, the more significant and sinuous line running through the Thigmotrichida, the Astomatida, and the Peritrichida, and, finally, it is presumed to be near the path which led to the Spirotricha.

ORDER GYMNOSTOMATIDA

Throughout the order the cytostome lies on the surface of the body, no special oral cilia are developed for feeding, and the somatic ciliature is uniform. These are the simplest of the holotrichs and where, as in some members of the Rhabdophorina, the cytostome is apical, the contractile vacuole subterminal, and the ciliary meridians run symmetrically from pole to pole, we discover the living image of a primitive ciliate. Gymnostomes are common and the species are numerous and many of the conspicuous ciliates found in freshwater collections belong to the order. Many classifications recognize 3 groups, the Prostomata, Pleurostomata, and Hypostomata, with the 'mouth' anterior, lateral, and ventral respectively, but a simpler and perhaps more rational arrangement is adopted here from Fauré-Fremiet (1950a). In this 2 suborders are recognized.

Suborder i. Rhabdophorina—the cytostome leads to a cytopharynx supported by articulated trichites in an expansible scaffolding (*Holophrya, Prorodon, Amphileptus, Dileptus*).

Suborder ii. Cyrtophorina—the cytostome, typically ventral, leads to a cytopharynx supported by a rigid pharyngeal basket (*Chilodonella, Nassula*).

SUBORDER RHABDOPHORINA

This is by far the larger suborder and it includes mainly carnivorous gymnostomes which feed through a distensible cytostome and cytopharynx. The latter, which may be extended slightly into occasional lateral diverticula, is supported by skeletal rods, the trichites, which form a sort of circular fence within its wall (Fig. 118). They may help in gripping the prey and they may permit a relatively enormous distension of the cytopharynx, for example, *Didinium nasutum* can devour specimens of *Paramecium* several times larger than itself (Mast, 1909, and see Kahl, 1927). In addition, trichocysts are common about the cytostome, and are also used in attack. The suborder includes not only the large carnivores, but also the truly primitive symmetrical forms like *Holophrya*; further, the mode of stomatogenesis is probably always primitive with all meridians equipotential. Nevertheless, the rhabdophorine gymnostomes seem to have given rise only to such evolutionary cul-de-sacs as the Trichostomatida and the Suctorida and the more fertile suborder of the Cyrtophorina. The common

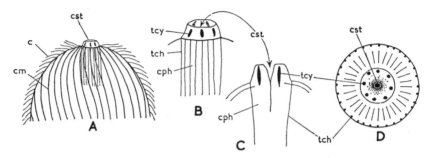

FIG. 118. *Balanophrya* (*Holophrya*) *mamillata* Kahl, a simple gymnostome, differing from the true *Holophrya* only in that the cytostome is borne on an unciliated, truncated, conical process. A, anterior end, showing cytostome and behind it, internally, the cytopharynx supported by a delicate curtain of trichites; B, cytostome and cytopharynx; C, the same, in L.S.; D, frontal view of the anterior end. (After Kahl, modified.)

c, cilium; *cm*, ciliary meridian; *cph*, cytopharynx; *cst*, cytostome; *tch*, trichite; *tcy*, trichocyst

genera (which include *Spathidium*, *Coleps*, *Lacrymaria*, *Amphileptus*, *Dileptus*, *Lionotus*, *Loxophyllum*, *Loxodes*) are usually well figured in textbooks, but for specific identification Kahl (1935) is indispensable.

Holophrya nigricans Lauterborn

This large species was described by Lauterborn in 1894 and more fully in 1908. It is pelagic in freshwater pools, where it feeds voraciously on dinoflagellates and other Mastigophora, which are conspicuous in its endoplasm. The other members of the genus do not depart significantly from it in structure, except that a few terminal cilia may be elongated as a steering tuft (cf. Fig. 121A, *rc*), and in some the cytopharynx may be obliquely set, slanting from the apical cytostome at an angle to the axis (Kahl, 1935; Penard, 1922).

The living organism

H. nigricans, like other species of *Holophrya*, is an active swimmer and is best observed after mounting in methyl cellulose. The body is shaped like a fat gooseberry, broadly rounded behind and very slightly truncated in front (Fig. 119), and measures 110–180 $\mu \times$ 100–150 μ. From the apical cytostome radiate evenly spaced ciliary meridians which converge on the aboral pole. The pellicle is sculptured by longitudinal and transverse

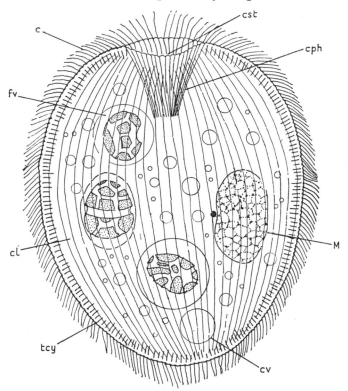

FIG. 119. *Holophrya nigricans.* $\times c.$ 650. (After Lauterborn.)

c, cilia; *cl*, ciliary line; *cph*, cytopharynx, supported by trichites; *cst*, cyto-stome; *cv*, contractile vacuole; *fv*, food vacuole; *M*, meganucleus: the micro-nucleus lies just to the left; *tcy*, trichocysts.

ridges into fields from each of which emerges a cilium. The cytostome is wide and circular and leads into a shallow, funnel-shaped cytopharynx, supported by a fence of delicate trichites. The clear ectoplasm, with nume-rous regularly disposed trichocysts, is plainly set off from the greyish endo-plasm, which is usually crowded with food inclusions. The contractile vacuole is terminal or nearly so. The meganucleus is ellipsoidal or slightly kidney-shaped; the micronucleus lies against it in a small bay. Almost nothing is known of the life-history and neither conjugation nor encysta-tion has been described.

Permanent preparations

The living animal best displays most of the structure, but S+A followed by D.H. will show the nuclei, and Ag preparations the infraciliature (p. 443).

Prorodon teres Ehrenberg

The widely distributed genus *Prorodon* is perhaps more commonly encountered than *Holophrya* and it has been more thoroughly studied.

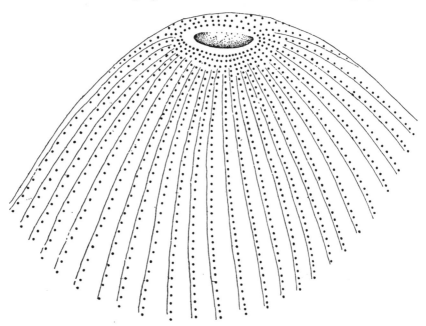

FIG. 120. *Prorodon teres*, showing the infraciliature of the anterior end as given by Maier in 1903.

Though still relatively primitive it shows slight but unmistakable signs of specialization. The mouth is no longer circular, but slit-like, the cytopharynx oval, and its trichites double (Fig. 121C). A few slightly stiffened cilia bend over the cytostome; set apart from them 3 rows of closely set cilia, the dorsal brush, mark the conventional dorsal side; posteriorly a few long cilia trail behind as a rudder; but otherwise the ciliature is regular and holotrichous (A, B). A beautiful drawing by Maier, published in 1903, plainly shows the orderly disposition of the kinetosomes and their accompanying kinetodesmata, and must be among the earliest illustrations of kineties (Fig. 120). There are many species, difficult to determine, typically found in fresh water but extending into brackish water and perhaps the sea.* *P. teres* is closely allied to other common species, especially *P. platyodon* and *P. griseus*, and it is very probable that the following general description applies to the whole *P. teres* group of species. For structure and taxonomy see Kahl (1927, 1935) and Penard (1922); the trichocysts have been well studied, first by Krüger (1934) and then with the electron microscope by Wohlfarth-Bottermann and Pfefferkorn (1952–3); the natural history and life-cycle of *P. griseus* were given by Tannreuther in 1926.

P. teres and its immediate relatives are common in ponds and rain-pools where they readily encyst, and they may appear among water-weed left standing for a few days in the laboratory

The living organism

Shape is important in classification and the animal must first be examined swimming freely in an uncovered drop of water and only later should this be mixed with methyl cellulose for high-power work. *P. teres* is very active and feeds on bacteria, starch grains, zoochlorellae, and small nematodes, but apparently it does not attack any sizeable prey; local strains may show their own food preferences.

The ciliate, 130 to 200 μ in length, resembles *Holophrya* but is more elongated, and the anterior end, rather truncated, is set a little askew. In animals undistorted by over-feeding, there is a slight lateral flattening of the anterior half of the body and an equally slight waist about the middle (Fig. 121A). The posterior end is round in section, and dome-shaped. The whole animal is covered with a uniform holotrichous coat of cilia, of which there are said to be about 11,600 in all (Wetzel, 1925). The somewhat stiffer cilia about the cytostome bend over it; nearby, a few closely set rows lie among the normal meridians and they form the so-called dorsal brush, in which the cilia point away from the cytostome (B). Posteriorly there is a little rudder of longer cilia. None of these ciliary specializations is more than slight.

The cytostome is a slit lying just out of the apex. The cytopharynx has a thickened wall and is supported by about 50 conspicuous double trichites (A–C). The contractile vacuole is terminal with lateral canals and may receive accessory vacuoles. The meganucleus is ellipsoidal, with clear, homogeneous ovoid bodies lying in a granular matrix. Alongside it lies the slim, long micronucleus, pointed at one end, rounded at the other. The trichocysts of *Prorodon* are pale rodlets lying below the pellicle and are admittedly most difficult to observe.

P. griseus encysts readily (Fig. 121D) and indeed cysts may be commoner

* The marine forms are not well known; according to Kahl (1935) the ciliate well described by Fauré-Fremiet (1924) and called by him *Prorodon marinus* belongs eslewhere, perhaps in the genus *Pseudoprorodon*.

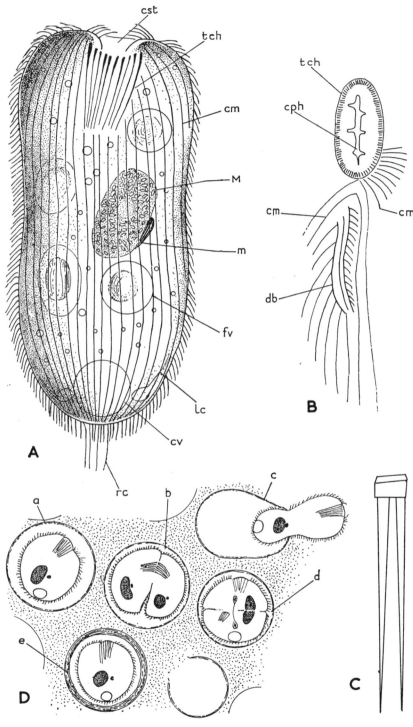

FIG. 121

in nature than the free ciliates (Tannreuther, 1926). The animal contracts, becomes spherical, and rotates while secreting its cyst wall; this is thin for temporary and thick for 'permanent' cysts. The former take about half an hour to form and contain animals which remain active; the latter take 3 to 5 hours and contain quiescent animals. Excystation, at least from permanent cysts, is preceded by the secretion of some substance that weakens the wall and the animal escapes by bursting through it.

Binary fission takes place either in the encysted or free stage and the new cytopharyngeal structures are laid down before division. If a cytopharynx is removed by cutting, tips of the new trichites appear in a ring within 4 to 6 hours and the rest of these organellae grow back from them, seemingly as at division (MacDougall, 1925); unfortunately nothing is known of the role of the infraciliature in either division or regeneration. Conjugation has been described by Tannreuther (1926).

Permanent preparations

As for *Holophrya*.

SUBORDER CYRTOPHORINA

This is a smaller and more specialized group than the foregoing and yet of great evolutionary importance, for the ancestors of the Hymenostomatida (and hence of the great majority of ciliates) were probably cyrtophorine gymnostomes. The cytostome has shifted from its anterior position on to one surface, now definitively ventral, of the animal, and the cytopharynx is supported by a non-expansible basket of fused trichites (Fig. 122). All species are herbivorous. There is a tendency for the cilia to be confined to the ventral surface, and even on this they may be reduced in number and simplified in arrangement. Some of the cilia near the mouth may adhere to compose a membrane, but no elaborate feeding organellae occur. In morphogenesis some specialization in the competence of the kineties is an advance upon the rhabdophorine state (see p. 244). The cyrtophorines are striking animals, usually occurring in fresh to brackish water; some are marine; some are ectocommensal on the gills and integuments of aquatic animals (see, for example, Kidder and Summers, 1935) and on the gills

---

FIG. 121. *Prorodon*. A, *P. teres*. ×c. 750; B, *P. platyodon*, view of the cytostome and dorsal ciliation; cilia are shown only on the right hand of the 3 short rows constituting the dorsal brush (*db*); C, double trichite; D, cysts of *P. griseus*. (A, B, and C after Kahl, A extensively redrawn; D after Tannreuther.)

a, temporary cyst; *b*, conjugation in cyst; *c*, hatching; *cm*, ciliary meridian; *cph*, cytopharyngeal lumen; *cst*, cytostome; *cv*, contractile vacuole; *d*, binary fission in cyst; *db*, dorsal brush (the guideline ends on the left-hand row); *e*, permanent cyst; *fv*, food vacuole; *lc*, lateral canal with accessory contractile vacuole; *M*, meganucleus; *m*, micronucleus; *rc*, 'rudder' cilia; *tch*, trichites (in A seen laterally, in B, the heads embedded in the cytopharyngeal wall).

of woodlice (Matthes, 1950). *Chilodonella* and *Nassula* are perhaps the best-known genera.

*Chilodonella** cucullulus* (O. F. Müller)

C. cucullulus is the largest and in many localities the commonest species. It occurs in fresh and brackish water, especially with a high organic content, as provided by decaying plant material, and here it feeds on bacteria and filamentous algae; it is often found in association with the 'sulphur bacterium', *Beggiatoa*, which is really a colourless blue-green alga oxidizing H_2S. Some account of the morphology will be found in Penard (1922) and Kahl (1935); conjugation has been described by Ivanić (1933 *a*, *b*), and fission by Fauré-Fremiet (1950*b*). Species of *Chilodonella* illustrate the cyrtophorine facies referred to on p. 232.

The living organism

The animal is extremely plastic and easily deformed as it passes against obstructions and its true form will be understood only by viewing it from all angles in an uncovered drop of water; this may be subsequently mixed with methyl cellulose before high-power examination.

The body (Fig. 122 A, B) is more or less oval, rather blunt anteriorly, with the right side slightly convex and the left slightly concave; the curve of the right side sweeps round the front to join the left in a beak, marking the left anterior point. The shape varies with nutrition and well-fed animals may be oval with a scarcely perceptible beak. The ventral surface is flat, ciliated, and, of course, bears the cytostome. The naked dorsal surface is flat in front for about a quarter or third of its area and then rises to a dome over the rest of the body. The total length is usually between 130 and 150 μ, but specimens up to 300 μ have been recorded.

The ventral ciliature is complete (cf. *C. uncinata*, Fig. 122c and p. 245). There are 19 or 20 kineties. Of these, 3 (the stomatogenic kineties marked *1, 2, 3* in Fig. 123) run a straight course down the middle from the cytostome. To the left, 8 or 9 run more or less parallel to the side of the body. To the right, 8 or 9 run parallel to that side as far as the level of the cytostome and then curve in front of it to meet the kineties of the left side in an oblique seam, which passes from the beak to the cytostome and bears somewhat longer cilia than found elsewhere. As they pass from right to left in front of the cytostome the 3 rows of cilia nearest to it dip into a slight concavity and here they tend to fuse into membranes; in this arrangement

---

• = *Chilodon* in the older books. This was Ehrenberg's name for the genus and it remained in use for nearly a century before Strand observed that it was preoccupied by a mollusc and introduced the present and accepted form.

there is detected a slight foreshadowing of a vestibulum. The dorsal surface is not quite devoid of cilia; just in front of the dome it carries a dorsal brush of stiff cilia, suggesting setae, in a single transverse row (Fig. 122B, *db*); the brush, which is not easy to detect, runs from the midline outwards

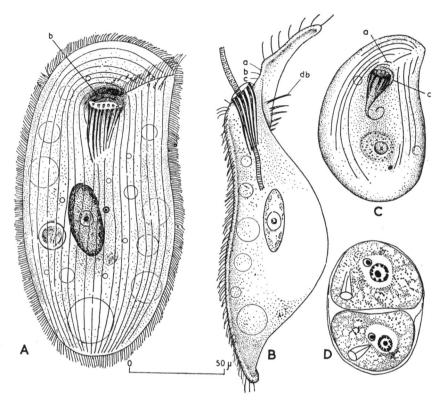

FIG. 122. *Chilodonella.* × 500. A and B, *C. cucullulus*: A, from the ventral side; B, from the left, the organism feeding on a filamentous alga; C and D, *C. uncinata*: C, from the ventral side; D, cyst. (A and B composite, mainly from Kahl and Penard, with ciliature from Fauré-Fremiet; C after Chatton *et al.*, modified, with additions; D after Ivanić.)

a, *b*, and *c*, pre-oral and circumoral cilia or ciliary lines; *db*, dorsal brush.

and slightly backwards and its cilia are very short at the inner end and grow progressively longer towards the outer end.

The cytostome lies in the anterior third of the body in the slight concavity bearing the membranes already mentioned. The cytopharynx is supported by 12 to 15 trichites, held together in a membrane, incapable of distension, but slightly protrusible from the cytostomal pit. The trichites are short, strong, embedded in the cytopharyngeal wall, and turning dorsally and slightly to the left towards their ends, where they are abruptly truncated; the whole structure is oval in transverse section. MacDougall (1925) found that the cytopharyngeal basket of *C. uncinata* was soluble in HCl and pepsin and concluded that it was proteinaceous.

The meganucleus is ellipsoidal and lies near the middle of the body. Like that of all species of *Chilodonella* it has a conspicuous karysome, containing a central granule, and heavier masses of material lying against the membrane. This is the heteromerous type of meganucleus referred to on

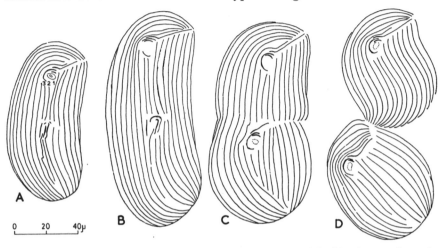

FIG. 123. *Chilodonella cucullulus*: fission and stomatogenesis. The kineties are shown by lines. A, elongation of the organism: the 3 stomatogenic kineties are interrupted; B, the cytostome of the proter has disappeared and the short isolated lengths of the stomatogenic kineties begin to arrange themselves to form the pre-oral ciliature of the opisthe; C, the cytostome of the opisthe has appeared and the definitive disposition of its pre-oral ciliature is evident: the transverse (perkinetal) cleavage of the kineties of the left-hand side is clearly seen; D, last stages of fission. (After Fauré-Fremiet.)

1, 2, and *3*, left, central, and right stomatogenic kineties, marked in A.

p. 227; in *C. uncinata* (c), where the granular material is more evenly distributed, Seshachar (1950) found that the karyosome was slightly and the granules heavily supplied with F+ substance. The micronucleus is spherical. There are 6 to 12 contractile vacuoles and one of them, larger than the others, tends to take up a terminal position.

It seems likely that *C. cucullulus*, like other members of its genus, encysts (p. 245), but no information is available.

Division is perkinetal, that is, the line of fission cuts through all the kineties, roughly supplying half a length of each to each daughter, but there is some degree of specialization in stomatogenesis (Fauré-Fremiet, 1950b). As the organism elongates to divide (Fig. 123) each of the 3 median kineties is interrupted behind the cytostome so as to liberate short lengths of some 10 to 12 μ, and these are rearranged to provide the 3 kineties in front of the cytostome of the opisthe generating the pre-oral (or circumoral) membranes and the adoral kinety which marks the seam; this last is no more than an outgrowth of the most anterior of the 3 pre-oral kineties. Early in division the cytopharyngeal basket has disappeared and a new one is generated in each daughter.

For conjugation see Ivanić (1933 *a, b*); here again the cytopharyngeal basket is dissolved and a replacement constructed for each exconjugant.

Permanent preparations

S+A followed by H.H. is the standard method, but fixation with Champy should be tried. For the infraciliature, the Chatton-Lwoff method (p. 443) is indispensable.

Culture

MacDougall (1925) successfully cultivated *C. uncinata* on Hogue's medium as follows. Add 2 eggs to 400 ml Locke's solution (p. 405). Boil over a bath for 15 minutes, filter through cotton-wool, sterilize. Add 1 part of this solution to a further 10 parts of Locke's solution plus 10 parts of distilled water, distribute in suitable small vessels and add more distilled water when the medium becomes cloudy with bacteria.

Chilodonella uncinata (Ehrenberg)

This smaller and more specialized species is sometimes commoner than *C. cucullulus* in similar habitats. The general morphology was studied by MacDougall (1925), who also gave an account of conjugation; a precise map of the infraciliature was given by Chatton, Lwoff, Lwoff, and Monod (1931*b*), who described its continuity during fission.

C. uncinata (Fig. 122C) is usually from 50 to 90 μ long, though considerably smaller forms occur. Apart from a dorsal brush of 6 to 8 setose cilia, cilia are restricted to a few clearly defined ventral kineties. There are 2 circumoral and 1 pre-oral kineties, and a continuation of the last forms the strongly ciliated seam towards which the kineties of the left and right converge. These are, on the left, 5, of which the outermost is short and anterior and the innermost short and posterior, with 3 long parallel lines of cilia between them, and on the right, 4 long parallel curving lines and a shorter anterior line. The cytopharyngeal basket is supported by 8 to 12, usually 10, trichites converging towards the posterior end, which, when at rest, winds in a curl, straightened when feeding. There are usually 2 contractile vacuoles. *C. uncinata* forms multiplication cysts (D) in which, after nuclear reorganization which may be a type of endomixis, the organism divides into 2 daughters, the cytopharyngeal basket degenerating and forming in each *de novo* (Ivanić, 1928, 1933*c*).

MacDougall (1925) found that larger ciliates, which were tetraploid, arose spontaneously in her cultures, and they became dominant; she gave some account of these and also (1929, 1931) of radiation-produced mutants in this species.

For accounts of other members of the genus see MacDougall (1936).

Culture and permanent preparations

See under *C. cucullulus*.

ORDER SUCTORIDA

This aberrant order consists of a number of highly characteristic ciliates which cannot possibly be confused with any other animals (Figs. 124–7). The adult stage, which is that usually observed, is always sessile, directly, or by means of a stalk; it never has cilia, though kinetosomes are scattered at random beneath the pellicle; it always bears, evenly distributed or in small groups, a number of tentacles with which it captures and ingests its prey, which is nearly always another ciliate; there is no mouth. The body is ovoid or globular, or may be lobed, sometimes extensively. There are one or several contractile vacuoles. In this striking phase, the only ciliate character is the dimorphism of the nuclei, and that is difficult to verify on account of the small size of the micronuclei, which vary very much in number. The meganucleus is compact and regular in young animals, but it tends to branch, and when the body is lobed, lobes of the meganucleus extend into its divisions (e.g. *Dendrosomides*, and see Fig. 125B). The tentacles are contractile and of 2 sorts: the commonest (Fig. 126A) are capitate and hollow, with a pellicular covering, a cortical layer, and a longitudinally striated wall to the internal canal—a structure described by Collin in 1912 and since confirmed by E.M. studies (Rudzinska and Porter, 1954; Rouiller, Fauré-Fremiet, and Gauchery, 1956); such tentacles can capture and suck the contents of prey down into the body (p. 251). Less common are prehensile organs, more like the axopodia of Heliozoa than tentacles; they are long, solid, sharp, needle-like, with a fibrillar core instead of a canal (e.g. some of the 'tentacles' of *Ephelota*). The stalk, if present, is never contractile; it is secreted, like that of the Peritrichida, by a specialized region at the anterior end of the larva, the scopula (Fig. 125, s, and pp. 248, 254).

The ordinary method of reproduction of Suctorida is budding, which produces a ciliated larva. This free-swimming stage is the only means of distribution; its structure affords the only clue to the affinities of the order; and the means of budding is important in taxonomy. The commonest method is internal budding (endogenous gemmation), as in *Tokophrya infusionum* (Guilcher, 1951, and see Fig. 124). The apical surface of the parent is invaginated to form a brood chamber (*bc*) lined with ectoplasm. The irregular scattering of kinetosomes in the floor of the chamber becomes aligned in rows, and the floor rises in a mound which will be constricted off as the embryo (c). At the same time it receives part of the meganucleus and a product of a micronuclear division. Cilia are sprouted from the lines of kinetosomes and the young larva, after living for a short while in the brood chamber, escapes through a birth pore. External budding

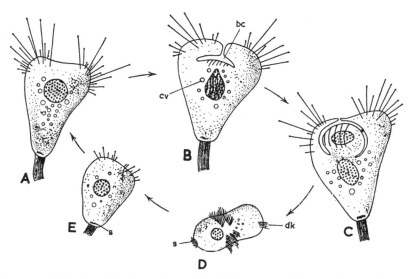

FIG. 124. *Tokophrya infusionum*: internal budding. A, trophic suctorian; B, formation of brood chamber and beginning of bud (the lines on its surface indicate the arrangement of kinetosomes); C, development of bud; D, larva; E, young suctorian. (After Guilcher.)

bc, brood chamber; *cv*, contractile vacuole; *dk*, divergent kinety; *s*, scopula.

(exogenous gemmation) is not essentially different except that the buds are produced as superficial outgrowths of the parent and there is no brood chamber (Fig. 125 A–C; and see Grell, 1950, who gives a fine description of budding during the life-history of *Tachyblaston*, a suctorian itself parasitic on *Ephelota*, Fig. 116C). Both types of budding may be multiple. A third and more involved method occurs in *Discophrya piriformis* and is described below (p. 252). In certain circumstances, usually unfavourable, the entire body of the adult may be converted into a free-swimming stage.

The larva (sometimes called the swarmer, or embryo) is usually elongated and often more or less flattened. The end usually in front during movement is called anterior and is marked by the scopula, and when, as often happens, the cilia are confined to one surface, this is called ventral. The cilia do not in fact form the circles sometimes described. They may be arranged in incomplete arcs behind the scopula, often more resembling a ventral horse-shoe, with one arm, the right, better developed than the other (Figs. 125D; 126E). The foregoing constitute the primary field of cilia; behind them may lie a secondary field (*sf* or k_2); in *Ephelota* these develop in continuity with the right arm of the primary field, become detached from it, move into a more central position, and their anterior kinetosomes turn into a ventral depression behind the scopula, where they possibly represent a vestige of a buccal ciliature (Guilcher, 1948). A small patch of isolated cilia, forming the so-called divergent kinety, may be present. The scopula is a group of close-set cilia at the anterior tip of the larva of *Tokophrya* (Fig. 124D, *s*) but more often it is in an antero-ventral position, within the loop of the primary field of cilia (Figs. 125D; 126E). It is by means of the scopula that the larva settles and secretes its stalk.

The light thrown by the study of larval structure upon the affinities of the Suctorida is a dim one. Yet two points emerge fairly clearly. There are, strictly speaking, no kineties, but only rows of kinetosomes, and these always conform to a simple, holotrichous pattern of parallel lines. Secondly, one repeatedly observes, from one larva to another, a tendency for the ventral ciliature of the larva to develop asymmetrically, and the asymmetry is precisely that seen in the cyrtophorine gymnostomes. Many groups have been considered as possible ancestors for the Suctorida (see Collin, 1912; Fauré-Fremiet and Guilcher, 1947) including the Thigmotrichida and the Peritrichida; but these are highly specialized orders and the common characters are as likely as not convergent. It is hard, in the face of so widespread a ciliary pattern as that here described for the larvae of *Discophrya* and *Ephelota* (and see, for reinforcement, Guilcher, 1951), to deny the suctorians a place among the Holotricha and with a remote gymnostome ancestry. A primitive origin is consistent with the interpretation of some of the nuclear phenomena referred to on p. 228 and discussed by Grell (1952, 1953a).

The larva has no mouth and its life is short, rarely more than a few hours. 'A free-swimming larva of *Tokophrya lemnarum* utilizes its few moments of liberty only to affix itself to some substrate as quickly as possible, a goal which is usually attained in less than a minute and within a few millimetres of its parent' (Noble, 1932). The larva settles by its scopula, which secretes a cement fixing it to the substratum, and the stalk is produced, within a few minutes or a few hours, apparently in the same way as in the Peritrichida (p. 320). The cilia are immobilized and regress from the apical pole downwards; their kinetosomes disperse and leave no trace in the adult of their orderly larval arrangement. In some cases a few tentacles appear before the larva settles, but usually they form later; they grow out as small protuberances which form suckers and then increase in length. The Kormoses (1957b) contend that the position of the ciliary girdle in the

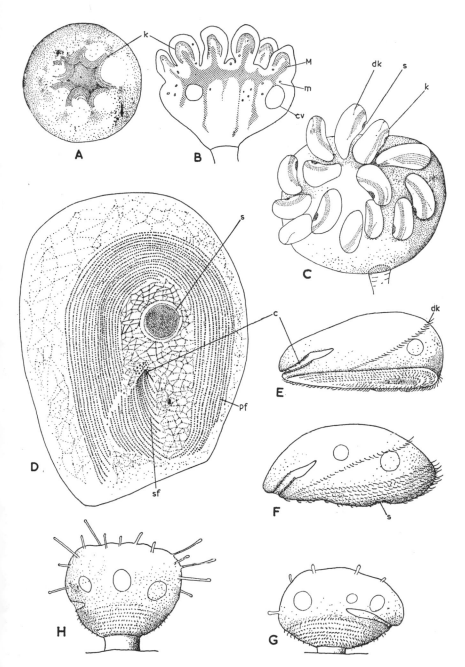

FIG. 125. *Ephelota gemmipara*: asexual cycle. A, surface of parent showing bud rudiments with ordered kinetosomes (*k*) after Ag impregnation. ×800; B, optical section of budding suctorian. ×250; C, external buds on surface of parent after Ag impregnation. ×800; D, larva in ventral view (Ag impregnation). ×1,000; E–H, larva and metamorphosis in lateral view. ×650. (A, C, D after Guilcher; B, E–H after Collin.)

c, vestige of cytostome (?); *cv*, contractile vacuole; *dk*, divergent kinety; *k*, kinetosomes of larva; *M*, meganucleus; *m*, micronucleus; *pf*, primary field of kinetosomes; *s*, scopula; *sf*, secondary field of kinetosomes.

larva of *Podophrya* determines the site at which the adult will eventually produce its buds.

Suctorians reproduce sexually by conjugation between neighbours. The conjugants may be of similar size, or one may be conspicuously larger than the other (macro- and micro-conjugants), again as in the sessile Peritrichida. Normally there is only a temporary union between conjugants, as in most ciliates, but sometimes, as in *Lernaeophrya capitata*, fusion is permanent so that only a single animal remains after conjugation. Descriptions, including examples of the variations mentioned, will be found in Noble (1932), Gönnert (1935), and Grell (1953*a*), the last with excellent illustrations of the nuclear phenomena, which are of special interest as they suggest early stages in the evolution of meganuclear polyploidy (p. 228), and in papers by the Kormoses (1957*a*, 1958).

In 1912 Collin published a memoir on the Suctorida which is still the main source of our knowledge of their biology and taxonomy, but to this the modern work of Guilcher, dealing especially with morphogenesis and the structure of the larvae, and summarized by her in 1951, is an indispensable complement.

Discophrya piriformis Guilcher

This animal, which is probably fairly common in fresh water, was originally described by Guilcher (1947) from material found among macerating aquatic plants. It is easy to cultivate, being remarkably resistant to fluctuations in pH, temperature, and other external factors; it has been well investigated by modern methods (Guilcher, 1951); it is now thought to be the organism used by Kitching (1951, 1952 *a, b,* 1954 *a–d*) in his important studies on the physiology of suctorians, and further, is very likely that studied by Root (1914). The following account assumes that the results of Guilcher, Kitching, and Root all apply to the same organism.*

The living organism

D. piriformis is most easily studied in culture (p. 255), where it feeds freely and reproduces rapidly by budding. The body is ovoid or pyriform, mounted on a non-contractile stalk attached by a disk to the substratum, and is covered by some 30 to 60 tentacles, sticking out from it like pins from a pin-cushion (Fig. 126A). It measures normally some $50 \times 40 \, \mu$, but may be much larger after feeding; the stalk is about $50 \, \mu$ long and does not

---

* Root called his animal *Podophrya collini*. In his earlier writings, Kitching called his *Podophrya* sp., and later identified it as *Discophrya piriformis*, the name now applied by Guilcher to her species. The name ought probably to be *Discophrya collini* (Root), not, as suggested by Hull (1954*b*), *Podophrya collini*. For a discussion of the taxonomy of the genus *Discophrya*, see Matthes (1954).

vary in length once it is fully grown. The young meganucleus is ovoid, but in older specimens tends to be lobulated. The micronuclei, of which there are up to a dozen, are very small and become visible only on staining.

The animal spends most of its time motionless in the water with its tentacles held stiffly out. Each tentacle (Dragesco and Guilcher, 1950) is hollow, pierced by a canal about $0·4 \mu$ in diameter, and surrounded by a wall, a cytoplasmic cortical layer, and an outer pellicle continuous with that over the body. The sucker is about $0·6 \mu$ in diameter, and shows some discontinuity of structure which may betray the presence of pores. The central canal is visible only by phase-contrast microscopy but its presence is betrayed under the bright field microscope by the path of material passing through it. When the tentacle contracts it shows a spiral thickening on its surface.

The suctorian feeds on other ciliates and depends on what prey happens to come into contact with its tentacles. There is some selection of food, and it is not based on size: *Spirostomum*, *Euplotes*, *Vorticella*, and the larvae of other suctorians are ignored, but *Paramecium* spp., *Colpidium*, and *Tetrahymena* are attacked. When suitable prey touches a tentacle, it adheres to it; the cilia may continue to beat for a while, and, if the ciliate is large, its rotation may twist the tentacle into a rope, and it may eventually break free, or its writhings may bring it into contact with other tentacles, and it will be retained. It is unlikely that suction alone can hold on to the prey, for the tentacular orifice must be minute; there is some evidence that a toxic effect is exerted at the tip of the tentacle. Thus, the cilia of the prey nearest to the tentacle tip are the first to stop beating, in, usually, about 3 to 4 minutes, and the stoppage spreads progressively through the body, sometimes in as little as 7 minutes, though remote cilia may beat for half an hour. It seems likely that some digestion takes place in this stage, for ciliates coloured with Congo Red show an acid reaction where held by a tentacle tip. Food, in the form of granules, passes down the central canal, and is squirted, so to speak, into the body as if along a defined path, suggesting that the canal is prolonged below the tentacle base. During feeding, two simultaneous changes have been noted in the suctorian—the contractile vacuole, or vacuoles, increase in activity, and the surface of the body is sometimes wrinkled until the body expands with food and the wrinkles are pressed out. The contents of small prey are totally exhausted and only the husk of an animal is discarded, but larger ciliates like *Paramecium* may be little damaged by the attack of a suctorian.

It is not easy to explain how food passes down the tentacle. The internal pressure of the prey cannot be invoked, for its pellicle is ruptured by the suckers. It is known that the tentacle can apply suction, and one species has been observed by Collin to draw its food from a distance, gathering it in like a tiny vacuum cleaner. Kitching (1952*a*, 1954*b*) points out that at the

beginning of feeding there is a real expansion of the pellicle, which is occasionally seen to wrinkle, and this would result in suction, drawing food
liquefied at the tentacle tip down the tentacular canal; any delay in the
supply of food would account for the wrinkling sometimes observed; where
feeding and increase in volume keep pace with expansion of the pellicle no
wrinkling would be seen. The increased vacuolar activity accompanying
feeding occurs when other activities of suctorians are heightened, as during
breeding (Rudzinska and Chambers, 1951; Hull, 1954a). Kitching (1952b)
explains that *D. piriformis* may increase to twice its size during a meal, and
the extra output of the vacuole is approximately equal to the decrease in
volume of the prey (the suctorian's intake) less the increase in the volume of
the suctorian; in effect this means that the animal is concentrating its food
by discharging liquid as it feeds, with the result that it makes room for more
food from a given meal than it could without its increased vacuolar activity.

The only means of reproduction so far reported for *D. piriformis* is budding, and the process is peculiar. In Root's cultures, budding followed
feeding. Thus, if a few drops of a *Paramecium* culture were added to a
watch-glass containing *Discophrya* the latter liberated a few larvae within
9 hours. Next day the culture swarmed with larvae and these had given rise
to adults by the third day. The free life of a larva is generally only about
2 hours though 24 hours is possible. Thus the whole process of budding,
larval life, and metamorphosis may be studied in the laboratory over a short
period. For the sake of continuity the facts learned from fixed material,
especially Ag preparations, are here added to what may be observed *in vivo*.

The first sign of budding in the living animal is the appearance of a
dimple eccentrically placed on the surface; this sinks into the cytoplasm
and is closed off as a vesicle without any connexion with the exterior. Ag
preparations show that the dimple is a focus for the concentration of kinetosomes previously scattered over the surface of the parent (cf. Fig. 115,
III. 1), and these are invaginated into the vesicle. On the walls of the vesicle,
or embryonic cavity, the kinetosomes multiply and arrange themselves in
parallel lines. The cilia appear early. The bud has now been formed; its
walls are those of the cavity, i.e. the external surface of the bud is the lining
of the vesicle. The relations become clearer as the bud evaginates (Fig.
127). The embryonic cavity opens and cytoplasmic streaming in the parent
accompanies contractions which force the lower part of the bud upwards
till it lies superficially but still attached to its parent, and with its anterior
surface still invaginated into its lower half. As the bud is pushed out from
its parent, so its own anterior half is evaginated like the finger of a glove
that has been turned inside out (Figs. 126C; 127 D–F). The whole structure
breaks free and swims away. The time taken to form a bud is about an
hour. This highly peculiar method of bud formation is typical of the genus
Discophrya (Guilcher, 1951; Matthes, 1954).

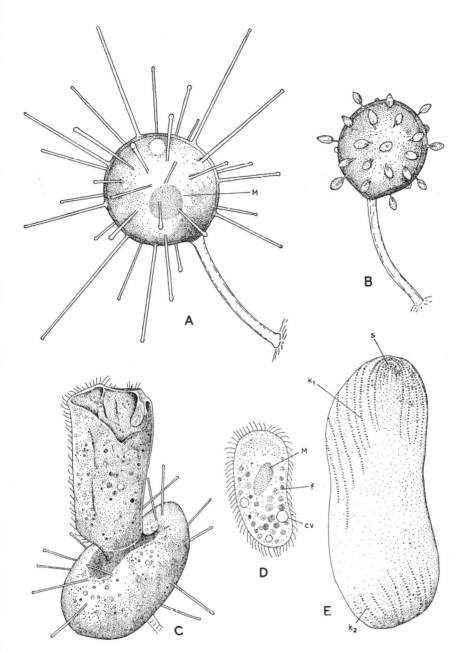

FIG. 126. *Discophrya piriformis.* A, adult suctorian. ×*c.* 750; B, encysted adult; C, evagination of larva (cf. Fig. 127, D, E); D, larva; E, larva (Ag preparation). (A, B, and D, after Root; C and E after Guilcher.)

cv, contractile vacuole; *f*, food inclusion; k_1 and k_2, kinetosomes (diplosomes) of the primary and secondary fields; *M*, meganucleus; *s*, scopula.

The larva is large, reaching 80 or 90 μ in length, somewhat reniform, with the anterior lobe a little larger than the posterior, and flattened, especially in the middle (Fig. 126 D, E). The cilia are almost confined to the ventral surface, and are arranged in incomplete loops in front of the scopula with

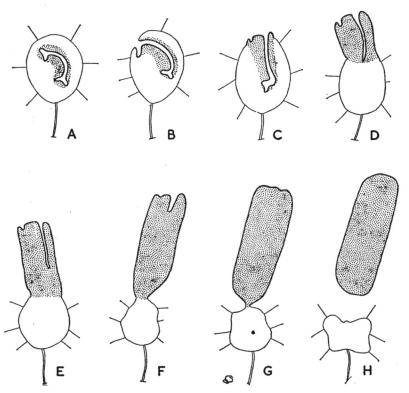

FIG. 127. *Discophrya piriformis*: budding. A–C, formation of bud; D, evagination of bud from parent; the bud is still turned in on itself and unfolds in E and F; G and H, liberation of larva. (After Guilcher.)

their free ends running backwards on each side; the rows of cilia are double and those on the right are longer than those on the left. Behind these, the cilia of the primary field, occur distinct rows forming a secondary field; in related species, the 2 fields may be in continuity (and cf. *Ephelota*, Fig. 125D). During its short free life, usually of about 2 hours, the larva swims ceaselessly in spirals, rotating on its axis, and showing avoiding reactions when it comes in contact with obstacles. It settles by its scopula, the tentacles appear within 10 minutes and may at once begin feeding. The stalk grows out from the scopula, the body becomes rounder, more tentacles grow out, and the thick pellicular investment of the adult is differentiated.

So rapid is reproduction that the parent that has liberated one larva may begin to form another within some 20 minutes.

According to Root, the entire animal could transform itself into a larva. The contents emerged as a mass from the pellicle, which with the tentacles was left behind, and the cytoplasm assumed the larval form and sprouted cilia. Except in one case, this occurred only when the whole organism had been ensheathed in a web of trichocysts of *Paramecium*; the exceptional case had many broken tentacles, presumably damaged in a struggle with large prey. Root's observation seems to confirm Collin's belief that transformation of entire adults into the free-swimming stage is a response to unfavourable conditions.

When left for weeks without food, Root's suctorians encysted (Fig. 126B). The pellicle thickened and the tentacles degenerated, withdrawing from their tips to form bulbous knobs which persisted, though some might be broken off, for months.

Permanent preparations

For nuclei, fix in B and stain in D.H. The micronuclei are difficult to show. Only Ag preparations can display the kinetosomes of the adult and their orderly arrangement in the larvae.

Culture

Root's animals were grown in tap water and fed on ciliates from hay infusions. They will often flourish in tap water if supplied with quantities of *Paramecium*, *Colpidium*, or *Tetrahymena*. Kitching has used silk threads to form a convenient substratum for attachment of Suctorida. Massive supplies of ciliates are introduced into tap water to a depth of about 1 cm, and on the surface are floated 1 cm lengths of threads frayed from parachute silk, which floats. The suctorians are introduced and left to feed for 7 to 10 days. At the end of this time *Discophrya* will have liberated many larvae that will have settled on the threads and transformed, and the threads can be lifted off with the suctorians attached and mounted for study.

ORDER CHONOTRICHIDA

This small, compact order consists of species living epizoically on the mouth-parts of Crustacea, usually marine, though *Spirochona* occurs on freshwater gammarids. The body is ovoid or flask-shaped, attached directly or by a stalk and expanded at the opposite end into a more or less complex feeding apparatus; this is a vestibulum, lined with extensions of somatic cilia, though it is often called a peristome. The rest of the somatic cilia, but not their kinetosomes, have been lost and the body is naked. There

is typically a heteromerous nucleus (p. 227), as in the cyrtophorine gymnostomes. Chonotrichs reproduce sexually and they conjugate (Tuffrau,
1953), but the commoner means of multiplication is budding, which is
external. From Guilcher's illuminating studies of the development, structure, and metamorphosis of the larva it appears that the Suctorida and
Chonotrichida have much in common, including a probable origin from
the Gymnostomatida, though perhaps from different regions of that order
(p. 258). We consider first the well-studied *Chilodochona* and then briefly
the common *Spirochona*.

Chilodochona quennerstedti Wallengren

The ciliates live on the endopodites of the first and second maxillae and
first and second maxillipeds of *Carcinus maenas*, and they are especially
abundant in spring and autumn, when 1 in 6 crabs may be infected; they
are also found on *Cancer pagurus*, *Scyllarus arctus*, *Portunus depurator*, and
Pachygrapsus sp. If the mouth-parts are isolated in dishes of sea water
made slightly alkaline the Protozoa may survive for some time. In nature
they live off particles of food dropped by the crustaceans. Wallengren's
description of the species (1896) is still useful, but must be supplemented
by Guilcher's report of the life-history.

The living organism and permanent preparations

C. quennerstedti has an ovoid body, $60-110\,\mu \times 35-40\,\mu$, mounted on a
fairly rigid, non-contractile stalk, arising from an intra-cytoplasmic rosette
from which radiate small refringent rodlets like the spokes of an umbrella
(Fig. 128 A, B). The sides of the body, covered by a firm pellicle, bear no
cilia, but Ag preparations reveal close, parallel rows of kinetosomes. The
apical surface (which, as will be seen, is really ventral) is expanded in
2 unequal lips, which can open to display on their inner sides the rows of
holotrichous cilia used in feeding; they constitute the vestibulum, and lead
through the cytostome to a long, unciliated cytopharynx. Only very small
particles of food are taken and apparently they are not envacuolated. The
meganucleus is heteromerous, with a karyosome. There are several micronuclei.

Bud formation begins with the appearance of a small protuberance below the level of the vestibulum. Kinetosomes are scattered on the surface
of this rudiment, and at its apex they concentrate, multiply, and arrange
themselves in an orderly field of 8 to 10 short parallel rows (Fig. 128c),
with a striking resemblance to the corresponding stage in a suctorian (cf.
Fig. 115, III. 3). The kinetosomes, greatly increased in number, group
themselves, again as in the Suctorida, into 2 fields, of which the right is

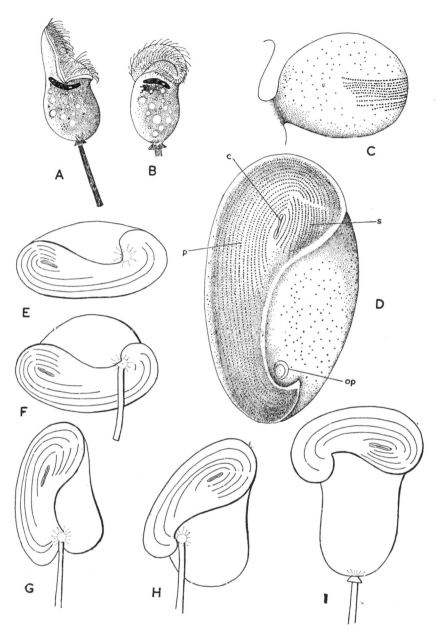

FIG. 128. *Chilodochona quennerstedti*. A, B, 2 adults: in B only part of the peduncle is drawn. × 500; C, bud, showing arrangement of kinetosomes into primary field: Ag preparation. × 1,500; D, larva: Ag preparation. × 1,500; E–I, metamorphosis: the courses of a few kineties are indicated diagrammatically. (After Guilcher.)

c, cytostome; *op*, rudiment of peduncle; *p*, kineties of primary ciliary field; *s*, secondary ciliary field.

much more highly developed than the left; they lie in a gutter on the ventral face of the bud, the folds of which make them difficult to observe. Meanwhile, the cytoplasm of the bud, near to the parent, forms a rosette, which is the rudiment of the organ of fixation. The ventral gutter unfolds to reveal the wide bands of cilia it contains. The larva breaks free. It is 40 to 70 μ long, with a flat, ciliated ventral surface, bearing a cytostome anteriorly and a rosette posteriorly (D). The dorsal surface is domed. There are 2 or 3 contractile vacuoles. Ventrally the kinetosomes (and, of course, cilia) are ordered in about 15 rows in the 2 unequal fields already mentioned; there are also kinetosomes on the dorsal surface scattered irregularly in the ectoplasm. At times the entire adult body may, without budding, transform into a larva.

The free life of the larva lasts usually for some 3 or 4 hours. After settling on its host, it changes its shape to ovoid and then to pyriform, the dorsal face bulging more and more, the ventral twisting and folding to form the lips of the vestibulum (E–H). The rosette is at first ventral and it is the centre of much cytoplasmic activity indicated by the streaming of the granules near to it. It produces a secretion which sets at once in a clot from which the stalk elongates. There is no resemblance between the rosette of the Chonotrichida and the scopula of Suctorida or Peritrichida and the former organ shows no trace of a ciliary origin. By growth and continued movements of adjustment the cytostome and rosette come to lie at opposite poles and the proportions and morphological relations of the adult are achieved.

From its inception as a bud, the larva establishes its holotrichous nature, and as it develops it reveals more and more in common with the Suctorida and the more primitive cyrtophorine gymnostomes. In both the larval Chonotrichida and the Cyrtophorina we find the flattened ventral surface, bearing unequal ciliary fields, of which the right is better developed and curves anteriorly across the cytostome to meet in an oblique seam the shorter rows of cilia belonging to the left side. These characters and the presence in both groups of the peculiar type of heteromerous nucleus very powerfully declare, in spite of the disparity of their adult habit, for their phylogenetic proximity.

Fix in B or S+A; stain in D.H. or H.H. or Feulgen for nuclear characters. Ag impregnations.

Spirochona gemmipara Stein

This well-known genus, the only one to occur in fresh water, has the anterior end expanded into a conical, spirally wound feeding apparatus, and the disposition of the ciliary lines within it, though now, thanks to Guilcher, well understood, is more difficult to interpret than it is in *Chilodochona*. *S. gemmipara* was the subject of long descriptive papers by Stein (1851), and Hertwig (1877), which have never been superseded, though Guilcher (1951) has added important comments. For species, see Swarczewsky (1928) and Kahl (1935).

S. gemmipara (Fig. 129) is sessile upon the branchial lamellae of fresh-water gammarids, including *Gammarus pulex*. The body is a slim, elongated

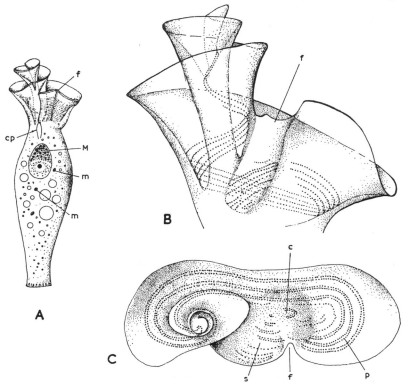

FIG. 129. *Spirochona gemmipara*. A, adult. × 500; B, the collar (vestibulum) with the internal kinetosomal paths plotted; C, the same, seen from above. B and C from Ag preparations and × 2,000. (A after Hertwig; B and C after Guilcher.)

c, position of cytostome; *cp*, cytopharynx; *f*, fold in collar; *M*, meganucleus; *m*, micronucleus; *p*, kinetosomes of primary field; *s*, secondary field.

vase, constricted at the neck and then expanded to form the conical spiral of the vestibulum (A). This is really a ribbon of cytoplasm, wound into a spiral, and ciliated in parallel lines on its inner face (B, C). The rows of cilia increase in number at each turn of the spiral. The last and widest circuit of the ribbon is folded at one point down its wall, and at the base of this fold lies the cytostome, leading to an unciliated cytopharynx. The whole body is faintly covered with fine kinetosomes in parallel rows. The heteromerous meganucleus is plainly differentiated into two regions, one coarsely, one very finely granulated, and the former strongly, the latter weakly, F+;

there is a karyosome which apparently disappears during division. The life-history, so far as it is known, appears to be very like that described for *Chilodochona*. For conjugation, see Tuffrau (1953).

ORDER TRICHOSTOMATIDA

The order assembles a diverse collection of adult forms, many of which have never been adequately studied. All are more advanced than any gymnostome, but none achieves the complex oral structure of the hymeno-stomes. The distinctive feature is the vestibulum, an ectoplasmic depression provided with feeding cilia which are extensions of the somatic ciliature. The simplicity of this arrangement is apparent in such primitive genera as *Pseudoprorodon* or *Coelosomides* (Fig. 130), and even in more advanced forms such as *Balantidium* the somatic kineties can with care be traced to the margins of the vestibulum into which they turn (Figs. 131, 132); but in very specialized genera such as *Colpoda* the continuity of vestibular with somatic kineties can be established only by a study of development (Figs. 134, 135).

Coelosomides marina (Anigstein)

This species, originally discovered and well described by Anigstein (1912), has more recently been studied by Fauré-Fremiet (1950c), who collected it from beach sand. The interstices between the grains are in-habited by a highly peculiar fauna, including a number of remarkable ciliates (Fauré-Fremiet, 1950c, 1951). Of these, the more specialized tend to be elongated, thin, vermiform, or ribbon-like, and they live among the finer sands, called microporal. *C. marina* is mesoporal, occurring between coarser grains (c. 1·7 mm) and where organic debris is provided by decaying algae. The species, which is morphologically very generalized, is thus ecologically most restricted.

Collect damp sand in about 250-gm lots to a depth of about 5 or 6 cm and keep it in suitable covered vessels below filtered sea water. With a wide-mouthed pipette separate a few c.c. of sand into a Petri dish of filtered sea water, agitate briskly, move most of the sand to one side and examine the space cleared for *Coelosomides*. (The more specialized ciliates are thigmotactic and will be dislodged only after adding a few drops of 12 per cent magnesium chloride to the water.) The ciliate must be ex-amined rapidly for, like others from this habitat, it is fragile and may under-go cytolysis when removed from its sand.

The living organism

C. marina (Fig. 130) is elongated, more or less ovoid, and in transverse section, circular. It swims rather rapidly, turning on its long axis without any marked deformation of the body. At first sight it looks like a gymnostome, with longitudinal rows of holotrichous cilia, but at the anterior end these rows turn inwards and then back into a depression, the vestibulum, where they beat towards the cytostome. This narrow aperture leads into a spacious

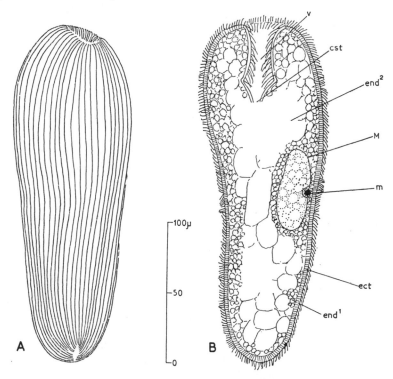

FIG. 130. *Coelosomides marina.* A, the whole organism after Ag impregnation, showing the primitive infraciliature with the meridians invaginated anteriorly at the vestibulum; B, L.S. showing the continuation of the somatic ciliature into the vestibulum. (After Fauré-Fremiet.)

cst, cytostome; *ect*, ectoplasm; *end*[1], peripheral endoplasm (finely vacuolated); *end*[2], vacuolated space in central endoplasm; *M*, meganucleus; *m*, micronucleus; *v*, vestibulum.

highly vacuolated region of the endoplasm, which receives the filamentous algae and bacteria on which the organism feeds. Peripherally, the endo-plasm is more compact, though still finely vacuolated, and here it contains the mega- and micronucleus.

Permanent preparations

Animals must be fixed immediately after separation from the collected sand. Fix in S+A; stain in H.H. or Chatton-Lwoff.

Balantidium entozoon (Ehrenberg)

Most members of the genus are parasitic in the alimentary canal of Amphibia, but some occur in mammals, including man (*B. coli*), and in other vertebrates, and species are found in invertebrates, such as cockroaches (p. 266), turbellarians, and coelenterates: the little known *B. hydrae*, briefly noted by Entz (1912) from *Hydra oligactis*, would repay attention. The most studied form is, not unnaturally, *B. coli*, which is much commoner in pigs than in man (McDonald, 1922, and see Wenyon's *Protozoology*, and Hoare's *Handbook of Medical Protozoology*), but the species from frogs are larger and more accessible. Although the genus has for long been well known and very frequently observed it has been widely misplaced in the classification; Stein (1867) allocated it to the Heterotrichida, and there it remained until 1955, when Fauré-Fremiet pointed out that, for the reasons stressed below, it was really a trichostomatous member of the Holotricha.

B. entozoon occurs in the rectum of *Rana temporaria* and *R. esculenta*, perhaps more often in the latter, and according to Stein it is also found in *Bombinator igneus*, *Triturus taeniatus*, and *T. cristatus*. Notes on related species and their distribution will be found on p. 264. The only good account is that of Stein (1867), now to be read in conjunction with Fauré-Fremiet (1955). Bhatia and Gulati (1927) offer a key to species.

The living animal

Frogs are dissected dry as for *Opalina* (p. 150) and mounts of living material sealed under No. o slips. *Balantidium* cannot be confused with *Opalina*, but it does bear a superficial resemblance to another ciliate, *Nyctotherus* (p. 355), which often accompanies it; *Nyctotherus* is usually slightly larger, has the 'mouth' placed laterally instead of terminally, and is of a yellowish, not, like *Balantidium*, a greyish tint.

B. entozoon (Fig. 131A) is an ovoid or egg-shaped animal; the anterior, narrower end is often turned slightly to one side, the posterior is domed. Most specimens are 50 to 85 μ long, but the measurements given by the authors vary extensively and much larger specimens certainly occur. The entire body is coated with holotrichous cilia arranged in longitudinal lines which converge on the lips of the vestibulum, where the feeding cilia are conspicuously longer. The vestibulum is a conical depression, set a little obliquely to the midline, and tucked into the interior at least as far back as the equator. *B. entozoon* does not display the vestibulum clearly and the continuity of somatic and vestibular kineties is not so plain as in, for example, *B. elongatum* (see below). It swims, rotating on its axis and squeezing its elastic body between obstacles. The meganucleus is kidney-shaped and carries the micronucleus in a lateral depression, rarely seen in the living subject. There arc 4 large (and a number of smaller) contractile vacuoles,

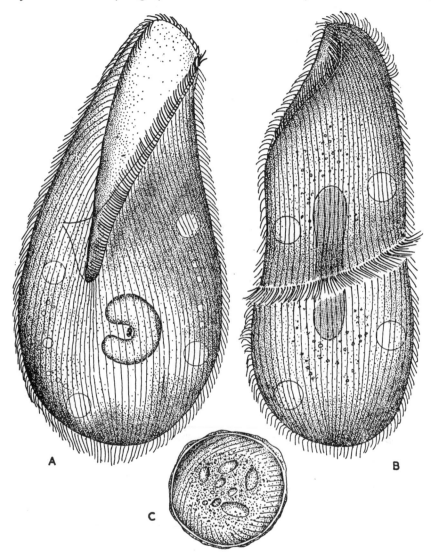

FIG. 131. *Balantidium entozoon.* A, adult; B, division, showing subequatorial girdle of strong cilia representing vestibular primordium of the opisthe; C, cyst. All × 1,000. (After Stein.)

and the number is used in taxonomy. There is apparently no permanent cytoproct in this species, but faeces are discharged from time to time, always at the same spot.

Fission is perkinetal and the vestibular cilia of the opisthe appear as an incomplete annulus below the equator (B, and see p. 265). Nothing is known of the sexual phase (but for conjugation in *B. coli*, see Jameson, 1927, and also Scott, 1927).

The animal forms subspherical cysts (c), about 30 μ in diameter. It stops feeding, rounds off, and secretes a smooth, transparent envelope, which for a time remains flexible and elastic. Within this the ciliate rotates for a while, but eventually comes to rest and the cilia disappear. Cysts, if kept moist, can survive for some time outside the host.

Balantidium elongatum Stein

This species (Fig. 133A) is easily distinguished from the foregoing. It is cylindrical, longer and slimmer than *B. entozoon*, usually 100–140 μ × 30–60 μ, and the vestibulum is short, confined to the anterior quarter of the body and its obliquity to the axis is less marked. There are only 2 contractile vacuoles, lying in the midline, one before and one behind the meganucleus, which is oval. *B. elongatum* is rare in *Rana temporaria* but commoner in *R. esculenta* and in the newts *Triturus taeniatus*, *T. cristatus*, and *T. alpestris*.

Balantidium duodeni Stein

Unlike the 2 foregoing species, *B. duodeni* (Fig. 133B) occurs in the anterior part of the small intestine, where it is the only entozoic Protozoan of *Rana esculenta*. It is a short, very broad form, measuring some 45–60 μ × 35–50 μ,* and the ventral surface is markedly convex, the dorsal flat or slightly concave. The vestibulum is deep and curves strongly to the right. There is a single contractile vacuole. The meganucleus is ovate or subspherical.

Permanent preparations

Smears fixed wet in B or S+A, and stained in D.H. or H.H. show the meganucleus but little else that cannot be observed in living animals. For an understanding of the infraciliature Ag preparations are indispensable. These reveal the reasons for removing *Balantidium* from the Heterotrichida to the Trichostomatida, and they are conveniently considered at this point (Fauré-Fremiet, 1955; Krascheninnikov and Wenrich, 1958).

The taxonomic position of *Balantidium*

The Heterotrichida (p. 345) are characterized by the possession of a peristome bearing a conspicuous and powerful AZM used in feeding. The

---

* Bhatia and Gulati (1927) found the specimens from *Rana tigrina* in India were larger, 74 to 115 μ.

membranellae composing this zone always consist of fused cilia beating together as a single paddle. The oral ciliature is either autonomous, that is, develops from kinetosomes supplied directly from previous oral kinetosomes, or it is proliferated from one or several specialized so-called, stomatogenic kineties (Fig. 115, IIB; IV), i.e. the oral ciliature either is from the start, or at a very early stage becomes, completely independent of the somatic ciliature. In the Trichostomatida, on the other hand, the vestibular ciliature always develops in continuity with the somatic kineties of which it is really no more than an extension (cf. *Coelosomides*, Fig. 130, and Fig. 115, IB).

Now, in *Balantidium*, the somatic meridians of the ciliature converge on the vestibulum, on the internal lips of which, to right and left, lie the short rows of feeding cilia. They are more numerous than the somatic meridians, lie closer together, at an angle to them, and their cilia are longer though the difference is slight where the 2 systems meet. The point is not easy to observe in living ciliates, though, of *B. coli*, McDonald (1922) wrote, 'The homology of the adoral and body cilia is evidenced by the complete series of gradations from one to another which exist in the cilia of the apical cone. The cilia which are proximal to the adoral cilia are almost identical with them.' It is most clearly seen in *B. elongatum* (but not *B. entozoon*) where the oblique rows of kinetosomes are, on the left, plainly prolongations of the somatic rows, though there is some specialization and discontinuity of the right (Fig. 132A). At no time has any author described any true membranellae and the only published observations on the subject suggest that the cilia of vestibular rows beat independently.

The facts of morphogenesis may be called into support. At division the organism elongates, the micronucleus divides, and below the equator there appears, before division of the meganucleus, an incomplete band of stronger and longer cilia, the primordia of the vestibular cilia (Fig. 131B). Before the dislocation of the kineties which makes way for fission, the vestibular cilia are seen as local developments of the somatic meridians. Some at least of the short vestibular lengths become duplicated (Fig. 132B) and so provide the additional rows seen in the adult. After fission the vestibular girdle elongates on the ventral surface and assumes its asymmetry, the left lip being deeper and more powerfully ciliated than the right. From all the foregoing evidence it is apparent that the vestibular cilia develop as prolongations of the somatic kineties, after which they may suffer some duplication and, of course, tend to a greater strength, as is common for oral cilia, but they never attain the organization of true membranellae. Both in origin and adult structure they place *Balantidium* firmly among the trichostomes.

Culture

According to Dobell (1909), *B. entozoon* may be maintained for some time on infusions made from the faeces of various animals, such as rats and snakes, and the ciliate will divide. Systematic study of the culture requirements is lacking. *B. coli*, according to Jameson (1927), may be grown on the HSre+S variant of Boeck and Drbohlav's medium (p. 414).

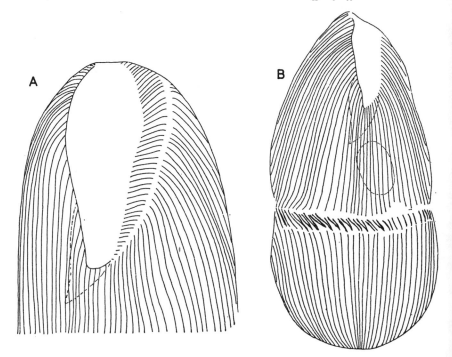

FIG. 132. *Balantidium*: infraciliature. A, the course of the kineties at the anterior end, showing the left lip of the vestibulum and the correspondence between its ciliary rows and the somatic kineties of which they are prolongations; B, division showing the oblique subequatorial segments of the somatic kineties and the duplication of some of them to give the vestibular primordium of the opisthe (cf. Fig. 131B). (After Fauré-Fremiet.)

Notes on *Balantidium* spp. from cockroaches

Cockroaches are so commonly used for parasitological examinations that the following species, though rare, must be briefly noted.

B. blattarum Ghosh. Body roughly pyramidal (Fig. 133C), 90 μ long, slightly more than half as wide, left longer than right side, posterior end obliquely truncate. Vestibulum short, not reaching middle of body. Meganucleus spherical. One large contractile vacuole. Noted in India from *Periplaneta americana* by Ghosh (1922a).

B. ovatum Ghosh. About the same length as the last, but reniform (Fig. 133E). Vestibulum short. Endoplasm dense. Meganucleus described as 'broadly oval'. One posterior contractile vacuole with a canal running to the exterior. Described from a single specimen of *Periplaneta americana* (Ghosh, 1922*b*).

B. praenucleatum Kudo & Meglitsch. From the colon of *Blatta orientalis* in North America where it infects only a minority of specimens, say, 7 to 8 per cent. According to the authors of the species (1938), it is 65·5 μ long

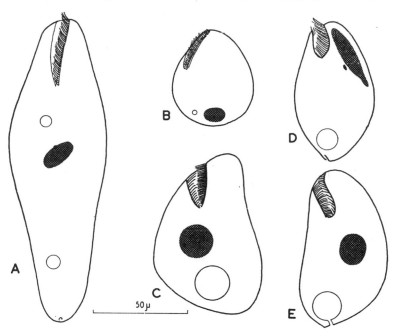

FIG. 133. *Balantidium* spp. from Amphibia and cockroaches. ×c. 500.
A, *B. elongatum*; B, *B. duodeni*; C, *B. blattarum*; D, *B. praenucleatum*; E, *B. ovatum*. (A and B after Stein; C and E after Ghosh; D after Kudo and Meglitsch.)

on the average, ovoid or oblong, with a small vestibulum (Fig. 133D). Meganucleus long, dorsal, and anterior, and slung by fibres to this region of the body. A single contractile vacuole. There is a cytoproct with a small canal which may be seen during defecation.

Colpoda cucullus O. F. Müller

Members of the genus *Colpoda* are among the most highly specialized trichostomes known (Figs. 134, 136). All are small, more or less kidney-shaped, with the 'mouth' displaced to the left or straighter side. The cilia are often paired, borne in deep furrows, and the kineties of the right, more curved side, converge above the vestibulum towards a notched keel; the number of notches is taxonomically useful. Asexual reproduction is almost if not entirely confined to an encysted stage, the multiplication cysts containing 4, sometimes 2 or 8, daughters; resistant cysts, tougher and longer lived, are also formed. *Colpoda* is common in nature, and in laboratory infusions, and it is easily cultured.

A clear general account of *C. cucullus* and a number of related species is given in Burt (1940) and there are useful notes given by Kahl (1935). A detailed study of the silver-line system and of stomatogenesis in the related *C. steinii* (= *C. duodenaria*) was given by Taylor and Garnjobst (1939); the facts apply in general to *C. cucullus* (Klein, 1929); morphogenesis in the family has been discussed by Tuffrau (1952). In nature *C. cucullus* is widely distributed in patches of moss growing in water well supplied with organic nutriment from decaying plant material; in the laboratory it is usually obtained from hay infusions, which will supply a mixture of species. These fall into 2 groups (Fig. 136): the smaller average about 30 μ in length (e.g. *C. steinii*, *C. aspera*), and the larger are over 50 μ. Of the latter *C. cucullus* is a fair example; it is admittedly difficult to distinguish from such closely related forms as *C. maupasi* and *C. inflata*; the facts given below for the most part apply to all.

The living organism

C. cucullus (Fig. 134) is 40 to 110 μ long, usually about 75 μ, and is bean- or kidney-shaped. The right side is broadly curved, the left indented less than half-way down its length and above the dent is the keel, bearing 8 to 10 notches; below it the side is convex. Pairs of cilia spring from 29 to 34 meridianal grooves, deep and close-set anteriorly, shallower, and more widely spaced posteriorly; a few of the posterior cilia may be single. The grooves which mark the positions of the kineties for the most part run to the right of and then above the vestibulum, and they converge on the keel; the notches referred to mark the points at which they meet it. At the mesial margin of the vestibulum runs a groove which is just interrupted in its course and this marks the position of kinety 1 (k^1 in Fig. 134D); to its left lies a small number of grooves (kineties) which never reach the keel but end at the vestibular margin. This group as a whole is of great importance in morphogenesis and its members proliferate the vestibular kinetosomes.

The vestibulum lies in the notch below the keel. Its opening is on the left and its cavity passes inwards and downwards to the cytostome, which thus is placed below the surface and near the midline. On the vestibular roof lies the right ciliary field, which is visible *in vivo*; on the floor lies the left field, much more difficult to observe in life, but plainly revealed in Ag preparations (D); the attribution to left and right sides is apparent only after considering their development (p. 272). Both fields consist of closely set rows of short cilia. *C. cucullus* feeds voraciously on very small bacteria,

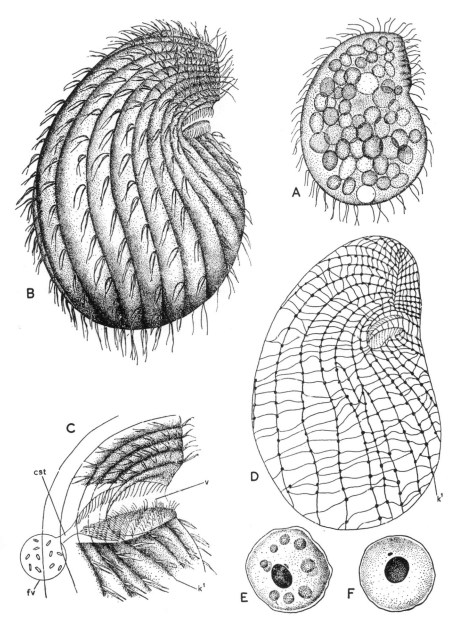

FIG. 134. *Colpoda cucullus*. A, the living organism with typical inclusions. ×500; B, stained specimen. ×825; C, part of the same with the vestibular region shown as a transparency; D, silver-line system. ×825; E, young resistant cyst still with food inclusions. × 1,000; F, mature resistant cyst with clear cytoplasm. ×1,000. (A, B, and D after Burt; C combined after various authors; E and F after Kidder and Claff.)

cst, cytostome; *fv*, food vacuole; *k¹*, kinety number 1; *v*, vestibulum with one line of the right ciliary field above and with the left ciliary field below.

T

which, on entering the body, are compacted into spherical masses, crowding the endoplasm and hindering observation; a ciliate of average size (70 μ long) may contain as many as 200 food vacuoles (A). The feeding mechanism is exceedingly efficient; a ciliate newly hatched from a cyst has clear cytoplasm, but 'within a few minutes . . . the cytoplasm will be found to be literally packed with spherical food vacuoles' (Kidder and Claff, 1938). Among these inclusions it may be possible to make out a more or less centrally placed meganucleus, and perhaps a posterior contractile vacuole.

Resistant cysts (E, F) are easily obtained by keeping animals in hay infusions for 48 hours without renewing the medium. Encystation in *Colpoda* is a response to a diet deficiency and occurs when the organisms are deprived of one or more of four essential vitamins (B_1, B_6, pantothenic acid, nicotinamide) or of an unknown complex, mainly protein, which is a heat labile, bacterial plasmoptyzate fraction (Garnjobst, 1947, and see discussion by van Wagtendonk, 1955). The division rate falls off, the animals become less active and decrease in size, and lay down a delicate transparent endocyst and a heavy wrinkled ectocyst. All resistant cysts are smaller than trophic ciliates, and usually about 20 μ in diameter. At first the cytoplasm contains food spherules but these are absorbed and their place is taken by numerous minute refringent bodies. These too are absorbed within a few hours, the cytoplasm is clear and the cilia are discarded. According to Kidder and Claff (1938) the meganucleus loses some chromatin to the cytoplasm where it is resorbed. In this condition the cyst may survive for long periods; Dawson and Hewitt (1931) claim to have recovered active ciliates within 24 hours of making an infusion from hay stored dry for 5 years, and dried cysts are said to resist exposure to 100° C for 3 hours. In some circumstances, e.g. evaporation of the medium, division cysts may be converted into resistant cysts by addition of the thick ectocyst, so that some resistant cysts may be found which contain 2 to 4 ciliates. Formation of resistant cysts may be inhibited by frequent renewal of the medium (Barker and Taylor, 1931). When the cysts are transferred to fresh medium they hatch. The ectocyst ruptures and discloses the transparent endocyst, within which the animal, now provided with cilia, rotates. The cyst wall increases in diameter until it disappears and Goodey (1913) considered that it was digested by enzymes produced by the contained organism. Excystation depends on temperature, with an optimum at about 24° C, and upon the concentration of hay in the infusion (Thimann and Barker, 1934), and the excystation factor is said to reside in a mixture of salts of inorganic acids present in hay (Haagen-Smit and Thimann, 1938).

The newly hatched organism feeds, grows, and then, within a few hours, rounds up and secretes about itself, while the cilia are still moving, a delicate membrane. This is the division cyst (Fig. 135 E, F). The cytostome becomes indistinct and the organism divides, almost always into 4, rarely into 2 or 8 daughters; 16 have been reported. Conjugation has not been observed, and in related species it is rare. The known life-cycle of *C. cucullus* thus consists of a trophic phase, asexual reproduction in a cyst, excystation, growth, and so on, with interruptions at any point by formation of a resistant cyst.

Permanent preparations

Kidder and Claff (1938) recommend the following method. Small circular flat-bottomed Petri dishes, 23×12 mm, will just contain $\frac{7}{8}$ inch cover slips. A slip, sometimes coated with egg albumen, is fitted into the bottom of the dish, which is filled with culture medium and inoculated with a single ciliate. When the culture has reached the required stage in the life-history, the slip is removed and dropped into fixative. Alternatively, the organisms may be centrifuged and attached to slides with celloidin, but the authors found that their method gave clean preparations, without much debris, and with the specimens attached side by side on the slip and not on top of one another.

Fix in S+A H.H. may be used but is apt to be opaque; it is useless for resistant cysts as it stains the walls. It is better to prepare nuclei and cilia-ture separately. For nuclei, Feulgen (see p. 436): hydrolysis, 15 minutes at 60° C, staining 4–5 hours, sulphurous acid 15 minutes with 3 changes. For somatic cilia, Bresslau's method with China Blue, Opal Blue or Nigrosin (p. 423). Morphogenesis cannot be understood without Ag preparations (Chatton-Lwoff, p. 443).

Ag preparations show the kinetosomes of the vestibulum and also the somatic kineties, which follow the courses of the pellicular grooves (Fig. 134D). Most converge upon the keel. Kinety number 1, and the few to its left, which never reach the keel, are stomatogenic. All the somatic kineties are irregularly connected by transverse lines. The apparently single kine-tosomes are nearly all double but very close together. The vestibular cilia-ture is set in two fields running transversely across the somatic kineties.

The meganucleus (Fig. 135 E, F) is more or less central, round, or oval, with the chromatin concentrated in a number of peripheral plaques applied to the inner surface of the nuclear membrane (Kidder and Claff, 1938; Burt, 1940). The micronucleus is small and lies close to the meganucleus.

The division cysts within which all reproduction occurs are transparent and the whole processes of fission and morphogenesis may be followed without interference, but different techniques are needed to disclose the behaviour of the nuclei (Feulgen, Azure A, or Haematoxylin) and of the infraciliature (Chatton-Lwoff).

The micronucleus divides by a regular mitosis. As it does so, the chromatin of the meganucleus is loosened from its peripheral plaques and distributed in granules throughout the nucleus. The granules form chromatic aggregates, believed by Piekarski (1939) to represent complete sets of genes, or genomes, of a nucleus far less polyploid than in many ciliates (see p. 229). As the micronucleus approaches its telophase, the meganucleus elongates, constricts, and partitions the aggregates between the daughters. According to Kidder and Claff (1938), some chromatin is extruded into the cytoplasm from each daughter meganucleus; a similar type of reorganization of the meganucleus is known to occur in related forms (Burt, Kidder, and Claff, 1941). Division is almost always repeated to form 4 daughter ciliates.

A clear and detailed account of morphogenesis has been given for *C. steinii* (= *C. duodenaria*), which does not significantly differ from *C. cucullus*, by Taylor and Garnjobst (1939); and see also Tuffrau (1952). At the beginning of encystation, as the ciliate rotates and secretes its transparent envelope, the vestibulum is evaginated, its ciliary fields are resorbed, and the whole cytostomal structure is lost. The organism has now almost completely regained a symmetrical, presumably primitive, disposition of its kineties, which converge towards opposite poles. Division is perkinetal, and the two halves, representing proter and opisthe, rotate in opposite directions twisting the kineties as shown in Fig. 135A. The oral structures differentiate after separation of the daughters and development in the proter precedes that in the opisthe. The right ciliary field is the first to appear from a multiplication of kinetosomes at the anterior end of its formative kineties (or single kinety in *C. steinii*); these mark out a crescentic field along the polar end of the kinety and arrange themselves transversely across it. The left field is derived from groups of kinetosomes proliferated by kineties adjacent to the crescent (B). They also arrange themselves in transverse rows at the polar ends of the kineties; there are usually 4 left groups in *C. steinii*, more in *C. cucullus*, and at this stage they show a passing resemblance to the *Anlagen* of membranellae in the Spirotricha. The upper ends of the kineties involved bend towards each other, bringing the components of the left field closer together, and they too mark out a crescentic field lying to the left of the first formed field (C, D). From the foregoing it may be seen how the vestibular cilia, so specialized and isolated topographically in the adult, develop from the ends of somatic kineties, and so betray during their ontogeny the trichostome affinities of *Colpoda*.

Culture

For ordinary purposes *Colpoda* is most simply grown in hay infusions (e.g., 10 gm dry timothy hay boiled in 1,000 ml tap water for 5 to 10 minutes and filtered). The ciliates feed on small bacteria. A more refined method is to sterilize the medium after filtration and feed the ciliates on a

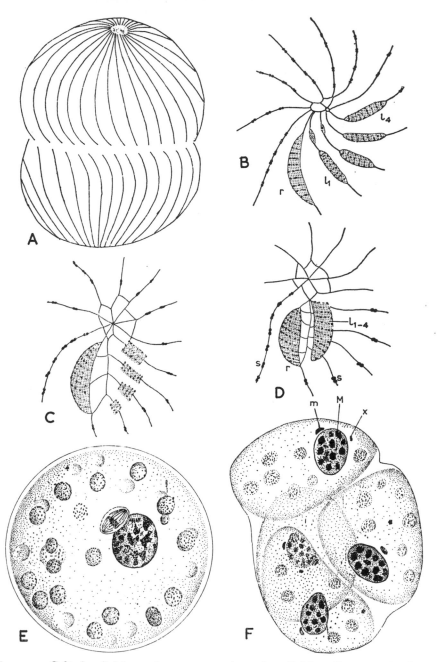

FIG. 135. *Colpoda*: division and stomatogenesis. A, first division, diagrammatic, from the side; B, polar view showing early stage in stomatogenesis: 1 somatic kinety has formed a field of kinetosomes which will produce the right ciliary field, and 4 kineties to the left of it have formed the separate *Anlagen* of the left field; C, later stage of same; D, later stage than C: the separate primordia (l_{1-4}) of the left field have united: the pairs of kinetosomes for somatic cilia are visible on the kinetodesmata, including those which are stomatogenic; E, early and F, late division cysts, both × 1,150. (A after Tuffrau; B–D simplified after Taylor and Garnjobst; E and F after Kidder and Claff.)

l_1 and l_4, 1st and 4th primordia of left ciliary field; M, meganucleus; m, micronucleus; r, primordium of right ciliary field; s, somatic kinetosomes; x, extruded chromatin.

known species of bacterium; different authors have used *Pseudomonas* spp. or *B. coli*, grown on slopes and mixed by the loop into the medium before use. The ciliates are cultured in small Petri dishes, with cover slips on the floor for making preparations. On this medium, even without controlled food, *Colpoda* will complete its cycle in about 48 hours. For a more precisely defined medium, see Barker and Taylor (1931) and Garnjobst (1947).

Related species of *Colpoda*

All the species are small, usually crammed with and distorted by food, variable in shape, and extremely difficult to distinguish. The following, based on Burt (1940), may assist in identification (and see Fig. 136).

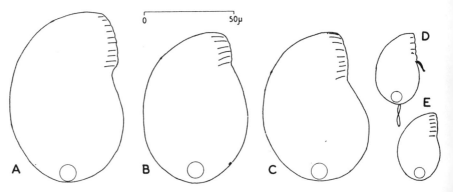

Fig. 136. *Colpoda* spp. showing the shape and size relations of well-fed specimens. A, *C. cucullus*; B, *C. maupasi*; C, *C. inflata*; D, *C. steinii*; E, *C. aspera*. (Redrawn after Burt.)

C. cucullus (A). 40–110 μ, usually 75 μ long. Bean-shaped, with the right side more sharply notched than in *C. inflata*. 29–34 meridians. May be almost black with food inclusions.

C. maupasi (B). 35–95 μ, usually *c*. 60 μ. Keel short, though the proportions of the body vary with feeding. 16–18 meridians.

C. inflata (C). 35–90 μ, usually *c*. 60 μ. Like the foregoing but with 21–24 meridians and a shallower notch.

C. steinii (D). 15–42 μ, usually *c*. 30 μ. Some vestibular cilia protrude as a beard, and two posterior (caudal) cilia are elongated. The species now includes *C. duodenaria* and is one of the best described (see Taylor and Furgason, 1938; Taylor and Garnjobst, 1939).

C. aspera (E). 12–42 μ, usually *c*. 30 μ. 14–16 meridians. Like *C. steinii* but without beard or caudal cilia.

ORDER HYMENOSTOMATIDA

The members of this order are the first to develop an oral ciliature which, both in origin and structure, is quite distinct from the simple holotrichous coat that clothes the body. In its primitive and complete form, the oral ciliature consists here, as it does in the more highly organized Spirotricha, of an undulating membrane (UM) of cohering cilia on the right of the buccal cavity and a modest AZM on the left (Fig. 137 B, D); the AZM has 3 membranellae in simple cases, and hence the buccal ciliature is quadripartite or tetrahymenal (with 3 membranellae and 1 UM). Many of the more advanced hymenostomes depart so far from this plan that its influence on their adult structure is not easy to recognize (e.g. *Paramecium*). In all cases the buccal ciliature develops either from kinetosomes proliferated from one or more stomatogenic kineties or directly from pre-existing buccal structures (cf. *Tetrahymena*, Fig. 137 E–H, and *Paramecium*). The hymenostomes, which stand very centrally among the Holotricha as the ancestors of a number of orders, appear to have originated from the Gymnostomatida, not the Trichostomatida, which have been by-passed. Of great interest is the small, rare ciliate, *Pseudomicrothorax dubius*, which possesses a shallow buccal cavity containing a tripartite AZM and a rudimentary prototype of the UM, all arranged as in the Tetrahymenina; at the same time it has a cytopharyngeal basket and so combines the characters of a cyrtophorine gymnostome with those of a primitive hymenostome (Thompson and Corliss, 1958; Corliss, 1958 a, b).

Most hymenostomes are free-living, freshwater animals. A few, like *Ichthyophthirius* (long mistaken for a gymnostome), are parasitic. The order contains 2 genera, *Tetrahymena* and *Paramecium*, which have been very extensively used in experimental studies; curiously enough it is only during the last few years that it has been possible to offer a clear account of the structure and development of either of them.

There are three suborders: the Tetrahymenina, with an UM on the right and a tripartite AZM on the left of the buccal cavity (*Tetrahymena*), the Peniculina, with compound ciliary organellae deeply placed in the buccal cavity and supposed to be homologous with membranellae (*Paramecium*), and the Pleuronematina, with a greatly enlarged (hypertelic) UM and the buccal cavity placed subequatorially (*Pleuronema, Cyclidium*).

Tetrahymena pyriformis (Ehrenberg)

Tetrahymena is a small ciliate and not easy to observe, but it is for a number of reasons too important to neglect. It embodies the most primitive type of organization found in the Hymenostomatida. It was the first animal ever to be maintained axenically, i.e. in a sterile medium completely free from all other organisms (Lwoff, 1923), and its usefulness to physiologists is reflected in a literature of some 500 contributions (Corliss, 1954). In this, unhappily, the present species appears under a wide variety of names,* for although an excellent description of it by Furgason appeared in 1940 (under the name of *Tetrahymena geleii*) it was not until Corliss (1952, 1953a) published the results of his investigations of nearly 30 strains of this and related forms that the limits of the species were plainly defined. Since then Furgason's findings have been largely confirmed and illuminated by E.M. studies (Metz and Westphal, 1954).

T. pyriformis is widely distributed in Europe and America, usually in fresh water, in ponds, streams, and stagnant pools, or in thermal springs. It probably also occurs in brackish water. It is found in the soil and is coprophilous. It is most likely that at least some strains are facultative parasites in various animals (Corliss, 1953, 1960; Kozloff, 1956; Thompson, 1958).

The living organism

The body is plastic, constantly changing shape in response to local pressures, and even when expanded so variable in shape that a pure culture may, as Furgason remarks, give the impression of consisting of several species. The animal is longer than broad, averaging $50 \times 30 \mu$, rounded posteriorly, pointed anteriorly (Fig. 137A). The shape varies from that of a pear to that of an egg or even a cucumber. The holotrichous cilia are arranged in meridians, closer together anteriorly than elsewhere. The buccal cavity (A, B, D) lies anteriorly in the mid-ventral line, and its aperture roughly mirrors the shape of the whole animal. The cavity is funnel-shaped, sinking inwards towards the dorsal surface and slightly to the left as it narrows to a cytostome; it is difficult to determine whether it empties at once into a food vacuole or whether there is a very short cytopharynx. The wide aperture is protected by an ectoplasmic flange extending from the apex, down the left side and along the posterior margin. The UM, especially when well extended, is easily seen in the living animal; it probably consists

* They are listed by Corliss (1953a). For the convenience of students, it may be mentioned that the commonest mistakes are *Colpidium colpoda*, *C. campylum*, *C. striatum*, and *Glaucoma pyriformis*. The trivial name is often misspelt as '*piriformis*'.

FIG. 137. *Tetrahymena pyriformis*. A, the trophic animal. $\times c.$ 2,000; B, anterior end showing buccal overture with the mouth-parts protruded; C, outline with meganucleus and basophil granules after Iron Haematoxylin staining; D, diagram to show argentophil structures; E–H, stomatogenesis. (A, C, E–H after Furgason; B and D, after Corliss.)

al, apical loop; *c*, cytostome; *co*, circumoral ring; *cp* and *cv*, positions of cytoproct and contractile vacuole pores, marking the 1st, 5th, and 6th meridians; *ic*, intermeridional connective; M_1, M_2, and M_3, 1st, 2nd, and 3rd membranellae; *n*, *n*-1, *n*-2, and *n*-3, last four primary meridians; *pm*, primary meridian; *po*, pre-oral suture; *s*, field of stomatogenic kinetosomes; *sm*, secondary meridian; *um*, undulating membrane; *1*, *2*, and *3*, 1st (stomatogenic), 2nd, and 3rd meridians.

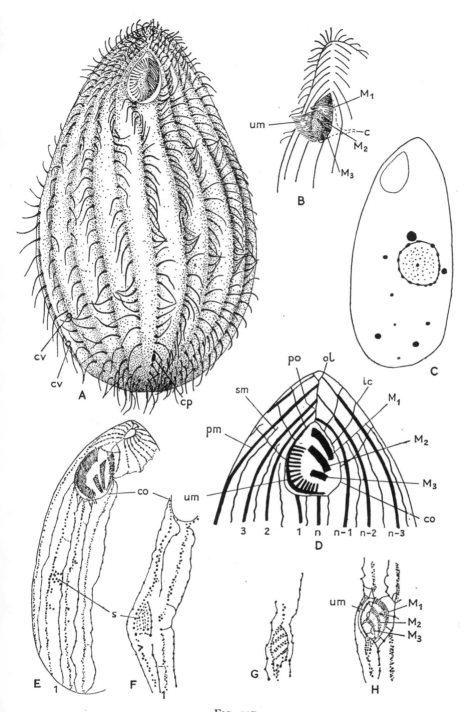

Fig. 137

of a single row of adherent cilia and it runs from the apex, down the right margin of the cavity and tucks into it posteriorly; with the flange opposite it forms a rim about the aperture leading into the cavity. Of the 3 membranellae forming the AZM only the first is at all clear in the living ciliate; it is the largest, is inserted obliquely to the body axis, and sweeps strongly downwards and inwards. The second is smaller, but sometimes visible. The third is almost impossible to discern except in stained material.

The endoplasm is homogeneous in axenic cultures, stuffed with food vacuoles in those containing bacteria. There is a single large contractile vacuole posteriorly and slightly to the right of the midline; it opens by usually two pores best seen in Ag preparations. Faeces are always discharged at a permanent cytoproct, but this is difficult to distinguish except during defecation.

The meganucleus (c) is round or oval, about $9 \times 11\,\mu$, with finely grained contents from which are differentiated larger masses of peripheral material and sometimes a central group of granules. A peculiarity of the species is the widespread occurrence of amicronucleate strains, which, of course, cannot reproduce sexually. All the strains studied by Corliss (1953a), though isolated in different parts of the world at dates extending over 30 years, were amicronucleate; so were his freshly isolated cultures, and therefore the condition is not a result of prolonged cultivation *in vitro*. Gruchy (1955) examined strains collected from over 150 sources and found that 60 of these could conjugate,* while 90, including 50 amicronucleate strains, could not. Over 60 per cent of the clones isolated from collections made in Central America by Elliott and Hayes (1955) were amicronucleate.

There are no division cysts and asexual reproduction occurs in the free stage. There are probably no resistant cysts; Watson (1946) claimed to have found cysts of *T. pyriformis* but neither in his nor in any other strain of this species could Corliss (1953a) confirm the observation.

Permanent preparations

Fixation in B or S+A and staining with H.H. or D.H. will reveal the meganucleus but little more. China Blue (p. 423) shows the ciliary meridians. The best results are given by Chatton-Lwoff preparations and for a study of the mouth-parts these are indispensable.

The cilia are arranged in 17 to 22, usually 19 or 20, meridians and are rather closer together anteriorly. Of the meridians (Fig. 137D) 2, rarely 3, placed ventrally, do not run from pole to pole like the others, but end at the posterior margin of the buccal overture; the right-hand member of this

---

* Of the 60, 8 were selfing, i.e. members of clones could conjugate with one another, and the other 52 yielded 30 new mating types divided into 7 'varieties'. Conjugation of selfers is commonly, but not always, lethal (cf. Elliott and Gruchy, 1952; Nanney, 1953; Gruchy, 1955; and Corliss, 1960). For some explanation of mating types and the use of 'variety' in the present sense, see p. 300.

pair is called kinety number 1, or the stomatogenic kinety, and from this the remaining meridians or kineties are numbered to the right; in the diagram, D, the normal values of $n-1$ and n are 18 and 19. Each meridian is double, consisting of a primary component (*pm*) bearing the kinetosomes and a shorter, more delicate secondary meridian (*sm*) bearing only a few granules. The anterior end is encircled by a small apical loop (*al*) towards which all the kineties converge though not all of them reach it. Ventrally the loop is connected by a pre-oral suture (*po*) to the circumoral ring (*co*) and a few of the ventral kineties join the suture instead of the loop. The circumoral ring surrounds the buccal overture and is a delicate structure, difficult to trace in its entirety. Also encircling the anterior pole, concentric with and posterior to the apical loop, are 3 intermeridional connectives (*ic*), which run from one side of the circumoral ring to the other. Near the posterior end are the 2 pores of the contractile vacuoles and the slit of the cytoproct (A, *cv*, *cp*).

Within the circumoral ring lie the UM and the AZM. The former appears as a thick arc (*um*) curving round the left and posterior margins of the overture, and from it there project inwards a number of short parallel rods, the nature of which is uncertain. There are 3 membranellae (M_1–M_3) and their bases are shown as 3 blocks of kinetosomes arranged in 2 to 4 rows.

In the meganucleus, the basophil, peripheral granules are F—, and the chromatin itself fills the centre of the nucleus in which a small karyosome with a halo may be differentiated. The quantity of DNA in the meganucleus is approximately doubled between one division and the next (McDonald, 1958).

At division, the first structure to differentiate is the buccal apparatus of the opisthe and stomatogenesis is well advanced before the meganucleus divides. All the rudiments are provided from the stomatogenic kinety (Fig. 137 E–H). This proliferates, below the equator and to the left, a crop of kinetosomes (*s*), which assume an orderly arrangement in 4 rows, of which 3 are bent to the left and downwards and are the rudiments of the membranellae, while the fourth remains to the right, and elongates, according to Furgason, as a single row, which is the base of the UM. The details are given by Chatton, Lwoff, Lwoff, and Monod (1931a) and by Furgason (1940). The buccal apparatus of the opisthe thus forms from the same somatic kinety which provided that of the proter. In more advanced hymenostomes, the continuity of the oral structures is even more direct and stomatogenesis is autonomous. For meiosis, see Ray (1956).

Culture

The species is readily grown in a variety of simple media of which the most obvious is hay infusion. Axenic cultures are easily maintained;

Lwoff's strain initiated in 1923 is still in existence and was studied by Corliss when 30 years old. A suitable medium is 1–2 per cent proteose-peptone solution or van Niel's yeast extract (p. 412). *T. pyriformis* has also been grown in completely synthetic media, in contrast to media containing substances such as serum or yeast extracts which include chemical un-knowns (see Hall's *Protozoology*, 1953).

Paramecium caudatum Ehrenberg

Some members of the genus *Paramecium* are large ciliates, cosmopolitan in distribution, easy to collect and cultivate, and they have accordingly been successfully used for many years as experimental animals. To the protozoologist, *Paramecium* is a highly specialized representative of a diffi-cult suborder, the Peniculina; to the student of biology it is one of the most important animals in existence, and it is as such that it earns its space in this book. There is a very extensive literature which, fortunately, has been clearly summarized in Wichterman's fine monograph (1953); in addition, reference should be made to von Gelei (1934*a*) and Lund (1933, 1941) for an understanding of the buccal ciliature and its functions, to a beautifully illustrated review by Ehret and Powers (1959) for the cell surface, includ-ing the ciliature, to Jennings (1931) for almost classical descriptions of behaviour, and to Sonneborn (1947, 1957) and Beale (1954) for studies on the life-cycle and genetics. In the following description of the structure, *P. caudatum*, as the heading implies, is taken as an example, but there must be frequent references, here and in the original literature, to other species, some of which are very common and of great scientific importance. On this account the following short taxonomic introduction is offered.

Common species of *Paramecium*

When numerous invalid or doubtful species are discarded, there appear to be 8 which are widespread, common and generally accepted.*

A key to these was given by Wenrich (1928) and further information is given by Wichterman (1953). The main characters used in taxonomy are size and shape, the pattern of the kineties on the oral surface, the position of the cytoproct, the condition of the contractile vacuoles, and the number and form of the micronuclei. The last may be compact, with the chromatin evenly distributed, or vesicular, with the chromatin concentrated in a small central mass. The 8 species fall into 2 groups, the *aurelia*, with 3, and the *bursaria* group, with 5, species. In the following brief outline (see

---

* Sonneborn and Dippell (1956) point out that the distinctions between *P. aurelia* and *P. multimicronucleatum* are bridged by giant strains of the former so that the latter name may become a synonym.

Fig. 138) it is assumed, unless otherwise stated, that there are 2 contractile vacuoles, and that when in motion the animal rotates on its axis in an anti-clockwise direction; the measurements given exclude extremes.

A. The *aurelia* group. Elongated and cigar-shaped, more or less circular in T.S., posterior end rounded. Cytoproct not subterminal. Most kine-ties on the right do not abut on the pre-oral suture but run forward more or less parallel with it (A).

1. *P. caudatum* Ehrenberg. 170–290 μ, one small compact micronucleus.

2. *P. multimicronucleatum* Powers & Mitchell. 180–310 μ. The largest species. 2–7, usually 3–4, very small vesicular micronuclei. Often dis-tinguishable *in vivo* from *P. caudatum* by a tendency to form additional contractile vacuoles, but some *P. caudatum* can do this and not all *P. multi-micronucleatum* can.

3. *P. aurelia* Müller. 120–170 μ. Smallest of the group. Two very small vesicular micronuclei.

B. The *bursaria* group. Short and broad, more or less flattened in T.S. Anterior end usually bent to the right and obliquely truncated to the left, posterior end rather blunt. Cytoproct subterminal. All anterior kineties of the right meet the pre-oral suture (Fig. 138B).

4. *P. bursaria* Focke. 85–150 μ. One compact micronucleus. Green with zoochlorellae. The cilia are set closer together in this species and cyclosis is more rapid.

5. *P. trichium* Stokes. 70–90 μ. The smallest species. One compact micronucleus. Two contractile vacuoles, each with accessory vesicles in-stead of the usually radial canals, and opening by a convoluted tube.

6. *P. calkinsi* Woodruff. 110–140 μ. Two, rarely 1 or 3–5, vesicular micro-nuclei. Oral groove very long. The only species to spiral clockwise when swimming.

7. *P. polycaryum* Woodruff and Spencer. 70–110 μ. 3–8, usually 4, vesicular micronuclei. Very like the foregoing but a little shorter and broader, with additional micronuclei, and the vestibulum not so far for-ward, and spirals anticlockwise.

8. *P. woodruffi* Wenrich. 120–210 μ. Largest of the *bursaria* group. 3–4, rarely up to 8, vesicular micronuclei, found anywhere in the body though most of them are usually, as in other species, near the meganucleus. Con-tractile vacuole with 10–12 radial canals, more than any other species.

Besides the above, Šramek-Hušek (1954) has briefly described *P. silesiacum*, which is like *P. calkinsi* but with the anterior contractile vacuole more centrally placed, and Diller and Earl (1958) *P. jenningsi*, which is like *P. aurelia* but slightly larger with relatively larger micronuclei.

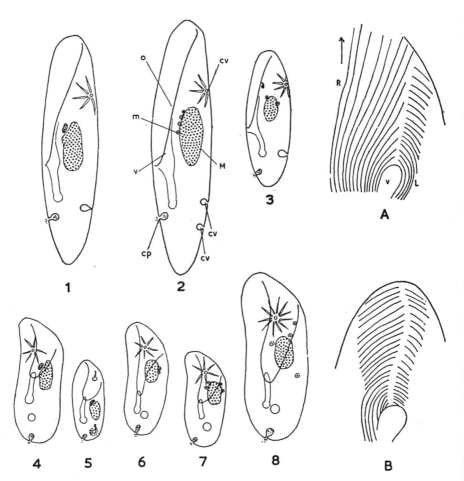

FIG. 138. *Paramecium*: the characters of the best-known species. Diagrammatic. Top row, (1–3, A), *aurelia* group: slim, elongated bodies, posterior end acute, cytoproct distant from posterior, in front of the vestibulum only a few ciliary meridians near it meet the pre-oral suture (A); bottom row (4–8, B), *bursaria* group: short, broad bodies, blunt posterior end, cytoproct subterminal, all or nearly all the ciliary meridians of the right side bend in front of the vestibulum to meet the pre-oral suture (B).

1, *P. caudatum*; 2, *P. multimicronucleatum*; 3, *P. aurelia*; 4, *P. bursaria*; 5, *P. trichium*; 6, *P. calkinsi*; 7, *P. polycaryum*; 8, *P. woodruffi*. All × 250. A, part of the anterior ventral surface to show the pattern of the ciliary meridians in the *aurelia* group; B, the same in the *bursaria* group. (1–8 after Wenrich, simplified; A after von Gelei; B after Lieberman: both simplified.)

cp, cytoproct; *cv*, contractile vacuole; *L*, left; *M*, meganucleus; *m*, micronucleus; *o*, oral groove; *R*, right; *v*, vestibulum; the arrow in A points anteriorly.

P. calkinsi may invade brackish water and even the sea. *P. woodruffi* occurs in brackish though it can survive in fresh water. All other species are fresh water, especially in stagnant pools.

P. caudatum: *the living organism*

The simplest and most reliable way to collect *Paramecium* is to take a litre of pond water with quantities of dead and living vegetation of all kinds and let the whole stand in the laboratory for 2 or 3 days. If present, *Paramecium* will then have multiplied and be visible either in the surface scum or in a ring just below it. The ciliates are then picked out under the binocular dissecting microscope and inoculated into one of the media given below (p. 407). From thin cultures animals may be concentrated as follows. Seal 50 cm of 5-mm or ¼-inch glass tubing at one end and fill to the top with the culture. Stand it upright. The animals are negatively geotropic and will collect at the open end within 24 hours.

Paramecium is generally observed on slides under supported cover slips, but the spiral course of movement and the avoiding reaction are far better demonstrated by a view through a dissecting microscope of a good culture in a Petri dish. The ciliates are very active when first mounted under slips but soon slow down and tend to aggregate about bacterial clumps, on which they browse. For high-power work they must be retarded with methyl cellulose. To see feeding, cyclosis, and defecation, powdered Carmine is added to the mount, and for pH of food vacuoles one drop of Neutral Red (1 : 50,000) to 1 drop of culture; Buck's method (p. 422) combines an indicator with particles and quietens the ciliates simultaneously. Trichocysts are discharged on adding 0·5 per cent Methylene Blue.

Paramecium caudatum is an elongated, asymmetrical organism, usually 170 to 290 μ and about 4 times as long as broad, roughly circular in cross section. The anterior end is cylindrical and blunter than the posterior and the second half of the body is somewhat expanded. On the oral surface is a long, shallow, obliquely set depression, the oral groove, leading to the vestibulum. The entire surface is covered with holotrichous cilia. They are set in parallel rows dorsally, but ventrally there are pre- and post-oral sutures towards which the ciliary lines are inflected; in *P. caudatum* and other members of the *aurelia* group the inflection is slight and most of the lines on the right of the suture run parallel to it (cf. Fig. 138 A, B).

When unimpeded, as in a Petri dish, *Paramecium* normally swims forward with a spiral motion, rotating on its axis, and this rotation is always to the left except in *P. calkinsi*, which swims in a right-hand spiral; all species rotate to the right when swimming backwards (Bullington, 1925, 1930). The rotation is not imparted by the oral groove; it is indeed the reverse (except in *P. calkinsi*) of what would be expected from a groove slanting backwards from left to right and the same is true of most spiralling genera with oral grooves, and, further, portions of animals without the groove spiral normally. Bullington considered that the spiralling was due to an oblique ciliary beat. Ordinarily, *Paramecium* spends much of its time browsing, and between whiles swims with a velocity of about 1 mm per second, but in bacteria-free cultures it may move at from 2 to 3 mm per second and can maintain such a speed for 2 hours (Ludwig, 1928).

On encountering in an 'unfavourable' intensity a wide range of stimuli *Paramecium* performs the well-known reaction recorded by Jennings over

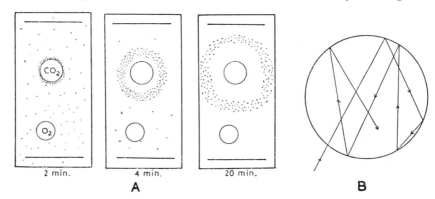

FIG. 139. *Paramecium*: concentration of ciliates in optimal zones. A, distribution of ciliates at various times after introduction of a bubble of carbon dioxide; as the gas diffuses outwards the optimal concentration is indicated by the concentration of ciliates: the bubble of oxygen is ignored. B, path of a ciliate within a drop of weak acid showing the avoiding reactions at the boundary of the optimal stimulus. (After Jennings.)

half a century ago (and see Jennings, 1931). The organism swims in its extended spiral, which approximates to a straight line, until it meets the threshold intensity of the stimulus; the cilia reverse their beat, and the animal backs, turns, advances in the new direction, and, if it again meets the stimulus, repeats the reaction until it is taken clear of the stimulus. Jennings called this 'trial and error' behaviour and the reaction an 'avoiding reaction', but the terms are now sometimes thought to be anthropomorphic, and the expression 'klinokinesis' may be substituted. The reaction may be used to trap *Paramecium* in optimal zones of a stimulus, as in a bubble of carbon dioxide (Fig. 139B). *Paramecium* avoids (relatively) strong chemical stimuli but not very weak ones, e.g. it collects in a drop of 0·01 per cent hydrochloric, acetic, or sulphuric acid. It does not normally respond to oxygen, but will do so in solutions poor in oxygen, and a bubble of air introduced into a mount has no effect unless the mount is sealed, when, as the dissolved oxygen is gradually reduced, the ciliates collect round the edge of the bubble. The positive reaction to CO_2 is important for, of course, the organisms produce this substance themselves, and in quantities which attract more individuals which then add to the CO_2; apparently spontaneous aggregates are thus explained. The effects of the two gases are seen in Fig. 139A, and recall the similar behaviour of *Bodo* (p. 103). While it can tolerate temperatures well outside it, *Paramecium* has an optimal range of 24–28° C and will aggregate at places within it if there is an opportunity. It does not react to light, except negatively to sudden increases in intensity, apart from *P. bursaria*, which has zoochlorellae, and is positively phototactic.

Discharge of the trichocysts is provoked by many chemical and other stimuli. It may be partial, as in response to local contacts and injuries, or total to more powerful stimuli, such as saturated picric acid or rapid heating. Although by now beautiful E.M. photographs of trichocysts are available (Jakus and Hall, 1946; Wohlfarth-Bottermann, 1950) their function remains uncertain. *Paramecium* is a micro-feeder and does not attack any sizeable organism. The use of trichocysts in defence is uncertain and is ineffective against *Didinium*, the principal predator. Trichocysts arrest an animal when they are discharged, but animals which have discharged all their trichocysts and not regenerated a new set are just as efficient at stopping. Jennings thought that 'the discharge is really an expression of injury —a purely secondary, even pathological, phenomenon . . .'; yet the complexity and wide distribution of these organellae seems to call for further explanation.

The natural food of *Paramecium* is bacteria, and it feeds when browsing or swimming slowly; it takes no food when swimming fast. Its feeding apparatus, as seen in the living animal, consists of a shallow gutter, the oral groove, running backwards from left to right across the ventral surface to the vestibulum, a depression lined with continuations of the somatic ciliary lines and leading to the buccal cavity, which contains a more specialized ciliature (Fig. 140, and cf. Fig. 141). As may be seen when the animal rotates from one to another of the positions shown in Fig. 140, the buccal cavity turns inwards, then bends posteriorly and bends once more, so that it opens to the endoplasm, not posteriorly but laterally. Though the details of the buccal ciliature cannot be distinguished *in vivo* it is evident that the cilia on the anterior dorsal wall of the cavity are those of the quadrulus and those to the (animal's) left belong to the peniculi (see p. 289). The cilia of the oral groove beat more strongly than those of the body and they can collect particles from a distance so long as the animal is stationary, and the particles flow to the vestibulum in a characteristic cone. In swimming, the force of the oral beat is to a large extent negated by the movement of the animal, and no feeding cone is formed; only particles approached very closely by the animal are then collected (Mast and Lashley, 1916). Many particles entering the vestibulum are at once rejected; the remainder reach the proximal part of the buccal cavity, from which again some are thrown by the cilia of the quadrulus back into the vestibulum and hence out of the body, while the rest pass into the distal part of the cavity, from which there is no escape. Some workers have maintained that *Paramecium* discriminates between different kinds of particles and that it may learn to do so, but it

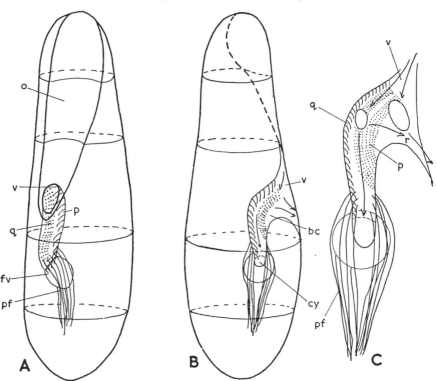

FIG. 140. *Paramecium*: the feeding apparatus (diagrammatic). A, ventral view, the animal turned slightly to its right; B, from the right side, with the feeding and rejection paths marked by arrows; C, part of B enlarged. (After Mast.)

bc, buccal cavity; *cy*, cytostome; *fv*, food vacuole; *o*, oral groove; *p*, peniculi; *pf*, post-buccal fibres; *q*, quadrulus; *r*, rejection path; *v*, vestibulum.

remains difficult to discover the basis of any selection there may be (Mast, 1947).

The food vacuole is formed laterally at the end of the cavity (Figs. 140, 141, *fv*, or FV_1). It grows rapidly at first and then remains at about the same size while it fills up with food particles. The means by which it is liberated are not completely understood, but it seems that the post-buccal fibres (*pf* or F) clasp the vacuole and help to start it on its course. It at once becomes spherical and moves towards the posterior, more rapidly than the endoplasmic flow, as if it had been pushed away from its moorings; it then turns forwards to circulate with the endoplasm (cyclosis) for 1 to 3 hours. Generally it moves in a wide ellipse round the body but there may be some preliminary circulation post-orally. Early in its journey the vacuole decreases greatly in size, then increases again, and these changes in volume are related to those in pH, the smaller vacuoles being more acid: the vacuole is first acid and then less so.* Defecation occurs at a permanent cytoproct (Fig. 138).

There are 2 contractile vacuoles which discharge alternately. Each is fed during diastole by some five to seven canals, which consist of a long terminal portion, an ampulla, which collapses when empty, and a short injector, which opens into the vacuole. According to King (1935) independent vesicles form at the end of each injector and these instantly coalesce to form the single vacuole. At systole the vacuole discharges through a permanent pore. *P. trichium* lacks the canals and is fed from vesicles (King, 1928).

The meganucleus is a conspicuous, ellipsoidal or reniform, granular structure just anterior to the middle of the body. There is a single compact micronucleus, but it is most improbable that it will be seen in a living animal. The vesicular nuclei of some species (Fig. 138), on the other hand, are visible in life.

It seems extremely doubtful that any species of *Paramecium* forms a cyst. As in the case of *Amoeba proteus* the evidence is not coherent and it has never been verified. Wichterman, who has tried and failed to produce cysts of *Paramecium* under the conditions described by the authors remarks that, if it exists at all, it is surprising it has not been seen more often. However, the student who wishes to read some accounts of cysts should consult Ivanić (1926) or, if preferred, Michelson (1928). Ivanić's cyst is spherical; that of Michelson is like a grain of sand.

The reproduction of *Paramecium* is discussed on pp. 292 f.

Permanent preparations

For nuclei fix in S+A, stain in H.H., Feulgen, or Azure A (pp. 436, 437); D.H. gives a fair general picture. *Paramecium* is best fixed to the slide by the celloidin method (p. 429), but it is brittle after fixation and so dangerous to centrifuge. However, it rapidly sinks to the bottom of a standing tube and the opaque animals are easily visible. For pellicular and infraciliary systems, use Chatton-Lwoff (p. 443).

* It is fair to say that there is hardly a fact mentioned in this account which could not be questioned. Many authors have contributed to our uncertainties about food selection, feeding, vacuole formation, and cyclosis in *Paramecium*, and their opinions are presented by Wichterman (1953). The present account follows largely that of Mast (1947), with help from Lund (1933, 1941).

The structures collectively known as the silver-line system, that is, all that is revealed by various silver-impregnation techniques, have been studied especially by Klein(1928), von Gelei (1932, 1934*a*, and earlier), Lund (1933, 1941), and Yusa (1957). To some extent they employed different techniques, different species, and different terminologies, and there are undoubted difficulties in collating their results. Some of these disappear when it is grasped that the so-called silver-line system has in fact no unity but consists of 2, possibly 3, parts, which may be considered separately. These are the pellicular pattern of ridges, well shown in dry preparations, the subpellicular infraciliature, best seen in wet preparations, and perhaps a 'neuro-motor system' of doubtful provenance.*

The body is covered by a pattern of pellicular ridges, forming polygons, usually hexagons (Fig. 141, bottom right) and running roughly in long parallel lines. On the dorsal surface this simple arrangement is preserved. Ventrally the lines converge before and behind the vestibulum towards pre- and post-oral sutures. In all species this flexure of the lines is well marked on the animal's left, but in the *aurelia* group of species a few of the lines are bent sufficiently to meet the pre-oral suture on the right and the rest pass forwards parallel to it (Fig. 138, cf. A and B). Each hexagon is slightly depressed into an ectoplasmic dimple from the centre of which a cilium emerges. A small spot on each anterior and posterior margin of a hexagon marks the position of a trichocyst. The elements of the somatic infraciliature trace below the pellicle the same pattern as the latter. The kinetosomes are connected by their kinetodesmata (Fig. 112F) and, especially in the region of the vestibulum, by additional transverse fibrillae (Fig. 141V). The real existence of these structures was shown by Worley (1933), who noted both series of fibrillae in layers of living ectoplasm spread on slides, and further confirmation comes from E.M. studies (Metz, Pitelka, and Westphal, 1953; Sedar and Porter, 1955; and see p. 215).

The intricate patterns produced at different levels by the foregoing (and other and dubious structures not here mentioned) have usually been supposed to represent more or less distinct pellicular and subpellicular fibrillar systems. Ehret and Powers (1959) have suggested that this interpretation is misleading. For them, the essential unit of structure at the surface of *Paramecium* is the 'ciliary corpuscle'. Each corpuscle is shaped rather like an apple and has an inner and an outer membrane separated by a space (Fig. 112B); the outer membrane is continuous over the cilium and the pellicle; both membranes are depressed in the centre of the corpuscle, where the cilium emerges. All the corpuscles are tightly packed so that

---

* The neuro-motor system of Lund (1933) included much that we should now regard as part of the buccal infraciliature, and the few remaining components are difficult to place. It is most doubtful whether the neuro-motor system described by Rees (1922) exists (see Worley, 1933), and it is omitted from the present account.

their walls produce hexagonal outlines. The various patterns reported at different levels by previous observers are sectional views of the outlines of the corpuscles. The kinetodesmata remain the only truly fibrillar elements.

The vestibulum is a shallow, irregularly conical depression into which the somatic ciliature, with its accompanying pellicular and subpellicular differentiations, is extended. The appearances here, as on the pellicle, are, in Ehret and Powers's interpretation, to be explained as the products of closely packed ciliary corpuscles. As the longitudinal kineties are invaginated, their ends meet and they form the circular or elliptical rows of the vestibulum. The 'fibres' transverse to them run longitudinally in the vestibulum and spread radially as they emerge on to the surface of the body. Within the vestibulum, the ordinary somatic cilia are continued for varying distances, except on the posterior wall, where they are either lacking or very short; it is from this naked area that stomatogenesis takes its origin. According to von Gelei (1934a) the cilia of this region are paired (Fig. 142). Below the vestibulum lies the buccal cavity, containing the specialized oral ciliature (Figs. 141, 142 BC), which consists of an endoral membrane, dorsal and ventral peniculi, and the quadrulus. Below the cavity there possibly exists a very short unciliated region, the cytopharynx, and, if so, the true cytostome lies at the junction of the ciliated and unciliated regions. The entire oral system is highly specialized and is difficult to examine and interpret.

The endoral membrane is a single row of cilia curving in an arc along the right wall of the funnel and marking the junction of the vestibulum and buccal cavity, or buccal overture proper (Fig. 113F; Figs. 141, 142E). It is more extensive in the *aurelia* than in the *bursaria* group. Its cilia are said to be conjoined and from its structure and position it is identified as the homologue of the UM of the Tetrahymenina (Corliss, 1956).

Opposite the membrane, on the left of the buccal overture, originate 3 ciliated bands which form the principal part of the feeding apparatus. They are, from left to right, the ventral peniculus, the dorsal peniculus, and the quadrulus (membrana quadripartita or *Vierermembran*). In the *aurelia* group, each of these organellae consists of 4 rows of cilia, but in the *bursaria* group there is some variation in composition of the peniculi. The ventral peniculus is short and simply follows the curve of the buccal cavity below the vestibular margin. The dorsal peniculus follows the same course but continues onwards to twist across the ventral wall of the cavity and end close to the point of formation of the food vacuole, i.e. at the cytostome. The quadrulus is less compact than the peniculi, and its lines of cilia tend to diverge along the middle part of their course. The quadrulus spirals down the cavity nearly parallel to the dorsal peniculus and ends very close to it. Thus the terminal cilia of these 2 structures form a group together, and according to Lund they beat towards the anterior; their effect,

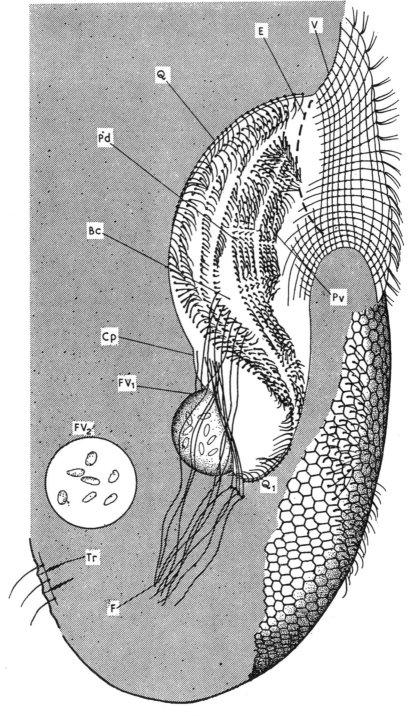

Fig. 141

combined with that of the downward beat of the tracts above them, drives
particles to the side and into the forming vacuole. (No reversal of the beat
is required; a posterior beat initiated at the anterior end of the tracts will
tend to point anteriorly as the tracts turn over the lower wall of the buccal

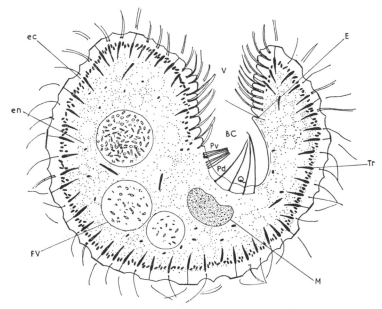

FIG. 142. *Paramecium*: schematic section at the level of the buccal cavity as
seen from an anterior position, and showing the vestibulum, lined with double
cilia, and the buccal cavity, containing the dorsal and ventral peniculi (*Pd, Pv*)
and the quadrulus (*Q*); one cilium of the endoral membrane is seen on the right
(*E*) at the boundary of the vestibulum and buccal cavity, i.e. buccal overture.
(After von Gelei.)

Abbreviations as in Fig. 141; *ec* and *en* are ectoplasm and endoplasm.

cavity.) The peniculi and quadrulus are interpreted as developments from
the membranellae of the tetrahymenal complex; in support of this view,
the cilia of the 4 rows of the quadrulus still appear to be longitudinally
coalesced, and the shortest component, corresponding to the third membranella, finds its correct position in the ventral peniculus.

FIG. 141. The oral ciliature of *Paramecium*. The animal lies with its oral (ventral) surface
facing the right of the page and with part of its right side removed to show the dorsal, left,
and ventral walls of the buccal cavity. (After Lund with modifications from von Gelei.)

Bc, buccal cavity; *Cp*, cytopharynx; *E*, position of endoral membrane on right border (removed) of
buccal overture; *F*, fibres in endoplasm enclosing food vacuole; FV_1; food vacuole during formation;
FV_2, food vacuole after separation; *Pd*, dorsal peniculus; *Pv*, ventral peniculus; *Q*, quadrulus; the
quadrulus runs down the dorsal wall of the *Bc* anteriorly, where part of its right-hand line of cilia
is shown in optical section, crosses the left wall of the cavity to continue on the ventral wall, where
its left-hand line is shown in section at Q_1; *Tr*, trichocyst; *V*, vestibulum.

From the posterior part of the buccal cavity a number of fibres (Fig. 141 *F*) depends freely into the endoplasm. They are heavy and flexible and undergo movements suggesting peristalsis; their function appears to be to guide and possibly propel the food vacuole along the first part of its course.

The life-cycle

The life-cycle of *Paramecium* is complicated. It consists of periods of growth interrupted by binary fission, which is its only means of multiplication, and periodic recourse to the curious sexual processes of conjugation, autogamy, and cytogamy. The last three not only fulfil their obvious function of effecting genetical recombination but they also provide the occasions for a regular reconstitution of the meganucleus from a daughter of the micronucleus. This nuclear reorganization appears to be indispensable for the continued health of stocks of *Paramecium* and further provision for it is seen in the experimentally produced type of meganuclear regeneration described below (p. 298). In addition, a variety of nuclear changes may occur without the intervention of the micronucleus; they are collectively known as hemixis (Diller, 1936) and their significance is uncertain. Here only binary fission, the regular sexual phenomena and meganuclear regeneration are considered.* Much further information is offered by Wichterman (1953) and Sonneborn (1947).

Under good conditions, healthy strains of *P. caudatum* may undergo binary fission, which lasts about 30 minutes, as often as two or three times in 24 hours.† The animal elongates, becomes spindle-shaped, stops feeding and its oral groove disappears. The nuclei move apart and the micronucleus divides mitotically, its daughters moving towards the extremities of the body but remaining connected by a thread for a long time; at no stage does the nuclear membrane break down. The meganucleus is partitioned without mitosis. Stomatogenesis begins early. The old buccal apparatus passes intact, but for the endoral membrane, which dedifferentiates but reforms later, to the proter, and a new set of organellae is generated for the opisthe.

* Wichterman (1953) calls attention to the fact that many of the books continue to give detailed accounts of endomixis, which almost certainly does not occur in *Paramecium*, while neglecting autogamy, which quite certainly does. Woodruff and Erdmann (1914) and Erdmann and Woodruff (1916) reported endomixis as a process in which the meganucleus is replaced from a product of micronuclear division without a sexual preliminary. The authors were probably observing stages of autogamy. Sonneborn was unable to find either cytological or genetical evidence for endomixis, but found both for autogamy. The subject is discussed by him (1947), and see, for a defence of endomixis, Woodruff, in Calkins and Summers, *Protozoa in Biological Research*, 1941, p. 646. Endomixis does occur in some of the lower ciliates (see p. 230).

† Curiously enough, we do not possess any complete account of binary fission in *Paramecium*. To the outlines given by Hertwig (1889), von Gelei (1934*b*) has added some notes on the behaviour of the pellicular and subpellicular structures, and Yusa (1957) has given some description of stomatogenesis; see also Ehret and Powers (1959).

The *Anlagen* of the latter are derived from elements of the parental buccal apparatus, i.e. stomatogenesis is autonomous. From its right side, towards the posterior, near the boundary of vestibulum and buccal cavity where the wall is devoid of cilia, a pouch grows backwards; it contains a disorderly group of kinetosomes ('anarchic field'); they become arranged in 6 rows, of which 4 at once constitute the quadrulus, while each of the other 2 forms the rudiment of a peniculus. The anterior and posterior contractile vacuoles become the posterior and anterior vacuoles of the daughters. The origin of the new endoral membranes remains uncertain.

The classical accounts of conjugation in *P. aurelia* are those of Hertwig and of Maupas, who both published in 1889, and the story they told is still widely accepted. It is convenient to begin with *P. aurelia*, because this is the species most widely used in genetical studies, the results of which are helpful in interpreting some of the cytological events. Conjugation takes place only between mature members of opposite mating types of the same variety (see p. 300), and is further conditioned by various other factors, such as the nutritional state of the animals, the time of day, and so on, which vary with the variety. Successful conjugants are usually rather smaller than the trophic forms, and they are slender.

When different mating types of the same variety are mixed in the circumstances favourable for the variety, an extremely striking mating reaction occurs, vividly described by Jennings (1939) for *P. bursaria*. Immediately on mixing the individuals become clumped in dense masses which grow in size until within a few minutes groups are formed consisting of hundreds of adhering ciliates, and when later these break up they are seen to be attached by their oral surfaces in pairs and they proceed to conjugate. When a pair is formed, the 2 ciliates adhere as if stuck together by their cilia. They may be attached at any part of the surface, there is no co-ordination of movement, and one animal is dragged about by the other, unless the two happen to be pointing the same way, when they swim together. As they move, other ciliates become stuck to them until large clots of scores or a hundred or so are formed. The contacts are in the first place accidental and the adherence occurs only between individuals of opposite types. This is elegantly shown in *P. bursaria*, which has symbiotic algae, by keeping a culture of one type in the dark until it loses its green colour, and then mixing it with a normal culture of an opposite type; all the pairs consist of a green and a colourless individual. The large clumps formed within 3 or 4 minutes of mixing usually remain dense for about half an hour or more and then, as they relax, many ciliates will be found united in pairs, at first by their oral cilia and later by their oral surfaces. Some ciliates form chains in which most are orientated in the same direction so that the chains swim like snakes. Many individuals remain which do not pair. The optimum time for clotting is a character of the variety; for example, in mating types of varieties 1 and 2, the tendency to clot appears about 8 a.m., grows stronger during the day, begins to weaken about 4 o'clock in the afternoon and disappears between 6 and 7 o'clock in the evening.

The time taken for conjugation varies with temperature and other factors, but in general *P. aurelia* and *P. caudatum* remain joined for 12 to 15 hours and *P. bursaria* for 20 to 48 hours. Events follow the same course in both partners and will be described for only one, in *P. aurelia* (Fig. 143), which has 2 micronuclei. The meganucleus disintegrates during the latter half of the conjugation period. It becomes loose in texture and unwinds into a complex and twisted skein. Constrictions appear which disrupt the nucleus into some 20 to 40 portions which will in time be resorbed into the cytoplasm. The differences reported in the times at which this has been seen to occur are possibly to be ascribed to nutritional differences; well-fed animals grow and divide more quickly, before disruption of the meganucleus is complete; in starved animals, these processes are delayed. The first micronuclear division begins early, before any changes in the meganucleus, and it lasts for about two-thirds of the total period. The 2 original nuclei enlarge from about 3 μ to 20 μ long and form characteristic crescents and then broad spindles. The chromosomes number between 30 and 40. There is no resting phase and the daughter nuclei at once divide again. Seven of the 8 products disintegrate and the remaining daughter divides once more to form the gametic nuclei (pronuclei), which are thus sisters. Meanwhile a cytoplasmic bulge, the paraoral cone, has developed in the vestibular region of each conjugant, and across it moves the migratory or male nucleus to fertilize the stationary or female nucleus of the partner. The zygotic nucleus (synkaryon) divides twice (three times in *P. caudatum*) and between the two divisions the partners generally separate and are now known as exconjugants. The 4 nuclei become 2 micronuclei and 2 meganuclei. The exconjugant divides, and so do the micronuclei, but not the meganuclei, which are distributed whole, so that the daughters have the normal complement of 1 meganucleus and 2 micronuclei. Subsequent divisions follow the normal course of binary fission.

It is generally assumed that the first two micronuclear divisions in a conjugant are reductional and the third is equational. But it has been suggested that (1) the last division is reductional, and (2) it is not true that all but one of the 8 micronuclei degenerate, but several may survive and begin a third division and so provide a variable number of gametic nuclei (Diller, 1936). The following facts speak against these two suggestions. Inheritance is biparental, as Jennings knew many years ago (Jennings, 1913; Jennings and Lashley, 1913). This is to say that when clones from 2 exconjugants are compared with nonconjugating clones of the same stock, they are not only seen to show more variation, as would be expected after genetical

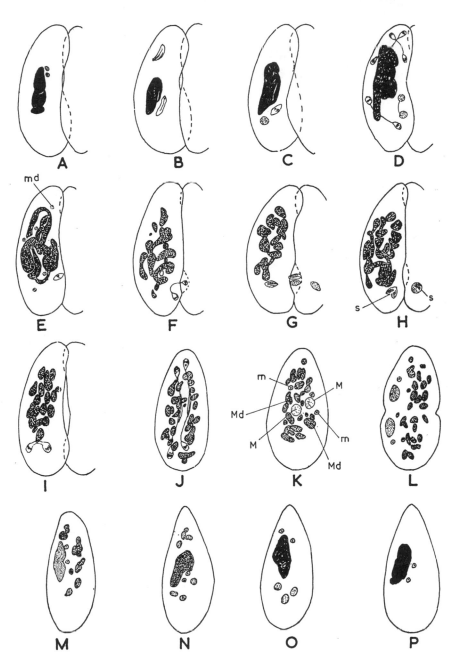

FIG. 143. *Paramecium aurelia*: conjugation. Only the left conjugant is completed. ×c. 400. A *mm* (micronuclei) enlarging; B, *mm* in crescent stage; C, *mm* in metaphase of 1st maturation division; D, 2nd maturation division: *M* beginning to skein; E, 7 *mm* degenerating (*md*), 8th in 3rd maturation division; F, telophase; G, migration of gametic nuclei; H, synkaryon (*s*); I and J, 1st and 2nd postzygotic divisions; K, the 4 products of the zygotic nucleus differentiate into 2 *M* and 2 *m* among the fragments of the old meganucleus (*Md*); L, fission of the exconjugant: the *mm* have divided, the new *MM* developed further, fragments of the old *M* are distributed among the daughters; M–P, animals after further fissions: P, after the 4th, is fully developed. (After Sonneborn, based on Hertwig: modified.)

M(*d*), meganucleus (degenerating); *m*(*d*), micronucleus (degenerating); *s*, synkaryon.

recombination, but their departures from the parental stock tend to be the same in the clones derived from both exconjugants. The consistency of this result cannot be explained unless there is cross-fertilization producing genotypically identical zygotes in each member of the pair. An extension of the same reasoning shows that reduction must occur during the first 2 divisions and, further, that the gametic nuclei are sisters. Fig. 144 shows the inheritance of a single pair of genes from heterozygotic mates on two different assumptions. If the third division is reductional it gives different types of gametes in each conjugant; half the pairs will give similar descendants, which will be heterozygotic, and the other half will give descendants which differ, being equally divided into opposite homozygotes. If the third division is equational, all the descendants of any pair must be alike, and again half will be heterozygotic, one-quarter of each being oppositely homozygotic. It is the second possibility that corresponds to the facts, and the results depend on the provision of gametic nuclei, not only by equational division of a haploid nucleus, but division of the same nucleus; that is, gametic nuclei are sisters. A fuller discussion of the points, with additional evidence, is given by Sonneborn (1947).

The course of events in *P. caudatum* is essentially similar (Calkins and Cull, 1907). The single micronucleus produces 4 daughters, of which 3 degenerate and the fourth divides to provide gametic nuclei. After fertilization, 3 divisions give 8 nuclei. Four grow into meganuclei and do not divide at the next 2 fissions. It seems most likely that 3 of the 4 remaining nuclei degenerate and the fourth becomes a micronucleus, which divides at all subsequent fissions.

Cytogamy is the name given to a process which is precisely similar to conjugation except that the gametic nuclei fuse with their sisters within the body of the same parent; there is no cross-fertilization. Its frequency, in *P. aurelia*, varies greatly with temperature; at 17° C about 95 per cent of the mating pairs undergo conjugation and the remaining 5 per cent cytogamy, but the proportion for cytogamy is greatly increased when the temperature is raised or lowered to 47 per cent at 10° C and 60 per cent at 27° C. The cytological evidence for cytogamy is confirmed by the genetical results, which are inconsistent with cross-fertilization, each partner retaining its own genes.

Autogamy is a rehearsal in solitude of the events which constitute cytogamy when they take place among pairs. It is in fact no more than self-fertilization accompanied, of course, by a reconstitution of the meganucleus. All the zygote nuclei are formed, as before, from the fusion of 2 sisters derived from a single haploid nucleus by one equational division,* and it

---

* The only other species in which autogamy has been studied in detail is *P. polycaryum*, where Diller (1954) found a clearer cytological indication than in *P. aurelia* that gametic nuclei are sisters.

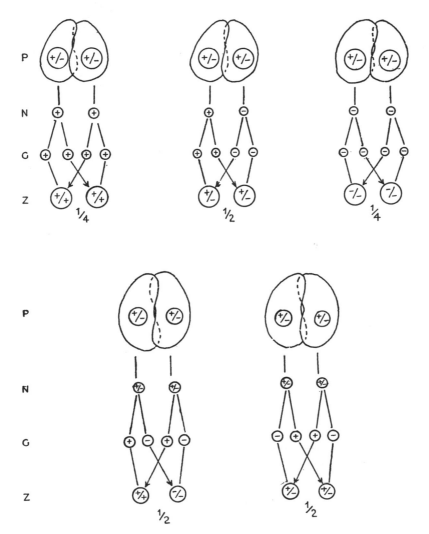

FIG. 144. *Paramecium*: behaviour of a pair of genes (+ and −) on crossing heterozygotic parents (P). N is the functional survivor of the 2nd maturation division; G and Z are
gametic and zygotic nuclei. The top row shows the result if the 3rd division (between N
and G) is equational: each pair gives equal exconjugants of which half are heterozygotes, a
quarter dominant and a quarter recessive homozygotes. The bottom row shows the result
if the 3rd division is reductional: half the pairs consist of equal heterozygotes and the
other half of unequal homozygotes. In both cases it is assumed that gametic nuclei are
sisters. Breeding results are in accordance with the assumptions illustrated in the top row.
(After Sonneborn.)

follows that all such zygotes are homozygotic. Now, autogamy is induced in the laboratory by maintaining stocks with a rich supply of food and then starving them, and when this is done the interval between successive autogamies on most stocks of variety I is 10 to 14 days, and in some it is as little as 3 to 4 days. That is, autogamy becomes of frequent occurrence, and periods of heterozygosis are brief, and, as both homozygotes are produced in equal numbers, recessive genes are easily revealed in this way. In fact, autogamy is a mechanism for inducing a high degree of homozygosis, and it provides a quicker means of genetical analysis than conjugation.

In all the above processes, except binary fission which is purely a means of duplication,* genetical recombination is accompanied by replacement of the old meganucleus from a micronuclear source. It is now known that reconstitution of the meganucleus is possible without the intervention of the micronucleus, for in 1940 Sonneborn discovered that fragments of the old meganucleus dispersed at conjugation could be distributed to subsequent fission products and each could give rise to a functional meganucleus. Growth and division of nuclei at this stage may be inhibited by heating animals to 38° C, when subsequent fissions give daughters that do not contain presumptive meganuclei but do contain surviving fragments of the old meganucleus; such fragments, instead of being resorbed into the cytoplasm, regenerate and provide functional meganuclei. Meganuclei obtained in this way may, of course, differ genetically from the micronuclei present in the same animal. For example, if opposite homozygotic conjugants mate, the zygotes and all their daughter nuclei will be heterozygotic; but if at the same time development of the presumptive meganuclei is inhibited, while fragments of the old, parental meganucleus are allowed to regenerate, then the definitive meganucleus will be homozygotic. Organisms produced in this way phenotypically express the constitution of the meganucleus, which overrides the micronuclei. The micronucleus is the only sexual nucleus and the only agent of genetical recombination and it normally expresses its message through a meganucleus derived from it. As the existence of amicronucleate stocks of *Paramecium* shows, it is not essential to the life of the individual. But there is some evidence that to the extent that it periodically renews the meganucleus it is needed for the continued viability of stocks, and this must now be considered.

When cultures of *Paramecium* are kept without conjugating their vitality commonly decreases and they die out. Vitality is usually measured by their rate of fission, which, in the circumstances, decreases. There has never been any doubt that this fate often does overtake non-conjugating clones, but about whether this is necessarily so, and whether conjugation really does in some way rejuvenate the stock, there have been two opinions. In the view

---

* Except for a possibility, which cannot be confidently denied, that there are inequalities in the meganuclear portions distributed at fission; but see p. 229.

associated with Maupas, Calkins, and others, there is a term to the life of a clone which does not conjugate, and it will inevitably reach a condition somehow analogous to the senescence of a metazoan body, and then, unless conjugation supervenes, it dies out.* The contrary opinion, held by Wood-ruff and his school, was that given correct cultural conditions and adequate food, non-conjugating clones could survive indefinitely. The conflicting evidence accumulated in support of both sides has been patiently reviewed by Wichterman (1953). Most of it is vitiated by two weaknesses. First, the life of a clone is affected by its culture medium, pH, temperature, and other factors, and it is dependent also on the species, and within the species, the variety of *Paramecium* employed. So little is known about these variables during the experiments performed in the past, that they cannot be strictly compared with each other, far less repeated. Second, the discovery of autogamy, unknown to the earlier workers, as a common occurrence, invalidated their studies, for it contributed to the clones just those elements of sex and nuclear reconstitution of which they were supposed to be de-prived. The problem has to be reformulated. What is the effect of conjuga-tion and autogamy on vitality? and: which is the effective element in these processes, sex or the nuclear reorganization which accompanies it?

From a study of over 10,000 exconjugants or the clones derived from them, Jennings (1944 *a, b*) showed that conjugation may have four effects. (1) It may be lethal. (2) Some exconjugants undergo a few fissions, but then their descendants die. (3) Exconjugants may produce weak, abnormal, or patho-logical clones, and some of these die while others survive, although weak and abnormal. (4) Conjugation has a rejuvenescent effect; the exconjugant clones divide vigorously, flourish, and at times are more vigorous than their parents. In general, mortality is high after conjugation in old clones and low in young ones; it varies from 0 per cent to 100 per cent and 'at random the mortality runs usually around 30 to 50 per cent of the exconjugants'. In fact, conjugation may arrest a decline in vitality, but it does not always do so, and many factors have to be taken into consideration. For example, the exconjugants of inbred clones may suffer very heavy mortality, and in some clones, especially old ones, conjugation may be fatal, though non-conjugants from the parents may continue to multiply in culture. The effect of autogamy is equally complex. In normally vigorous clones, autogamy

---

* As pointed out by Comfort (1956), 'it is . . . probably misleading to identify the decline of protozoan cultures with the metazoan senescence which it superficially re-sembles. It is doubtful if analogies can properly be drawn between acellular organisms and metazoan cells . . .'. The attempt to regard the sum of all the bodies of all the asexual generations of ciliates derived from a single exconjugant as somehow the equivalent of all the cells of a metazoan body is very strained. The controversy about ciliate senescence has been much bedevilled with analogies of this sort, as with, for example, the unhappy attempts to discover in the history of clones, where fission leaves no corpses, a potential, if somewhat theoretical, immortality. The question whether there is a natural term to the life of an individual protozoan is a different one: see p. 14.

usually yields strong, more rarely weak or non-viable clones. Clones which have begun to decline have a normal fission rate restored. Old clones, far gone in decline, die whether they undergo autogamy or not and it may hasten their ends. According to Sonneborn (1954), one or the other process eventually becomes indispensable, though either may be harmful, especially to old clones; without them decline leads to death. He concluded that 'in spite of all the risks involved, the animals must undergo autogamy (or conjugation) or perish. Of those that take the risk, if they have not waited too long to do so, some will survive and be rejuvenated.'*

It is difficult to point to any single element of autogamy and fertilization as the factor promoting viability. It cannot be cross-fertilization, which is absent from autogamy, or recombination, for this is absent from all but the first autogamy of a series and thereafter the homozygosis which it initiates is perpetuated at all subsequent autogamies. (In this connexion it is to be noted that the invigorating effect of crossing 2 stocks of *P. aurelia* survives the first autogamy, i.e. homozygosis does not here impair hybrid vigour, which cannot therefore be ascribed simply to a state of heterozygosis; see Siegel, 1958.) Fauré-Fremiet (1953) has suggested an agency to explain the decline of a clone and its revival by meganuclear reconstitution on the assumption that the distribution of genes in the meganucleus is disorderly. If the nucleus contains many sets of genes arranged haphazardly, then, though there are several ways in which the nucleus may be divided which by chance will provide each daughter with a complete set of genes, eventually daughters must come to receive defective sets and as time goes on they will become commoner than complete ones until only reduplication of the complete genetic equipment from the micronucleus can restore the losses, and this, of course, is what occurs at autogamy and conjugation. It will be noted that this suggestion cannot be reconciled with the view discussed elsewhere (p. 228) that the meganucleus contains, not a random assortment of genes, but a collection of genomes in orderly arrangements. Sonneborn (1954), after reviewing various opinions about the revitalizing effect of autogamy and conjugation, concluded that none of them was satisfactory.

Mating types and the species problem

Paramecium has developed an extraordinarily high degree of sexual differentiation, on an entirely physiological, never a morphological, plane, and it is reflected in the production of an elaborate system of mating types discovered by Sonneborn (1937) in *P. aurelia*. Individuals may be sorted

* One of the clones used by Sonneborn was Woodruff's old Methuselah strain of *P. aurelia* which has been maintained for over 50 years without conjugating, though it can still do so when given the opportunity. Sonneborn confirmed Woodruff's view that conjugation was unnecessary, but we now see, of course, that autogamy occurs.

into groups the members of which never mate with others of the same group. The group is called a mating type. Members of one mating type may conjugate with all members of one or more other mating types, and all the mating types capable of conjugating together constitute a variety. For example, if a variety of a certain species contains mating types A, B, C, and D as its 4 mating types, then all members of A may conjugate with all of B, C, and D, all of B with A, C, and D, and so on, but A's cannot conjugate with A's, or B's with B's. A species may contain a considerable number of varieties; most varieties contain only 2 mating types. In 1957, Sonneborn reported that 16 varieties were known in *P. aurelia*; 15 contained 2 mating types each, and the sixteenth (originally reported as belonging to *P. multimicronucleatum*, now united by Sonneborn to *P. aurelia*) had 4. *P. caudatum* likewise has 16 varieties each containing 2 types. The position in *P. bursaria* is rather different. Six varieties have been reported though the status of 1 is doubtful. Of the other 5, one has 2 mating types, 3 have 4, and 1 has 8. A great deal remains to be discovered about the number and distribution of mating types. Some are cosmopolitan, while one variety of *P. aurelia* is at present believed to be restricted to Madagascar. Mating systems comparable to that of *Paramecium*, though less elaborate, are known in some other ciliates, such as *Euplotes* and *Tetrahymena*. The subject is reviewed by Sonneborn (1947, 1957) and by Beale (1954).

It is evident that the organisms which we distinguish on morphological grounds as species, and which are shown on p. 282, are really compounds of many reproductively isolated groups, the so-called varieties, which are fertile within themselves. It is these subgroups which correspond with the modern concept of a species, that is, a population among which gene flow is possible. There is no doubt that varieties are restricted in this way. It is true that mating between some, but not all, varieties is possible, but it never occurs as readily as between types in the same variety and is usually ineffective in that most of the products of inter-varietal breeding are non-viable or their descendants rapidly become so. It is difficult to prove the existence of a complete intervarietal barrier to gene flow, but, as Sonneborn remarks, the flow can at the most be but a trickle and it is always in danger of drying up. Apart from their mating reactions, varieties differ in many physiological characters, such as the time taken for conjugation, the time of day at which it occurs, the length of the period of immaturity (if any) during which mating is impossible, in serological traits, and so on. Some groups of varieties show size differences, but they cannot be used to separate all varieties, and no clear-cut, consistent morphological distinctions such as would appeal to the taxonomist are as yet known. In practice only the mating type difference can be used to distinguish between varieties and much remains to be discovered about them. The decision whether to regard the varieties as species must depend on how far one is prepared to extend a species concept to organisms which in the end may turn out to be unsuitable to receive it. The question of nomenclature is more easily decided. If all the varieties were recognized as species and accordingly named, we should require to add at once some 30 new names, with the prospect of more to come, to the 2 we at present employ to label *P. aurelia* and *P. caudatum*, and it would be difficult if not impossible for all but a handful of experts to apply them correctly.* Nomenclature is the hand-maiden, not the mistress, of taxonomy, and if it is to remain so, we must not invent names we do not know how to use.

Culture

Paramecium is usually maintained in the laboratory on infusions of hay or lettuce leaf (p. 407). Axenic cultures have been available since 1942 and can now be grown in a medium which is chemically defined except for one constituent (Miller and Johnson, 1957).

Cyclidium glaucoma Müller

This small ciliate is easily obtained and cultured and it clearly illustrates the features of the suborder Pleuronematina. In nature it is fairly common in fresh water and in soil, and it penetrates brackish water. It frequently appears in faecal suspensions (see p. 303). Specimens have been described from the sea, but freshwater strains cannot be adapted to sea water, and, though the morphological differences between fresh- and salt-water strains are very slight, they seem to be physiologically isolated, and would not normally have opportunities to interbreed. In some localities *Cyclidium* may be regularly obtained by uprooting a handful or so of grass, boiling it for a minute and, after cooling, inoculating a little grass and soil from the same source: *Cyclidium* appears in the surface scum in 4 to 6 days, and is transferred to hay or faecal media. The following account is based on fresh-water material, which is common. *C. glaucoma* has been described very thoroughly by Hoare (1927); the related, euryhaline *Uronema nigricans* (= *U. marina*) has been studied by Párducz (1939) and the 2 genera have been compared by him (Párducz, 1940). For other pleuronematine ciliates, see Noland (1937).

The living organism

C. glaucoma is small, 14–23 $\mu \times$ 6–13 μ, ovoid in outline, and striped by 10 longitudinal grooves bearing the somatic cilia (Fig. 145). These are few in number (15–20 in each row), long, especially towards the posterior where they are more widely spaced, and they do not reach the front of the

* For a sharp retort to this counsel of convenience, see Hairston (1958).

body, which is left as a naked, slightly swollen cap. A conspicuous feature is the undulating membrane, which, during feeding, stands out from the long right margin of the exposed buccal cavity (effectively a peristome) like a sail; it is the *Segelmembran* of German authors. It curls posteriorly around the lower limit of the peristome and so acts as a trap for food (bacteria) directed backwards from the anterior by some of the somatic cilia. As noted below, there are very few cilia within the peristomial area itself, but possibly some of them, springing from the posterior transverse rows seen in Fig. 145B, assist in directing food to the cytostome; there is a long, narrow cytopharynx.

When feeding the animal is stationary, lying on its dorsal surface, pegged down by its long, motionless, somatic cilia, which, except for those just anterior to the buccal cavity, lie spread out around the body. These long, motionless cilia, which in contact with a substrate act as organs of attachment, are thigmotactic. They are not highly developed in *Cyclidium*, but in the related Thigmotrichida they form powerful fields of adhesive cilia (cf. Figs. 147–9). The habit of prolonged rest seen here during feeding may account for some of the pleuronematine characters—the sparse ciliature, the hypertelic UM (many sessile animals tend to produce efficient means of capturing what food comes their way), and the long, adhesive, thigmotactic cilia. Movement is usually erratic; a stationary animal suddenly flicks away from its anchorage as if knocked out of position, and almost at once settles nearby, but sustained swimming is possible, and then the UM, which would be a hindrance if extended, is folded against the side of the body. There is a large contractile vacuole at the posterior end, and below it trails a long, stiff cilium or caudal seta.

Permanent preparations

B followed by H.H. should be used for nuclei. The meganucleus is spherical and anterior, with an adjacent micronucleus. Temporary preparations with Opal or China Blue (p. 423) show the cilia, but Ag impregnation is more precise. The infraciliature is shown in Fig. 145B. Lying transversely to the length of the UM are groups or lines of kinetosomes of which only the 2 long ones posteriorly and the anterior group bear cilia. These and the vestigial kinetosomes accompanying them represent the remains of the membranellae seen in the Tetrahymenina; they are better developed in *Uronema* (C) where their homologies are more obvious.

Culture

Cyclidium has a marked coprophilous habit and probably the simplest way of maintaining it is to dilute a small portion (about the size of a pea) of human faeces with about 40 ml of tap-water and use this as a medium

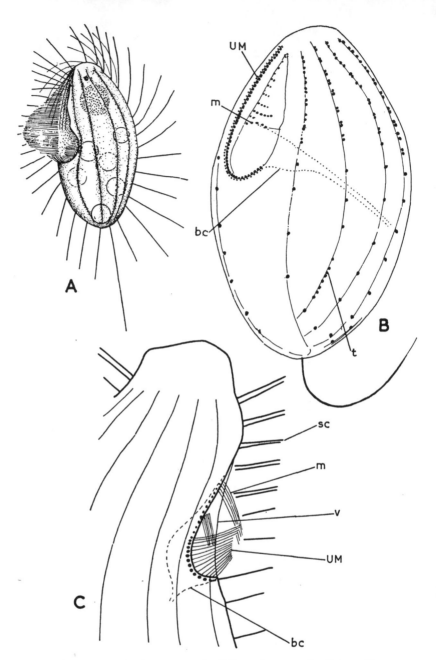

Fig. 145. *Cyclidium* and *Uronema*. A, *Cyclidium glaucoma*: the living ciliate. × 2,000. The feeding cilia are shown beating over the vestibulum. B, *C. glaucoma*: Ag preparation. × 3,200. The kinetosomes of the undulating membrane, *UM*, are obvious on the animal's left; *m* marks the last row of a group of kinetosomes perhaps representing vestiges of membranellae; only the posterior granules bear cilia. The cilia thought to be thigmotactic are marked by kinetosomes at *t*. The existence of the buccal cavity, *bc*, is doubtful. c, *Uronema*: diagram to show buccal ciliature. × 4,000. The anterior kinetosomes of the undulating membrane, *UM*, lack cilia; there are 2 membranellae, the anterior labelled *m*. (A after Hoare; B and C after Párducz.)

bc, buccal cavity; *m*, membranellae or their kinetosomes; *sc*, somatic cilia cut short; *t*, kinetosomes of thigmotactic cilia; *UM*, undulating membrane or its kinetosomes; *v*, vestibulum.

distributed in test-tubes or heavy watch-glasses. *Cyclidium* and a variety of other Protozoa will often appear in the surface scum of infusions (pp. 302, 397). Drops containing as many *Cyclidium* as possible are picked out and inoculated into the faecal suspension; where the *Cyclidium* reasonably outnumbers the other organisms it soon overgrows them and after a few transfers from promising cultures (made at intervals of 2 or 3 days) pure cultures may be obtained, and should be sub-cultured weekly. An alternative method is given on p. 403.

ORDER THIGMOTRICHIDA

The thigmotrichs form a natural group of ciliates, mostly living in the mantle cavities of molluscs, especially lamellibranchs; a few are probably parasitic, most are harmless commensals. There are 2 suborders, the Arhynchodina,* which have a buccal cavity with a cytostome, and the Rhynchodina, which are mouthless, with a sucker. All possess thigmotactic cilia by which they adhere to their substratum. In the more generalized forms the thigmotactic field is no more than an anterior part of the ventral surface where some of the cilia are set more closely together and employed in adherence. In more advanced genera (e.g. *Ancistrum*, Fig. 147) the field is more clearly defined and its cilia rather more specialized. In some of the Rhynchodina (Fig. 149) the somatic ciliature is much reduced and almost the only cilia remaining are those of the thigmotactic field. The buccal cavity, or peristome, is usually a shallow trough on the right side, tending to elongate till it reaches the posterior and to which eventually, as in *Boveria*, it may be confined (cf. Figs. 146–8 and Fig. 155 C–E). In the Rhynchodina the mouthless animal adheres to its host by means of a sucker (Fig. 149) and in *Gargarius* (H–K), where all the cilia have been lost, the structure superficially suggests that of a fluke and the animal has become a highly specialized parasite.

The topography of the thigmotrich body is variously explained by different authors and the interpretation adopted here is not the only possible one. In what appears to be the relatively unspecialized genus *Thigmophrya* (see Fig. 146 and Raabe, 1936) there is a complete investment of holotrichous cilia set in parallel rows originating from an anterior and transverse suture on the ventral face. The cilia behind the suture are set closer together than elsewhere, because the body here is narrower, and they form the thigmotactic field. The oral apparatus lies to one side and posteriorly. Behind it the kineties converge on a posterior suture, which is oblique. The longitudinal kineties are all more or less twisted and the extent of their torsion may be thought to indicate the extent of the 'mouth's' displacement

---

* = Stomatina, a good name, but previously used in protozoology, and so now abandoned for the weaker but unoffending Arhynchodina (see Corliss, 1957).

from an original median and ventral position. If, in Fig. 146, the body be supposed to be untwisted until the kineties are straightened and the mouth is restored to its original position, it will be seen that that position is behind the thigmotactic area on the same side as the anterior suture. This surface is here called ventral and thought to correspond to the ventral surface of a hymenostome; it is always marked by the suture and the thigmotactic

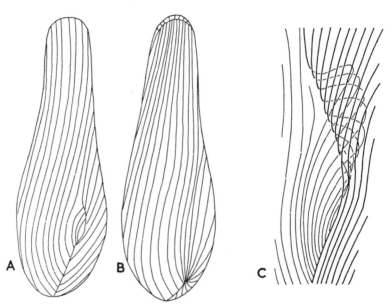

FIG. 146. *Thigmophrya macomae.* A, right side, showing torsion of the kineties and displacement of the mouth; B, ventral side with anterior suture; C, the arrangement of the vestibular kineties. (After Raabe.)

field, when present; it may be identified in other related ciliates (Astomatida). In the Thigmotrichida, the oral apparatus is assumed to have migrated to the right side. This is understandable. In the Arhynchodina, the body is fixed by its ventral, thigmotactic surface to the ctenidial or some other epithelial surface of the host, but the ciliate does not feed on the tissues it touches: it feeds on bacteria and other matter entering the mantle cavity, and which could not reach a mouth placed on a surface pressed against the host. To function, the mouth must move to a position of free exposure on one side or the other and it has moved to the right.*

The oral ciliature is simplified though often powerful. *Thigmophrya* has an obvious vestibulum (Fig. 146c), recalling in principle if not in detail

---

* If the position of the stomatogenic kinety is taken as fixed, then the oral surface is ventral. But must not the stomatogenic kinety migrate with the oral apparatus?

that of *Paramecium*; unhappily nothing is known of any deeper oral cilia-ture referable to a possible buccal cavity. In most of the Arhynchodina, 2 long, powerful kineties with sweeping fringes of cilia run the length of the peristome to curl below the cytostome, always in an anticlockwise arc (Figs. 147 A, C; 148 A, B). Of the 2, the right is regarded as the representative of the UM, and the left the remains of a much modified AZM; the 2 kine-ties are called 1 and B respectively and kinety number 1 is stomatogenic (Chatton and Lwoff, 1936); the oral excavation is thus the homologue of a buccal cavity or peristome.

The evidence points to the Hymenostomatida as the group ancestral to the Thigmotrichida. Some of the Pleuronematina already possess the thigmotactic habit, and in them too the oral complex has begun to migrate to the right and to elongate, and the buccal ciliature has suffered a simpli-fication foreshadowing the arrangement in thigmotrichs (cf. Figs. 145, 147–8); in both groups stomatogenesis calls upon a single kinety. For further comment, see p. 328 and Fig. 155.

The monographic studies of Chatton and Lwoff (1949, 1950) on this group are of great theoretical as well as taxonomic value. Shorter and very vivid accounts of many genera are offered by Raabe (1934, 1936, 1938, 1949, 1950) and the American protozoologists, Kidder (1933 *a–d*, 1934 *a, b*) and Kozloff (1945 *a, b,* 1946 *a–d*).

It conveniently happens that the common mussel, *Mytilus edulis*, sup-ports enough species of thigmotrichs to provide some notion of the variety of the order, and they are here presented for study. They are:

Suborder Arhynchodina: with an oral apparatus. *Kidderia mytili, Ancistrum mytili.*

Suborder Rhynchodina: with a sucker instead of a mouth. *Crebricoma kozloffi, C. carinata, Raabella helensis, Isocomides mytili, Gargarius gargarius.*

Of these, *Kidderia* is the most primitive, but *Ancistrum* is described first because it is commoner, easier to maintain on hosts in captivity, and has been more extensively studied.

Ancistrum mytili (Quennerstedt)

A. mytili lives ectocommensally in the mantle cavity and on the ctenidia of *Mytilus edulis*, where it has been known for nearly a century. It is very common and may form heavy infections. Good descriptions of it have been given by Kidder (1933*c*) and Raabe (1934, 1936), but on some points of importance the authors do not agree, and they should·be read in the light of the comments by Chatton and Lwoff (1949), who also studied the genus.

The living organism

The ciliates will live for some months on mussels kept in the laboratory in aerated sea water, running or static. The mussels are opened and the contents of the mantle cavity washed out into small Petri dishes from

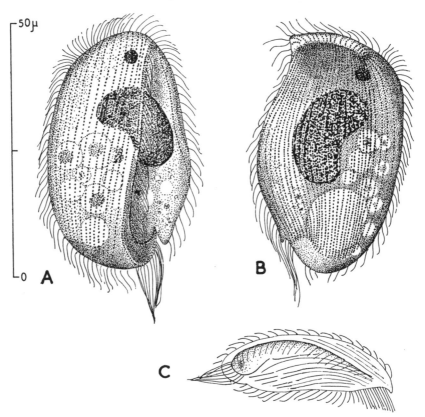

FIG. 147. *Ancistrum mytili.* A, dorsal aspect: there is a large naked vestibular field on the right with kineties 1 and B running down its left side and turning forward below the site of the cytostome; B, ventral aspect, showing the anterior suture with the thigmotactic area just behind it, meganucleus with distinct micronucleus anterior to it, food vacuoles, large posterior contractile vacuole and behind it the naked end of the animal; C, sketch of living ciliate from the side, showing the thigmotactic cilia extended from the anterior part of the ventral surface. (A and B from Ag preparations; C from life. All after Raabe.)

which the ciliates may be removed with a pipette under the dissecting binoculars.

A. mytili (Fig. 147) is oval, somewhat flattened, usually between 30 and 55 μ long and about 25 μ broad, but the proportions vary and from their differences Raabe (1936) has named five variations. The ciliate attaches to its substratum by the cilia of the thigmotactic field. Its grip is good, but in a Petri dish it constantly leaves its position and flutters up to the surface in a series of jerky somersaults and then returns to its base. These free-swiming intervals may account for cross-infections.

The pellicle is stiff and thick, though elastic. The somatic cilia are set in longitudinal rows originating from the anterior suture on the ventral surface. There are normally 55 rows of cilia, of which 16 are dorsal. The rest are crowded on to the ventral surface in closely set rows (Fig. 147B) and here, towards the anterior end, they are pulled even closer together by the longitudinal approximation of their kinetosomes. These thickly crowded cilia constitute the thigmotactic field, and during attachment they are held stiffly against the substratum while the general somatic cilia continue their beat (C). The ventral cilia do not reach the posterior end, which remains naked. The dorsal cilia are set farther apart (A). Outside the thigmotactic area the cilia are long and wavy. During adherence, a small naked cytoplasmic nipple may appear at the anterior end, possibly foreshadowing the suctorial tentacle of the Rhynchodina.

The buccal cavity (peristome) begins anteriorly as a narrow cleft which broadens towards the posterior end into a shallow depression. Its lower (ventral) margin is prolonged into a little triangular flap underlying the cytostome. This last leads to a cytopharynx opening to the endoderm. The oral ciliature consists of two strongly ciliated kineties, 1 and B, which run the length of the peristomial field on its dorsal side, and then curve ventrally behind the cytostome.

There are numerous food vacuoles and a single, posterior contractile vacuole, usually on the left side. The meganucleus is large, thick, and curved. There is a single spherical micronucleus, small but conspicuous, at the anterior end, lying clear of the meganucleus.

Thin-walled cysts have been described by Raabe (1936), who found them during the winter. The wall fits the body closely but is drawn out to an anterior point by which the cyst is attached to ctenidial tissue. At room temperatures, viable cysts will hatch in 7 to 8 hours.

For conjugation in the related *A. isseli* see Kidder (1933*d*).

Permanent preparations

As for *Kidderia* (p. 311), but the Ag system is better known.

Kidderia mytili (De Morgan)

The genus is less specialized than the last. The mouth has not retreated so far towards the posterior and the continuous pelt of holotrichous cilia shows no morphologically distinguished thigmotactic area though the animal may adhere strongly by means of its ventral cilia. Both De Morgan (1925), who discovered the species at Plymouth, and Kidder (1933 *a, b*), to whom we owe the best description, regarded it as a species of *Concophthirus*,* but it seems to require its own genus (Raabe, 1934). *K. mytili* is found creeping about on the muscles and the foot of *Mytilus edulis*, large specimens of

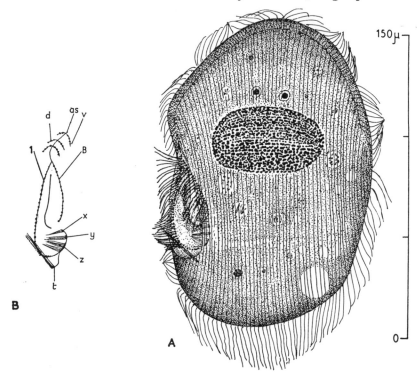

FIG. 148. *Kidderia mytili.* A, from the ventral aspect; B, diagram of the oral ciliature. (After Kidder.)

as, anterior suture; B, kinety B; *d*, dorsal somatic kinety arising from anterior suture; *t*, tuft of immobile cilia; *v*, ventral somatic kinety; *x*, *y*, and *z*, ciliary brushes lying behind the cytostome: the cytoplasmic shelf separating kineties 1 and B is indicated.

which may yield up to 75 ciliates, though 5 to 10 are more likely. The mussels must be fresh or kept in running sea water; in static water, the mussels survive but lose their ciliates (of this species) rapidly.

The living organism

The body is bean-shaped, about 170 $\mu \times$ 100 μ, dorsally convex, ventrally flat except posteriorly, where it is slightly concave. The feeding

* Species of *Concophthirus* are readily accessible on the palps and ctenidia of freshwater mussels (e.g. *Anodonta*) and they do not greatly differ from *Kidderia*. For details see Kidder (1934 *a, b*). Dr. J. O. Corliss informs me *in litt.* that *Concophthirus* must now supersede the usual *Concophthirius*.

apparatus lies on the right side. The animals may swim with a rotating movement, and in this stage infect other hosts, but more usually they creep about the host tissues with the ventral surface applied to them. There is a thick pellicle. The close-set lines of cilia arise from grooves originating in an anterior suture near the antero-ventral margin. The cilia are somewhat longer posteriorly; those of the ventral surface generally are used in adherence and there is no specialized thigmotactic area.

As in *Ancistrum* the buccal cavity is shallow and its ciliature is fundamentally similar. Kinety 1 is long and curls posteriorly below the mouth. Kinety B consists of a long anterior row of kinetosomes behind which lie 3 short brushes of cilia which, when stimulated by particles moving in their neighbourhood, beat together like the components of a membranella, though in fact they appear to be independent cilia. Behind this apparatus lies a long tuft (*t*) of immobile cilia of unknown function.

There are very numerous trichocysts, never seen to discharge, set in pellicular ridges, more numerous ventrally than dorsally. They have a marked affinity for Neutral Red which even in great dilution shows them in a bright cherry red colour. Food vacuoles are numerous. There is a single large contractile vacuole. The meganucleus is large and oval. There are usually 2 or 3 micronuclei. During fission the meganucleus discharges chromatin into the cytoplasm and this is absorbed by the daughters.

Permanent preparations

Most of the structure may be seen in the living animal, but fix in S+A to show nuclei, or Champy for cytoplasmic inclusions, and stain in H.H. The Ag system needs reinvestigation by modern methods.

Crebricoma kozloffi Chatton and Lwoff

This ciliate seems to be genuinely parasitic on the gills and palps of *Mytilus edulis* in that it attaches itself to and probably feeds on the tissues of its host, though the damage may be inconsiderable. With a suctorial tentacle, no mouth, and the ciliature practically confined to the thigmotactic area on the anterior part of the ventral surface, the animal is much more specialized than any arhynchodine thigmotrich. A good description of it, under the name *C. carinata*, has been published by Kozloff (1946a).*

---

* The taxonomy and nomenclature of this and the following species have been confused and in the interests of those consulting the literature it must be explained that in 1934 Raabe described a ciliate from *Mytilus edulis*, and which he called *Hypocomina carinata*. This animal bore the same name in his paper of 1938. Kozloff (1946a) studied a ciliate, which he supposed to be Raabe's, from *Mytilus edulis*, and transferred it to his new genus *Crebricoma* as *C. carinata* (Raabe). In 1950, Chatton and Lwoff pointed out (1) that the organism reported by Kozloff was not Raabe's ciliate, but a new species, and they called it *Crebricoma kozloffi*, and (2) that Raabe's ciliate nevertheless belonged to Kozloff's

The living and fixed organism

The ciliate (Fig. 149 A, B) is pear-shaped in outline, pointed at the anterior end and swollen posteriorly, compressed dorsoventrally, with a shallow concavity on the anterior part of the ventral surface containing the thigmotactic cilia. The dorsal surface and the part of the ventral surface behind the thigmotactic area are convex. The animal measures some 65 $\mu \times$ 30 μ, and is about 25 μ thick. The anterior end is not quite symmetrical but obliquely truncated, and set towards the right is the suctorial tentacle by which the animal adheres to the host. The tubular canal into which this leads is not so evident in *C. kozloffi* as in some other Rhynchodina, but it may often be seen after staining with H.H., when it appears to pass first dorsally, then ventrally, and then to the right side.

Nearly all the cilia are contained in the thigmotactic depression occupying about two-thirds of the ventral surface, and here they are arranged in some 32 to 36 rows, becoming longer from right to left. The front of the animal is considerably narrower than the rest and in fact several of the kineties of the left side originate dorsally and then twist on to the ventral surface to contribute to the thigmotactic field. On the extreme right, set apart from the main group, lie 2 longer and more widely spaced kineties. The cilia are long, about 10–11 μ, sluggish when the animal is attached but beating metachronally during swimming.

There is a large contractile vacuole. The meganucleus is ovoid. The micronucleus is circular and distinguishable in the living animal.

Crebricoma carinata (Raabe)*

This species (Fig. 149 C, D), which is uncommon, resembles the foregoing in general size and shape, but the anterior end is more pointed, there is a pronounced ventral curvature, and the thigmotactic area is formed of about 20 kineties, straight in the middle, asymmetrically curved, and longer towards the edges of the field; this is bordered by 2 ribs on which are borne, on the right 2, on the left 3, longer and more widely spaced rows of cilia. The convex dorsal surface is said to bear a keel along its anterior half. For details, see Raabe (1934, 1938) under the name *Hypocomina carinata*.

Raabella helensis Chatton and Lwoff

This attractive little ciliate (Fig. 149 E, F) is best known to us from the descriptions of Raabe (1938) and Kozloff (1946*b*), both of whom knew it

---

new genus and should be called *Crebricoma carinata* (Raabe). Thus *Crebricoma kozloffi* C. & L. 1950 = *C. carinata* (Raabe) Kozloff 1946*a*, and *C. carinata* (Raabe) C. & L. 1950 = *Hypocomina carinata* Raabe 1934, 1938.
    * See preceding footnote, p. 311.

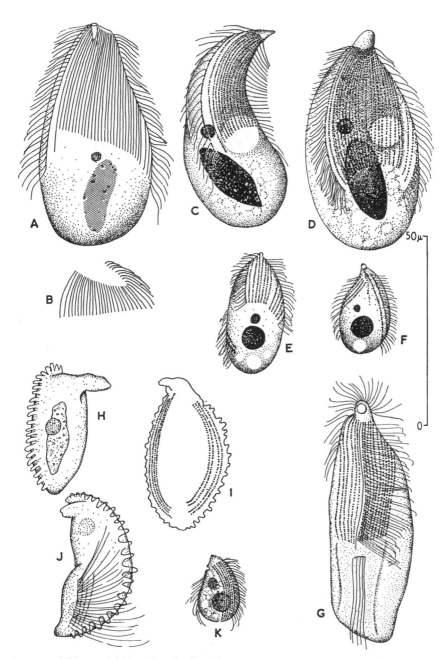

FIG. 149. Thigmotrichida Rhynchodina from *Mytilus edulis*. A, *Crebricoma kozloffi*, ventral; B, the same, anterior end to show dorsal origin of some left-hand kineties; C and D, *C. carinata*, right and ventral aspects; E, *Raabella helensis* forma *major*, ventral; F, *R. helensis* forma *minor*, dorsal; G, *Isocomides mytili*, ventral: the small group of very long flagella depend from the vestigial kinety; H–K, *Gargarius gargarius*: H, adult, dorsal view; I, ventral aspect, with kinetosomes impregnated by Ag (there are no cilia); J, adult, budding a larva posteriorly; K, ciliated larva. (A and B after Kozloff; C–F, K after Raabe; G–J after Chatton and Lwoff.)

under the name of *Hypocomides mytili*;* it was transferred to a new genus created for it by Chatton and Lwoff in 1950. Raabe found it rare at Hel, which is a place on the Gulf of Danzig; Kozloff found it common on the ctenidia and palps of 80 per cent of the mussels he examined from San Francisco Bay. They further disagreed so often on minor points that Raabe's account is given here and the main differences observed by Kozloff then noted.

The living and fixed organism

The body is ovoid, slightly flattened dorsoventrally, and narrows anteriorly to a point bearing the suctorial tentacle by which the ciliate attaches itself to the epithelium of its host. The tentacle is hollow and its passage is continued into a canal in the endoplasm which may be followed in fixed material for about half the length of the body. When the ciliate is swimming freely the tentacle is withdrawn. The anterior part of the ventral surface is flattened and forms the thigmotactic area. The cilia, arranged in longitudinal rows, are long (about 8·5 μ). All the rows originate at the base of the tentacle and form three systems. These are (1) a central system of 7 or 8 rows, about 1 μ apart, and of approximately equal length, extending rather less than half-way down the body, (2) to the left 5 or 6 rows winding round the body from dorsal to ventral surfaces and becoming longer towards the left (outer) side of the system, and (3) 2 much longer kineties to the right, also winding from dorsal to ventral surfaces, but in a contrary direction to the kineties of the second system. Raabe considered that the last 2 kineties represented a vestige of the somatic ciliature of more primitive thigmotrichs. Both nuclei are spherical and there is a posterior contractile vacuole.

Raabe recognized two distinct forms of his ciliate and found no intermediate stages between them:

			Number of kineties in system		
Forms	Length	Breadth	(1)	(2)	(3)
Major	26–36 μ	19–21 μ	8	6	2
Minor	17–26 μ	15–17 μ	7	?5	1

The ciliate studied by Kozloff from San Francisco was obviously closely related to Raabe's, but it was larger (34–38 μ long), the ciliary system was less distinct, the kineties of the middle row were not subequal but increased in length towards the left side, the meganucleus was ovoid, the contractile vacuole central, not posterior. On the face of it there seems reason to think that Kozloff's animal was at least a distinct subspecies.

* But it is not the same animal as that called *Hypocomides mytili* by Chatton and Lwoff in 1922; that is now *Isocomides mytili*, see p. 315.

Isocomides mytili Chatton and Lwoff

This is an imperfectly known ciliate from the ctenidia of *Mytilus edulis* figured by Chatton and Lwoff (1950). It is an oblong thigmotrich (57–63 $\mu \times$ 20–22 μ), tapering anteriorly to a process bearing the suctorial tentacle (Fig. 149 G). The thigmotactic field is longitudinally subdivided by a keel with 6 or 7 kineties on one side and 8 to 11 on the other (left side in the present convention). To either side of the field or as posterior continuations of it lie long cytoplasmic extensions which bear no cilia but correspond to the elongated kineties of some related genera (e.g. *Hypocomides*, and cf. the long kineties on the right side only of *Crebricoma* and *Raabella*). A most distinctive feature is the so-called vestigial kinety running transversely in a groove behind the thigmotactic field and bearing extremely long cilia.

Gargarius gargarius Chatton and Lwoff

This is one of the most specialized ciliates known (Fig. 149 H–K). It has no cilia, but retains kinetosomes which develop cilia in the larval stage. Almost all the ventral area is converted into a large sucker bordered by a papillate fringe. The animal is always attached to the gills of *Mytilus edulis*, where it is not common. According to Raabe (1938), it is found only on hosts bearing few or no other ciliates. It was originally discovered by Chatton and Lwoff in 1934 and redescribed and illustrated by them in 1950; some excellent pictures are given by Raabe.

The living and fixed organism

The body (25–35 μ long according to Chatton and Lwoff, or 40–60 μ according to Raabe) is ovoid and flattened, shaped like a liver fluke, and at once recognizable by its anterior proboscis, which is directed to one side (H–I). The proboscis contains a canal leading into the interior of the animal. There is a lateral fringe of papillae, blunt, pointed, or capitate, of uncertain function; they have nothing to do with feeding. Their bases are inserted on marginal filaments encircling the body behind the proboscis, and they are further supported by filaments which pass into the endoplasm. Farther from the proboscis run 2 strong basophil fibres, which may be skeletal or may possibly represent the borders of a canal continuous with the proboscis. The kinetosomes, which in the adult are the only evidence that the animal is a ciliate, form 2 rows of 4 kineties (or, more accurately, lines) on each border of the ventral face (according to Raabe, 4 lines on one side and 6 on the other). They bear no cilia.

The meganucleus is a large, elongated structure, and the micronucleus is remarkable for its size, nearly half that of the meganucleus. There appears to be no contractile vacuole. The animal reproduces by budding off a ciliated larva posteriorly. A constriction divides daughter from parent, and the former develops cilia from its kinetosomes, a sucker, and the marginal papillae (J, K). Conjugation has not been seen.

ORDER PERITRICHIDA

With over a thousand species, including the well-known bell animalcules, the Peritrichida form the largest order of ciliates. It is divided into two suborders, the Sessilina, attached, usually by a stalk, to the substratum, and the Mobilina, which have secondarily regained considerable freedom of movement. All the peritrichs are highly specialized. Their somatic ciliature is either reduced or suppressed. The larvae of the Sessilina have developed, as a locomotor organella, a fringe of obliquely set membranellae, and sometimes this persists for a while in the adult, fixed stage (Fig. 151 C–E); if so, it is the only somatic ciliature of the suborder. In the Mobilina the same structure is a highly important, elaborate, and permanent organella (Fig. 153A, *tm*). The oral ciliature is always well developed; it consists of 1 or 2 inner wreaths (the polykinety) and a single outer wreath (the haplo-kinety) which run a complete anticlockwise circuit round the rim of a more or less flattened peristome and then plunge into a funnel-like depression, the infundibulum, at the base of which lies the cytostome (Fig. 150 A, B). The cilia of these wreaths may be basally fused but they are distally free and there are never any membranellae. The membranellae of the telotroch or of the adult Mobilina are independently developed structures and have nothing to do with any possible ancestral AZM. It is a question whether the entire peristomial field represents an expanded buccal cavity (as in, for example, *Euplotes*) with the infundibulum remaining as the only persisting excavation about the cytostome, or whether the infundibulum should be regarded as the whole cavity out of which the oral ciliature has migrated to spread on to an originally somatic surface (Fig. 113, cf. G and H).

Peritrichs are highly contractile animals and there is a well-developed system of myonemes. There are always contractile vacuoles. In the fresh-water species most of the water which enters the body does so osmotically; some is added with the food but this is only a fraction of the total and the main function of the vacuoles is osmoregulatory. But in the marine species there is, of course, no osmotic intake from the sea, and we find that the vacuolar output practically balances the volume of water taken with food, and it is probable that it is the need to discharge water accepted while feed-ing that accounts for the retention of contractile vacuoles in these and other marine ciliates (Kitching, 1934, 1936, 1938, 1939). Both attached and free forms encyst (p. 321, and see Rosenberg, 1938).

The distributive phase of attached peritrichs is the telotroch, a cylindrical larva, swimming with the aboral pole foremost and with a circlet of membranellae, already mentioned, placed near it, and with the oral apparatus at the opposite, hinder end. A telotroch may be formed by the conversion of the entire adult body, which deserts its stalk and swims away; epidemics of swarming in this way may occur (Fox and Newth, 1936). One of the products of binary fission, which must escape from the stalk, is always a telotroch, and so, also, in sexual reproduction, is the microconjugant (Fig. 152). The larva settles by its aboral pole where a scopula secretes the stalk (Fig. 150 D–H). The genus *Telotrochidium* appears to be a permanent telo-troch; no stalked phase for it is known and the organism encysts and con-jugates in the free stage (Rosenberg, 1938; Kofoid and Rosenberg, 1940); it may therefore be considered as a neotenous member of the Sessilina. As already pointed out, one of the most distinctive characters of the suborder Mobilina is the teletrochal girdle, a structure which almost certainly originated as a larval adaptation in the life-cycle of a fixed, Sessiline peritrich, and if this is so the origin of the Mobilina provides a further instance of neoteny.

Binary fission in the Peritrichida differs from that of other ciliates in being often unequal and always in a plane that is (topographically) longi-tudinal or nearly so. In the stalked forms (Fig. 152) one daughter retains the peristome and stalk and the other swims off to settle elsewhere. Little is known of morphogenesis except in a highly specialized member of the Mobilina, *Cyclochaeta astropectinis* (Chatton and Villeneuve, 1937). Here the old peristomial apparatus proliferates a new one and the two products disengage at division (Fig. 154), i.e. stomatogenesis is autonomous.

In the Sessilina, conjugation (Fig. 152) is peculiar in that the participants are sexually differentiated into an attached macroconjugant (or female) and a free-swimming microconjugant (or male); fusion is complete, producing a single zygote; the subject has been reviewed by Finley (1952). In the Mobilina the conjugants may or may not be unequal and the differences are possibly no more than those of age (Davis, 1947); fusion again is complete and there is one synkaryon and one zygote. The condition is clearly in-herited from a sessile ancestor; the freedom of the Mobilina is secondary.

The Peritrichida are common, well-known, widely distributed animals in fresh water and the sea, where they are generally attached to submerged objects such as plants or other animals; some are epizoic, and a few live within their hosts. Among modern taxonomic studies, those of Kahl (1935), Stiller (1939, 1940), and Biegel (1954) form an adequate introduc-tion.

SUBORDER SESSILINA

The adults are sessile, directly or by a stalk; the somatic ciliature is lost, or rarely represented by a persistent telotrochal wreath. Like many other sessile forms they tend to produce colonies, e.g. *Epistylis* with a non-contractile and *Carchesium* with a contractile stalk. Some (*Vaginicola, Lagenophrys*) produce a pseudochitinous container, the lorica. Many are attached to plants and animals and the commensal associations with their hosts may become obligatory; a few (*Operculariella*) are entozoic.

Vorticella L.

Although over 200 species of this common genus have been described they differ only in minutiae, and it is convenient to offer a general account of it. For identification see especially Kahl (1935). A very useful introduction to 7 common species is given by Noland and Finley (1931).

The body of *Vorticella* is like an inverted bell fixed to the substratum by a contractile stalk (Fig. 150). The bell is covered by a pellicle transversely ringed by parallel striae, plainer in some species than in others (Fig. 151A). Its mouth is filled by a disk, the peristome, bearing the oral ciliature and bordered by a projecting shelf of cytoplasm. There are 3 circlets of cilia; the inner 2 are closely associated and are inserted on the polykinety, and distinct from the outer circlet, belonging to the haplokinety. All the circlets run a complete or slightly overlapping anticlockwise turn about the margin of the disk and then diverge as they enter the peristomial funnel or infundibulum. The cilia tend to be joined in longitudinal series near their bases but they are distally free; they do not form membranellae. Those of the outer circuit lie more or less horizontally and form a shelf along which food particles are swept by the more upright inner circlets. The action of the latter is extremely rapid and is never clearly observed except in animals whose activities are slowing down. Within the funnel the cilia of the haplokinety lengthen and fuse to a true undulating membrane, descending the external wall; the 2 ciliary lines of the polykinety pass down the internal wall. According to Noland and Finley (1931) there is a feeding current directed between the 2 kineties and a rejection current between the inner cilia and the wall of the funnel (arrows in Fig. 150B).

The cytostome lies at the base of the infundibulum and leads into a narrow cytopharyngeal tube usually stretching to the base of the bell. Its path is outlined by food vacuoles, which are constricted to a spindle shape until they escape as spheres into the endoplasm. The body may be dense, even opaque, with inclusions. There are one or two contractile vacuoles; one lies between the meganucleus and the funnel and discharges into the rejection current, and if there is a second it lies on the outer side of the funnel. The meganucleus passes up the centre of the body, its lower end a little bent, its upper end forming a horizontal limb beneath the disks. The micronucleus is rarely seen in living animals. The whole body is strongly contractile and may be rapidly clenched into a ball by means of a myoneme system clearly

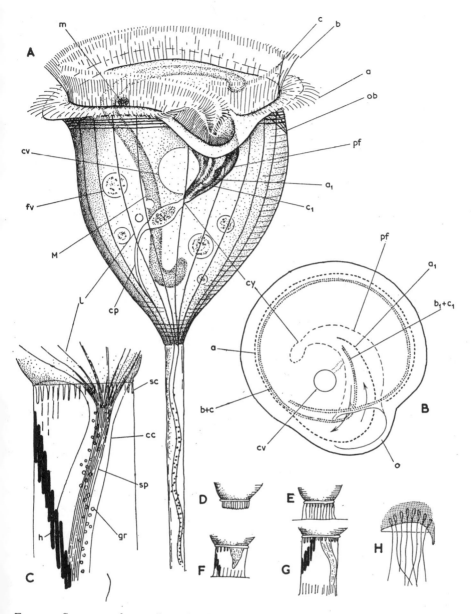

Fig. 150. Structure of a sessile peritrich. A, *Vorticella*, the living animal; B, diagram of peristomial field of *Vorticella*; c, *Carchesium*, the stalk; D–G, development of the stalk in *Vorticella*; H, scopula of *Campanella umbellaria* showing resemblance of the immobile filaments to cilia. (A compiled from various sources; B after Noland and Finley; C–H after Fauré-Fremiet.)

a, outer peristomial wreath; *b* and *c*, the inner wreaths; a_1–c_1, the same within the peristomial funnel; *cc*, contractile cord in the stalk; *cp*, cytopharynx; *cv*, contractile vacuole; *cy*, cytostome; *fv*, food vacuole: one is shown compressed within the cytopharynx; *gr*, granule (mitochondrium?) of stalk; *h*, helical thickening in stalk wall; *l*, longitudinal myoneme; *M*, meganucleus; *m*, micronucleus; *o*, opening into peristomial funnel; *ob*, oblique myonemes: they cross over the circular; *pf*, peristomial funnel (infundibulum); *sc*, scopula; *sp*, spasmoneme.

described by Schröder (1906). Longitudinal myonemes (Fig. 150A, *l*) shorten the body, and the peristome is pulled inwards by oblique myonemes (*ob*), while the rim is contracted by circular myonemes.

The stalk (Fig. 150 C–H) consists of a wall containing a liquid and a contractile cord. The wall is double and thickened by vertically placed rodlets forming a spring which expands after contraction of the stalk. The cord contains cytoplasm and a specialized myoneme called the spasmoneme, and there may also be some granules which are possibly mitochondria. The spasmoneme is continuous with the myonemes of the bell. The development of this structure has been described and interpreted by Fauré-Fremiet (1905, 1910). The telotroch settles by its aboral pole on which is situated the scopula, which secretes the stalk. Whether the scopula is present at the beginning of the telotroch's life is not clear, but it is certainly evident at the time of attachment. In *Vorticella*, the scopula (D) happens to be small, but it does not differ essentially from the larger organella of other genera (C). It consists of a circlet of stiff cytoplasmic processes, usually short and stubby, but occasionally longer and finer (H); these processes are, for reasons discussed below, regarded as homologous with the thigmotactic cilia of, for example, *Ancistrum* or *Boveria*. The telotroch touches the substratum with its scopula, which secretes the wall of the stalk, enclosing a circular space within which the central cord grows down (D–G). The cord is not strictly central, but hangs to one side, and as the organism slowly rotates about its axis, the point of attachment of the cord describes a tiny circle. Now the secretion of the inner wall is discontinuous and confined to a section opposite the cord; these facts, and the observed rotation, explain why the thickening is spiral and consists of independent rodlets. For encystation and reproduction see pp. 321–3.

Vorticella microstoma Ehrenberg

The species is common in fresh water containing abundant organic matter and one of the most frequently seen in laboratory infusions. Most of the life-history is known from the studies of Finley (1936, 1939, 1943) and those of von Brand (1923) on the cyst.

The living organism

The body (Fig. 151A) is slender and rather long, about $55 \times 35\ \mu$, with a small peristomial field, $23\ \mu$ in diameter on the average. The pellicular striae are faint. The contractile vacuole has a mean diameter of $10\ \mu$ at diastole and pulsates about once in 15 seconds. The stalk is very narrow and the turns in the spasmoneme are spaced at intervals of about $30\ \mu$: no cytoplasmic granules are visible in it during life. The species is very like

V. striata but the latter is smaller ($33 \times 19\,\mu$) with a peristome $18\,\mu$ wide and has 20 to 30 well-marked pellicular striae on the wall of the bell.

Under the presumably rather unfavourable conditions offered by a microscope mount, *V. microstoma* very readily forms telotrochs. Within 15 to 30 minutes the bell forms an aboral wreath of cilia and swims away (C–E); or it encysts (von Brand, 1923) on the stalk, from which it eventually falls.

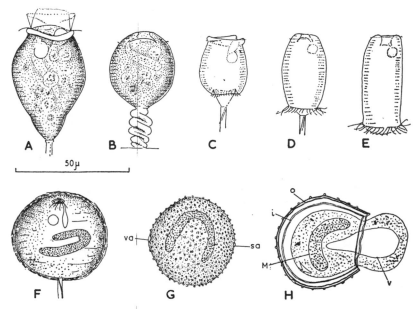

FIG. 151. *Vorticella microstoma.* A, trophic ciliate; B, the same, contracted; C–E, conversion of body into a telotroch; F, beginning of encystation; G, the mature cyst with the outer endocyst as the recognizable cyst membrane; H, excystation. (A–E after Noland and Finley; F–H after von Brand.)

i inner endocyst wall; *M*, meganucleus; *o*, outer endocyst wall; *sa*, umbilicus left by stalk; *v*, vacuole; *va*, umbilicus left at point of discharge from contractile vacuole.

The body loses water, rounds off, and is surrounded by an outer gelatinous ectocyst (F). The ectocyst is soon reduced to an inconsiderable, wrinkled membrane, and the character of the cyst is imparted by the endocyst, a double membrane of which the outer component is much wrinkled or papillated (G). The myonemes and pellicular striae of the contained organism become indistinguishable, and the contractile vacuole works more and more slowly until the animal is isolated from the water surrounding it. After some time (up to a week) the peristome is absorbed. The completed cyst has a mean diameter of $38\,\mu$, and its poles are marked by 2 scars, one indicating the previous point of attachment to the stalk, and, opposite, the other marking the last point of escape for excreted water. Von Brand hatched cysts by removing them to fresh water supplied with bacteria. The vacuole enlarged greatly, and perhaps as a result of the pressure it exerted, the organism escaped, almost explosively (H), grew an aboral circlet of cilia, and swam off as a telotroch.

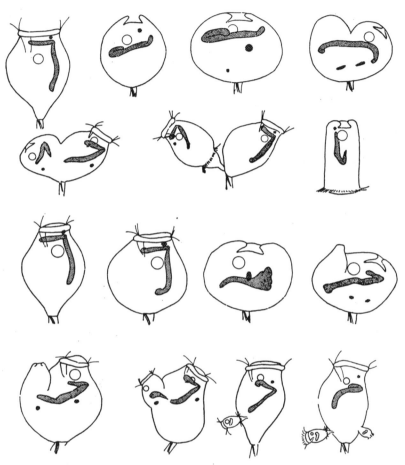

FIG. 152. *Vorticella microstoma*: fission. The top 2 rows show normal binary fission, which is equal and reproductive; one daughter escapes as a telotroch. The 2 bottom rows show unequal binary fission producing conjugants; in the last drawing a foreign micro- conjugant is fertilizing the macroconjugant before its own daughter microconjugant escapes from it. (After Finley.)

Normal binary fission (Fig. 152, top) is subequal and takes 20 to 30 minutes (Finley, 1939). The animal contracts into a sphere and broadens. The endoplasmic circulation remains vigorous and the vacuole pulsates throughout division. The fission plane appears early and cuts off the daugh- ter so that the parent retains the old peristome and the stalk. The daughter peristome is formed. The parent resumes feeding. The peristome and contractile vacuole of the daughter become functional and the aboral circlet of cilia appears. While the parent contracts sharply on its stalk the daughter rotates, and between their efforts the two are separated and the daughter leaves as a telotroch. During fission the micronucleus has divided mitotically and the meganucleus like the cytoplasm has been divided subequally.

The sexual forms are produced by a similar type of fission except that very unequal quantities of cytoplasm and meganuclear material are apportioned to the male and female products (Fig. 152, lower half). (In some species more than one male is produced at a time, Finley, 1952.) The male or microconjugant is free-swimming and can live for 24 hours at the most; if by then it has failed to fertilize a macroconjugant it dies; it does not feed or encyst. The female or macroconjugant is morphologically indistinguishable from normal trophic individuals but is physiologically specialized and for about 2 hours it can attract males which swim within 1 mm of it. A male undertakes trial searches until it touches a female, fuses with her, always in the lower third of the body, which it enters, leaving behind its pellicle. Fusion is complete. According to Finley (1943), both meganuclei degenerate, the male micronucleus undergoes 3 and the female 2 divisions, of which the last, rather surprisingly, is said to be reductional (cf. *Paramecium*, p. 294). The diploid number of 4 chromosomes is immediately restored in the synkaryon. Within the zygote the nucleus divides 3 times and one of its products becomes a micronucleus, the other 7 meganuclei, and subsequent cytokineses provide 7 daughters. As these develop they normally acquire aboral wreaths and migrate as telotrochs, but some may encyst and the development of these is unknown.

Permanent preparations

When fixed, vorticellids withdraw their peristomes and contract. Use Flemming or Champy for myonemes, S+A for nuclei, followed by H.H. or, in the last case, D.H.

Culture

Vorticellids may be maintained in hay infusions if fermentation is not too rapid. Boil 2 gm hay in 100 ml filtered pond-water, make up to 200 ml, leave 2 or 3 days and add the vorticellids. Growth is slow. Sub-culture every few weeks. For other methods and for axenic cultures see Levine (1959) and Finley, McLaughlin, and Harrison (1959).

Conjugating stocks are obtained by enforcing encystation and then activating the cysts. Prepare the following: 2 gm alfalfa hay, 3 gm wheat kernels, 100 ml glass-distilled water; boil and filter; make up to 100 ml with more water; sterilize at 15 lb for 10 minutes. Add twice the volume of filtered sterile spring water. Tube in 15 ml lots and store; the liquid remains good for 10 days. Obtain cysts by starving animals in small Petri dishes or tubes, under glass. When ready, introduce cysts into the tubes and add 1 mm drop of bacteria (e.g. *Achromobacter liquefaciens*). Keep in a damp chamber. Excystation begins in 30 to 55 minutes and conjugation after 14 hours, reaching a maximum 24 hours after inoculation. For further details see Finley (1936).

SUBORDER MOBILINA

These are ectozoic, or more rarely entozoic, peritrichs without a stalk but with the aboral end differentiated into an elaborate disk. *Trichodina pediculus*, which is often seen scurrying about the surface of *Hydra*, is very well known: it is possibly the same species as that seen on the larval gills of some tadpoles and neotenous urodeles (Fulton, 1923). *T. urinicola* and *T. vesicularum* are common in the urinary bladder of amphibians (Fulton, 1923; Fauré-Fremiet, 1943). Trichodinids are common and sometimes pathogenic parasites of fishes, living on the gills, fins, and body generally, where they skim over epithelial surfaces or swim freely for short periods in water. In swimming they defy the probabilities by moving with the disk held in front. An excellent account of the habits, structure, and reproduction is given by Davis (1947). Infection is direct and in some cases must necessarily be rapid. For example, *Urceolaria mitra*, which is ectozoic on the eddy-worm *Polycelis*, is known to occur in plankton, though it can live apart from its host for only about 6 hours, and it can quickly discover hosts in relatively large volumes of water, e.g. in 6 hours in 5,000 ml. Once the infection is established the population of urceolariids on the worms is seasonally more stable than that of free-living Protozoa (Reynoldson, 1950, 1951). Reproduction (Fig. 154) has been studied by Chatton and Villeneuve (1937), Padnos and Nigrelli (1942), Colwin (1944), and Davis (1947). As already mentioned, the conjugants may be of different sizes, but the differences do not seem to be, as in Sessilina, sexually significant, but rather due to age.

Trichodina myicola Uzmann and Stickney

From among many this species is chosen because an excellent account of it, with a useful distribution table for the genus, has been published by Uzmann and Stickney (1954). In Maine it occurs in up to 62 per cent of its host, the bivalve *Mya arenaria*, especially on the palps, where it may be very numerous. It is sometimes accompanied by the thigmotrich *Ancistrocoma myae*, and may itself be infected by a suctorian, *Endosphaera* (? *engelmanni*).

The living organism

T. myicola, seen from above, is circular in outline, with a diameter of 62–103 μ (mean= 81 μ). From the side (Fig. 153) it is domed, or the top may be pulled down like the crown of a gibus, so that the height is variable (31–86 μ). The surface directed away from the host carries the peristomial ciliature, consisting of 2 rows of cilia, united, as in *Vorticella*, at their bases, but distally free. The outer row is mounted on a single line of kinetosomes, while those of the inner row seem to be double (Fig. 153 *ic*, *oc*). The 2 rows separate as they pass into the infundibulum, where they descend the wall spirally, out of phase with each other, towards the cytostome (B). The funnel also receives, through a permanent canal, the contents of the contractile vacuole.

The aboral disc (A, C) is an extremely elaborate structure, rimmed by a thin, flexible band (*mb*), just above which 3 rows of cilia are set. The cilia of the upper and lower rows (*doc*, *dic* in Fig. 153A), are single, fine, and rather short; their function is not known. Between them lies the conspicuous girdle of membranellae (*tm*), each membranella set obliquely, and each a powerful strap, frayed at the end into its constituent cilia; this is the loco-motor organ, and it corresponds to the telotrochal wreath of the Sessilina.

Below the membranellae are set radial striae marking the positions of rods from which run myonemes to the bases of the membranellae (dotted lines in A, running from a rod, *sb*, to a membranella). Below the striated band runs a circle of 26 to 36 articulated, skeletal denticles which irresist-ably recall vertebrae. Each denticle is a hollow cone, fitted into the one next in front, and it bears an inwardly directed spine and outer blade. The whole disk is flexible and is normally applied to the host. The meganucleus is C-shaped with its opening towards the infundibulum and contractile vacuole. The food vacuoles tend to congregate towards the oral pole.

Permanent preparations

Much of the structure of *Trichodina* may be clearly seen in the living animal. For details, fix in Flemming, Champy, or S+A, stain in H.H., or, for nuclei, D.H. The kinetosomatic pattern has been studied by Ag methods, but the subject is not easy.

The affinities of the Peritrichida

The Peritrichida are successful animals and they appear to have enjoyed a long, isolated history during which they have evolved the specializations which now distinguish them. Most of these are plainly related to the sessile habit, such as the loss of somatic ciliature, the eversion of the buccal cavity to increase the food-collecting area, the evolution of a swimming larva with

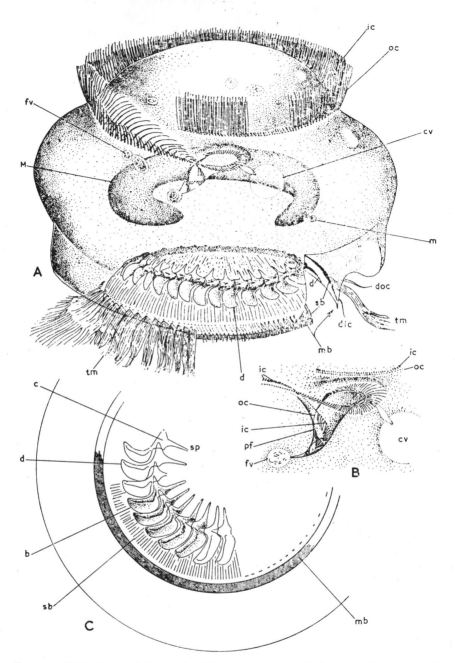

FIG. 153. *Trichodina myicola*. A, the living organism, semi-diagrammatic: part of the foreground is seen as a transparency to show the structure of the aboral disk, and at the bottom right a slice has been removed to show the same in section. × 1,000; B, the peristomial funnel, enlarged; C, part of the aboral disk: diagrammatic. (After Uzmann and Stickney.)

b, blade; *c*, centrum; *cv*, contractile vacuole; *d*, denticle; *dic*, inner cilia of disk; *doc*, outer cilia of disk; *fv*, food vacuole; *ic*, inner circlet of cilia (polykinety); *M*, meganucleus; *m*, micronucleus; *mb*, marginal band; *oc*, outer circlet of cilia (haplokinety); *pf*, peristomial funnel (infundibulum); *sb*, striated band; *sp*, spine; *tm*, membranellae of telotrochal wreath.

a telotrochal wreath as a larval adaptation, the unusual fission plane, and the production of motile microconjugants. None of these characters throws any light on the origin of the Peritrichida. Nor, in seeking some, are we much helped by good morphological studies, which are hard to find; further, the little that is known of morphogenetics refers to a single and highly specialized member of the Mobilina (Fig. 154). In most classifications the Peritrichida are implausibly settled somewhere towards the end of the Spirotricha, where it is difficult to explain the direction of their adoral wreaths. This is anti-clockwise; in all Spirotricha, it is clockwise. Indeed, so long as the adoral wreath of a peritrich is compared to the AZM of a spiro-

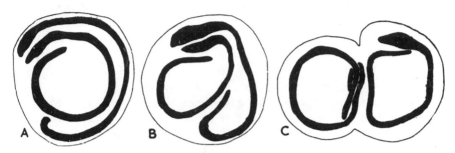

FIG. 154. *Cyclochaeta astropectinis*. Division of the peristomial field during fission. A, duplication of peristome; B–C, separation of parent and daughter peristomes. (After Chatton and Villeneuve.)

trich, no explanation of the apparent reversal of its direction will be possible. The view is here taken that this comparison ought never to be made, that the peritrichs are not spirotrichous but holotrichous, and they are related through the Thigmotrichida to the tetrahymenal group of ciliates (Fauré-Fremiet, 1905, 1910, 1950a; Corliss, 1956; and see also a discussion by Chatton, 1936).

In the Spirotricha there is always a well-developed adoral zone of clearly differentiated membranellae circling clockwise towards the 'mouth'. The Peritrichida never develop any membranellae on the oral face and their ciliary tracks move counter-clockwise. Both points make it impossible to regard them as good spirotrichs. The condition in the Hymenostomatida and their relatives is different and much more variable. Fundamentally here the mouth-parts consist of a UM lying to the right of the buccal cavity and sweeping towards it in an anti-clockwise curve. On the left is a set of membranellae; they are never numerous, are often disrupted, vestigial or ill-defined, and though primitively (*Tetrahymena*, Fig. 137) their path was, if anything, clockwise, its course is not well marked, and sometimes it is plainly anti-clockwise within the same order (Figs. 145–8). In the family Lembidae, for example, the AZM is represented by ciliary fields, and in some of its genera (e.g. *Anophrys*) these have crossed from left to right of the buccal cavity and lie next to the UM, whose anti-clockwise path they follow (Fig. 155, cf. A and B).

In the Thigmotrichida we have an anti-clockwise arrangement of the mouth-parts in an order with a strong tendency towards the sessile habit, accompanied by a reduction in the somatic ciliature. At the same time the mouth retreats towards the posterior end, i.e. away from the pole by which the animal normally attaches itself to the substratum (Fig. 155 C, D). *Boveria* is a ciliate with a thigmotactic field at one end and a 'mouth' at the other surrounded by an anti-clockwise spiral of cilia (Fig. 155E, and see Stevens, 1904; and Pickard, 1927). The correspondence in position and orientation with comparable structures in the sessiline telotroch is so exact that it is difficult to resist the belief that their relation is genetic as well as functional. A vorticellid, then, must be regarded as having settled by its anterior end; its posterior surface is oral, the cilia of the haplokinety represent the UM of the tetrahymenal apparatus, and those of the inner circlets, which in some cases are mounted on kinetosomes in tracks three rows thick (Schröder, 1906), are the modified remains of the old AZM. The scopula, which still bears thigmotactic cilia, represents the anterior thigmotactic field of an advanced thigmotrich. Fig. 155 attempts to illustrate the affinities which these views imply, but not, of course, to embody anything in the nature of a linear phyletic series.

ORDER ASTOMATIDA

All the members of this order are entozoic and mouthless, with a holotrichous coat of cilia showing little if any differentiation. Nearly all of them inhabit the alimentary canals of annelid worms, especially oligochaetes, and, like many other gut parasites, they frequently develop some sort of skeletal apparatus for attachment to the host epithelium. This varies from the elaborate hooked structure of *Metaradiophrya* to the mere vestige of a skeleton found in *Durchionella* (Fig. 159); the very successful genus *Anoplophrya* (Fig. 156) is unarmed. There are nearly always contractile vacuoles, whose number and arrangement are of taxonomic · importance. Contractile vacuoles are, of course, characteristic of Protozoa living in hypotonic media such as fresh water, where their function is primarily osmoregulatory, and their persistence in this entozoic order is exceptional and unexplained. A curious feature of the group, though it is known elsewhere, is the presence in many of bacteria, occurring in various parts of the cytoplasm. The bacteria may be typical of a species, with different forms occurring in different species of astomates from the same host. They are never in vacuoles and they are not food and they may survive for a time the autolysis of their hosts. Hovasse, who discovered them, suggested that they were facultative symbionts (Hovasse, 1945 a, b, 1946).

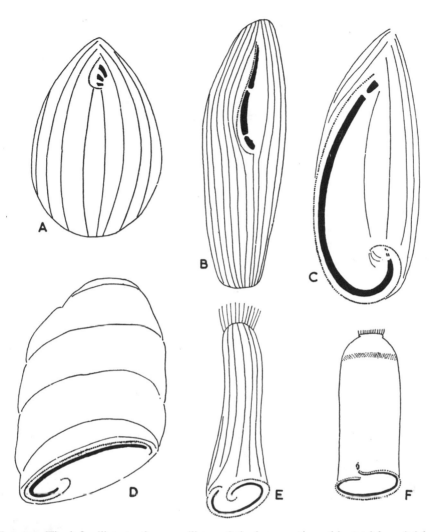

FIG. 155. The infraciliature of some ciliates of the hymenostome-thigmotrich-peritrich group to show the homologies of the tetrahymenal complex. The undulating membrane, on the right-hand side of the buccal cavity, is shown as dotted lines; the AZM or its homologues is black; the somatic ciliature is indicated by light black lines. (All figures simplified: A after Corliss; B after Mugard; C and D after Chatton and Lwoff; E after Stevens and Chatton and Lwoff; F original.)

A, *Tetrahymena* (Hymenostomatida); the primitive arrangement, UM on the right-hand side, AZM on the left; B, *Anophrys* (Hymenostomatida): the ciliary fields corresponding to the AZM have moved to the right-hand side of the buccal cavity and pursue an anti-clockwise path; C, *Ancistrospira* (Thigmotrichida): the oral ciliature is on the right of the animal with the anti-clockwise pattern typical of the stomatine thigmotrichs; D, *Hemispeira* (Thigmotrichida): oral ciliature posterior; E, *Boveria* (Thigmotrichida): the thigmotactic cilia are indicated; F, a telotroch (Peritrichida).

Astomates occur only seldom outside annelids and never in vertebrates. Some are very common and may occur in large numbers, such as those found in earthworms of the family Lumbricidae, which may harbour several species at once, and if so, they may be distributed along fairly well-defined and separate lengths of the gut so that there is little interspecific competition. In such cases, de Puytorac (1956a) has shown that the principal factors influencing distribution of the astomates are the pH and osmotic pressure of the gut fluid. On the other hand, infections in other hosts may be both light and rare. Mackinnon and Adam (1924) examined 1,250 specimens of tubificid worms, hosts which live in close association with each other and might be thought to provide continuous opportunities for cross-infections. Yet only 2 animals were infected with *Radiophrya tubificis* and these contained only 3 ciliates between them; 15 hosts contained two or three specimens each of *Intoshellina maupasi*. *Radiophrya rossolimoi* is both rare and sparse (Cheissin, 1930); so is *Metaradiophrya falcifera* (Heidenreich, 1935). The writer found a species of *Anoplophrya* in only one out of over 400 specimens of *Amphitrite gracilis*. The survival of these small and unsuccessful populations, which apparently cannot spread even when surrounded by suitable hosts, suggests an unexplored ecological problem. Nothing is known about the means of infection; though cysts undoubtedly occur, they are extremely rarely seen: for example, Cheissin (1930) examined 2,062 oligochaetes and found 1,520 of them infected with trophic astomates, but he did not find a single cyst. Very little is known about conjugation and no complete account of it exists. Asexual reproduction is common and may be rapid with the production of chains of daughters attached *in tandem*.

The classical studies of Cépède (1910) on the Astomatida were continued by the surveys of Cheissin (1930) and Heidenreich (1935): see also Rossolimo (1926) and, for skeletal structures, Rossolimo and Perzewa (1929). Apart from the skeleton, which may be reduced or absent, astomates display few characters of obvious use to the taxonomist and for years their systematics has been in confusion. It is in the work of de Puytorac (especially 1954), with references to earlier publications, and also 1955 a, b, 1957 a, b, c, 1959) that we find at last the outlines of a coherent system and a critical discussion of phylogeny. But the characters used, such as number and pattern of kineties, though stable, are often difficult to determine, so that, while genera may be recognized and studied as such, species are not easily identified.

It seems likely that astomates are related to the Thigmotrichida or to their ancestors and so belong to a fundamentally tetrahymenal stock, though probably to a peripheral part of it. When *Anoplophrya* and *Kidderia* are compared (Figs. 148, 156, 157), it is seen that the body is of the same shape, flattened but with distinguishable dorsal and ventral surfaces; the latter, in each, has a shallow depression which is adhesive and it carries the thigmotactic cilia, which need not be structurally differentiated, and although the thigmotactic behaviour of *Anoplophrya* is less striking than that of *Kidderia*, it is still recognizable (Fig. 156). In both, just in front of the thigmotactic area lies an anterior suture, interrupting the dorsal and ventral meridians. The kineties are closely placed, parallel, in the same pattern, and bearing holotrichous cilia. *Conchophthirus* (? *Kidderia*) *caryoclada* has even developed the long, ribbon-like meganucleus which is typical of *Anoplophrya* and some other astomate genera (Kidder, 1933e). Such resemblances as these may point to a general relationship between the Astomatida and the tetrahymenal complex of ciliates, but they do not point very precisely, and the exact location of the ancestral astomates remains disputable; the group may, as de Puytorac himself points out (1954, 1957a, 1959), be polyphyletic.

Anoplophrya alluri Cépède

All members of the common genus *Anoplophrya* are oval, flattened ciliates with close-set, longitudinal kineties, and no trace of skeleton. Apart from slight, and for the most part only recently observed, details of the infraciliature, the species are much alike and the distribution remains uncertain.* *A. alluri*, originally described from *Eiseniella tetraeda*, is also common, together with another species of *Anoplophrya* and two of *Maupasella*, in the gut of *Eisenia foetida*. *A. lumbrici* from the gut of various earthworms commonly used for dissection is very similar to *A. alluri*. The latter was well described by Cépède for his period but the notes of de Puytorac (1954) are now an indispensable supplement.

The living animal

The ciliate is commonest in the part of the gut just behind the male reproductive organs though it may occur, more sparsely, for some way behind the clitellum. Very small pieces of gut may be teased in a drop of 0·6 per cent saline and mounted.

The flat, oval ciliate (Fig. 156) measures 50–150 $\mu \times$ 35–60 μ, and, in lateral view, 25 μ deep. The elasticity of the pellicle is evident as the animal squeezes between obstacles. It swims rapidly, either side up, and when free to do so in a wide circle, tilting from side to side or rotating completely on its axis. Occasionally it pauses and behaves in a way that has

* Thus *A. alluri* is not recorded from *Eisenia foetida* in France, but has been repeatedly found in this host in the West of England over some 12 years (R. S. J. H.). Imperfect identification of hosts and incomplete descriptions of the parasites make it impossible to collate much of the literature of the past into a reliable host list. For present purposes the difficulties may be largely ignored. For other parasites of *E. foetida*, see index, under *host-lists*.

never been explained. Either it slowly revolves by working its way round and round in a series of jerks, or, without moving from its place, its whole

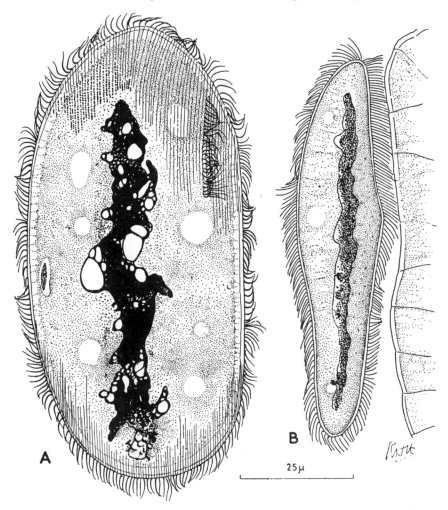

FIG. 156. *Anoplophrya alluri.* × 1,200. A, the animal from the dorsal aspect. Only a few of the cilia are drawn. At the anterior end the thin parallel lines on the right are pellicular grooves and the rows of dots on the left are the kinetosomes below the pellicle. B, L.S. of ciliate adhering to the surface of the host epithelium. The slight concavity of the thigmotactic area (upper right of the drawing) is sometimes seen to be more deeply excavated in T.S. Note dorsal position of contractile vacuoles. (Original.)

body vibrates in a prolonged, rapid quivering. In spite of its superficial appearance of symmetry both surfaces and both sides are in fact slightly different, though this is not always easy to appreciate by watching living animals. The curve of the anterior margin is a little bolder on one side than the other, and this is conventionally described as the left side (Fig. 156A, and note the asymmetry of the anterior suture in Fig. 157). As in many thigmotrichs the dorsal surface is gently convex, and the ventral surface, just behind the suture, is scooped into a slight concavity (Fig. 156B). Long ago Cépède regarded this depression as adhesive and the correctness of his observation may be confirmed if small patches of epithelial cells are contained in the preparation. Should a specimen of *Anoplophrya* then fortuitously settle in side view against such a clump of cells, the cilia in the concavity remain motionless while elsewhere they continue their beat. In these circumstances the animal again tends to quiver, and one of the reactions already noted may be no more than thigmotactic behaviour against the glass surface of the slide, as sometimes exhibited by thigmotrichs. The resemblance to a thigmotrich is very striking (cf. Figs. 147C and 156B) and the habit of thigmotactic attachment is common in nature, as is seen in sections of the host gut.

The cilia, 5 to 7 μ long, form a thick holotrichous coat, and those of the thigmotactic area are not morphologically distinct. There are two rows of contractile vacuoles, one on each side. The largest, when spherical, are 8 μ in diameter. According to de Puytorac there are 4 to 9 vacuoles in each row, but 100 specimens noted by the writer showed 1 to 6, usually 3 or 4. The endoplasm seems to be highly viscous and the vacuoles are frequently irregular in outline and their shape changes slowly when watched. Cépède noted that each vacuole is fed from small satellites at its periphery and the fact is easily confirmed by mounting specimens in dilute (e.g. 3 per cent) saline solution, when the normally slow pulsation is accelerated. Symbiotic bacteria may be present near the axis of the animal or about the vacuoles or they may be absent from some or all ciliates in a single host.

The meganucleus is long, ribbon-like, granular, and plainly visible in the living animal. In healthy animals its outline is smooth and the irregularities that appear at death, whether by fixation or not, are artefacts. The micronucleus is lateral but rarely visible. Division is perkinetal. De Puytorac has observed couples united broadly by their posterior ends and also by a narrow anterior zone of contact; the partners lie parallel. But conjugation has never been followed to its conclusion in this or any other astomate.

There are very few reports of cysts occurring naturally. In earthworms collected after a spring frost, de Puytorac found spherical specimens of *Anoplophrya* turning slowly round and round and expelling a transparent liquid which formed a fine pellicle about the animal. This was almost certainly the beginning of encystation. Similar phenomena may be induced by mounting specimens in the host's fluid and partially desiccating them by heat. As already mentioned, cysts are evidently rare in nature and the means of transmission are not understood.

Permanent preparations

Most of the structure of *Anoplophrya* is best seen in the living animal, including features absent from or concealed in fixed material. Good Champy/H.H. preparations show the pellicular striae above the kineties, the cilia, vacuoles, and other cytoplasmic structures. Nuclear fixation is always poor. Silver impregnations are necessary to see the pattern of kineties about the anterior suture (Fig. 157) and they show that there are

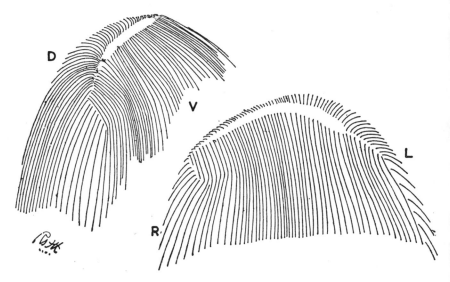

FIG. 157. *Anoplophrya alluri*: anterior end to show the course of the kineties and anterior suture from the right and ventral aspects. (Original from Ag impregnations.)

more kineties on the dorsal than on the ventral surface; in fact, there are 80 dorsal and 64 ventral kineties, but they can only be counted on an enlarged photomicrograph.

Culture

No astomate has yet been cultured.

Anoplophrya vulgaris de Puytorac

This species, briefly noted from *Eisenia foetida* by de Puytorac (1954), generally resembles the foregoing, but has the anterior suture more posteriorly placed so that it is easier to examine. The ciliate measures 105–50 $\mu \times$ 45–75 μ, and has 115 kineties, of which 60 are dorsal.

Maupasella Cépède

The revision of this genus by de Puytorac (1954) has so drastically cut across the old arrangement of species that the literature before the date of his monograph is hardly intelligible without the following explanation. In 1910 Cépède described and figured, under the name *M. nova*, a ciliate from the gut of various oligochaetes, and for many years thereafter apparently the same organism was remarked, always in oligochaetes, until a considerable number of distinct but related species had accumulated under Cépède's name. Unfortunately, Cépède did not identify his hosts and his description is defective in just those particulars by which the species now recognized are distinguished, so that it is impossible to tell which of these corresponds with that seen by the original author or, in many cases, those seen by his successors. Thus the name that is so common in the literature, *M. nova*, can no longer be applied to any species. The present taxonomy is mainly based on the number and arrangement, especially about the apex, of the kineties, points rarely noted by older authors. As in the case of *Anoplophrya*, while the systematics of the genus are being more firmly established, much remains to be learned about the distribution of the new species. At least two of these occur in *Eisenia foetida*, though only one is recorded by de Puytorac himself.

Maupasella mucronata (Cépède)

This is the organism originally described by Cépède (1910) as *Schultzellina mucronata* from the gut of *Eiseniella tetraeda*. It has been found consistently over some dozen or more years in specimens of *Eisenia foetida*, where it is less common than *Anoplophrya alluri*, but still plentiful especially in the part of the gut just behind the seminal vesicles, that is, in the gizzard and anterior part of the intestine.

The living organism

Smears from the gut are prepared in the same way as for *Anoplophrya* (p. 334).

M. mucronata (Fig. 158A) is smaller than *Anoplophrya*, slim and sausage-shaped or sometimes with the posterior part somewhat swollen, when it resembles a pear. The body is flexible and may bend during swimming, though more often it is held straight. The anterior often appears to be truncate and the posterior rounded or slightly tapering. Our specimens, after fixation, measured 52–102 $\mu \times$ 18–33 μ, with a mean of 80 $\times$ 25·5 μ. Anteriorly, one surface, conventionally called ventral, is somewhat flattened (G); the rest of the body is circular in section. From the anterior end, which is naked, projects a slender, pointed splinter of ectoplasm, like a spike (A, B, H, I). The spike is movable and can be projected from or folded against the body. It is covered by an extension of the pellicle and its cytoplasmic core rests proximally on a thickened ring from which a number (6–10) of hyaline fibres depend into the body. So much can be plainly seen in the living animal under good optical conditions but the apparatus is said by de Puytorac to be far more complicated and to resemble that, described below, of *M. cepedei*.

The cilia are sparser than those of *Anoplophrya* and form a shaggier coat. They are set in 46 longitudinal rows and the number is remarkably constant for the species. Both anterior and posterior ends of the body are left naked of cilia and the terminal patterns of the meridians, better seen in Ag preparations, are taxonomic characters (cf. C, F). Cépède figured contractile vacuoles in his *Maupasella nova* but they have apparently been seen by no other observer.

The meganucleus is elongated, axial, and granular. The living micronucleus is rarely seen. Binary fission is perkinetal, and the dislocation of the kineties begins always, as in *M. cepedei*, ventrally and nearer to the left than the right (D, E). The opisthe develops the fixing apparatus before separation from the proter.

Permanent preparations

Fix in B. or Champy: stain in H.H. The cytoplasmic characters are mostly well shown; the meganucleus fixes better than in *Anoplophrya*. Only sections show the skeletal apparatus and even in well-fixed material the details shown in Fig. 158H are exceedingly difficult to verify; the ordinary appearance is that drawn in B. Specific determination calls for Ag impregnation, which will reveal the apical pattern of the kineties (C); they leave a heart-shaped unciliated area which may contain a few irregularly disposed kinetosomes. This pattern very closely resembles that found in *Juxtaradiophrya*, one of the more conventionally armed astomates, and it is to this group, not to *Anoplophrya*, that *Maupasella* seems to be related.

Maupasella cepedei de Puytorac

This species, also from the gizzard and anterior part of the intestine of *Eisenia foetida*, is very like the foregoing, but smaller (40–60 $\mu \times$ 20–35 μ), and with only 26 kineties (Fig. 158 F–I). It was from studies on it that de Puytorac (1954) described the structure and action of the remarkable organ of attachment, which that of *M. mucronata* is said to resemble.

The apparatus (H, I) consists of a spine, covered by the pellicle, and mounted on a base which is prolonged into 3 leaf-like feet. The base is hollowed out as a socket, resting on a domed rotula. Against the under

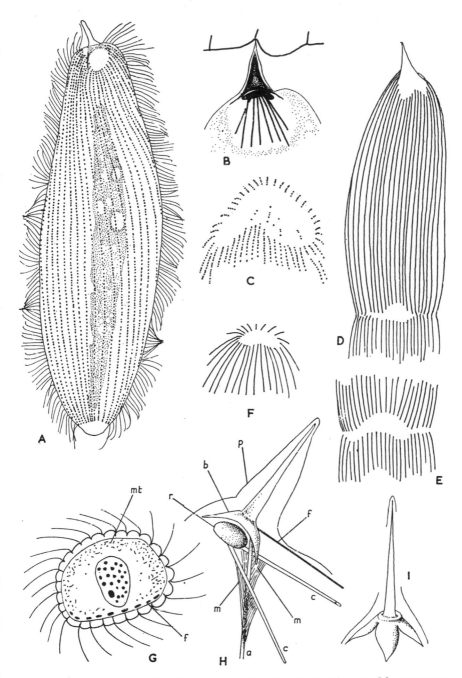

Fig. 158. *Maupasella* from the alimentary canal of *Eisenia foetida*. A–E, *M. mucronata*: A, ventro-lateral view of the ciliate (Flemming; H. H.). × 1,250; B, L.S. anterior end (B.; H.H.); c, apical pattern of kinetosomes (Ag); D, E, successive stages in binary fission showing kinetal pattern: the ventral surface is seen in focus from above so that the animal's right is on the right of drawing (Ag); F–I, *M. cepedei*: F, apical pattern of kineties; G, T.S. anterior region with ventral surface below; H, the organ of fixation and its accessory components; I, spine. (A–E original; F–I after de Puytorac.)

a, axis; *b*, base; *c*, arms of compass; *f*, fibre; *m*, myonemes; *mt*, mitochondria; *p*, pellicle over the spine; *r*, rotula.

surface of the rotula are articulated 2 rods, bound together at their proximal ends and constituting the arms of a compass. Between these arms and
attached to them by sheets of myonemes, depends an unpaired rod, the
axis, the head of which passes the rotula and abuts on the socket. To the
upper part of the base are attached the fibres that are so conspicuous a
feature of the ventral aspect of the animal both in life and in stained sections
(cf. B). When the spine is pointed anteriorly the angle between the compasses is acute and the vertical axis between them is raised. As the spine
leans towards the side of the body, which it does rather slowly (in about
2 seconds), the axis sinks into the endoplasm, the myonemes slacken, and
the angle between the compasses widens. To raise the spine, the myonemes
contract, pulling the arms of the compasses towards each other, until,
presumably, they are somehow arrested before they meet, and the pull of
the myonemes is transmitted to the axis, which moves upwards, pushes
against the base, and tilts this on the rotula until the spine is vertical.
It is possible that the fibres are contractile or elastic or both but it is not
clear what part they play in moving the spine. The spine is only 3 to 5 μ
long and the whole apparatus is on a minute scale. It will be noted that
there are no fixed points on which any part of the apparatus can find a purchase; all the components move (except the rotula?) and the resistance that
the myonemes must encounter before they can exert a force on the axis
presumably comes from the viscosity of the cytoplasm. There is no doubt a
considerable movement of the gut contents in just the region occupied by
Maupasella; and its need for some organ of fixation to the gut wall is
evident and, further, any such organ must be flexible enough to allow the
body to bend and sway in the lumen. What is not so easy to understand is
the evolution of so much minute complexity to fulfil so simple a function, if
indeed attachment is the only function of the organ.

Permanent preparations

As for the preceding species.

Durchoniella brasili (Léger and Duboscq) and D. legeri-duboscqui (Léger and Duboscq)

An astomate ciliate from the polychaete worm, *Audouinia tentaculata*,*
has been known for over half a century, and Léger and Duboscq (1904b)
published a good account of it under the name *Anoplophrya brasili*, but
they missed the cytoskeleton. This was discovered by Hentschel (1925),
who transferred the animal to the genus *Hoplitophrya*. In 1954 de Puytorac
pointed out that there were really 2 species in this host and he created for

* For other parasites of this host, see index, under *host-lists*.

them the new genus *Durchoniella*. The smaller species (90–195 $\mu \times$ 60–70 μ) with 68 kineties, is *D. brasili*; the larger (180–350 $\mu \times$ 75–90 μ), with 138 kineties, is *D. legeri-duboscqui*. The other differences are so slight that a single description serves.

Living and fixed organisms*

Both species are elongated, circular in cross section except anteriorly, where the 'ventral' surface is flattened (Fig. 159A). Posteriorly the body is truncated or rather flatly rounded and anteriorly it is an obtuse process, devoid of cilia, and containing the cytoskeleton. The cilia are set in close, long rows. There is a single line of contractile vacuoles (3 to 5 in the small, up to 14 in the large species).

When seen from ventral or dorsal surfaces the cytoskeleton looks like a hyaline circumflex with a slight backward projection between the arms. It is a pyramid, four angles of which (three in *D. legeri-duboscqui*) are more or less prolonged so that the base is concave; the apex forms the papilla marking the anterior tip of the animal (B). The apparatus is supported by a number of ectoplasmic fibrillae stretching backwards between the kineties. The skeleton of *Durchoniella* is reduced to a state in which its function is doubtful; Hentschel thought it might be used to push a way through intestinal debris. In related genera (e.g. *Metaradiophrya*, Fig. 159 C, D) it may be highly developed for attachment.

The kineties leave a naked area anteriorly into which the skeleton fits. Ag preparations reveal an argyrome of interlocking links between the kineties (Tchang-Tso Run, 1931). The meganucleus is a ribbon, excavated for some of its length by a gutter so that it is C-shaped in transverse section. The micronucleus is larger and more easily seen than in the astomates of oligochaetes and, from the frequency with which it is observed, its mitosis must be prolonged.

The cyst of *Durchoniella*, described by Tchang-Tso Run, is ellipsoidal or pyriform with a double-contoured wall, within which the ciliate, which apparently retains much the same structure as in the trophic phase, continuously rotates.

ORDER APOSTOMATIDA

This small order of some dozen genera, all of which are parasitic, is characterized by the following features. There are never more than 33 somatic kineties, and these are always spirally twisted in the adult feeding stage (Fig. 160C). The cytostome is very small (in one genus it is lost) and is associated with a peculiar rosette organ (C, I), not found elsewhere. The

---

* Methods as for the foregoing species.

free-living infective stage, called the tomite (H), is equipped with a ventral group of thigmotactic cilia which fasten it to the host. The commonest hosts

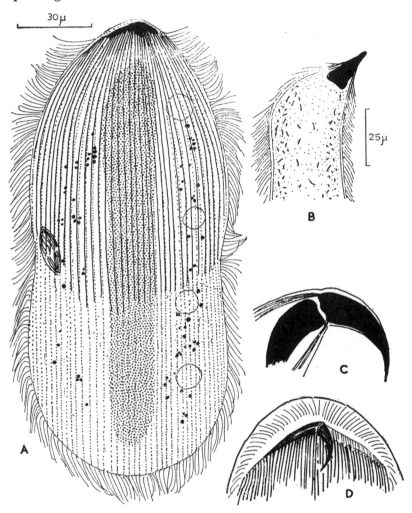

FIG. 159. Astomatida. A, *Durchoniella brasili*: ventral surface, the black spots are lipid droplets; B, the same, L.S. anterior end showing the cytoskeletal process; C, *Metaradiophrya lumbrici*: L.S. showing the fully developed astomatid skeleton in the form of an articulated hook; D, the same, ventral view of the anterior end to show position of the cystoskeleton. (A–C after de Puytorac; D, sketched from a figure by Heidenreich.)

are marine Crustacea and the ciliates may be digenetic; for example, the well-known species *Foettingeria actiniarum* is very common in actiniid anemones and passes part of its life-history in the crustaceans on which they feed. The life-history is always complicated, but conforms fairly constantly to the following plan. There is a feeding, growing (and also sexual) stage, called the trophont, which is parasitic; its kineties are spiral, and encircle the body in a clockwise helix or arc when seen from the apex of the animal. When full of food, the trophont encysts and becomes a tomont; its kineties straighten and it divides, once, twice or many times to give the free-living tomites, which are the infective stages. On the host the ciliate again encysts, as a phoront, and emerges from the cyst to feed again in the trophont stage. The sketchy treatment which the apostomes receive here does not do justice to their interest. They have been fortunate in their students. They are the subject of a monumental work by Chatton and Lwoff (1935*b*) and they also form the source from which André Lwoff drew many of his illustrations in expounding the principles of ciliate morphogenesis (Lwoff, 1950).

Gymnodinioides inkystans Minkiewicz

The genus *Gymnodinioides* is widely distributed* and the species differ little from *G. inkystans* as it occurs on *Eupagurus prideauxi* and, probably, other Crustacea. The encysted phoronts are found on the gills of *E. prideauxi* and cannot hatch until the host moults, when they penetrate the discarded exuvium and feed on it as trophonts. These, when gorged with food, escape, encyst as tomonts, and divide; their products, the tomites, excyst and swim freely to find new hosts, on whose gills they settle and become trophonts. It must be admitted that the encysted stages are difficult to interpret *in vivo* and for the sake of a simple presentation of the life-cycle, the results obtained from both living and fixed material are here considered together. Fixation with B. or other standard mixtures is good, provided that the fixatives are made up in sea water. The fixed material is stained with H.H. Ag preparations are indispensable for an understanding of morphogenesis.

Living and fixed ciliates

A gill of the host is excised and spread on the slide, its lamellae being turned back on either side from the axis. The phoronts (Fig. 160A) occur fixed to the axis, where they appear as small ellipsoidal bodies, often coloured. They are commonly of two sizes, one group with a mean of 100 × 50 μ, the other 53 × 25 μ. The larger (B) are phoronts of the related apostome *Polyspira delagei*; the smaller are *G. inkystans*. Where there is doubt, stages of *Polyspira* may be diagnosed by the presence of plainly visible lines of refringent rods, the trichocysts, which accompany the kineties.

---

* *G. corophii* on *Corophium acutum* and *C. volutator*, *G. calkinsi* on *Palaemonetes* sp., *G. humorale* on *Harpacticus gracilis*, *G. zonatum* on *Gammarus pulex*, *G. aselli* on *Asellus aquaticus*, *G. caridinae* on Japanese shrimps.

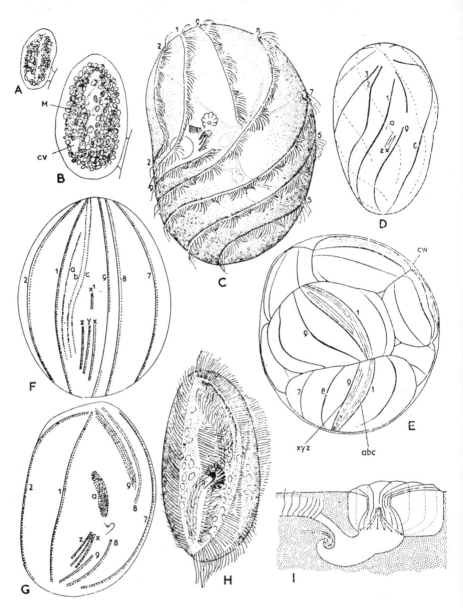

FIG. 160. *Gymnodinioides inkystans*. A, young phoront, living. ×350; B, same, of *Polyspira delagei*, for comparison; C–H, *G. inkystans*: C, grown trophont. ×675; D, young tomont, shortly after encystation, with kineties straightening. ×500; E, tomonts dividing in cyst. ×500; F, infraciliature of young tomite at the beginning of its development: diagrammatic; G, ventral infraciliature of tomite; H, living tomite, ventral view. ×1,100; I, diagrammatic L.S. rosette of *Foetteringia actiniarum*: at the bases of the septa lies part of the circlet of internal cilia, a passage bearing buccal cilia leads from the left (of the drawing) into the buccal atrium, and a narrow internal canal (cytopharynx) leaves the atrium. (After Chatton and Lwoff.)

a, b, c, parabuccal cilia or their kineties (in G, the kinetosomes, derived from *a,* for the thigmotactic cilia); *x, y, z,* buccal cilia; *1–9,* somatic kineties; *cv* and *M,* positions of contractile vacuole and meganucleus among food reserves in B; *cw,* cyst wall enclosing tomonts.

The phoront fills the cyst, which has a thin transparent wall attached to the host by a sort of foot so that it lies parallel with the axis of the gill. The food inclusions, in turn, fill the ciliate, which is stuffed with platelets of reserve material, colourless, violet, or pink, according to the source of food and its stage of digestion. The meganucleus is visible as a clear, cylindrical area. In the living phoront, the ciliary striae are only faintly visible. There are 9 of them, twisted into a clockwise spiral when observed from the anterior end; their cilia are motionless or, in ciliates which are near to hatching, they stir with a languid undulation. There is one slowly pulsating contractile vacuole. On staining, the meganucleus is seen to be long and central; the micronucleus is tiny and spherical.

Excystation occurs only at the moult, and Chatton and Lwoff found no experimental method (however successful with other genera) which could evoke it except that cysts from non-moulting hosts would excyst when placed on fresh exuvium from another host. The young trophont, on emerging, swims into the exuvium and begins to feed voraciously. During the next 6 or 8 hours the ciliate will ingest all the food it requires for the rest of its life-cycle and it increases rapidly and sometimes enormously in size. It will be understood that phoronts themselves vary very much in size, and small ones give small trophonts which may expand to over 60 times their original volume during their short trophic life. The food is the exuvial fluid (and possibly, though the mouth is minute, some particulate matter) of the host; if this contains, as it often does, a violet pigment, the pigment is concentrated by the ciliates, and this accounts for the pigmentation found in other stages and retained by the phoronts.

The grown trophont (c) is reniform, up to 120 μ long, stuffed with a single large mass of food so that the cytoplasm is reduced to a mere skin holding the nuclei and food reserves. On its ventral face, in, so to speak, the hilum of the reniform body, lie the rosette, cytostome, and contractile vacuole. The rosette is a laminated or septate organ, one wall of which is slightly eroded to admit the cytostome. The septa run down perpendicularly to the body surface to an incomplete ring of cilia which guard the entrance to an oral chamber from which runs off a cytopharyngeal tube (Fig. 1601, of *Foettingeria*, where the structure of the rosette is better known than in *Gymnodinioides*). Towards the end of its free life, the food mass of the ciliate begins to divide. The trophont is now ready to leave the exuvium. It has 9 spirally twisted somatic kineties, 3 short rows of buccal cilia, called *x*, *y*, and *z*, below the cytostome, and, to the right of the rosette, a short line of parabuccal cilia, sometimes doubled, called *a* (or *a+b*, and eventually, when it trebles, *+c*). This creature, after a trophic life of not more than 10 hours, swims away from the exuvium, settles on the substratum, and encysts.

The second encysted stage, which is the more difficult to examine alive, contains the tomont, which will multiply asexually, sharing the food reserve among its daughters, who, as they digest it, will change colour, if they have any, from violet to pink. The divisions may be few or several, giving 2 to 64 tomites, and they are attended by a complicated and unique process of morphogenesis. The kineties of the tomont straighten (D) and run as meridional lines down the body; *a*, *b*, and *c* (as soon as the last is developed) lengthen, and so do *x*, *y*, and *z*, but the latter group of 3 shorten again between fissions, which are perkinetal (E). In the final products, the young tomites (F) *b* and *c* regress, while *a* shortens and proliferates a long ellipse of kinetosomes from which will grow the thigmotactic cilia of the developed tomite (G). The somatic kineties 8 and 9 are interrupted and their anterior portions also proliferate a kinetosomal field, whose cilia possibly reinforce those from *a*. Finally a short length of *x* separates anteriorly (F, x^1), migrates below the surface, and lays down the origins of the cilia for the rosette. The tomites which now hatch from the cyst naturally vary greatly in size according to the number of divisions that has produced them. They may swim freely for about a week and settle on the gills of a host by their thigmotactic cilia, or, failing to find one, they die.

Conjugation is extraordinary; it begins between trophonts but is carried into the next encysted stages and completed by tomites; a description is given by Chatton and Lwoff (1935*b*).

SUBCLASS SPIROTRICHA

The conspicuous and distinguishing character of the subclass is the AZM, here developed as a powerful organ of feeding and locomotion.* An AZM of course appears among the Holotricha but never in the dominating proportions which mark that of the spirotrich. The somatic ciliature, complete and unremarkable in the Heterotrichida, is elsewhere reduced or absent. It is represented by stiff, bristle-like cilia, long and locomotor in the Oligotrichida (Fig. 165), short and possibly sensory in the Hypotrichida (Fig. 168F), or by cirri. Cirri (Fig. 168), which are described in more detail below (p. 369), are like membranellae except in shape—membranellae are blades of cilia with rectangular bases and cirri have round bases and taper to a point—and it is sometimes difficult to know which term to apply (e.g. in the Entodiniomorphida). As the somatic cilia disappear in the more advanced orders the increasingly naked pellicle tends to stiffen into a permanent shape, which may be only slightly or not at all deformable. At the same time the surface organellae become more widely spaced and it is perhaps in relation to their distances from each other that there appears in the most highly evolved orders (Entodiniomorphida and Hypotrichida)

---

* Except in the small, specialized order Odontostomatida, the affinities of which remain most uncertain. See p. 380.

an internal system of fibrillae, called the neuro-motor system, which has been thought to sustain conduction and co-ordination (see pp. 368, 374).

Morphogenesis remains primitive in some of the Heterotrichida where, as in *Spirostomum* (Fig. 163 C–F), there is a single stomatogenic kinety, or (*Stentor*) several adjacent kineties (Villeneuve-Brachon, 1940). Elsewhere the process is specialized, and in the Hypotrichida development is so complicated that only very careful observations and analysis have revealed that the behaviour of the kinetosomes conforms with theoretical expectations (see p. 377 and Chatton and Séguéla, 1940).

Most of the Spirotricha are free-living. One whole order, the Tintinnida, is loricate and planktonic (Fig. 166). All the Entodiniomorphida are entozoic (and possibly symbiotic) in the stomachs of herbivorous mammals; they exhibit the elaborate speciation within a uniform environment seen in some other groups of entozoic Protozoa, and, also like them, they attain perhaps the highest degree of morphological complexity seen in their class (Fig. 167).

ORDER HETEROTRICHIDA

These, the least specialized of the Spirotricha, exhibit considerable diversity of form and are uncommitted to any single pattern of morphogenesis. Many are large, up to 3 mm in length, and their size has made them suitable subjects for experimental study (see under *Stentor* and *Spirostomum* below). They are the only spirotrichs to retain a typical somatic ciliature; it is holotrichous, generally set in close parallel lines. The oral ciliature consists of a well-developed, but not enormous, AZM, and there is often an UM in addition. Some of the heterotrichs are pigmented: *Blepharisma* is pink, and *Stentor coeruleus* ('the king of the ciliates') is one of the few freshwater animals to be pale blue. A few are loricate (*Folliculina*). Encystation is relatively common. The size and beauty of some species has made them celebrated objects for illustration.

The group may be divided into 2 suborders, which are very unequal (Corliss, 1959). In the larger, the Heterotrichina, the somatic ciliature is well developed and the typical characters of the order as given above are present. The small suborder Licnophorina (here neglected) consists of a single genus, *Licnophora*, without a general somatic ciliature, and with a complicated basal disk for attachment to the host; all species are ectocommensal with marine animals.

Stentor coeruleus Ehrenberg

Species of *Stentor* are common in ponds and slowly moving streams containing enough bacterial food. They are all large and, when expanded, trumpet-shaped, with a conspicuous AZM encircling the peristome.

S. polymorphus is inclined to be long and slim, brown in colour, or green with symbiotic algae; it tends, when feeding, to attach itself to vegetation, and may at times form a gelatinous lorica. *S. roeseli* is long and slimmer and the lorica is almost permanent. *S. coeruleus* is at once distinguished by its blue colour and it is without question one of the most beautiful animals in existence. It is generally found in foul water and though tolerant of a fairly wide range of temperature, carbon dioxide content, and pH, it appears to select environments with an exceptionally low oxygen content, though in the laboratory it can rapidly adapt to water containing much more dissolved oxygen (Sprugel, 1951).

The large size of *Stentor* has made it a favourite object for the study of behaviour (Jennings, 1931), grafting and regeneration (Weisz, 1954; Tartar, 1953, 1954), and ciliary movement (Sleigh, 1956, 1957). On the other hand, surprisingly little is known of its cytology and morphogenetics. Probably the best description is that of Dierks (1926), whose report ought to be reviewed in the light of the important E.M. studies by Randall and Jackson (1958). For much general information, Johnson (1893) still remains useful.

The living organism

Stentor coeruleus (Fig. 161A) is often between 1 and 2 millimetres long and so visible to the naked eye. When expanded the anterior end forms a flattened or slightly convex peristomial disk with the membranellae set around it. The body expands below the disk and then tapers to the posterior where it forms a foot by which the animal frequently attaches itself. The whole surface, including the peristome, is covered with short cilia in rows related to the striations of the body noted below; the cilia on the peristome are shorter than those on the body and on the foot they are slightly longer.

The body is striped by alternate bands of clear and pigmented ectoplasm, converging on the foot. These are the *Zwischenstreifen* and *Rippenstreifen* respectively of German authors and both may branch towards their peristomial ends. The cilia are inserted along the *Zwischenstreifen* and the *Rippenstreifen* contain the pigment, which, in *S. coeruleus*, is a blue substance called stentorin by Ray Lankester; it is distributed in granules which look blue-green by natural incident light and grass-green by transmitted light under the microscope. The granules are very basophil, stain strongly with Sudan Black, and are the only inclusions to react with Janus Green B, and on these and other grounds Weisz (1949b, 1950) concluded that they were mitochondria.

Stentor is highly contractile and a number of authors have contributed descriptions of fibrillar systems supposed to mediate the contraction (see especially Neresheimer, 1903; Schröder, 1907; and Dierks, 1926). The subject has become confused and we are fortunate in having from Randall and Jackson (1958)—and see also Fauré-Fremiet and Rouiller (1958)—a very clear account of the facts based on E.M. studies. In living animals, 2

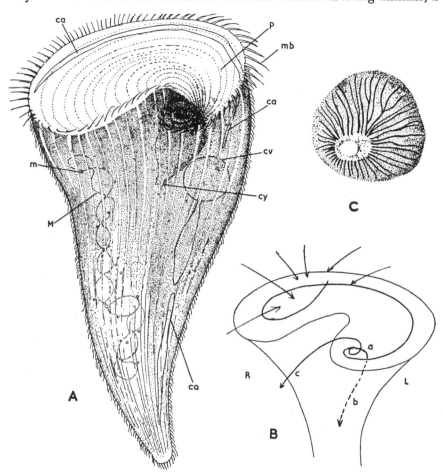

FIG. 161. *Stentor coeruleus.* A, the trophic ciliate: semi-diagrammatic. × 100; B, the feeding and rejection paths: particulate food reaches the peristome in the area indicated by the small arrows, follows the track around the peristome to the selection point (*a*), where it rotates above the entrance to the buccal funnel, and passes down the latter (*b*) or is rejected (*c*); C, a specimen seen from below and stained to show the *M* bands. (A original; B and C after Dierks.)

a, selection point; *b*, path of accepted food; *c*, rejection path; *ca*, canals feeding *cv*, the contractile vacuole; *cy*, cytostome; L, left side; *M*, meganucleus; *m*, micronucleus; *mb*, membranella of AZM; *p*, peristome; R, right side.

fibrillar systems may be distinguished. One is obvious and consists of longitudinal fibres lying in the clear stripes (*Zwischenstreifen*) of ectoplasm, very superficial, and corresponding to the ciliary meridians. They stretch from peristome to foot. They may have a wavy course, but in much extended or much contracted animals they straighten and thicken. These structures, easily seen by phase contrast and also by bright field microscopy, are kinetodesmata; their finer structure and possibly contractile function are discussed on p. 217. Deeper to the kinetodesmata are thicker fibrillae structures, oval in section, called M bands or endoplasmic myonemes (Fig. 161C). They actually extend throughout the length of the organism though *in vivo* they are seen only in its posterior half. They too may be contractilᵉ. Now the confusion in the literature appears to arise very largely from the fact that the earliest authors saw the kinetodesmata in the living animal and the M bands in their fixed and stained preparations, and assumed they were dealing with different aspects of the same organellae, which they called myonemes.*

The AZM surrounds the peristome like a fence within which the everted floor is carpeted with cilia. Both the AZM and the cilia are used in feeding. The peristome is notched on the ventral side and the AZM begins to the (animal's) right of the notch, circles the rim and turns into a corkscrew-shaped depression (representing the enclosed part of the buccal cavity) which leads to the cytostome (cy). The membranellae (mb) are fairly conspicuous throughout most of the zone, but they become smaller as they approach the depression and they tend to lose their integrity so that much of the spiral tract below the level of the peristome is composed of individual cilia. In *S. polymorphus* most of the membranellae have 3 rows, each containing 20 to 25 cilia, but they are reduced to 2 rows near the peristomial funnel (buccal cavity). Feeding has been studied by Schaeffer (1910), Dierks (1926), and Jennings (1931), and all agree that the organism exercises some selection from the particles brought to the peristome. The action of the AZM creates a vortex which delivers a mixture of particles on to the peristomial disk (Fig. 161B, small arrows) and these are taken to the entrance to the funnel (a), where they rotate, and it is here apparently that selection occurs and some particles are rejected (c) by a momentary reversal of the ciliary beat. The food is bacteria, small rotifers and Protozoa, and *Stentor* is sometimes cannibalistic (von Gelei, 1925).

The meganucleus (M) in trophic specimens consists of a string of elliptical nodes held together by delicate cytoplasmic bridges—the moniliform type of nucleus. The number of nodes varies: there were 7 to 23 in specimens studied by Schwartz (1935) and 6 to 12 in those of Burnside (1929). The equivalence of meganuclear nodes is different in young and old animals. For example, after fission all nodes are alike in that any one of them is able (other conditions being suitable) to support regeneration, but as time

---

* Thus the well-known figures of branched 'myonemes' from Dierks (1926) show M bands drawn from fixed specimens, while his descriptions of their behaviour refer to living kinetodesmata.

goes on the posterior nodes progressively lose their capacity to maintain fragments, which achieve less and less differentiation, and more and more nodes become involved in failure until only anterior nodes are effective (Weisz, 1949a). The meganucleus, as in *Spirostomum* (Fig. 163), contracts before dividing; in the daughter ciliates, the nuclei regain their moniliform arrangement and for a time the faculty for supervising regeneration is distributed along the whole structure again. The number of micronuclei (*m*) is usually large, e.g. 10 to 42 with a mean of 25 (Schwartz); they are small, difficult to observe, and usually they are closely associated with the meganucleus.

The first sign of division is the appearance between the peristome and the foot of a field of kinetosomes proliferated by some of the ventral kineties, which have previously been duplicated in this area (Fig. 162A). They provide the peristomial apparatus of the opisthe which grows around the constriction between the daughters as it is formed (B–E). More details are given by Schwartz (1935). For conjugation, see Mulsow (1913).

It is just possible that *Stentor* forms cysts: Stein described them. But if they exist they have apparently not been seen for nearly a hundred years.*

Permanent preparations

Stentor is an unsatisfactory subject because it is so contractile; most of the structure is easily seen in the living animal.

Culture

Some strains may be maintained on wheat or barley water, made by boiling about 20 grains in a litre of water and allowing it to stand until enough bacteria or small ciliates have developed to feed the specimens of *Stentor* which are then introduced. More refined methods are given by Hetherington (1932) and by Dawson (1953); see p. 411.

Spirostomum ambiguum Ehrenberg

This fine ciliate, sometimes 3 or 4 mm long, occurs in ponds rich in organic material from decaying vegetation, especially in slime with much hydrogen sulphide. It is not, as sometimes thought, a facultative anaerobe —it disintegrates in the absence of oxygen—but its oxygen requirements are small (Specht, 1934). It is very intolerant of alkalinity above pH 7·6 (see p. 354). To the naked eye *Spirostomum* appears as a whitish thread, often attached to the sides of its container, and it may be taken for a rhabdocoel turbellarian. The description and figures by Stein (1867) remain indispensable, supplemented by the work of Bishop (1923, 1925, 1927) and that on

---

* 'I have never seen the cysts of *Stentor*, and I have never met anyone who has.' D. L. M.

fine structure by Randall (1957). For behaviour see Blättner (1926) and Clark (1946), and for regeneration, Sokolow (1923, 1924) and Seyd (1936).

Two varieties were noted by Bishop (1923): *S. ambiguum major* is 800–900 μ long, its posterior end rounded, its cytoplasm yellowish, the cytostome behind the midpoint, and the contractile vacuole is about half as large

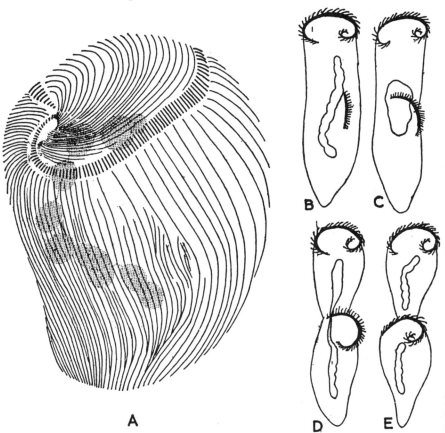

FIG. 162. *Stentor coeruleus*: binary fission. A, ciliate in a preparatory stage seen from the left and ventral aspects: the nucleus is still moniliform and some of the ventral kineties have multiplied to form the rudiments of the new peristomial apparatus; B–E, differentiation of the peristome and fission. (A after Schwartz; B–E after Weisz.)

and pulsates twice as fast as that of the smaller variety (it is up to one-eighth of the length of the body with an interval of about 8 minutes); *S. ambiguum minor* is 400–500 μ, truncated posteriorly, greyish-white, with its cytostome in the anterior third of the body; its vacuole occupies a quarter, a third, or even more of the body and pulsates every 16 minutes on the average.

The living organism

The ciliate (Fig. 163 A, B) is slim and long, somewhat flattened laterally, so that most of the peristome lies on a narrow ventral surface. The body is covered with rows of short cilia which follow a slightly spiral course which is anti-clockwise when seen from in front. It is probably owing to their co-ordinated action, and not that of the peristomial membranellae, that the animal rotates as it swims, for the rotation is maintained by isolated fragments of the body. On even slight mechanical stimulation *Spirostomum* contracts vigorously and the spiral course of the cilia becomes more obvious. On generalized stimulation, as, for example, on tapping the sides of the container, the animal contracts, reverses the direction of its ciliary beat, darts backwards a short distance, gradually relaxes, and continues forwards again. A similar effect is produced by stimulation in the anterior half of the body, but in the posterior half it causes contraction and then swimming forwards at an increased speed, i.e. the organism is moved away from the direction of the stimulus. The local properties which cause these differences in the direction of the reaction are retained for a time by fragments. When *Spirostomum* is bisected and the halves allowed to recover, if the vessel is tapped, both halves contract, but the anterior half then moves back and the posterior half forward. In this respect the portions do not begin to behave like physiological wholes until they have regenerated sufficiently to be recognized as morphological wholes (Clark, 1946). The anterior end of *Spirostomum* appears to be more sensitive than the posterior and the same is true of anterior fragments as compared with posterior fragments of similar size.

The peristomial membranellae, like those of all Spirotricha, follow a clockwise course to the cytostome, though this is not obvious. The AZM begins at the anterior end of the animal and runs along its length and it is not until it nears the cytostome that it begins to spiral. Thus much of its course is straight unless it is involved, as it often is, in the whole body's contraction, and then it twists into an anti-clockwise spiral. There is no UM, but a single row of cilia appears on the right wall of the depression that represents the enclosed part of the buccal cavity.

S. ambiguum normally feeds on bacteria or small flagellates but has been seen to take *Chilomonas paramecium* which is 30–40 μ long. After ingestion the food spheres, which may be large, follow a fixed cycle, forward to the anterior end, and then back on a parallel course, down the narrow strip of endoplasm between the contractile vacuole and body wall (Fig. 163G). Undigested remains are evacuated at a cytoproct which lies in a little terminal pit. Inorganic particles such as Indian ink or Carmine, as well as some food which apparently cannot be digested, follow a different course; they begin, like natural food, to move forwards, but soon take a short cut

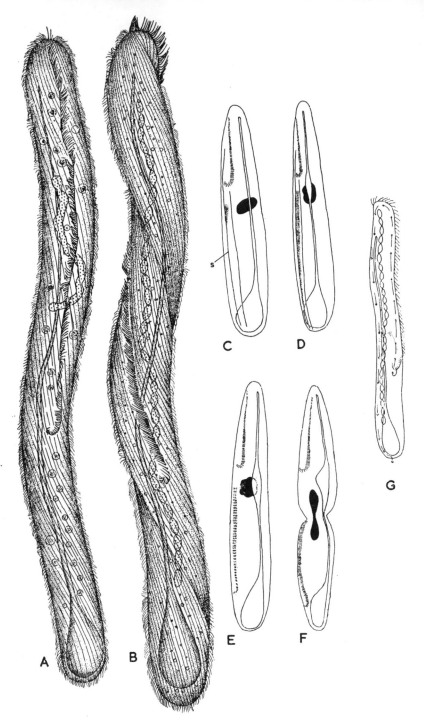

Fig. 163. *Spirostomum ambiguum*. A and B, trophic ciliates. × 125; in A the animal has recently divided and the nucleus has not yet regained the typical moniliform structure; C–F, binary fission in *S. teres*: in C the stomatogenic kinety (*s*) has proliferated kinetosomes at the level of the nucleus; in D the *Anlage* of the new vacuole is forming in the proter; E and F show further differentiation; G, cyclosis: food particles take the long path marked in arrows, Carmine and Indian ink the short cut dotted across the midline. (A and B after Stein; C–F after Villeneuve-Brachon; G after Bishop.)

across the body to turn into the last half of the normal course towards the cytoproct. The contractile vacuole is always conspicuous. It lies in the posterior part of the body and is fed by a long canal stretching dorsally from the anterior end. The vacuole empties posteriorly. The meganucleus is moniliform in *S. ambiguum*; at division it becomes first vermiform and then compact, and these two conditions are seen respectively in the adults of an unnamed species from India (Seshacher and Padmavathi, 1956) and in the common *S. teres*.

Binary fission (C–F, which illustrate the process in *S. teres* with a compact nucleus) occurs, as far as is known, at any time of the clock, and takes about 8 hours. It is more frequent at high temperatures and Bishop (1923) found that animals at 20° C divided so often that they never had an opportunity to reach the length of those living at 16° C. Ciliates about to divide are longer than the average and the additional length is formed by growth mainly behind the cytostome. The first indication of fission is the formation of a ridge running posteriorly from the level of the cytostome. Along this ridge the membranellae of the opisthe develop, small at first, and uncoordinated until the final separation of the daughters. When stomatogenesis is well advanced the meganucleus loses its lobulation (cf. B and A), straightens, and contracts; as its anterior end remains stationary the result is that most of the nucleus is drawn forward and it may come to lie entirely in the anterior half of the body. It now moves to a central position and contracts still further until it is roughly oval in outline. At this stage a dilation appears on the canal of the contractile vacuole at the level of the anterior end of the nucleus, and this is the primordium of the new vacuole. The nucleus elongates, a constriction appears about the animal and the daughter vacuole begins to discharge by a pore of its own. The final constriction separates daughters containing unequal lengths of vermiform meganucleus, which then lobulate.

The behaviour of the micronuclei cannot be followed *in vivo*. They are beginning their division by the time that they accompany the meganucleus in its forward migration and have completed it at its return to the central position or soon after. The daughters are scattered irregularly throughout the cytoplasm and although they eventually align themselves with the meganucleus, they do so haphazardly and their products are unequally distributed to the daughter organisms (Bishop, 1925).

Villeneuve-Brachon (1940) has reported something of stomatogenesis in *S. teres*: the process can be seen in the living animal. The stomatogenic kinety (C, *s*) is the one immediately on the right of the peristome and it proliferates kinetosomes which become arranged in short parallel rows; these approximate in pairs to give the bases of the membranellae of the opisthe.

Conjugation has been seen during the early summer (May–June) between individuals of smaller and less variable size than other members of the culture. They pair by their peristomial faces and their membranellae are not resorbed. The process takes from 2½ to 3 days (Bishop, 1923). The cytological details are incompletely known.

Encystation has not been clearly reported. *Spirostomum* is known to disappear from time to time from populated habitats and to reappear after long intervals. The disappearance may be due, as Jenkin (1927) suggested, to slight increases of pH above an optimum value. *Spirostomum* survives indefinitely at pH 7·4 to 7·6, but its life was disproportionately shortened by slight increases in pH outside this range. The reappearance is not understood. Stein described structures which might have been cysts of *Spirostomum* but their identity was uncertain, and like the supposed cysts of some other genera, they have never been seen again.

Permanent preparations

Spirostomum always contracts violently when fixed, but shows the nuclei well after S+A or B, and D.H. with Orange G or Eosin. Bishop's well-known studies of the structure are now confirmed and expanded by the E.M. investigations of Randall (1958). There appear to be no *M* bands (cf. *Stentor*, p. 348) and it may be that the only contractile elements are kinetodesmata.

Culture

Bishop (1923) obtained good stocks on simple wheat infusions. Two grains are boiled for a few minutes in aquarium water. The tubes stand for 4 to 5 days to produce a good crop of bacteria and *Spirostomum* is then added. Bishop was successful only with long narrow tubes in which the amount of dissolved oxygen was small. Others have found it impossible to repeat these results, but the medium is a good one if mammalian faeces are added, i.e. two pellets from rats to 30 ml wheat infusion (Clark, 1946). For a more precise method, see p. 410.

Nyctotherus Leidy

The genus comprises entozoic ciliates distinguished by the form of the AZM. This begins anteriorly and follows the ventral surface for a distance and then plunges into a more or less prolonged internal passage which winds in the ordinary clockwise direction towards the cytostome, below which there is a narrow cytopharynx; that is to say, less of the original buccal cavity has been everted on to the surface of *Nyctotherus* than in most of the Spirotricha. To the right of the AZM as it bends inwards there lies an inconspicuous UM. Most species inhabit the alimentary canals of anuran Amphibia and Reptilia, but there are some from other vertebrate and from a number of invertebrate hosts. Host lists are given by Bhatia and Gulati (1927), who also provide a key, and by Zeliff (1933), and some additional species are listed by Wichterman (1937). Good descriptions were given by Stein (1867) for a few species; cytoplasmic inclusions were studied by Horning (1927) and Dutta (1958).

Nyctotherus cordiformis (Ehrenberg)

This well-known species occurs in the common frog, *Rana temporaria*, in company with *Opalina* and *Balantidium* (pp. 150, 262) in the rectum, and has also been recorded from *R. esculenta*, *Hyla aurea* and *H. versicolor*, *Bombinator igneus*, *B. cinereus*, and in India, *B. melanostictus*, and it probably infects other Anura. Frogs are opened dry, the rectum removed whole, moistened with Frog Ringer's Solution and examined as for *Opalina*. The frogs should be freshly collected; they tend to lose their ciliates when kept in captivity.

The living animal

The ciliate (Fig. 164 A, B) is laterally flattened, oval when seen from the side or sometimes a little more pointed anteriorly than posteriorly, 150–200 $\mu \times$ 80–95 μ. As it swims slowly among the rectal contents it is at once distinguishable from *Balantidium* by its prominent S-shaped peristomial line of membranellae. The dorsal side is convex and the ventral is slightly concave at about its mid-point, where the AZM enters the interior of the animal.

The holotrichous coat of somatic cilia, consisting of 66 to 72 kineties, is arranged in parallel lines on the dorsal and right sides of the animal, on which they follow the main curvature of the body. But on the left (A) there is a median longitudinal suture separating dorsal and ventral groups of kineties. A small terminal spot is unciliated and bears the cytoproct, which is here a permanent structure fed from an endoplasmic canal. The AZM follows the ventral margin of the body, but set back a little way, for less than half its course and then passes into the unexposed buccal cavity towards the cytostome, from which the cytopharynx continues the lower limb of the S-shape. The UM is inconspicuous and parallels the middle part of the AZM. There is a contractile vacuole in the posterior part of the body discharging through a small canal to the cytoproct. The anterior half of the body contains a store of glycogen that tinges brown in Lugol's Iodine Solution. The meganucleus (mean, 16 × 24 μ) is a plump, ovoid or reniform structure in the anterior part of the endoplasm, with a small micronucleus (2 to 4·5 μ) lying against it.

The cysts (B) are rounded or oval, greenish yellow, and within them the oral apparatus is dedifferentiated, and the cilia, but not the kinetosomes, are lost.

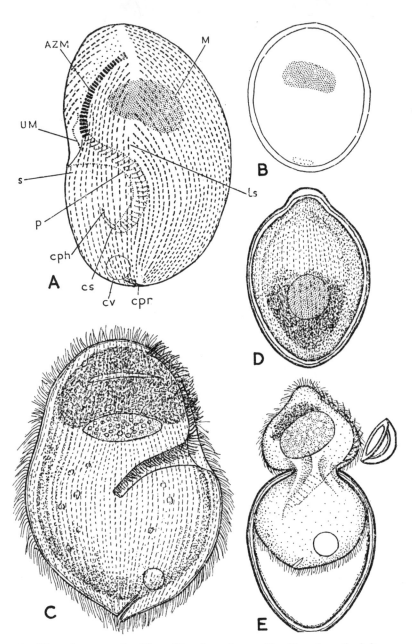

FIG. 164. *Nyctotherus.* A and B, *N. cordiformis*: A, the trophic ciliate from the left; B, cyst: C–E, *N. ovalis*: C, the living ciliate, from the right: D, cyst, the posterior end is uppermost and the ectocyst is not visible; E, excystation. All ×c. 500. (A mainly after Villeneuve-Brachon, modified; B after Wichterman; C after Stein; D and E after Lucas.) (D. L. M.)

AZM, adoral zone of membranellae; *cph*, cytopharynx; *cpr*, cytoproct; *cs*, cytostome; *cv*, contractile vacuole; *ls*, longitudinal suture; *M*, meganucleus; *p*, peristomial passage; *s*, area in which stomatogenic kineties proliferate the rudiments of the new peristomial ciliature of the opisthe at division; UM, undulating membrane.

Binary fission takes place at all stages of the life-cycle. According to Villeneuve-Brachon (1940), the new oral ciliature is derived from kinetosomes proliferated by 7 kineties just below the parent AZM at the point where it turns into the body (A, s).

The life-cycle in *Hyla versicolor* has been studied by Wichterman (1937). Tadpoles are infected by cysts, excystation follows, and the young ciliates divide and establish an infection in the intestine. They may at this stage again form cysts. It is only at the host's metamorphosis, and especially during its early stages, that conjugation occurs, that is, conjugants are commonest in tadpoles which are developing their hind legs, they may also occur in older tadpoles, but not in transformed frogs, in which the earliest stages of the ciliate are exconjugants.

Nyctotherus ovalis Leidy

This species occurs in the colon of cockroaches (*Blatta orientalis, B. germanica, Periplaneta americana*) and also in the mole-cricket, *Gryllotalpa vulgaris*, and species of *Julus*, and is probably capable of infecting other invertebrates.* The incidence varies greatly from place to place, and has been found in up to 50 per cent or even 100 per cent of some populations of cockroaches. It was described by Stein, and again by Kudo (1936) and by Pai and Wang (1948); excystation was studied by Lucas (1928).

The living organism

N. ovalis (Fig. 164 C–E) varies in size from 70 to 360 μ in length. It resembles the foregoing species in general, but is darker in colour, less flattened, pyriform when seen from the oral or aboral surfaces, with the anterior walls slightly concave. The internal limb of the AZM is shorter and the cytostome accordingly farther forward. The meganucleus measures 30–70 $\mu \times$ 15–25 μ and, when viewed from the side, as it usually is, it is biconvex, with the posterior more boldly curved than the anterior, which may be nearly straight. The micronucleus is spherical or ovoid and lies close to the anterior side of the meganucleus.

The cyst of *N. ovalis* (D) is 70–100 $\mu \times$ 60–80 μ, with a thickened knob at one end which is posterior in relation to the enclosed ciliate. The wall is three-layered; the thin ectocyst is usually invisible unless it is ruptured, and is not shown in the drawing; the middle layer is also thin except at the knob; most of the thickness elsewhere is contributed by the inner layer. The encysted organism shows pellicular striae but no cilia or membranellae.

* Dr. K. Vickerman informs me that it appeared in two out of many hundreds of leather-jackets (Tipulid larvae) examined by him in Devon. For other parasites of cockroaches, see index, under *host-lists*.

Although almost all cockroaches in the population studied by Lucas (1928) were infected by ciliates, only 4 per cent carried cysts. Excystation, which was followed in o·5 per cent saline maintained at 28° to 30° C, takes 6 to 8 hours. It is initiated by streaming movements in the endoplasm and the nucleus moves towards the knob from the far end of the cyst, and the new organellae will develop in relation to the new position of the nucleus, that is to say, the polarity of the animal is reversed. The peristome appears first as a clear broad streak on one side, without membranellae. The first ciliary activity is seen at the base of the buccal cavity. The body retracts from the wall, the somatic cilia develop, and the animal begins to revolve about its long axis. The contractile vacuole and cytoproct become visible and the membranellae develop. The ciliate is now ready to emerge, a sudden rupture pushes off the knob of the cyst like an operculum and the ciliate screws its way out, taking about an hour to do so (E).

Permanent preparations of *Nyctotherus* spp.

Ag preparations show the infraciliature. Nuclei are good after S+A and D.H. or Feulgen, but Kudo (1936), who especially studied the meganucleus, found that the truest picture was given after Flemming (the strong solution, i.e., 15 : 4 : 1 of 1 per cent chromic acid: 2 per cent osmium tetroxide: glacial acetic acid).

Culture

There are no good methods. Kudo (1936) kept *N. ovalis* by transferring the whole colon of infected animals (apparently the presence of the organ itself is necessary) to Petri dishes containing a medium made up of 3 eggwhites in 200 ml Ringer's Solution. When bacterial growth became excessive, about half the quantity of medium was replaced with fresh. The ciliates lived for 6 weeks at 18° to 22° C and divided.

Balch (1932) replaced human with rabbit serum in Smith and Barret's medium. On 19 parts of o·5 per cent NaCl+1 part non-activated rabbit serum, at room temperature, *N. ovalis* lived for 40 days, divided and sometimes encysted. It was sub-cultured weekly.

ORDER OLIGOTRICHIDA

This very small order* of freshwater and marine ciliates retains and develops the AZM but almost or completely loses the somatic ciliature. If any of the latter remains it is in isolated patches of locomotory bristles or

---

* *s. str.* In some classifications the Tintinniid and Entodiniid ciliates, here treated separately, are united with the oligotrichs to form a larger and more varied order Oligotrichida *s. lat.*

cirri. The AZM itself is used in locomotion. The members of the order tend to be small, commonly about 50 or 60 μ long, and are easily over-looked, but both *Strombidium*, with many, and *Halteria*, with few, species are common. *Strombidium inoculatum* exhibits an unusual diurnal rhythm adapted to tidal conditions. It inhabits littoral pools, and when, at low tide, these are isolated, it swims freely in the plankton for about 6 hours, but at high tide, when the pools are submerged into unguarded communication with the open sea, the ciliates sink and encyst in great numbers on solid surfaces (Fauré-Fremiet, 1948*b*). Stomatogenesis is autonomous and the new AZM faces away from the old, i.e. towards the hind end of the parent, so that the polarity of the opisthe reverses that of the proter, which is unusual in ciliates (Fauré-Fremiet, 1953*a*).

Halteria geleiana Szabó

The genus consists of about half a dozen species of small, spherical animals bearing groups of long, stiff cilia or bristles, some of which may be united into cirri. These project from the body, and by rapidly flicking cause the sudden erratic jumps which characterize locomotion; between whiles the animal may rotate slowly by means of its powerful AZM. The species are much alike and the present one is selected only because it was fairly completely described by Szabó (1935); the common *H. grandinella* differs mainly in having 7 groups of 3 bristles instead of 9 groups of 4, and 7 membranellae within the buccal cavity instead of 10. Szabó gave a key to the species, and there are taxonomic notes in Kahl (1935) and Penard (1922). *Halteria* occurs frequently in fresh water and in wet, mossy turf. All speci-mens are difficult to observe unless mounted in some viscous medium such as methocel which of course destroys the character of the motion.

The living organism

H. geleiana is ovoid, 55–60 $\mu \times$ 40–50 μ, with a flattened anterior peri-stome round which runs the conspicuous AZM (Fig. 165). The only somatic cilia are the bristles, in 9 groups, each emerging from a slight pit just anterior to the equator. Each group consists of 4 bristles, of which the 2 anterior are single and the posterior pair stuck together, so that there is an incipient cirrus. In life the bristles stand out to a length of about half the diameter of the body. The AZM has 15 very prominent membranellae about the peristome and is continued within the enclosed tunnel of the buccal cavity by a further 10 membranellae of decreasing size. There is an UM of some 40 to 50 cilia, and at the base of the cavity, near the cytostome, lies a further small group of 6 cilia, also used in feeding, and of uncertain homology. A contractile vacuole lies to the left of the buccal cavity, the normal position in *Halteria*, and there is a caudal, slightly ventral, cytoproct, visible only when functioning. The meganucleus is 20–25 $\mu \times$ 8–10 μ. It is a curved structure in the anterior part of the body with its concave surface facing inwards. The micronucleus has not been described. The life-history, except for binary fission, is unknown.

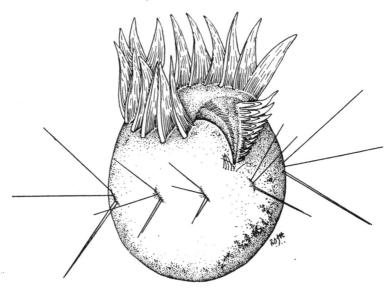

Fig. 165. *Halteria geleiana.* × c. 1,000. There are 15 large membranellae encircling the peristome and 10 smaller ones within the buccal cavity, here shown as laid open; and on the right of the latter, opposite the membranellae, is a small undulating membrane. (Modified from Szabó.)

Permanent Preparations

The ciliates require centrifugation until they are fixed to the slide with celloidin (p. 429) for ordinary staining, or gelatin for Ag impregnation. Fix in Champy, stain in H.H.

Culture

No method is known.

ORDER TINTINNIDA

Most of the 900 or so species composing this large order live in the open seas where they may contribute great numbers to the plankton. Some are coastal; a few are freshwater. The distinctive feature is the lorica, a cup- or vase-shaped structure secreted by the animal and sometimes reinforced by attached debris (the arenacious loricae, Fig. 166A); only very rarely is the lorica absent. Inside it the ciliate lies loosely, usually attached to the base by a contractile cord of cytoplasm and with the peristome extended from the aperture. The AZM is very powerful, with 12 to 24 flame-like membranellae, and is surrounded by a contractile peristomial rim or lip. Between the membranellae and lip are arranged the tentaculoids, which are claviform organellae of unknown function (*t*). The somatic cilia are reduced usually to some sparse groups below the peristome, though one line of cilia here may be developed as a vertical and dorsal membrane (*cm*) and some long elastic cilia about the peristomial rim can act as stays holding fast the body as it leans out of the lip of the lorica. There are generally 2 meganuclei, sometimes more, even as many as 100, with an equal number of small micronuclei. In the form and development of the AZM and reduction of the somatic ciliature the tintinnids are related to the Oligotrichida with which they are sometimes classed.

Tintinnids do not live well in laboratories and most of them occur in relatively inaccessible places. It is not surprising that there is no good detailed description of a single species, and almost nothing is known of the infraciliature. The good monographs of Entz (1909) and Fauré-Fremiet (1908, 1924) are valuable, and some further information may be extracted, in spite of an almost impenetrable style, from Campbell's paper on *Tintinnopsis nucula* (1926). For taxonomy, which is based almost entirely on the form of the lorica, see Kofoid and Campbell (1929), and Campbell (1942); Kahl (1935) deals with the freshwater forms, which are all species of *Tintinnidium*, *Tintinnopsis*, *Strombidinopsis*, and *Codonella*.

Tintinnopsis campanula (Ehrenberg)

The species is common and widely distributed from the Baltic to the Mediterranean Seas, where, like most members of its genus, it occurs in coastal rather than open waters. It disappears from the plankton during the winter and reappears during the warmer months with an optimum towards the end of the summer. Like all tintinnids it can be studied profitably only when alive. For descriptions see Fauré-Fremiet (1924) and Entz (1909).

The living organism

The lorica is a thin transparent structure secreted by the animal and plastered with an opaque arenacious coat of foreign particles. It is shaped like a hand-bell, 130–55 μ long, including about 40 μ for the handle, or basal process. The ciliate (Fig. 166A) loosely occupies the lorica and is attached to its base by a contractile, slightly eccentric, cytoplasmic pedicle. The body is cylindrical to oval, a little narrowed below the peristome, which is emphasized by an encircling lip. The peristome itself is flat except

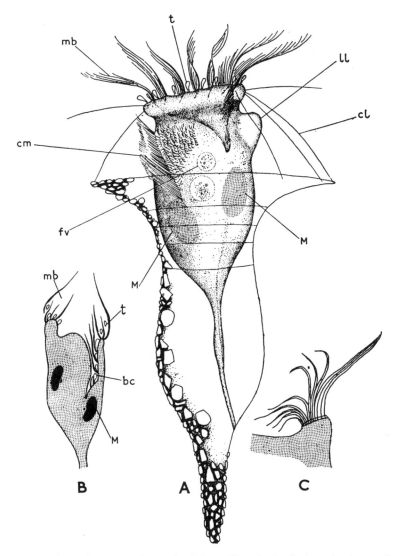

FIG. 166. *Tintinnopsis campanula*. A, the living ciliate in its lorica: the inorganic encrustation is drawn only on the left of the lorica. ×*c*. 700; B, schematic L.S. through the plane of the buccal cavity; C, diagram of a single membranella showing the cilia coalesced on the outside and free on the inside. (A and C after Fauré-Fremiet; B after Entz.)

bc, buccal cavity; *cl*, elastic cilium attaching the peristomial lip to the edge of the lorica; *cm*, ciliary membrane; *fv*, food vacuole; *ll*, lateral lobe; *M*, meganucleus (in B only one is labelled and each is accompanied by a micronucleus); *mb*, membranella; *t*, tentaculoid.

where it dips into the buccal cavity and the spiral wreath of membranellae is inserted just within the lip. The animal swims, either forwards or backwards, with about half the body protruded from the shell.

There are about 20 membranellae, used for feeding and swimming. They are set in a spiral but the distal and proximal ends overlap so closely that they appear to form a circle which is extended down into the buccal cavity (B). In each tall membranella the outer cilia are fused to form a sort of cytoplasmic flame about 35 μ high while the inner cilia are frayed loose (c). Between them are set the stalked, claviform tentaculoids (t). The somatic cilia are of two sorts. There is a sparse patch of some 10 to 12 vertical rows, more or less opposite the buccal cavity, and the members of the extreme dorsal row are longer than the others and coalesced into a membrane (cm). Fauré-Fremiet observed such a membrane only in species with arenacious loricae and thought it might be concerned in shell building; it may also serve to clean the interior of the shell of excreta and other debris. About the lip long elastic cilia like guyropes tether the animal to the rim of the lorica. Opposite the ciliary field is a rounded protoplasmic lobe like a permanent pseudopodium; according to Campbell not only is some of the substance of the shell secreted in this region in *T. nucula* but the lobe assists in shaping its form. The endoplasm contains food vacuoles and the meganuclei with attendant micronuclei.

Permanent preparations and culture

The living animal shows more, except of the nuclear structure, than preparations. No method of culture is known.

ORDER ENTODINIOMORPHIDA

Morphologically and physiologically the members of this order* are among the most complicated and interesting of Protozoa, and they are in many ways imperfectly understood. There are no free somatic cilia, though an unconfirmed note of Kantor's (1956) states that meridians of kinetosomes have been found. There is a crown of membranellae which in fact are much more like cirri, representing the AZM, which is used for both feeding and locomotion. There is a firm pellicle, often protracted into spines, which are used in classification. The internal structure is extraordinarily elaborate and the feeding, digestive, and defecatory apparatus achieves a continuity and permanence which justify the use of such a term as 'alimentary tract'. There are 2 families. In the Ophryoscolecidae, which occur in the first and second divisions of the stomachs of ruminants, the AZM may represent the entire ciliary equipment (*Entodinium*) but more often it is accompanied by another and similar wreath of cirri, not connected with the 'mouth', and

* See footnote on p. 358.

known as the dorsal zone of membranellae, or DZM (*Ophryoscolex, Diplodinium*). In the Cycloposthiidae, from horses and anthropoid apes, patches of cirri or membranellae occur posteriorly as well as anteriorly (*Cycloposthium, Troglodytella*). For taxonomy see Dogiel (1927), who also gives much information about distribution, Crawley (1923), and Kofoid and MacLennan (1930, 1932, 1933). For structure, in spite of the great interest of the subject, we still largely rely on a single paper on *Epidinium* published by Sharp in 1914. Very little is known about development except that stomatogenesis occurs, as in the related Oligotrichida and Hypotrichida, within a pellicular pocket. For sexual reproduction, which is remarkable for the highly differentiated male and female pronuclei and for the resemblance of the former to spermatozoa, see Dogiel (1925).

In spite of reports to the contrary, ectodiniomorphs do not form cysts and outside their hosts they soon die. Infections cannot be acquired by eating unsterilized hay, grass, water, faeces, or even the dried stomach contents of known hosts. But the ciliates occur in saliva, and infections are rapidly gained by clean animals which are allowed to mix with infected ones most probably by eating food still damped with contaminated saliva and possibly also from licking among members of herds (Becker and Hsuing, 1929).

The ciliate fauna of cattle, sheep, and some wild ruminants is a mixed one of holotrichs, especially *Isotricha* and *Dasytricha*, and many species of entodiniomorphs. Estimates of the numbers present vary but have been put as high as 200,000 holotrichs and 450,000 entodiniomorphs per ml. Hungate found on an average about 7,000 *Diplodinium* per ml. in cows, and *Entodinium* was more numerous. The numbers vary, and so does the composition of the fauna, and the variation continues in hosts fed on a constant diet. Be that as it may, it is likely that ciliates are always present and usually in very large numbers indeed, and it has naturally been supposed that they are useful, perhaps indispensable, to their hosts. Some of them store polysaccharides in their skeletal plates and elsewhere in their cytoplasm. They are obligate anaerobes and consequently obtain their energy by fermentation, the products of which could contribute materially to the needs of the host. Further, about half the contents of the rumen are emptied daily, the Protozoa are consumed and replaced by division of the remainder so that a contribution of protein is ensured. One genus, *Diplodinium*, is known to digest cellulose, possibly by means of intracellular symbiotic bacteria (Hungate, 1942, 1943). Over a century ago, Gruby and Delafond, who discovered the rumen fauna, suggested that it might supply about one-fifth of the host's food, and 'the results of investigation during the succeeding 110 years have not significantly modified the estimate', as Hungate (1955), in a particularly lucid review of much difficult evidence, observes. But the symbiosis between ciliates and ruminants is not well understood and it is certainly not so clear cut as that between flagellates and termites, which in some ways it suggestively resembles. Without each other, termites and flagellates die. But calves may be bred without ciliates and are none the worse for it (Pounden and Hibbs, 1950) and hosts do not deteriorate after defaunation. It is easy to misunderstand the implications of some of the facts; for example, it is true that *Diplodinium* is able to digest cellulose, and, of course, mammals have no cellulase: but the amount of reserve carbohydrate contributed by ciliates to, say, a sheep, would represent only about 1 per cent of its requirements. It is quite possible that the Protozoa themselves do not secrete a cellulase, but rely on symbiotic bacteria as agents of digestion, and, in any event, without the Protozoa, the bacteria seem well able to take over all digestive activity required by the host. All that has been demonstrated so far is that some of the Protozoa have the means of contributing to the welfare of their hosts; it seems likely that in normal circumstances they do so; it is certain that without them hosts are otherwise sustained (see the reviews of Oxford, 1955, and Hungate, 1955, for discussions and references).

Epidinium ecaudatum (Fiorentini)

A fine paper by Sharp (1914) on this animal contains not only most of what is known of the morphology of the order but also the first account of a 'neuro-motor' system, an internal system of fibrillae which, whatever its true function may be, is highly developed and easy to study in *Epidinium*. Sharp's description is old and doubtless reinvestigation would suggest some amendments, but it is the best we have and the following is little more than a précis of it.

Rumen ciliates must be seen alive and freshly killed animals are needed and a means of conveying the contents of the rumen or reticulum without cooling to the laboratory. A vacuum flask of warm water (37°–40° C) is taken to the slaughter-house and emptied when a stomach is made available. The rumen is opened and its contents scooped into the flask. Even 3 or 4 hours later the ciliates, if examined at about 35–37° C, will be vigorously active, but if allowed to cool much below 30° C they deteriorate and become useless for any purpose. The rumen will usually contain many species of ciliates, including holotrichs, and the genera *Entodinium* and *Diplodinium* are likely to be present. The latter is very like *Epidinium*, which is sometimes regarded as a subgenus of it: the present species was called *Diplodinium ecaudatum* by Sharp. The form described below is *Epidinium ecaudatum ecaudatum*; one or more of a number of closely related species or subspecies differing only in the presence and arrangement of posterior pellicular processes are likely to be found in the same habitat. Dogiel (1927) may be used for identification.

The living organism

The animals move rapidly. Sharp thought that *E. ecaudatum* covered about 20 times its length in a second. But on cooling to 30° C the behaviour, though slower, remains normal, and observation is possible.

E. ecaudatum ecaudatum (Fig. 167) is roughly cylindrical, largely transparent, and it displays a number of characteristics distinguishing it at once from all other ciliates so far considered. It is naked of cilia, with a prominent AZM marking the antero-ventral crown of the body, and opposite this is an independent DZM. Below the pellicle, ventrally and to the right and left, lie skeletal plates, and dorsally is a long meganucleus, harbouring at its side a small, shiny micronucleus. The most curious differentiation is something approximating to an alimentary canal: the cytostome leads through the cytopharynx into a large endoplasmic sac, which empties through a permanent rectal passage by a cytoproct. All these structures may be seen in the living animal.

Measurements vary with the locality, but probably 120–30 $\mu \times$ 40–45 μ are near the average. The body is broader in the anterior half, rounded or truncated at each end. The firm pellicle is smooth except where it overlies the skeletal plates and anteriorly it is flexible to allow movements of the membranellar zones. At each end of the body, i.e. at the cytopharynx and cytoproct, it is, according to Sharp, tucked in like the stomodeum and proctodeum of a metazoan.

The skeletal plates which are such a conspicuous feature of many Entodiniomorphida and which certainly in some species are important centres for the storage of polysaccharides are here three in number. The middle or ventral plate is much the largest. On either side of it smaller, triangular plates taper towards the posterior. Each plate is laminated in inwardly projecting shelves and the sides of each lamina diverge in the middle. Elsewhere the cytoplasm below the pellicle is alveolar. In the application of the terms ectoplasm and endoplasm usage varies: Sharp considered all outside the endoplasmic sac to be ectoplasm, while others have regarded the skeletal plates and the alveolar layers as endoplasmic. There is perhaps a tendency at times to treat the question more seriously than it deserves, as if ectoplasm and endoplasm were germ layers. Below the alveolar and skeletal structures, and completely enclosing the sac, is a clear, heavily staining bounding layer (*b*) within which the undoubted endoplasm is more liquid than the cytoplasm elsewhere. The long meganucleus, some 65 $\times$ 15 μ, and thinning towards the posterior, lies outside the bounding layer, which is probably better regarded as limiting the digestive 'tract' than as defining the endoplasm. The micronucleus is a small, refringent body lying in a depression half-way up the dorsal surface of the meganucleus.

The organs of feeding, locomotion, and digestion are as follows. There

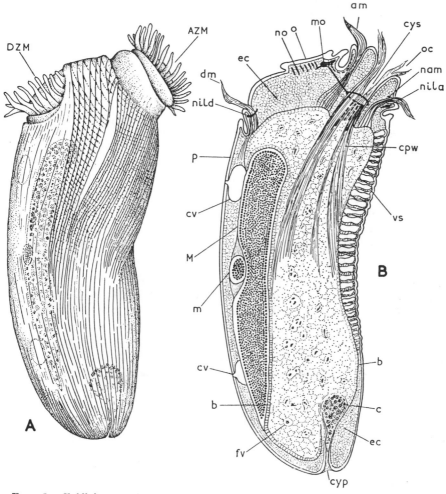

FIG. 167. *Epidinium ecaudatum.* A, the living ciliate, right ventral view; B, L.S. of the same. Both × 900. (After Sharp.)

am, adoral membranella; *AZM*, adoral zone of membranellae; *b*, bounding layer of endoplasmic sac; *c*, 'caecum'; *cpw*, extension of cytopharyngeal wall with contractile fibrillae and thick broken lines of neuromotor fibrillae; *cv*, contractile vacuole; *cyp*, cytoproct; *cys*, cytostome; *dm*, dorsal membranelle; *DZM*, dorsal zone of membranellae; *ec*, ectoplasm; *fv*, food vacuole; *M*, meganucleus; *m*, micronucleus; *mo*, motorium, with solid fibre to circumcytopharyngeal ring and dotted fibre to inner lip of AZM; *nam*, neuro-motor fibre to AZM; *nila*, same to inner lip of AZM; *nild*, same to inner lip of DZM; *no*, same to operculum; *o*, operculum; *oc*, oral cilia; *p*, pellicle; *vs*, ventral skeletal plate.

are two zones of membranellae, or, rather, cirri, and both are used for locomotion. The DZM is arranged on an arc surrounded on the outer side by two parallel lips, one folded into the other, and capable of extrusion, as when a finger-stall folded into itself is everted. The line of membranellae is placed, not between the lips, but in a groove within the inner lip. There are 26 or 27 of them and they are high, pointed, and they beat from left to right. When irritated the DZM contracts, the lips are unfolded and pulled over towards the operculum so that the whole zone is covered. The operculum is a flexible area between the two zones.

The AZM is the only feeding organella and is also used in locomotion. It consists of an almost complete circlet of 30 to 36 cirrus-like membranellae, beating clockwise, and from its end trails a curve of smaller, freer cilia leading to the cytostome. The crown is set on a peristomial field, surrounded like the DZM by a double lip and tilted outwards towards the left. The smaller circlet or curve of oral cilia is very different in structure from the AZM itself: it is made up of coarse independent cilia, of uncertain homology, and extending some way into the cytopharynx. The cytostome is the elliptical entrance to a cytopharynx which is prolonged for some distance into the endoplasmic sac, its walls being marked by the presence of powerful fibrillae, thought to be contractile, and also by the so-called 'neuro-motor' fibres described below. The contractile fibres are numerous, some appear to be inserted on the skeletal plates and others possibly run all the way from the cytopharynx to the rectal wall. As the anterior part of the feeding apparatus is pulled down, the lips extend over the AZM to protect it. The more fluid endoplasm in the sac moves in currents from the cytopharynx towards the rectum, then forwards along the left dorsal wall, and again to the posterior end where dejecta are accumulated in a defined area inappropriately called the 'caecum'; from here they pass into the rectum and out through the cytoproct.

There are two lenticular vacuoles, each with a pore, lying dorsally near the ends of the meganucleus. They are said to contract slowly and only slightly and then to fill again.

Permanent preparations

Fixation in S+A or B, provided it is carried out on healthy animals, followed by Haematoxylin or Mallory's Stain (p. 439), will reveal the nuclear structure, the basophil bounding layer of the endoplasmic sac, and it will also demonstrate the system of fibrillae called by Sharp the neuro-motor system, which on various grounds is held to serve co-ordination. The system is basophil and stains with Haematoxylin or is red with Mallory's Triple Stain.

The neuro-motor system (Fig. 167B) consists of a small mass of differentiated cytoplasm, the motorium (*mo*), lying just dorsal to the AZM, from which strands, or fibrillae (or more probably bundles of fibrillae) pass to various organellae as follows. (1) A strand runs about the base of the DZM giving a branch to each membranella, and, on its way, (2) a further strand (*nild*) to the inner dorsal lip. Similarly, (3) a strand (*nam*) surrounds the base of the AZM, with a branch (*nila*) (4) to its inner lip. (5) A number of prominent tracts (*no*) run into the operculum and are perhaps comparable to those in the collar of some species of *Euplotes* (Fig. 168C, *c*). A branch runs to the cytopharynx and encircles it as a ring (6). Finally (7), many branches are found in the extension of the cytopharyngeal wall as it passes through the endoplasm; they mingle with the contractile fibres, and it is not clear whether they originate from the ring (as shown in the drawing) or come directly from the motorium.

Culture

See p. 417.

ORDER HYPOTRICHIDA

The hypotrichs, which are common and familiar animals, sum up the specializations variously manifested by the orders of Spirotricha so far described. They possess no generalized somatic ciliature. The only cilia they have are very short 'sensory' (better, 'dorsal') bristles springing from rows of tiny pits on the dorsal surface (Fig. 168F). All other cilia are combined to form cirri or membranellae (A). Except in *Aspidisca* the AZM is dominating, sweeping across the front of the animal from right to left, down the left side and then inwards to a small buccal cavity. On the right of this is an insignificant UM, at its base the cytostome. The body is more or less flattened and is held in shape by an almost rigid pellicle.

Cirri are tapering bundles of cilia adhering like the hairs of a damp camel-hair brush; sometimes the ends are frayed. Except that they taper and have rounded bases, they are constructed like membranellae. Their cilia, like those of membranellae, are roughened with small processes which assist them to grip their neighbours; there is no bounding membrane (Roth, 1957). The cirri may, like the AZM, be used in swimming, but more frequently hypotrichs walk on them with a characteristic scurrying movement.

Specialization extends to the kinetosomes. Those of the dorsal bristles are ordinary, that is, they are the bases of the cilia themselves and at fission they divide to form new bristles. The bases of the cirri and membranellae, on the other hand, show, after Ag impregnation, two kinds of kinetosomal bodies (Fig. 168 D, E). There are numerous small granules called secondary kinetosomes, grouped in rounded plates for cirri and oblongs for membranellae; they do not divide and they are probably the ends of the cilia composing the organellae. Associated with each such group is a small number of much larger primary kinetosomes and each of these is related to a rosette of rodlets or granules (D, E, F); the nature of these is uncertain: in E.M. photographs they appear as minute vacuoles, and Chatton and Séguéla (1940) regarded them as trichocysts, though they do not discharge.

Primary kinetosomes do not appear to be structurally related to cilia of any kind (though those of dorsal bristles are), but it is from among them that the stomatogenic kinetosome originates at fission, and it is almost certain that they proliferate the kinetosomes which initiate new cirri (pp. 377–379). Where, as in *Opisthotricha monspessulana*, new organellae are derived from erratic kinetosomes occurring freely in the cytoplasm, these are primaries, though they lack the distinguishing rosettes of *Euplotes*. It seems as if the functions of the kinetosomes of more generalized ciliates have in this order become divided. The secondaries are merely ciliary ends and have a limited life; they do not divide. The primaries retain their morphogenetic functions; they sustain the genetic continuity of the infraciliature. The kinetosomes of dorsal bristles, which are still relatively unspecialized, retain both their structural and reproductive functions.

Morphogenesis is peculiar. At binary fission and conjugation the animals submit to a drastic process of reorganization in which all the cirri, and sometimes the other cytoplasmic organellae, are resorbed and replaced; the facts are a little different for the two processes and are given in some detail below (pp. 375, 380). Here it may be noted that similar types of reorganization, which may be extremely complicated, may be evoked during regeneration after injury. It appears as if essentially the same series of morphogenetic events may be called into play by a number of different events, or, there is a single morphogenetic pattern and all of it is evoked by a selection of causes (see Taylor (1928) and the discussions in Balamuth (1940), Fauré-Fremiet (1948*a*), and Weisz (1954), who also give many references). During encystation, folding and invagination may make it difficult to observe the persistent organellae, but they do not dedifferentiate and there is no reorganization except that proper to an exconjugant when it encysts (Fauré-Fremiet, Gauchery, and Tuffrau, 1954).

Some unusual meganuclear conditions are seen in the order. The nucleus is single in *Euplotes* (for its reorganization see p. 375, and Fig. 169); in *Stylonychia* it is double and in *Urostyla* multiple, with about 100 dispersed fragments, but in all cases the components are united before division. There are one to many micronuclei.

Hypotrichs are usually of medium size, free-living in fresh or salt water. They are common in collections from standing pools or ponds, and in laboratory infusions. For taxonomy, see Kahl (1935).

Euplotes patella Ehrenberg

E. patella is common in standing freshwater pools and ponds and extends into brackish water. Yocum (1934) found that it would survive well and divide in 66 per cent sea water provided that the concentration was gradually increased; the activity of the contractile vacuole diminished and became imperceptible at concentrations above 10 per cent. The species was well described and figured by Stein (1859) and again by Pierson (1943), who distinguished it from a number of closely related forms. Its mating system, discovered by Kimball, and reviewed by Sonneborn (1947, 1957), is similar to but less elaborate than that of *Paramecium*. A useful E.M. study by Roth (1957) illuminates much of the structure to be seen with the light microscope. Further references are given under the various headings below.

Some confusion in the study of *E. patella* arises from the fact that much of the better-known work supposed to be about it was in fact performed on the related *E. eurystomus*, which was raised to specific rank in 1932; e.g. the reports of Yocum (1918) and Taylor (1920) on the 'neuro-motor system' and of Turner (1930) and Hammond (1937) on division and conjugation, which are ascribed to *E. patella*, are to be referred to *E. eurystomus*. The differences between the two, though plain enough on inspection of living material, are not profound, but for the sake of clarity the main features of *E. patella* are here described first, and then the distinctive characters of *E. eurystomus* are noted, before a treatment of division, metamorphosis, and conjugation, based on information gleaned from either species and almost certainly true in all significant respects of both.

The living organism

The motion of *Euplotes* is characteristic. Using especially its AZM it can swim in spirals or circles or straight forwards or backwards with occasional turns. But more commonly it scurries about on its cirri, and then its habit is to creep forwards, snap back a little, and then again forwards with a slight turn, as if it were butting its way through a trial and error motion like that of *Paramecium* (see Taylor, 1920, who described the uses of the membranellae and cirri involved). The suddenness and speed of these bursts of activity make the animal difficult to observe and in a viscous medium it is distorted; study is helped by a gentle narcosis and some vital staining (p. 422).

The flattened body (Fig. 168A) varies in outline from elliptical to ovoid and the extremes are seen within the same clone. It may be 150 μ long, but a good mean is 90 × 30 μ. The dorsal surface is slightly concave and marked by some 6 ridges, parallel and equidistant and each bearing a row o bristles. The bristles spring from small pits and each is surrounded by a rosette of rod-shaped vacuoles (F). As already noted they are really cilia. They are often called sensory bristles; they do not share in the neuro-motor system and no intracellular connexion between them and any other organellae has been demonstrated (von Gelei, 1929, 1934c; Roth, 1957).

The peristome is a large depression occupying most of the left anterior

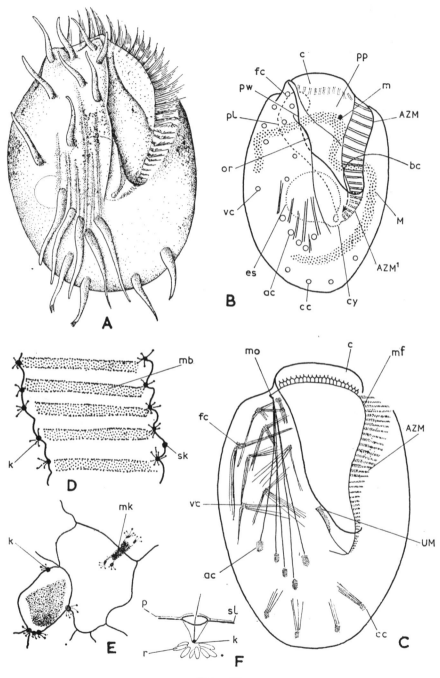

FIG. 168

quarter of the flat ventral surface. The floor of its own left anterior region is raised in a so-called peristomial plate (Fig. 168A, and cf. B, *pp*). On the right the peristomial cavity undercuts its own wall, so that a shelf projects inwards over this side and is continued back as the wall of the buccal cavity (*bc*). Further, the shelf itself is overlain for much of its course by another projection, the oral lip (*or*) which in many species of *Euplotes*, but not *E. patella*, is continued as a collar (B, *c*) across the anterior margin of the animal. The lip assists in holding the larger sorts of prey and directing its course to the cytostome. There are about 35 to 45 fine membranellae curling round the peristome into the buccal cavity. Opposite them, and posteriorly, lies a small UM. The cytostome opens into a spacious endoplasmic sac (*es*), circular when seen from above or below, with an incomplete dorsal wall. Digestion apparently begins within the sac and food is then passed through the gap into the rest of the endoplasm. There are said to be no food vacuoles in *Euplotes*.

The cirri are constant in arrangement. There are 6 frontals, in 2 rows of 3, and 3 ventrals, more widely spaced in an oblique row. Behind lie much larger anal cirri, posted at the ends of grooves guarded by 6 parallel ridges; the first and fourth ridges are longer than the rest. The powerful anal cirri lash to and fro in a motion restricted by their ridges. There are 4 conspicuous caudal cirri, of which the right 2 are fimbriated, i.e. their ends are frayed into their constituent cilia.

The meganucleus, always gigantic in this genus, is C-shaped with a small micronucleus lying in its left anterior margin. There is one contractile vacuole near the outer anal cirrus.

Euplotes eurystomus Kahl

Often mistaken for *E. patella*, this species may be readily distinguished *in vivo* as follows (Fig. 168B). It is larger (mean, 140 × 80 μ). The meganucleus is shaped like a figure 3. The peristome is wider, its plate larger and more triangular. Both the plate on the left and the wall on the right are

---

FIG. 168. *Euplotes*. A, *Euplotes patella* from the ventral side. ×700; B, *E. eurystomus*: diagram; C, *E. eurystomus*: internal fibrillar or 'neuro-motor' system: D, *E. crassus*: origin of the stomatogenic kinetosome; E, *E. crassus*: origin of a new cirrus rudiment; F, *E.* (? *patella*) dorsal bristle. (A mainly based on Pierson; B after Pierson; C after Hammond; D and E, after Chatton and Séguéla; F after von Gelei.)

ac, anal cirrus; *AZM*, adoral zone of membranellae; *AZM*[1], the same, within the buccal cavity; *bc*, buccal cavity; *c*, collar (with its lattice in C); *cc*, caudal cirrus; *cy*, cytostome; *es*, endoplasmic sac; *fc*, frontal cirrus; *k*, kinetosome; *M*, meganucleus; *m*, micronucleus; *mb*, membranellae base; *mf*, membranelle fibre; *mk*, multiplication of a kinetosome which has apparently migrated from *k*; *mo*, 'motorium'; *or*, oral lip; *p*, pellicle; *pl*, limit of peristomial undercut beneath right wall; *pp*, peristomial plate; *pw*, right peristomial wall; *r*, rodlets or vacuoles of bristle rosette; *sl*, silver line of argyrome; *sk*, stomatogenic kinetosome originating from outer wall of AZM; *UM*, undulating membrane; *vc*, ventral cirrus.

undercut so that the peristome is overlain by shelves on both sides. The AZM is flexed inwards during the left part of its course which is thus sigmoidally curved. The oral lip is well developed and continued anteriorly as a collar. The dorsal ridges are weak but their positions are marked by rows of bristles.

The fibrillar and argentophile systems of *Euplotes*

Most of the structure is well displayed by the living organism, but permanent preparations disclose, besides the nuclei, three apparently independent systems—the internal fibrillar or neuro-motor system, the argyrome, and the infraciliature.

The internal fibrillar or neuro-motor system

Some of this system is seen on vital staining with Neutral Red, Toluidine Blue, or Methylene Blue, but it is better revealed by fixation in Schaudinn, followed by Mallory's Triple Stain (p. 439), when it appears red, or by a Haematoxylin. It was described by Yocum (1918), Taylor (1920), and Hammond (1937), who all called it the neuro-motor system. The system will be the more easily understood if it is grasped at once that what the light microscopist calls the 'neuro-motor' system is the part visible to him of a wider system of connecting fibrillae between cirri and membranellae, much of which is disclosed only by the electron microscope.

The system (Fig. 168c) consists of a bilobed granular structure called the motorium (*mo*) upon which fibres converge. Five, seen *in vivo*, run from the bases of the cirri. A long fibre (*mf*) runs below the AZM and is connected to the bases of the membranellae; it gives off perpendicular fibres to the collar, where this is present, and they combine to form a lattice. Finally, from the bases of the cirri run short fibrillae which seem to peter out, but are, as explained, continued beyond the range of the light microscope. Yocum considered that the collar lattice was sensory, the rest of the system motor, and the motorium a coordinating centre. There is some experimental evidence (Taylor, 1920) at least for the view that some of this fibrillar system is indispensable for coordinated movement. Thus a cut across the right of the equator, but not across the left, disorganizes the activity of the cirri. It does not, of course, follow, as the unfortunate name 'neuro-motor' appears to suggest, that the system has a mode of action comparable to that of the metazoan nervous system.

The argyrome

This subpellicular network of silver lines may be impregnated by wet or dry methods (Turner, 1933; Chatton and Séguéla, 1940). Dorsally it consists of regular rows of polygonal links alternately bearing the kineto-somes of the dorsal bristles and their rosettes (Fig. 170D). Ventrally the system suggests, as Dr Turner put it, 'badly treated chicken wire' (Fig. 170A). The system is replaced at each division.

The infraciliature

Membranellae and cirri are implanted on bases consisting of numerous small secondary and fewer primary kinetosomes (Fig. 168 D, E, and see p. 369). The precise numbers and relations of the primaries vary slightly with the species. In *E. patella* and some others, all primaries are strictly related to existing membranellae or cirri, but in *E. crassus* there is a number of free (erratic) kinetosomes. Some of these are the products of old cirri and will be the progenitors of new ones, but it seems unlikely that this function can exhaust all the free kinetosomes to be seen and they require more investigation; in *Opisthotricha monspessulana* the free kinetosomes gain greatly in number and importance.

Binary fission

At fission, the meganucleus undergoes a process of reorganization before it divides, the peristomial apparatus for the opisthe is constructed (that of the parent passing entire to the proter), all the parental cirri are replaced by two sets of new ones, the argyrome is reconstituted, the dorsal bristles are multiplied so that each daughter receives some new and some old ones, and, of course, the animal divides. Most of these morphogenetic revisions are repeated during conjugation and are so important that they must be described in some detail. They have been studied in recent years especially by Yocum (1918), Turner (1930), and Hammond (1937), who described the external events, by von Gelei (1934c), who studied the dorsal bristles, and by Chatton and Séguéla (1940) and Bonner (1954), who used Ag methods. A great deal may be seen in the living animal, but direct observation must be supplemented by Ag impregnation and other methods given below. Division lasts about 8 hours and it will be understood that the processes described separately in fact take place concurrently.

In preparation for division the micronucleus migrates from the corner of the meganucleus to a position on its left (Fig. 169). Originally some 2 to 3 μ in diameter, it enlarges to two or three times this size. During mitosis there are 8 chromosomes and the daughter nuclei are connected by a siderophile thread for a long time.

The meganucleus, before dividing, suffers a reorganization noted long ago by Stein and described carefully by Turner (1930); there is an E.M. study by Fauré-Fremiet, Rouiller, and Gauchery (1957) and a most important analytical study by Gall (1959). At the time of migration of the micronucleus, a reorganization band appears at each end of the mega-nucleus. The bands move slowly towards each other and after a few hours meet in the middle; and as they pass through the nucleus its substance is seen to undergo alterations in their wake (Fig. 169 A–D). Each band consists of an anterior or inner deeply staining disk called the solution plane and a posterior or outer disk or reconstruction plane. After treatment with

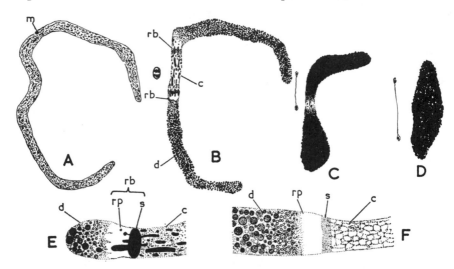

FIG. 169. *Euplotes eurystomus*: reorganization of meganucleus. A, interphase nucleus; B, reorganization bands approaching each other near centre of meganucleus: micronucleus dividing; C, reconstruction planes have joined; D, meganucleus contracted before its division; E, end of meganucleus at beginning of reorganization: fixed Schaudinn; F, part of meganucleus about reorganization band: fixed Flemming. A–D, × 420. E–F, × c. 1,800.
(Redrawn from Turner.)

c, central, and d, distal regions of meganucleus; m, micronucleus; rb, reorganization band; rp, reconstruction plane; s, solution plane.

Schaudinn's Fluid and Iron Haematoxylin the solution plane is dark and homogeneous, and the meganuclear material in front of it (before reorgani-zation) is coarsely and loosely granular, containing rods, spheres, and inter-mediate bodies; some of the rods may enter the plane and project from the other side of it (E). Probably the rods and other uneven masses are artefacts, for in material fixed in Flemming (F) the granules are finer and arranged in a reticulum giving the central part of the nucleus an alveolar appearance. The reconstruction plane is always clear, and distal to it the alveolar struc-ture of the nucleus is lost, and the granules, which are small near to it and larger farther away, are more compact (d). The nucleus as a whole now con-denses into a thick rod (c, D) which, just before fission, elongates and divides. Reorganization bands occur in other hypotrichs; they may start in the middle and move outwards, as in *Aspidisca*, or there may be more than one meganucleus (*Stylonychia*), but the behaviour of the bands is essentially similar to that described here (see Summers, 1935). Gall (1959) has beautifully shown that during reorganization the nucleus doubles its content of DNA and a basic nuclear protein, probably histone, and that synthesis takes place only in the region of the reorganization bands. What is observed during reorganization is in fact the passage through the enormous nucleus —it contains about 200 times as much DNA as the micronucleus—of two converging zones of synthesis to meet in the middle. Such a process of orderly duplication of DNA is consistent with a suggestion of Sonneborn's that reorganization in hypotrichs is a wave of mitoses successively dividing sub-nuclei along the length of the meganucleus.

At fission, but not at conjugation, the AZM of the parent is retained for the proter. The rudiment of the AZM for the opisthe first appears as a minute granule to the right of and near the posterior end of the parental peristome (Fig. 170A, *sk*). Its original has not been traced in *E. patella* but in *E. crassus* it comes from the division of a primary kinetosome at the external end of one of the parental membranellae (Figs. 168D; 170A, *sk*); in fact there is here a single stomatogenic kinetosome. It invaginates and the sac which contains it elongates and its products arrange themselves in transverse rows which are the *Anlagen* of the membranellae. The sac stretches first forwards and then backwards, still communicating with the exterior through its small original aperture (Fig. 170B); this orifice enlarges (C) until all but the posterior length (buccal cavity) of the AZM lies exposed on an open peristomial field.

The new cirri appear before the old ones are resorbed so that for a time the undivided organism possesses 3 sets of these organellae, 2 peristomes and, as will be seen, a partially renovated argyrome. In *E. crassus* the secondary kinetosomes forming the base of a parental cirrus are grouped within a loop of the argyrome and about them is set a number of primary kinetosomes (Fig. 168E). Nearby may be seen similar primary kinetosomes apparently in the course of division (*mk*) and it seems likely that these have arisen by migration from the parental base. They cannot have originated, as Klein (1936) supposed, from the argyrome, which exhibits no changes until after the new cirri have appeared. Each rudiment becomes surrounded by a small, finely reticulated field from which the argyrome is gradually replaced, and the fields, with their cirral rudiments, form 2 rows of 5 just anterior to the parental anal cirri. Of the 5 rudiments in each row, the outer 2 divide into 2, and the inner 3 into 3 (Fig. 170B), so providing 13 cirral rudiments in all, or one less than the total required (not counting the caudals, which have a separate and later origin). The reticulated plates, which are slightly excavated, enlarge and fuse, so that much of the ventral surface is covered by an irregular depression distinguished by the fineness of

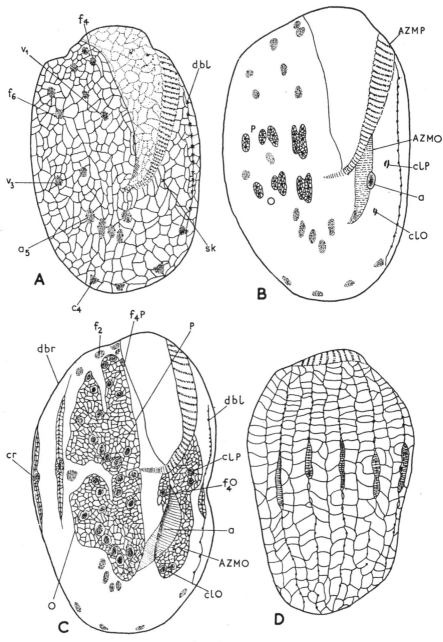

FIG. 170

its silver network from the old argyrome (which, in Fig. 170, is omitted from B and C). The cirral rudiments take up positions roughly corresponding to those of the frontal, ventral, and anal cirri, except that the innermost member of the second row of frontals is always missing. This missing cirrus (f_4) is provided from the adjacent margins of the old and new peristomes for proter and opisthe respectively (C, f_4P and f_4O). The 2 left caudal cirri (B and D, clP and clO) with their argyrome fields arise on the left of each peristome, and according to Hammond (1937) the right caudals (C, cr) appear dorsally near the middles and ends (for proter and opisthe respectively) of the 2 right rows of bristles, and they do not migrate to their final positions until fission.

At division the pits in which the dorsal bristles are set evaginate sufficiently for their kinetosomes to come almost flush with the surface. Near the equator regions of multiplication occur in each row to provide kinetosomes from the new bristles, and these equatorial patches are surrounded by new argyrome fields which spread to replace the old (Fig. 170D). Most of the new bristles required are generated before fission, but some appear later and according to Bonner (1954) the number is always proportional to the size of the ciliate.

A few cirri, especially among the frontals, are resorbed before fission, the rest later. The process is rapid: a cirrus stops its movement, becomes thinner and shorter and disappears in about 2 minutes. Before their loss, the new cirri develop the internal fibres of the neuro-motor system, which are plainer proximally than distally, so suggesting that they grow out from the bases of the cirri.

It is doubtful if any more specialized process of morphogenesis is known among ciliates than that described above, and for many years, until the work of Chatton and Séguéla, it seemed to abrogate the rule of genetic continuity of the infraciliature. It is now hardly possible to doubt that in *Euplotes* the ciliary derivatives of the daughters originate from primary

---

FIG. 170. *Euplotes patella*: organogenesis at fission, from Ag preparations. A, onset of reorganization: argyrome and impregnated bases of parent organellae are shown, and at *sk* the stomatogenic kinetosome; B, new peristome and rudiments of cirri have appeared, the latter surrounded by primordia of new argyrome for both daughters (*P* and *O*); C, new argyrome has spread over much of the right ventral face of the parent and has been augmented by that developed about rudiments of left caudal cirri (*clO* and *clP*) and the right caudals (*cr*) have begun to develop and so have f_4P and f_4O which are the successors to f_4; D, dorsal view of about the same stage with proliferation centres near the equators of the bristle rows and new argyrome. (After Chatton and Séguéla.)

a, opening of cavity within which new peristome develops; a_5, right anal cirrus (parent); *AZMO*, AZM for opisthe; *AZMP*, same of parent and for proter; c_4, right caudal cirrus (parent); *clO*, left caudal cirrus (opisthe); *clP*, same (proter); *cr*, right caudal cirrus (daughter); *dbl*, dorsal bristles, left row; *dbr*, same, right row; f_2, f_4 and f_6, frontal cirri (parent); f_4O, inner frontal cirrus (opisthe); f_4P, same for proter; *O*, argyrome field(s) for opisthe; *P*, same for proter; *sk*, stomatogenic kinetosome; v_1, inner ventral cirrus; v_3, outer ventral cirrus.

kinetosomes of the parent. In *Opisthotricha monspessulana*, where morphogenesis follows a different course, continuity is more evident. Here the parent possesses a reserve of free kinetosomes randomly distributed through the cytoplasm like those of Suctorida (p. 246), and it is from these that the daughter organellae are generated. Enough is now apparent to warrant the assumption that even in this highly specialized and difficult order the infraciliature retains its autonomy.

Conjugation

The early work of Maupas on conjugation has been largely confirmed and expanded, especially by Hammond (1937), and some important details were added by Chatton and Séguéla (1940). Conjugants touch by their left ventral faces and fuse by a small triangular area at the left anterior end of the peristomes. The micronucleus divides in the usual way to provide, eventually, 2 haploid gametic nuclei. The zygote nucleus divides twice, 2 of the 4 daughters degenerate, one becomes a micro- and the other a meganucleus.

These unremarkable events are accompanied by a process of cytoplasmic dedifferentiation and reorganization essentially similar to that seen at binary fission, except that the AZM is reformed, and, of course, only a single set of cirri is produced in each conjugant. The posterior part of the AZM is resorbed first, though it is the last to be replaced; conversely the anterior region of the new AZM appears early though the old one persists till after separation of the exconjugants. The new cirri develop just as they do at binary fission except that the missing cirrus (f_4) cannot be formed at separation because the region of the AZM from which it will originate has not yet been differentiated. Thus each exconjugant has at first only 17 instead of 18 cirri and only the anterior half of its AZM; its meganucleus is spherical and elongates to its definitive shape only after 2 to 3 days. At the same time the posterior half of the AZM begins to develop in continuity with the existing portion, the posterior membranellae being added from kinetosomes proliferated in front. Finally the missing cirrus at f_4 originates from the recently constructed part of the AZM. This completes the exconjugant which at once undergoes fission with its attendant reorganization.

ORDER ODONTOSTOMATIDA*

This small order of about 30 species diverges in a number of ways from the tendencies seen elsewhere among the Spirotricha (Fig. 171). They are all small (30 to 35 μ, rarely up to 60 μ, long). The body is asymmetrical,

---

* = Ctenostomata of many authors. The present name was introduced to avoid confusion with the order of Ectoprocta.

wedge-shaped, covered with long, ectoplasmic plates. Not only the somatic but also the buccal ciliature is reduced. The former consists mostly of patches of long, coarse cilia, differently developed on opposite sides of the body. The AZM (?) consists of 8 membranellae, set close in a row like the teeth of a comb and hence the name 'ctenostome', with a tiny ninth near the cytostome. The buccal cavity itself is a small, compressed chamber opening on the thick edge of the body, nearer to the left than to the right side. Nothing is known of the infraciliature or morphogenesis in the order, and its position in the Spirotricha—or indeed its right to one there—is equivocal.

All odontostomes are rare, restricted to waters (usually fresh waters) heavily charged with organic material. There are notes on species by Penard (1922), and Kahl (1926, 1932), the principal student of the order, has given a general account of it as well as a taxonomic conspectus.

Epalxis antiquorum Penard

With a length of 80 μ, this is the largest member of the order, and it appears to be widely distributed, though never in large numbers, in foul water. Penard's description is brief and the best account is by Kahl (1932).

The living organism

The body is flattened and asymmetrical (Fig. 171). The dorsal boundary, marked by a keel, is gently curved along most of its length and then bends over the anterior end to project as a beak above the crest described below. The keel itself is asymmetrical, extending farther over the left than the right side. The right side is the simpler, composed of 6 or 7 tall ectoplasmic plates, separated for most of their length by deep furrows. Some of the furrows are interrupted by oval fenestrations, 4 in all, of uncertain significance; Kahl thought they might facilitate osmotic communication with the external medium. All the plates end at the same level and none is produced into a spine so that on the right side the posterior surface has a truncated appearance.

The left side is covered by 4 plates bounded by deeper furrows and with slightly overlapping edges. As already remarked, the keel on this surface extends farther than on the right. There are 3 fenestrations. The posterior ends of the plates on this side, though not spinous, are moulded into processes which give an uneven appearance to the posterior border.

The somatic cilia are long and coarse, set in isolated and asymmetrically arranged groups or rows, most emerging between teeth along the borders of the plates. The left side is better ciliated than the right. A frontal band of 5 rows (*fbc*) begins on the left and passes to the right where it is more extensive. On the right are dorsal and ventral lines of long, single cilia, and

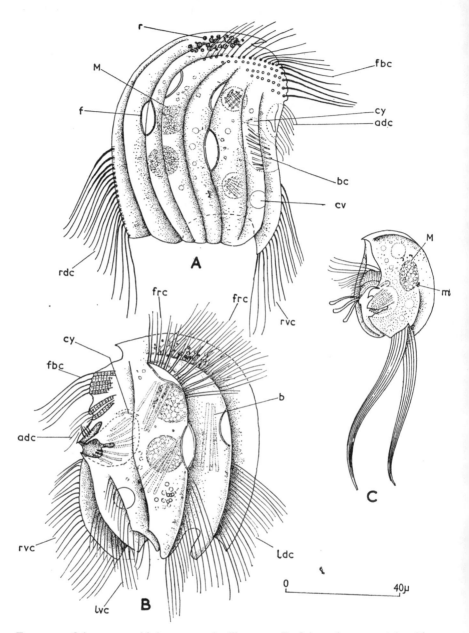

FIG. 171. Odontostomatid (ctenostome) ciliates. A, *Epalxis antiquorum*, right side; B, the same, left side; C, *Mylestoma bipartitum*: the ciliature is reduced to a short frontal band, adorals and 3 ribbons of coalesced cilia on the ventral surface, and 2 enormous cirri posteriorly. (Redrawn from Kahl.)

adc, adoral cilia (the short preorals lie in a pit just below them in B); *b*, symbiotic (?) bacteria; *bc*, buccal cavity containing 8 membranellae; *cv*, contractile vacuole; *cy*, position of cytostome guarded by the 9th minute membranella; *f*, fenestra; *fbc*, frontal band cilia; *frc*, frontal row cilia; *ldc*, left dorsal cilia; *lvc*, left ventral cilia; *M*, meganucleus; *m*, micronucleus; *r*, carbohydrate reserves; *rdc*, right dorsal cilia; *rvc*, right ventral cilia.

they are posterior (*rdc, rvc*). Similar lines occur on the left (*ldc, lvc*) with 2 middle lines between them; again all 4 lines are posterior, but in front of the dorsal and dorsal middle lines are anterior frontal lines (*frc*, and not to be confused with the frontal band); both frontals consist of paired cilia.

The ventral surface bears a crest carrying various cilia described below, and below them, the buccal cavity (*bc*), which is complicated and, like so much of the body, asymmetrical. It opens so much nearer the left than the right side that its left wall is no more than the ectoplasmic covering of the body itself; it, but not the right wall, is eroded by an irregular horizontal fissure. Above and below the cavity are beak-like processes between which stretches, only on the right side, a membrane; this forms the right wall of the buccal cavity. The cavity itself is narrow and rather high and it contains the 8 membranellae lying close in a row and, above them, in a sickle-shaped pocket just in front of the cytostome, is the ninth minute membranella. In a cleft below the anterior beak is a small group of very short stout cilia, and above them, on the crest itself, are 2 lines of adoral cilia (*adc*) which are long and like ordinary somatic cilia; the lines begin on the left side, stretch across the crest, and turn down the right side towards the buccal overture.

The endoplasm is finely granulated and contains numerous fat droplets and an anterior mass of carbohydrate (paraglycogen?) reserves. Apparently there are no food vacuoles in *E. antiquorum*, though there are in other species, and it has been suggested that it never takes particulate food and further that the fenestrations which interrupt the ectoplasmic armature facilitate an osmotic exchange. In addition, the species entertains very distinctive bacteria, sometimes free in the endoplasm (in B) and sometimes envacuolated (as in A); they are rods, from 10 to 20 μ long, and they lie in groups of 3 to 7. Kahl considered that they were symbionts. Be that as it may, it is difficult to discover a function for the buccal cavity, which nevertheless does not differ from that of any other species in which it seems to function normally.

There are 2, rarely 3, meganuclei and apparently the same number of micronuclei. There is a single posterior contractile vacuole.

The life-history is unknown for this or any other species.

Permanent preparations and culture

More is likely to be seen in living than in fixed animals, but S+A and D.H. will bring out the nuclei. Dry silver methods have been used to outline the plates which are not obvious *in vivo*. No means of culture are known.

V

METHODS IN PROTOZOOLOGY

ON THE USE OF THE MICROSCOPE

A CORRECT and confident use of the microscope is indispensable to the study of protozoology. Work of a sort can be done with it by blindly following a set of instructions, but it is obviously an advantage to have some understanding of the principles on which it works. The notes* that follow are meant to do no more than assist the student towards sound practice with the type of monocular microscope, fitted with low- and high-power and oil-immersion objectives and a substage condenser, usually provided in teaching laboratories. Much of what follows is not meant to apply to the more elaborate instruments used for critical work and is, indeed, untrue of them.

The microscope stands on a foot, on which the rest can be tilted by grasping the limb. Attached to the limb is a stage, pierced by a hole in the middle. Below this is the substage condenser, which can be moved by a screw up and down for focusing, an iris diaphragm, opened and closed by a handle, and a ring for holding light filters. Below them is a mirror, with one plane and one concave surface. Above the stage is the body tube, which also can be racked up and down for focusing. At the top of the tube is inserted a removable cylinder, the eyepiece, containing a system of lenses, and at the other end is a rotating nosepiece, holding the three objective lenses. More or less transparent objects for examination are placed over the hole in the stage and light is transmitted from a lamp in front of the microscope, reflected upwards by the mirror, through the substage iris, the condenser, the object, the objective, and the eyepiece, and the magnified image is seen through the last. Unless the whole of this optical system is in alignment, i.e. centred, observations will suffer.

The formation of the image

The lenses fitted into the objectives and the eyepiece may be numerous and they form a complicated system, but they submit to the following simplified explanation (Fig. 172). When an object PQ is set up in front of a lens OO, rather outside its focal point (Fo', Fo), it forms an image at $Q'P'$, as

* Barer's *Lecture Notes on the Use of the Microscope* (Blackwell Scientific Publications, Oxford, 2nd edn., 1956) and Martin and Johnson's *Practical Microscopy* (Blackie, London and Glasgow, 3rd edn., 1958), to both of which the writer is much indebted, offer better introductions to the subject.

shown in the diagram A. The image is magnified and inverted, and it is a real image, that is, it would show upon a screen placed at $Q'P'$. This is the primary image and it is further magnified by treating it as the object for enlargement by a second lens, EF, housed in the eyepiece, as in diagram B.

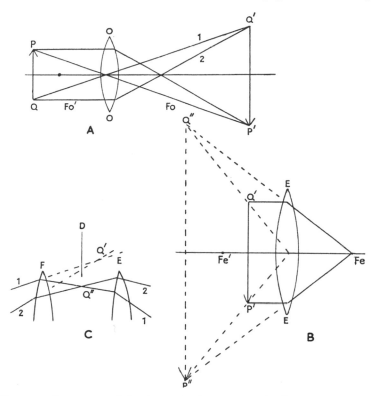

FIG. 172. Formation of the image in the compound microscope: greatly simplified. A, Formation of the primary image by the objective; B, magnification of the primary image by the eyepiece; C, the action of the field lens in the eyepiece. (See text.) (From Barer, *Lecture Notes on the Use of the Microscope*, Blackwell, Oxford, 1956.)

EE is placed so that the primary image is on the nearside of its focal point (Fe', Fe), and the further enlarged image at $Q''P''$ is formed on the same side of EE; it is not again inverted; and it is not real, but virtual, that is, it cannot be projected on to a screen, but can be observed by another system of lenses, such as those of the eye. The position at which $Q''P''$ is visible depends on the focusing of the system; it is usually taken as 25 cm from the eye looking down the eyepiece, but as individuals vary, each must focus for his own clarity and comfort. One further adjustment is performed in the eyepiece. In the system so far described, rays from the primary image would strike the periphery of *EE* very obliquely and this would cause defects in the second image. Such defects are considerably reduced by interposing a so-called field lens in front of $Q'P'$ at F (in diagram C). This converges the rays from the dotted path so that E may receive its marginal content less obliquely. The field lens, which is housed in the eyepiece, slightly reduces the size of the image provided by the objective system here simplified as the single lens OO.

The objective lenses

No objective lens is as simple as the preceding paragraph suggests. In the course of improving magnification, preserving the detail of the image, and correcting the weaknesses which arise from its nature, lens designers have evolved a complicated and expensive piece of apparatus, and upon its quality the usefulness of the microscope largely depends.

Two of the main sources of imperfection in the image are chromatic and spherical aberration. White light is, of course, composed of vibrations with different wavelengths, and when it is passed through the lens the blue and red components (with wavelengths of 0.4 and 0.7μ respectively) are differently affected by the glass. In Fig. 173A, blue light focuses at B and red at R, and a white light at W will appear blue with a red margin at B and red with a blue margin at R. This is chromatic aberration, and it is most readily corrected by combining in one lens different types of glass having different refractive indices. Lenses made in this way are called achromatic, and they can bring light of two colours to a common focus. They give the best results with green light. Higher-quality lenses, called apochromatic, combine fluorite with different types of glass to bring three colours together in one focus, and they also reduce other aberrations and give better resolution (see below). Spherical aberration (Fig. 173B, which, like A, is grossly exaggerated) is due to the curvature of the lens, which refracts more strongly at the margin than the centre, so that rays in different parts of the field come to different foci. The means of correction is found in combining lenses of different shape (C) so that the rays come to a focus in one plane; such a lens is called aplanatic.

There is no great difficulty in magnifying objects, in the sense of obtaining larger and larger images of them. But all magnified images are imperfect versions of their originals, and at high magnifications the inherent imperfections limit the usefulness of further enlargement. As Fig. 174 shows, from an object at P emitting light in all directions, only some can enter the lens OO to form an image at P'. P' is thus always to some extent imperfect; it lacks the information contained in all that part of the light outside the cone POO. It is evident that the measure of what the lens can accept from P—in this case the cone POO—is a fundamental property of its efficiency; this measure is expressed in a constant for each lens called the numerical

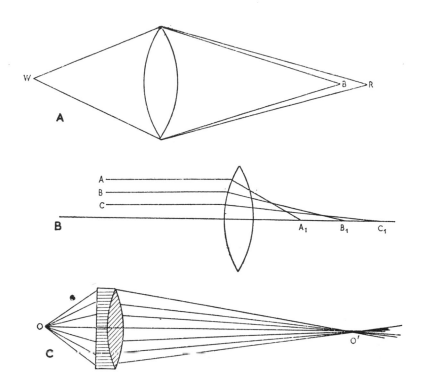

FIG. 173. A, Chromatic aberration; B, spherical aberration, and, C, its correction. (See text.)

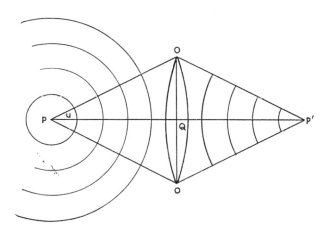

FIG. 174. The numerical aperture of a lens expresses the amount of light from a source P which can enter it. N.A. $= n.\sin u$, where n is the refractive index of the medium. For air, $n = 1$, and N.A. $= \sin u = \dfrac{OQ}{OP} = \dfrac{D}{2} \times \sqrt{\left(\dfrac{D^2}{4} + PQ^2\right)} = \dfrac{D}{2}\sqrt{\left(\dfrac{D^2}{4} + f^2\right)}$, where $D =$ diameter and $f =$ focal length of the lens.

aperture (N.A.). N.A. $= n.\sin u$, where n is the refractive index of the medium between P and OO, and u is half the apical angle of the cone. In air, $n = 1$. The N.A. of a lens directly affects its resolving power. Resolution is the capacity of a lens to discern detail. It is well known that very small objects may be seen by eye but their shapes cannot be distinguished. For example, we may note a tiny point of light but not know whether it is circular or rectangular. Resolving power is the smallest distance at which two adjacent points may be separately distinguished. Beyond the resolving power of a lens separate points will seem to be one and no amount of further magnification will separate them. High resolving power is therefore of the greatest importance in objectives used in microscopes, and, in practice, the higher the N.A. the better the resolving power of the lens. (The other condition for good visibility is contrast, which is an expression of the difference between the density of an object and that of its background, and, as will be seen, if the first step towards successful microscopy is the provision of good resolution the second is usually the sacrifice of some of it in the interests of contrast.)

The N.A. is the product of the refractive index of the medium, which for air is unity, and the sine of an angle which can never be more than unity. It follows that the N.A. of a lens used in air, i.e. a dry lens, can never be more than 1. But the lenses of very high-power objectives may have their effective N.A.s increased by inserting a suitable liquid medium between the object and the lens, and both oil and water lenses are manufactured. The latter are most useful in protozoology for obtaining high-power views of living animals unrestrained by a cover slip or sometimes for very difficult differentiation; the former give higher magnifications of cover-slip preparations or dry material, such as blood smears. A drop of cedar-wood oil is placed on the tip of the objective, and as this is lowered into position the drop spreads between the lens and the cover slip and rectifies the outward refraction of rays which, in air, would escape from the optical system (Fig. 175). The refractive index of cedar-wood oil is 1·51 and the N.A. of most achromatic oil immersion lenses with a focal length of 1·8–2·0 mm (about $\frac{1}{12}$ in) is 1·25–1·30.

Objectives are generally referred to by their focal lengths, and we speak of the low and high powers and oil-immersion lenses as 16, 4, and 2 mm lenses, or, in an odd and inappropriate survival of insular usage, as the 'two-thirds', 'sixth', and 'twelfth', which are the approximate equivalents in fractions of an inch. The magnification is given by the mechanical tube length, which is the distance between the top of the objective and the top of the body tube, divided by the focal length. In nearly all modern microscopes, the tube length is 160 mm (170 mm in Leitz instruments). Thus the magnification given by the low power on most microscopes is $\frac{160}{16} = \times 10$, by the high power it is $\frac{160}{4} = \times 40$, and by the oil-immersion lens, which is rarely exactly 2 mm, × 90 to 100. These figures are for the objectives only, and for the observed magnification they must all be multiplied by the power of the eyepiece which is engraved upon it.

Besides their N.A.s and magnifying power, objectives differ in other ways. As the power increases, the working distance, that is, the distance between the tip of the objective and the object in focus, decreases: high powers work nearer the cover slip. The depth of field diminishes as the N.A. increases. When a lens is set to bring into sharp focus one plane of an object it is also possible to see a little above and below the plane and the range for fair inspection without refocusing is called the depth of field. For low-power lenses with an N.A. of about 0·25, this may be as much as 10 μ,

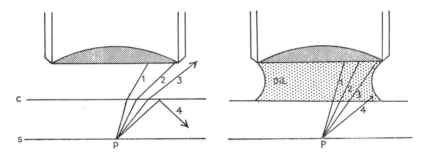

FIG. 175. The effect of an oil-immersion lens. On the left, in air, of the 4 rays shown, *1–3* are refracted and no. *4* is reflected by the cover slip (*c*); only *1* and *2* reach the objective. On the right the oil corrects the paths of all rays and *1–3* enter the objective.

c, cover slip; *s*, slide.

which means that all of a slice 10 μ thick is on view at one time. With an oil-immersion lens of N.A. about 1·25 the depth is about 0·5 μ and this is practically as good as an optical section of no thickness. With high-power lenses the depth of field can be increased by reducing the aperture of the substage iris so that it transmits a narrower cone and thus decreases the effective N.A. (see below); it is a useful means of searching for very small objects in depth but not, of course, for inspecting them when they are found.

With a given eyepiece, the diameter of the field of view decreases as the power of the objective increases; with the same objective, the field decreases as the power of the eyepiece increases. It is very important to know the three diameters of field given by the 16, 4, and 2 mm objectives with the eyepiece most often used, and some average values are set out below; from them it is easy to assess the approximate size of nearly all Protozoa. It is a curious fact that many people who use microscopes almost daily have very little sense of their scale, though this is much more useful than knowing the magnifying power. A rough estimate is made by examining a strip of mm squared paper under the low power. If, say, $1\frac{1}{2}$ squares stretch over the field its diameter is $1,500\ \mu$. Suppose that the objectives magnify $\times 10$, $\times 40$, and $\times 90$ (figures probably marked on the lenses). Then, with the same eyepiece, the diameters of the fields by high power and oil immersion are $1,500 \times \frac{10}{40} = 375\ \mu$ and $1,500 \times \frac{1}{9} = 166\ \mu$. It is worth remembering, for verification or comparison, that a human erythrocyte is $7\ \mu$ in diameter.

Some of the above information is engraved by the manufacturer on the objective. This usually includes the N.A. (a figure between 0·2 and 1·3), the magnification (10, 40, something near 100), sometimes the focal length (in mm or inches), some word or initials such as 'Oil', 'Oel', 'O.I.' or 'H.I.' for oil (homogeneous) immersion, 'Apo' for apochromatic (unmarked lenses are usually achromatic), more rarely a figure of 160, 170 or, on old microscopes, 250 mm, which is the tube length for which the objective was designed,* a serial number, which is that of the particular objective, the name of the maker and, usually, that of the laboratory to which it belongs.†

The table gives some approximate average figures useful to students.

Useful Information for Achromatic Objectives

Focal length	N.A.	Magnification	Working distance	Diameter‡ of field	Depth of field
16 mm (2/3 in)	0·20–0·30	10	4–8 mm	1–2 mm	10 μ
4 mm (1/6 in)	0·65–0·85	40	0·2–0·6 mm	0·25–0·50 mm	1–2 μ
2 mm (1/12 in)	1·2–1·3	90–100	0·11–0·16 mm	0·1–0·2 mm	0·5 μ

‡ Combined with a $\times 10$ eyepiece. Many of the other figures are averages (from Barer *Lecture Notes on the Use of the Microscope*, Blackwell Scientific Publications, Ltd., Oxford)

Eyepieces

The ordinary microscope is equipped with Huyghenian eyepieces. Each consists of a tube holding a plano-convex lens at each end, with a diaphragm pierced by a central aperture at the focal plane of the upper (eye) lens. The lower is the field lens (Fig. 172C) which concentrates the primary image from the objective on to the diaphragm where it is observed by the eye lens. With apochromatic objectives, more elaborate 'compensating eyepieces', designed to correct chromatic effects given by the objective, must be used.

* Modern practice is to equip a student's microscope with objectives designed for use with a fixed tube length. Old microscopes had tubes which could be lengthened to suit the objective. The point is one to watch when buying objectives to fit on a particular microscope, and especially when buying second-hand equipment.

† On the 4 mm objective there may be a number, usually 0·17, which is the correct thickness of cover slip to use with that lens. With other thicknesses there may be some spherical aberration. The means of correction for inaccurate cover slip thickness are not easy, and on students' microscopes are usually impossible. Low power lenses are very little affected and oil-immersion lenses not at all.

The range of magnifications manufactured is surprisingly large—from ×6 to ×30—and the figure is marked on the eyepiece. Sometimes only one eyepiece is supplied, usually a ×10 or a ×12; if there are several they are likely to be ×6, ×10, and ×15, or nearly so. If a choice can be made the points to bear in mind are (1) the final magnification should not generally be more than 1,000 or less than 250 times the N.A. of the objective, (2) the field of view of high-power eyepieces is smaller than those of low powers, (3) the higher N.A.s admit more light at the same magnification than the lower N.A.s, and the depth of field is greater with lower than with higher N.A.s—a fact of importance in photography, (4) the initial magnification by the objective is more important than that with the eyepiece.

The substage condenser: illumination

It is one of the unexplained facts of biological science that most of its students, when presented with a substage condenser, either ignore it or misuse it. The subject is best understood in the general context of illumination. The following remarks apply to an ordinary student's microscope fitted with an Abbé condenser and illuminated by an electric lamp.

Nearly all biological objects are examined by transmitted light, usually supplied by a 60 watt bulb placed 6–12 inches in front of the microscope. The light should be housed in a box with an iris diaphragm in front of it to control the amount of illumination, or, if there is no iris, one or more screens of ground glass may be interposed between the lamp and mirror. The best image is obtained when the field of view is evenly lit, and when interference from light, except that actually needed by the objective, is at a minimum. The light should fill the objective exactly and when it does so resolution is at its maximum. If more light is admitted it will cause glare and detract from the image. With very low powers (giving a final magnification of less than ×30) light may be reflected upwards from the concave side of the mirror. With all ordinary powers of the microscope a condenser is needed and this is usually an Abbé condenser.

The Abbé condenser (Fig. 176A) consists of two lenses in a cylindrical case and it has, below it and usually attached to its lower rim, an iris diaphragm. The whole structure can be moved up and down for focusing by turning a screw. The purpose of the condenser is to concentrate at the tip of a cone, which can be made to coincide with the object, O, all the light that passes through it. The iris diaphragm is to regulate the size of the cone so that it will just fill the objective in use with the amount of light it requires, and this condition is fulfilled when the effective N.A. of the condenser is the same as that of the objective. The real N.A. of a dry Abbé condenser is sometimes engraved on it: it is a figure approaching unity. It can be increased by oiling the top of the condenser and holding the drop against the lower surface of the slide, so that the condenser then forms an oil-immersion system like that of an O.I. objective only upside down, but in practice, for reasons explained below, this is not often necessary. It is not the real N.A., but the effective N.A. as determined by the aperture of the iris diaphragm which is relevant to correct illumination. The steps to be taken are far simpler than the following directions suggest, and they take longer to relate than to perform.

Setting up the microscope for use: low power

1. Place the lamp squarely, never askew, about 6 inches in front of the microscope. Using a 16-mm objective and rather low-power eyepiece ($\times 6$–12), bring a stained preparation into focus. Rack the condenser nearly to the top of its range and set the diaphragm stop about half-way between its extremes. Tilt the plane side of the mirror at about $45°$ to the light. If the field is brighter in one place than another manipulate the mirror until it is evenly illuminated. Focus up and down with the coarse adjustment; if the image moves laterally, adjust the mirror again until it stays still during coarse focusing. These quick preliminaries give a roughly correct arrangement which is now to be improved.

2. Remove the eyepiece and look down the draw tube. At the bottom is a circle of light: it is the back lens of the objective and all the light in the tube must enter through it. It ought, at this stage, to be evenly lit, but if by chance it is not adjust the mirror till it is. Still looking down the tube, open and close the substage diaphragm, and the circle of light will expand and contract. Close it: the image of the small aperture left in the centre of the diaphragm should now lie in the centre of the back lens of the objective. If it is not the condenser is out of centre. Some condensers have centring screws, and, if they are there, turn them one by one till the spot of light is centred. If there are no screws, small deviations must be tolerated (they will not seriously interfere with much work), but if the condenser is badly out of centre (half-way or so towards the margin of the objective) the instrument must be turned in for repair.

3. Expand the iris until its image exactly fits the margin of the back lens of the objective. In this position the effective N.A. of the condenser is the same as that of the objective (Fig. 176B) and the condition for optimum resolution is provided. Paradoxically the best position for resolution lets so much light through the specimen that usually it cannot be seen for lack of contrast. A compromise is made by closing the diaphragm until its image occupies from two-thirds to three-quarters of the area of the back lens (Fig. 176C). Some resolving power has, of course, now been lost in order to gain contrast, and the step is difficult to justify in theory, though in practice it makes the best of the limited capacities of the instrument.

There is no point in constructing ideal conditions for resolving an object which remains invisible. Replace the eyepiece, and look at the object. Slight adjustment of the iris is allowable for the needs of one object or another, but apart from that, its aperture is now set for the particular

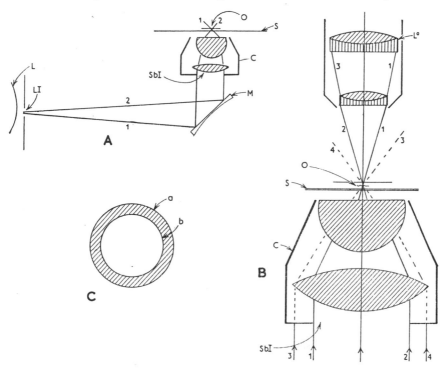

FIG. 176. *The substage condenser.* A, the general principle of the condenser in focusing light rays from the mirror (M) on to the object (O) on the slide (S); B, by partially closing the substage iris (SbI) so that the effective N.A. of the condenser equals that of the objective, the back lens (L^o) of the latter is completely filled with light: admission of the rays *3* and *4* would cause glare; B shows the setting for optimum resolution; the distance between the slide and the objective is greatly exaggerated; C, view down the draw tube of the back lens of the objective with the substage iris slightly diminished from its position in B so as to give better contrast: *a* is the margin of the back lens and *b* the limit of illumination for good contrast. (Redrawn after Martin and Johnson, *Practical Microscopy.* Blackie, 1958.) Other abbr. C, condenser case; L, lamp; *LI*, lamp case iris.

objective in use and it must be reset in the same way each time the objective is changed.

4. It is now necessary to focus the light source on the object without disturbing the arrangements so far made. Hold the point of a pencil in front of and just touching the lamp screen or bulb (the light source is the screen or bulb, not the filament) and move it. A shadowy image of it will be seen down the microscope. Slowly move the condenser until the image

cannot be improved. The light source is now focused on the object as in Fig. 176A. So, very likely, is the name of the manufacturer or other printing on the bulb. With a slight turn of the condenser screw, throw this out of focus. Like the iris, the condenser has a little play without spoiling the optical efficiency of the arrangement.

The high power

5. On changing from the 16- to 4-mm objective, swing the new lens into position if it is parfocal with the old (i.e. if it comes into focus on the swing, without much adjustment) and focus with the fine adjustment. Remove the eyepiece and look at the back lens of the high power. The circle of light from the iris as it was will fill about one-third of it. If it is out of centre, use the centring screws, or try the objective in a different socket. Fill the back lens with light by opening the iris. If a fully open iris is not enough move up the condenser; usually only a slight movement is needed to fill the back lens. Narrow the iris as before till only about two-thirds to three-quarters of the lens is lit. Replace the eyepiece. Focus the light source as before. Make any slight adjustment needed for the particular object.

The oil-immersion objective

This objective works even closer to the object (and cover slip) than the dry high power, and it is an expensive and delicate piece of apparatus. Obviously, it is easy to ram it through the slide. It is a rule with an oil-immersion lens that it is focused always with the fine adjustment, never the coarse screw, and that, after it is swung into position, the first focusing movement is upwards; only if the image fails to appear may the lens then be focused down, and always with care; the depth of field with this lens is very little, often only half a micron, and, it is easy to pass through it without noticing. Focus, then, extremely slowly, and until thoroughly accustomed to the lens in use, first on to a brightly stained mass of crowded material; faint and scattered objects may never appear in the field of view, or only so dimly that they are missed.

6. Place a drop of oil (cedar-wood oil or an immersion oil supplied by the makers of the lens) on the tip of the objective. With the tube well up, swing the lens into position and slowly lower it till the oil drop touches the cover slip. Now, with an eye level with the cover slip, watch carefully as the lens is further lowered till it nearly touches the glass. Look down the eyepiece, rack very slowly up with the fine adjustment, and so bring the image into focus. If, during these preliminaries, dark waves cross the field of view, the oil contains bubbles or there is not enough of it. Wipe it off with a tissue and begin again. Wipe the slide too; the bubbles may be on that.

Remove the eyepiece. The back lens will be incompletely filled, and this is only partly because the iris and condenser are set for a lower power lens. The oil-immersion objective will have an N.A. of about 1·25 or 1·3, as marked on it. The N.A. of the condenser is nearly 1, and, as already explained, in air it can never be more. It follows that the objective cannot be filled with light unless the condenser is oiled. In practice this is not necessary because, in the interests of contrast, only about two-thirds to three-quarters of the lens should be lit. Open the diaphragm all the way and rack up the condenser till it gives the maximum illumination. A dry condenser of N.A. 1 will light enough of an O.I. objective with N.A. 1·33 to give the same effect as lighting the whole lens and partly closing the diaphragm for proper contrast; indeed, it may still be necessary to close the diaphragm a little for some objects. (A clear image of the light source is more difficult to obtain with the 2-mm lens, and an approximation is quite good enough for practical purposes.)

Cleaning the lenses

Lenses are dusted with camel-hair brushes if they cannot be reached by hand, and they may be wiped clean with a little, a very little, xylol. If they are stained with blood (and a few other substances) use distilled, not tap, water instead of xylol. Lens-cleaning tissues may be bought, but a scrap of clean silk or face-cleansing tissues are just as good. Cleaning can be overdone. The front lenses of objectives are cemented into position and xylol, left to act on it, dissolves the cement; the slightest displacement from its position, of course, makes the lens unusable, therefore clean discreetly and always wipe quite dry. Dust out of focus does not usually affect work but must not be allowed to accumulate too long. Eyepieces are easier to clean than objectives, which must never be taken to pieces. To find the dirt on the eyepiece turn its components one by one and the dirt revolves with its part.

Oil must always be cleaned off lenses with a little xylol, and never allowed to dry on the glass.

Other practical points

Once the microscope is set up it cannot be moved without undoing the work of centration and so on. Therefore begin where you mean to go on and where you can examine your material, write, and draw in comfort.

Test the range of the objectives on unfamiliar microscopes. If you can switch from one to another without much focusing, the lenses are said to be parfocal. If they are not parfocal, rack up the tube before switching powers in case the longer, more powerful, lenses strike the slide as they swing into position.

Do not close one eye: it produces strain. If this seems difficult at first place a hand over one eye but keep it open and look down the microscope with the other. Remove your hand. With very little practice both eyes can be kept open and this makes for comfort.

There is no simple rule about spectacles. If possible, remove them, for both spectacles and eyepieces may be scratched. But spectacles for much astigmatism should be worn all the time.

Use a horizontal, not a tilted, stage for protozoological work, or liquids from wet preparations may disgrace your apparatus. When examining material in a watch-glass of liquid, first place a clean slide over the hole in the stage and then the watch-glass on that and it will not wobble.

Do not cut down the light by lowering the condenser or by closing the iris diaphragm, for this, as explained above, defeats their purposes. Light is best controlled by an iris diaphragm just in front of the source, or, failing that, by shielding it with plates of ground glass.

Slides examined under oil immersion, and to a less extent under high power, should be held in position by clips or a mechanical stage. The slightest accidental movement will take the object out of the small field of view and it may be very difficult to find again.

Always clean both lens and slide after using oil-immersion lenses (see above) and never let the oil dry on them. At the same time look for oil which has been accidentally smeared on the other objectives.

THE COLLECTION AND MAINTENANCE OF PROTOZOA

Elementary means of obtaining and maintaining most of the species described in the systematic chapters I–IV are given in their contexts, and the following generalities with some additional methods are meant to supplement these. More information will be found in *Culture Methods for Invertebrate Animals* (1937) edited by Galtsoff *et al.* (Ithaca, New York), and in Kirby (1950).

Free-living Protozoa

(from fresh water and the soil)

The richest and usually the most accessible source of Protozoa is likely to be a large pond or slow-moving stream with plenty of vegetation to maintain a fairly high organic content. Within it a few species may be ubiquitous but most will be more or less confined to the parts of it supplying the particular conditions they need, and it is essential to collect from all of these. Water, with living and dead plant material, twigs, floating and sunken debris, from the surface, bottom (including mud), and intermediate regions, from the damp, exposed margins, from shallow and deep water, light and shady parts, should all be collected. Foul water or mud, such as that contaminated by sewage or farmyard outlets, and stagnant water smelling of hydrogen sulphide have their own fauna. Water and debris from the bottoms of freshwater aquaria are useful sources of Protozoa.

In the laboratory the material should be distributed in large and small, deep and shallow containers, placed in the cool away from strong light and allowed to stand till next day. During this time the Protozoa will to some extent sort themselves, e.g. pigmented flagellates collect towards weak light, creeping rhizopods on the bottom, and ciliates at various levels. Crude collections may in this way yield many species, but generally in numbers too small for convenience. To encourage cysts to hatch and the Protozoa to multiply the collection must be fortified.

Boil wheat grains for 10 minutes and add them to the collections at the rate of 3 or 4 to each 100 ml of liquid. Or boil 10 gm of timothy hay in a litre of water and add 1 part of this infusion to 4 of the collection. The aim is to build up a population of bacteria on which some of the Protozoa feed, and, as they multiply, provide food for others, and in addition the organic supplement offers essential factors directly to the Protozoa. The last multiply at different rates, the food-supply, chemical composition, pH, and other characters of the infusion change; the composition of the fauna varies both with time and with position, in the surface scum, on the bottom, and at different levels between the two. Infusions should be kept covered in the cool, away from strong light, and they should be examined daily. Their populations may be very profitable for general study, but they are unpredictable and uncontrollable.

Culture methods

Culture methods are directed towards the indefinite maintenance of a single species, usually accompanied by other organisms among which it is dominant. The commonest example is the growth of a single species of Protozoa in a medium containing an undetermined mixture of bacteria on which it feeds. For example, a watch-glass of sterile hay infusion is inoculated with mixed bacteria from a natural source of, say, *Colpoda*, and allowed to multiply for 24 hours to provide a diet, and ciliates are then added. All the organisms reproduce and their waste products accumulate. Before they reach a toxic level, a small amount of the culture (ciliates, bacteria, and liquid) is transferred to another watch-glass of fresh, sterile medium; this process is sub-culturing, and the interval at which it is found by experience to be necessary is normally given in culture directions. At all stages the culture, which begins with sterile medium, is treated with the ordinary precautions for asepsis, though in fact it swarms with bacteria; the object is to exclude 'foreign' organisms, which may harm the ciliates. All the organisms present should be descendants of the bacteria deliberately introduced and of the ciliates of the inoculum.

Cultures of this kind containing many unknowns are sometimes called agnobiotic, and they are extremely useful for maintaining stocks of identified Protozoa and for some research purposes. Nearly all the techniques described here and in Chapters I and IV give agnobiotic cultures.

A step towards the better definition of the environment is taken when the many unknown strains of bacteria are supplanted by a single known strain. A culture in which a single species of Protozoa is maintained with a single other organism (usually a bacterium) is called monoxenic. The agnobiotic culture of *Colpoda* used as an example in the preceding paragraph could be converted into a monoxenic culture by the following means. Isolate a single specimen of the ciliate in a watch-glass of sterile medium. In picking it out of the mixed culture, an unknown number of bacteria will be transferred with it. Wash it in the sterile medium by gentle agitation and repeat with successive transfers through six changes of sterile medium. Finally transfer it to a watch-glass of medium previously seeded with a single known strain of bacterium. It is usual to initiate about six such monoxenic cultures at the same time, in case some of them turn out to contain bacteria or moulds accidentally transferred through the washes. After a few days the bacterial population is plated and incubated to test for the presence of any but the selected strain. Any culture initiated by a single individual and maintained by asexual reproduction is called a clone. It is not necessary, of course, to begin monoxenic cultures as clones, but it minimizes the risk of importing unwanted organisms.

The axenic culture, a further improvement, is one in which a single species lives unaccompanied by any other living organism. It is essential for some kinds of investigation (e.g., in nutritional studies) and it has the added advantage that growth over very long periods is unimpeded by accumulating bacterial toxins and sub-culture is needed only infrequently. The variables are few and the behaviour of the culture is more accurately predictable. The first axenic culture was that of *Tetrahymena* by André Lwoff in 1923. By now about 160 species of Protozoa, of which about four-fifths are phytoflagellates, are thus available from laboratories throughout the world.

A most valuable list of cultures of Protozoa was compiled and published in 1958 by the Society of Protozoologists (*J. Protozool.* 5, 1), and this gives not only the name of the species, but the medium, with its composition, and notes on maintenance. Some laboratories supply for teaching purposes and at a charge, while others present cultures as a courtesy to research workers. It is recommended that applications for strains of Protozoa should always in the first instance be made to one of the following three great collections:

Algensammlung, Pflanzenphysiologisches Institut, Göttingen, Western Germany.

Curator of the Culture Collection of Algae, Botany Department, Indiana University, Bloomington, Indiana, U.S.A.

The Curator, The Culture Collection of Algae and Protozoa, The Botany School, Downing Street, Cambridge, England.

Many of the following media, or at least their more troublesome ingredients, are available commercially. See dealers' catalogues.

The compositions of media printed in small capitals in the text will be found in their alphabetical places.

ACTINOPHRYS SOL

Bělař (1923) grew this in 0·1–0·01 KNOP'S SOLUTION in flat-bottomed glass vessels of about 5 cm diameter and 10 ml capacity, covered, and by a north light. For rapid growth incubate at 21° C. Feed on green algae (e.g. *Gonium pectorale*, *Chlorogonium euchlorum*) which are grown separately on Knop's agar (0·5–1·0 per cent agar dissolved in 0·05 per cent KNOP'S SOLUTION). Pour this into a Petri dish, inoculate with algae, and leave under a strong light. They are ready as food after 5 days. Sub-culture algae about once a fortnight.

Looper (1928) boiled 3 wheat grains in 100 ml filtered spring water and left it for 24 hours before introducing *Actinophrys*, and, as food, *Peranema* and *Colpidium*, covered, and left in the darkest part of the room. Add 5–10 ml boiled spring water weekly. *Actinophrys* is usually abundant after a month.

ACTINOSPHAERIUM

Actinosphaerium grows well in 0·01 per cent KNOP'S SOLUTION with large ciliates (*Paramecium*) or *Chilomonas* or rotifers for food.

AGAR

Agar is a preparation from seaweed which is soluble in water, liquid when hot, cools slowly, and is solid when cold. It is usually made up as 1–2 per cent and is useful in itself as a firm substrate; further, it may be fortified by nutrients. A great many varieties of supplemented agar are known and most are available commercially. To make slopes, pour enough hot agar into tubes or screw-topped bottles so that when tilted the liquid surface stretches from one side of the base to the opposite wall about 6 cm above it (cf. Fig. 177). Allow to cool in this position. For plates, pour a few mm of agar into Petri dishes and allow to set.

AMOEBA PROTEUS

CHALKLEY'S MEDIUM is good for this and other species.

To initiate cultures, Dawson (1928) recommends the following. Distribute water and plant material from a collection in finger bowls in 30–40-ml lots. Add 10 ml distilled water daily for 3 or 4 days and allow to stand. If amoebae are present they will become numerous within 10 to 30 days. They will not develop in the presence of small Crustacea or rotifers. When amoebae occur they are built up into hay-infusion cultures by transferring them first to small and then to large containers and at each step adding hay and water gradually as follows. Transfer about 5 ml of liquid containing amoebae and bacteria to a Syracuse watch-glass;* add at once a slip of timothy hay, about 15–20 mm long, sterilized by boiling for 15 minutes. Over the next few days add gradually a total of 5 ml distilled water. Initiate a number of such small cultures; some will die. In others the amoebae will flourish in 1 or 2 weeks. Transfer the whole contents then to finger bowls, make up to about 30 ml with distilled water. Add about 3 more slips of hay. At intervals of 5 to 10 days add about 10 ml distilled water with another 3 slips of hay until there are about 65–70 ml of liquid present. When established the culture will live for at least a month. Sub-culture by drawing off rather less than half the liquid. Dislodge the amoebae from the bottom and mix them in the remaining liquid. Remove half of it. Gradually make up the volume with water and hay, as directed above, until it is about 70 ml again, and leave for another month and so on. In most cultures made in this way, other Protozoa are present and some of these serve as food. An improvement is to remove only amoebae and bacteria from the collection in the first place and then inoculate with a culture of *Chilomonas* as food.

The foregoing and other methods using hay or wheat infusions are uncertain, slow, and never very productive. An original approach to the problem of breeding amoebae offered by Prescott (1956) is far more efficient; a single 9-inch Petri dish may yield a million amoebae. The basis of Prescott's technique is to seed an inorganic medium with washed amoebae and then supply them with axenically grown *Tetrahymena* as food. It is possible that all the bacteria inadvertently transferred to the medium with the amoebae may be consumed by the ciliates and then the culture would be truly monoxenic; but this is not the object and it is not guaranteed. The object is to supply rapidly growing cultures of amoebae which are extremely clean, with an insignificant bacterial flora and with the conditions well standardized.

Culture in flat-bottomed dishes, between 2 and 10 cm high, the size is not important. The dishes must have well-fitting tops and be washed in glass-distilled water before use. Cover the bottom with a thin layer of

---

* A Syracuse watch-glass has a circular flat base and its cavity is a flat-bottomed, very shallow cylinder. It is sometimes catalogued in English and continental lists as a Minot watch-glass. Small Petri dishes, about 3–4 cm in diameter, serve as well.

agar, made up in glass-distilled water, free from contaminating nutrients that might support bacteria. The inorganic medium is

$$MgSO_4 \quad 2 \text{ mg}$$
$$CaHPO_4 \quad 4 \text{ mg}$$
$$KCl \quad 6 \text{ mg}$$
$$\text{Aq. D. 1,000 ml}$$
$$\text{(glass-distilled)}$$

Grow the food organism as follows. *Tetrahymena pyriformis* is available in axenic culture on proteose-peptone medium. Make up a litre of the medium (1–2 per cent proteose-peptone) and distribute in 25 to 50 amounts in Erlenmeyer flasks, put cotton stoppers into them, autoclave, and inoculate with ciliates as required. All apparatus used in handling them must be sterile. Incubate at 22° C, and use as food populations that are 2 to 3 days old. Older cultures may contain damaged and therefore unsuitable animals. To prepare the food, centrifuge a culture slowly (a few hundred times gravity for 2 to 4 minutes) in conical tubes, decant the proteose-peptone quickly (before the ciliates disperse) and replace it with amoeba inorganic medium, suspend the ciliates, and repeat several times to wash. If ciliate medium (which is a nutrient) is transferred to the amoeba culture it will encourage bacterial growth. Washed ciliates will live for several days in the inorganic medium for amoebae.

Inoculate the inorganic medium with amoebae. If there are less than 100 of them use a dish 4–6 cm in diameter with 5–10 mm of medium. The amoebae must be singly and carefully washed before inoculation. Add *Tetrahymena*: the amount required (about 1,000 times as many ciliates as amoebae) is estimated by seeing that there are always 1 or 2 ciliates within a few hundred microns of each amoeba. Keep at 20° C. The amoebae should double their numbers within 40 hours. Add more *Tetrahymena* every 2 or 3 days. After 7 or 8 days subdivide the culture. As populations grow, transfer to larger containers, e.g. inoculate 1,000 amoebae into a dish 10–12 cm across. Young, active cultures double their numbers of amoebae every 24 hours. The amoebae are confined to the agar surface. As they become more crowded their growth falls off. Occasionally clean a culture by removing most of the medium, replacing it, mixing the amoebae and repeating this after the amoebae have again settled on the agar. New medium should be about 1 cm deep and the amoebae are fed at once on *Tetrahymena* as before. As populations rise they must be fed daily and cleaned fairly frequently. A culture needs cleaning when it looks dirty, the amoebae do not attach firmly to the agar, and the growth-rate falls off. Do not overfeed; the amoebae should be able to consume all their ciliates within 24 hours or nearly so. Keep cultures in weak light or darkness at 18–20° C if possible, but 17–26° C will serve.

With slight modifications to take account of its larger size, the giant amoeba, *Chaos chaos* (*Pelomyxa carolinensis*) may be cultured by the same method.

ARCELLA

Hegner (1929) recommends the following. Shake pond weeds vigorously in a container half-full of their own water and strain the lot through 8 thicknesses of cheese-cloth. This holds back the larger particles and also *Arcella* itself, but it lets through the smaller organisms on which the latter feed. Pour the filtrate into Petri dishes, allow to stand until a film has settled on the bottom, and then introduce the rhizopods; if they are allowed in too early the film settles on top of them with harmful effects. Alternatively, seed *Arcella* into weak hay infusion plus 2 wheat grains per 100 ml with ciliates as food.

Bles (1929) obtained his *Arcella* from the leaves of water-plants from which they were detached by vigorous shaking in a tube with filtered rain-water. They grew in watch-glasses of this liquid with diatoms and green algae. Keep near north light. Add rain-water, filtered, from time to time and remove such predators as small crustaceans and rotifers.

BODO

Bodo grows on many liquid media if they are rich enough, and on nutrient agar flooded with MUSGRAVE AND CLEGG'S MEDIUM.

CHALKLEY'S MEDIUM

This medium with wheat grains, rice, or hay will support a wide variety of freshwater Protozoa. It is as follows:

NaCl	0·1 gm
KCl	0·004 ,,
CaCl$_2$	0·006 ,,
Water (glass-distilled)	1,000 ,,

For amoebae, use 200–50 ml plus 4 or 5 grains of polished rice, seed with 50 to 100 amoebae, cover and leave in a cool place. Good crops are obtained in a month. One culture may last even as long as a year, but it is better to sub-culture monthly (Chalkley, 1930).

CHLAMYDOPHRYS

Bělař (1921a) grew *C. minor* (and *Rhogostoma schlusseri*) on Knop's Agar made slightly alkaline with a little 1 per cent Na$_2$CO$_3$ and in the presence of a mixed bacterial flora. Knop's Agar is

1% KNOP'S SOLUTION	10 ml
Agar	1 gm
Aq.D.	190 ml

Bělař also used Knop's 'amoeba agar', which was,

Meat extract (0·5%)	0·2	ml
Agar	1	gm
Aq.D.	200	ml

CYCLIDIUM GLAUCOMA and some other Pleuronematina.

For *C. glaucoma*, *Uronema nigricans*, and *Lembus pusillus*, Hoare (1927) recommended a FAECAL SUSPENSION, or HAY INFUSION, or 1 litre LOCKE'S SOLUTION with the white of 1 egg, or the following modification of MUSGRAVE AND CLEGG'S MEDIUM:

Agar	25	gm
NaCl	0·5	,,
Lemco beef extract	0·5	,,
Aq.D.	1,000	ml

The times for sub-culture must be determined. The author found that *C. glaucoma* did excellently in faecal suspension in covered solid watch-glasses if sub-cultured once a week.

DINOFLAGELLATES (see also under NOCTILUCA and OXYRRHIS)

Although most dinoflagellates are difficult to culture some success has been attained with media including SOIL WATER. From the work of Barker (1935) and Sweeny (1951) it appears that some species can be cultivated indefinitely only in the presence of unidentified factor(s) present in soil water; these cannot be replaced by any of the numerous growth-promoting agents tried by the authors.

Barker obtained pure cultures of a number of species on the following: potassium nitrate, 0·01 per cent; dipotassium hydrogen phosphate, 0·001 per cent; ferric chloride, 0·00001 per cent; soil extract, 2 per cent; the whole made up in 'aged sea water'. Aged sea water is sea water that has stood in large glass bottles in the dark for some months or years. Species of *Prorocentrum*, *Exuviella*, *Peridinium*, *Gonyaulax*, and *Ceratium* grew well in pure culture; *Oxyrrhis* was fed on diatoms.

EUGLENA

Most species of *Euglena* do well in SOIL WATER. Pringsheim (in Pringsheim and Hovasse, 1948) found that the best medium for *E. gracilis*, both in the light and the dark, was sodium acetate, 0·1 per cent; beef extract Difco, 0·1 per cent; bacto tryptone Difco, 0·2 per cent; yeast extract Difco, 0·2 per cent. Or the beef extract can be omitted and 0·1 per cent substituted for 0·2 per cent tryptone. The optimum temperature is 25° C, but the different species have different requirements; for discussion and further information, see Pringsheim (1946a, 1956).

EUPLOTES (especially *E. patella* and *E. eurystomus*)

Boil 2 gm rye grains in 200 ml spring water for 10 minutes. Filter hot, stand, covered, for 24 hours, pour the liquid into a finger bowl, add 12 of the boiled rye grains and inoculate with a good culture of *Chilomonas paramecium*. This is the food and in 6 days the fluid is swarming with it. Cohen (1934) used it at this stage for growing *Euplotes* on depression slides. Add *Euplotes* to 2 drops of the fluid with flagellates in the depression and transfer the ciliates daily to fresh medium. Pierson (1943) and others have used the medium for mass culturing of *Euplotes*. Inoculate good cultures of *Chilomonas* with the ciliates and leave for a week, when the latter will be numerous in a ring about 5 mm below the surface of the liquid. Subculture 'at short intervals'.

FAECAL SUSPENSIONS

Used especially for coprophilous organisms and those from manured soils. There are many recipes. Hoare (1927), for various Pleuronematina, shook a small proportion, about the size of a pea, of human faeces in 40 ml or so of distilled water. This is used in tubes, watch-glasses, or flooded over a layer of agar.

HAY INFUSION

This not only yields a good growth of bacteria but itself supplies essential factors for the growth of many species of Protozoa. For most purposes, boil 2–3 gm of chopped timothy hay in 500 ml distilled water. Cool, leave, with the hay in it, for 24 hours.

For stock, boil 10 gm timothy hay in 1 litre of distilled water. Cool, filter, sterilize in the autoclave or by filtration, and store in the refrigerator. Dilute for use with distilled or filtered spring water. 0·2 per cent is weak and most generally useful, but some species may require up to 0·6 per cent.

KNOP'S SOLUTION

Knop's Solution is the basis of many media for freshwater species. There are various methods of making it up, of which the following is useful.

Keep the following stock solutions:

Calcium nitrate	10%	A
Potassium nitrate	5%	B
Magnesium sulphate	5%	C
Potassium phosphate, monobasic	5%	D

and mix in the following proportions to get the named strengths:

1% Knop's solution:	10 ml	soln. A
	5 ml	of each of B, C, and D, adding the last drop by drop while shaking. A drop of ferric chloride (0·1%) may be added
	150 ml	Aq.D.
0·05% Knop's solution:	10 ml	of the 1% solution
	190 ml	Aq.D.
0·001% Knop's solution:	40 ml	of the 0·05% solution
	160 ml	Aq.D.

For Knop's agar see under *CHLAMYDOPHRYS*.

LOCKE'S SOLUTION

This is an ingredient of many media for both free-living and parasitic Protozoa.

NaCl	0·9	gm
$CaCl_2$	0·025	,,
KCl	0·042	,,
$NaHCO_3$	0·02	,,
Dextrin	0·25	,,
Aq.D.	100	ml

MEAT EXTRACTS

These are best obtained commercially. They are used in very weak (0·025–1 per cent) concentration, either alone or in combination with other substances, especially for bacteria feeders.

MUSGRAVE AND CLEGG'S MEDIUM

Walker's modification is:

Agar	2·5	gm
Sodium chloride	0·05	,,
Liebig's beef extract	0·05	,,
Normal solution of sodium hydroxide	2·0	ml
Aq.D.	100	,,

It is especially useful for many coprophilous Protozoa. The medium is plated in Petri dishes and streaked with faecal material. Bacteria develop first and then the Protozoa. From mixed cultures thus initiated single species can be picked out and transferred to fresh plates to set up single lines.

NAEGLERIA GRUBERI

Methods for coprophilous Protozoa are generally good and many variants have been described. Willmer (1956) gives:

Agar	7·5 gm (dissolve in distilled water and filter)
Lemco meat extract	0·5 ,,
Glucose	1·0 ,,

Make up to 500 ml with distilled water. Tube in about 4 ml lots and autoclave. The amoebae are large and active for the first 3 or 4 days at room temperature and after that cysts become commoner. Sub-culture every 10 days approximately. Wash the slopes with about 5 ml distilled water and spin at about 3,000 rpm, repeat in another 5 ml, suspend the amoebae in about 0·5 ml of distilled water and inoculate drops of this on to fresh slopes. The washing, which is not very thorough, helps to keep down the bacteria, but not so much as to deprive the amoebae of necessary food.

Dr K. Vickerman recommends to the writer:

Agar	1·5 gm
Peptone	0·5 ,,
Aq.D.	100 ml

Slope in tubes or plate in Petri dishes, seed with a loop of *Aerobacter*, incubate for 24 hours at 37° C, and then inoculate with *Naegleria*.

NOCTILUCA

Gross (1934) successfully cultivated *Noctiluca* for long periods in Föyn's 'Erdschreiber' medium, which is a sea-water variant of the SOIL-WATER medium used by Pringsheim (p. 408).

$NaNO_3$	0·1	gm
Na_2HPO_4	0·02	,,
Soil extract	50	ml
Sea water	1,000	,,

Gross (1937) boiled 1 kg of good garden or potting soil in 1 litre of glass-distilled or tap water. Allow to stand. After 2 or 3 days decant and sterilize the dirty brown liquid. After standing for 3 or 4 weeks, the fluid is a transparent brown or red and ready for use after, if necessary, further sterilization. Transfer to another flask, boil, add the nitrate, phosphate, and sea water. Use 'outside' sea water, i.e. collected from the open sea, well away from inshore sources of contamination, boiled and allowed to stand for 3 to 4 weeks. Keep in a refrigerator.

Wash the *Noctiluca* in several changes of sterile medium to avoid introducing small flagellates, which will overgrow the culture. All apparatus must, of course, be sterile, though axenic cultures are not required. Grow in flat-bottomed dishes with overlapping lids.

In this medium it was difficult not to encourage, but to suppress, sporulation, but the gametes developed little or not at all. To observe copulation and early zygotes lower the pH of the medium by adding a few drops of $1/100N$ HCl or H_2SO_4. Only gametes from different clones will copulate.

OXYRRHIS MARINA

Hall (1925a) got good results with Allen and Nelson's modification of Miquel Solution for diatoms, as follows:

Solution A	KNO_3	20·2 gm
	Aq.D.	100 ml
Solution B	$Na_2HPO_4 . 12H_2O$	4 gm
	$CaCl_2 . 6H_2O$	4 ,,
	$FeCl_3$ (melted)	2 ml
	HCl	2 ,,
	Aq.D.	80 ,,

To make B dissolve the calcium chloride in half the water and add the acid; dissolve the phosphate in the other half and add the melted ferric chloride. Mix the two slowly.

To make Miquel Solution add 2 ml of A and 1 ml of B to 1 litre of sea water. Heat to 70° C, cool, and decant the clear supernatant liquid. Sterilize. Diatoms are given as food. Hall obtained dividing forms after a few days and cultures were maintained for 2 years.

PARAMECIUM

Wichterman (1953) recommends either hay or lettuce infusion as follows.

Boil 6 gm of cut timothy hay (spikes and stems cut into 1-in segments) in 1 litre of water for 20 minutes; cover the flask opening with a snugly fitting beaker and boil for about 15 minutes. Leave the covered flask to stand for 24 hours and then inoculate with Protozoa. It is more convenient to prepare the infusion in 250 ml Erlenmeyer flasks. This medium does well for all species except *P. aurelia* and *P. bursaria* which are said to do better on a more dilute version (4 gm hay per litre instead of 6). The cultures may be maintained for long periods simply by adding a few pieces of boiled hay about once a month.

Separate the clean leaves of a head of lettuce and dry them slowly in an oven until brown and crisp, but not burnt and black. Grind in a pestle and mortar; the powder may be kept indefinitely in a stoppered jar. Add 1·5 gm desiccated lettuce leaves to 1 litre of boiling distilled water and allow to boil for 5 minutes. Filter while hot into smaller (250 ml) flasks and autoclave. Leave in stoppered flasks overnight and then the medium is ready. Mix

2 parts of the medium and 1 part of distilled water to obtain the right strength. Sealed flasks of the medium may be kept for long periods. An excess of $CaCO_3$ may be added to bring the pH to 7·2. All species grow on this (except *P. calkinsi* and *P. woodruffi*) but it is especially good for *P. bursaria*.

P. calkinsi and *P. woodruffi* from brackish water require a mixture of sea water. Wichterman used 2 parts of filtered sea water and 3 parts hay or lettuce infusion successfully.

PERANEMA TRICHOPHORUM

This colourless, phagotrophic euglenoid is normally given other flagellates (*Euglena* spp., *Ochramonas*, *Chilomonas*) to feed on, but can also be grown in pure culture.

For mixed cultures, boil 1 gm wheat cereal in 1 litre tap water; allow to stand overnight. Decant the supernatant fluid in roughly equal parts of about 200 ml into finger bowls. Introduce the food flagellates. After a few days add *Peranema*. Good growth is found after 2 weeks. Cultures may be maintained for months by adding a few grains of cereal weekly (Pitelka, 1945).

If axenic cultures are available they grow best on milk and soil water (Chen, 1950). Storm and Hutner (1953), who studied the nutritional requirements of *Peranema*, obtained good growth within a month on whole milk, 1·0 ml; soil extract, 10·0 ml; distilled water, 100 ml. The soil water was obtained by autoclaving soil with an equal weight of water and filtering. The medium deteriorates and is used fresh. Cultures last 2–3 months at 25–30° C; they deteriorate suddenly and sub-cultures should be started at fortnightly intervals.

SOIL PROTOZOA

Well-manured soil from pasture, gardens, or that from potted plants yields an extensive fauna. Most species feed on bacteria and do well on hay infusions, especially on an agar base or on the media given for *Naegleria gruberi*.

Damp soil is collected and usually kept damp till used, but many of the Protozoa encyst and for these the samples may be stored dry for months or even years. Flood agar plates in Petri dishes with hay infusion to a depth of about 1 cm. Spread small samples of soil thinly over about half the surface of the agar. Leave undisturbed, and covered. The Protozoa emerge and explore the agar where they may be picked out under the dissecting microscope for inoculation into fresh media.

SOIL-WATER CULTURES

The method, which has been elaborated to great effect by Pringsheim, is based on the capacity of soil to yield into solution, gradually over a period, small quantities of nutrients required by many micro-organisms; the medium is, in effect, no more than soil and water supplemented where necessary with small amounts of organic substances. It is a medium simple to make and to vary, and although success cannot be guaranteed for any organism unless its requirements are known, a few tubes, prepared as indicated below, are likely to include the needs of a wide range of species. The technique has been successful with a large number of organisms including Chrysomonadina, Phytomonadina, and Euglenoidina, as well as filamentous algae and other species lying outside the scope of the protozoologist.

Ordinary garden soil or the surface soil of arable land is dried and sifted before use. It should not contain too much humus, which will produce excessive putrefaction of the liquid. For special cases, to obtain an acid medium, use peat, covered with garden soil, or leaf mould; for alkaline media, add lime to the soil.

Some organisms will require organic additions to what is supplied by the soil. Casein, gelatine, dried cheese have been used. Natural mixtures of protein and carbohydrate are supplied by wheat or barley grains and these have been very successful. Starch may be used in their place; if so, calcium carbonate must be added to neutralize the fatty acids produced by anaerobic fermentation. Organic supplements are always placed in the bottom of the tube and covered with soil so that their contributions to the overlying liquid, in which the organisms grow, are made gradually.

Tap water may be used unless it is chlorinated or very hard, when distilled water should be substituted.

Preparation. The medium is prepared in hard-glass (e.g. Pyrex) thick-walled test-tubes, as follows. Place small quantities of organic substances (e.g. 1 or 2 wheat grains or their equivalents), if needed, in the bottom of the tube and cover with a column, 3 or 4 cm high, of dried and powdered soil. Add water to about 5 cm short of the top of the tube. Plug with cotton-wool. Place in a cold steamer, heat, and keep for 3 hours just below boiling-point. The object of heating is not to sterilize the system in the tube but to kill unwanted organisms. Allow to cool and use as soon as possible, certainly not more than a fortnight after preparation.

When the requirements of the organism to be cultured are known the medium is made up accordingly. In dealing with an unknown, Pringsheim suggests that it should be inoculated into a set of tubes containing water with (*a*) ordinary soil, (*b*) soil with $CaCO_3$, (*c*) a cereal grain with soil, and (*d*) peat and soil; this ought to meet the demands of a fairly wide range of chlorophyll-bearing species.

After inoculation (see below), colourless forms are left in the dark. Green forms are placed in a north light in spring and summer; in autumn and winter natural light is insufficient and is supplemented by grouping the tubes about a single large 500 Watt lamp, with a water screen between. Some cooling is necessary but the lamp will have the additional advantage that it raises the temperature a little, even with the screen in use.

Once good growth is obtained, the tubes are covered with wax-paper, cellophane, or tin-foil and sealed with Sellotape. If protected from desiccation, soil-water cultures last for 6 months or more without sub-culturing.

Inoculation. The quickest growth is obtained by the inoculation of large numbers of organisms and this may be satisfactory if only mixed cultures are needed for class work, or if cultures of single species are available for sub-culture into soil-water. The technique is adapted for the growth of clones, i.e. a culture consisting of the asexual descendants of a single individual initially inoculated to form the primary culture. For most purposes, however, it is enough to have cultures derived from inocula of several individuals of the same species. These are obtained as follows.

Single cells are picked up from the primary source in sterile capillary pipettes, washed in sterile fluid, and then inoculated into a test-tube of the medium. Three or 4 sterile watch-glasses are used, which must be large (5–6 cm diameter) and must have curved bottoms, not flattened ones which would allow the drops of liquid to spread. Each watch-glass is kept in a Petri dish, steadied on a triangle of metal or glass, and the whole system is sterilized by heat. The first watch-glass contains the primary source of the material, the others 2 or 3 drops of sterile washing fluid, e.g. soil-water of approximately the same pH as the primary material.

The watch-glass containing the primary material is observed under the binocular, and the tip of a capillary pipette is approached to a specimen of the required species. (If there is difficulty in recognizing individuals under a binocular, the species must be studied under first high, then medium and low powers of the microscope until the characteristic shape, colour, and manner of movement is known.) As soon as a specimen enters the capillary tube of the pipette, it is withdrawn from the water. Several cells may be picked up at the same time. These are emptied, also under the binocular, into the washing fluid, allowed to swim for some minutes, picked up again by the same method, and so on till the last wash. Finally, as many as possible of the organisms are pipetted into the tubes of medium. An obvious adaptation of the technique may be used to initiate single-cell (clone) cultures.

For a full description of the technique, see Pringsheim (1946*b*).

SPIROSTOMUM AMBIGUUM

Specht (1935) found that this species would not grow in the wheat medium described by Bishop (see p. 354). The following was simple and very successful. To 1 litre of spring water add 10 gm timothy hay and 10 gm wheat, boil, allow to cool, and add 1 tablespoonful of fresh cow manure. Leave for 2 to 3 days. Add *Spirostomum*. The pH rapidly adjusts to 7·6 and remains there for several weeks. Flourishing stocks were obtained 7 to 10 days after inoculation. Large shallow dishes will serve as well as tall narrow jars with this medium. The cultures are revived by the addition of fresh cow manure when the population begins to fall off. In this way, Specht's cultures continued to yield good stocks nearly a year after their inauguration.

Carter (1957) recommended the following:

Potassium chloride	0·5 mM/l
Sodium chloride	2·0 ,,
Magnesium chloride	0·2 ,,
Calcium chloride	0·5 ,,
Potassium dihydrogen phosphate	0·1 (approx.)
Potassium hydroxide	0·01 ,,

The last 2 substances are added as buffers until the pH is adjusted to 6·3. Boiled wheat grains are added as food for the bacteria on which the ciliates will feed.

STENTOR COERULEUS

The food organism is the pink ciliate *Blepharisma undulans*, maintained as follows. To about 70 ml spring water in finger bowls about 11–12 cm in diameter, add 2 grains of wheat, boiled for 1 minute and cut in two. From a rich collection of *Blepharisma*, add about 5 ml containing the ciliates, water, and the bacteria on which *Blepharisma* has been feeding. In 7 to 10 days the liquid will be pink and the culture is now rich. Sub-culture at this point by pouring off half the liquid, making up with fresh spring water and adding 1 or 2 more grains of wheat. Cultures made in this way have been maintained for over 30 years by Dawson (1953).

To obtain mass cultures of *Stentor*, isolate 10–50 ciliates with a coarse pipette and add to 30–40 ml spring water in a similar finger bowl together with 5 ml rich culture of *Blepharisma*. Ingestion begins at once and within 5 minutes nearly all the specimens of *Stentor* contain *Blepharisma* and division follows rapidly. Specimens thus well fed will live without further attention for 2 or 3 weeks. Sub-culture by discarding half the liquid, replacing with spring water and adding *Blepharisma*. A few short pieces of timothy hay may be added to provide growth of moulds as a foothold for *Stentor*. Cultures were maintained for 6 years.

Dr M. A. Sleigh (personal communication) kindly recommends the following simple method. To about 100 ml CHALKLEY'S SOLUTION add 5 or 6 wheat grains boiled for a minute. Add, as food, *Chilomonas*: the culture need not be pure. Twenty-four to 48 hours later add 10–20 specimens of *Stentor*. Keep at room temperature away from bright sunlight. Times vary, but good numbers of *Stentor* are usually obtained in a fortnight at summer temperatures or near a radiator in winter. Add 1 or 2 wheat grains once a month. The culture will keep for 6 months or more without sub-culturing.

TETRAHYMENA PYRIFORMIS

According to Phelps (1947) this species can withstand concentrations of streptomycin as high as 1,000 units per ml, and on this account may sometimes be isolated in axenic culture by the following very simple method. To a sterile 1 per cent solution of proteose-peptone add 500 units of streptomycin per litre. To 25 ml of this add 5 ml of a sample containing *Tetrahymena*. In about one-third of the trials the bacteria are killed and from such Protozoa as survive specimens are isolated for pure culture.

Furgason (1940) found that axenic cultures of *T. pyriformis* grew well in van Niel's Yeast Extract, as follows. Mix 1 lb of pressed fresh baker's yeast, broken small, in 500 ml distilled or non-chlorinated tap water, and incubate at 50° C for 24 hours. Boil. Adjust pH to 7 with NaOH, dilute 10 times, and parcel out the liquid in convenient lots in flasks. Autoclave at 15 lb for 15 minutes. This is the stock and before use it is diluted again to 10 per cent and autoclaved. Furgason found that the ciliates grew better in medium prepared in this way than in a 0·2 per cent aqueous solution of commercially prepared yeast extract.

WHEAT INFUSION

Boil 2 to 6 wheat grains for 10 minutes in distilled water and make up to 100 ml. Allow to stand for 24 to 48 hours before use. Most species do well on 3 or 4 grains per 100 ml. Fungal hyphae soon develop round the grains and are centres for concentrations of, especially, amoebae.

The culture of entozoic Protozoa

Many entozoic Protozoa, especially amoebae and flagellates from the intestinal tract, are relatively simple to culture. Sporozoa are either very difficult or quite impossible, and so, too, are almost all parasites of the blood and coelomic spaces. Ciliates vary. For obvious reasons, it is easier to handle parasites from poikilothermic than from homoiothermic hosts.

Cultures, even when swarming with bacteria, are treated as if they were sterile. The medium is sterilized by heat or filtration before use and is dispensed into sterile tubes. All operations are performed with sterilized Pasteur pipettes or other sterile instruments and with all the usual aseptic precautions. The object is not, of course, asepsis (which in most cases would kill the culture) but protection against the entry of any organisms except those introduced with the original inoculum or their descendants. Protozoa from homoiothermic hosts must be incubated at fairly constant temperatures, but not necessarily as high as those of their hosts; many amoebae of mammals do as well at 30°–33° C as at 37° C and some of them do better. Gut parasites are, or should be treated as if they were, obligate anaerobes. The medium should rise about 5 cm in the tube and the Protozoa grow at the bottom. When sub-culturing, material from the bottom of an old culture is gently deposited, without bubbling from the pipette, at the bottom of a tube of fresh medium.

It is, of course, very much easier to initiate cultures from material already growing *in vitro*, when the supplier will give all the information about the medium best suited for good growths, conditions for encystation and excystation, and intervals for sub-culture. Starting new cultures from infected hosts is more troublesome but for some species is by no means difficult. Material is obtained either by dissection or from freshly passed faeces. For the former, sterilize the area of skin to be incised and dissect 'dry' (i.e. not in water) with heat-sterilized instruments. Remove the portion of gut or other organ to a sterile dish as quickly as possible. Deposit the contents, or some of them, according to size, at the bottom of the tube of sterile medium; the initial inoculum should usually be something about the size of a pea. Inoculate likewise a similar quantity of freshly passed faeces; the material must be fresh or it may be contaminated with coprophilous organisms which may mislead and interfere. Incubate from homoiothermic animals at 33°–37° C (mammals) or 38°–39° C (birds), and from poikilothermic animals at 20°–23° C or keep at room temperature. Withdraw a very little material from the bottom of the tube with a fine Pasteur pipette daily and examine until the organism is well established and its growth understood.

The inoculum may include, not only the desired species, but a number of undesired and possibly harmful organisms, which flourish in the tubes and compete with the required species. Cultures of *Entamoeba* from nearly all hosts are commonly contaminated with *Blastocystis*, which is a nearly ubiquitous intestinal fungus. Other Protozoa may be present. The intestinal amoebae of mammals encyst; their flagellates commonly do not. Exposure in the refrigerator to temperatures of 3°–4° C will usually rid cultures of the latter after a few days without killing the encysted amoebae. *Blastocystis* may be discouraged by adding starch (which, in any event, the amoebae will need) to media, and by frequent sub-culturing. In obstinate cases only empirical art can find a remedy.

BALAMUTH AND SANDZA'S MEDIUM

This simplification of BOECK AND DRBOHLAV'S MEDIUM was originally proposed for *Entamoeba histolytica*, and, although it has been largely replaced by the yet simpler HSM MEDIUM, it still finds employment for this and other organisms.

Hard boil 2 eggs for 15 minutes, cool, and discard the whites. Crumble the yolks in a beaker with 125 ml 0·8 per cent NaCl. Boil for 10 minutes, make up to 125 ml, filter by suction, make up again, and autoclave at 15 lb for 20 minutes. Cool: a slight yellow precipitate settles: filter. Add to the filtrate 125 ml M/15 phosphate buffer (pH = 7·5); this brings the final concentration to M/30 phosphate in 0·4 per cent NaCl. Tube, autoclave, and store. Made in this way the medium is free of lumps and nearly transparent. Add a loop of rice starch before inoculation (Balamuth and Sandza, 1944).

BOECK AND DRBOHLAV'S MEDIA

All the variants of the media are diphasic, i.e. each consists of a solid slope (inspissated horse serum, *HS*, or coagulated egg, *E*) covered with a liquid component (dilute horse serum, *hs*, or dilute egg-white, *re*), and, for most purposes, a little rice starch is added as a powder (*S*). In the abbreviations, the solid phase is given in capitals, the liquid in lower-case letters, and the possible combinations are shown in Fig. 177. The entire medium in its tube is called a Boeck tube and it is, of course, a sterile system.

The ingredients are composed as follows:

HS—sterilize whole horse serum by filtration, tube, and inspissate (i.e. cook) at 80° C for 60 to 80 minutes, not more, on the slant.

E—wash 4 eggs, paint the shells with alcohol, break into a sterile dish, add 50 ml RINGER'S SOLUTION, and mix. Tube, slant, and cook at 70° C till good firm slopes are formed. Autoclave.

hs—dilute 1 part of inactivated horse serum with 8 parts of RINGER'S SOLUTION

re—put the whites of 4 eggs in 1 litre of RINGER'S SOLUTION; sterilize by filtration.

The liquid component is poured over the solid to reach the top of the slope at least, and either liquid may be combined with either solid. In Dobell and Laidlaw's amended media a loop of sterile powdered rice starch was added. The complete tube is then incubated to test for sterility. Amoebae will grow (though not at their best) without rice starch but they do not encyst. Further, in the presence of starch (unless starch-splitting bacteria are present) *Blastocystis*, the most resistant and perhaps the commonest contaminant of cultures of intestinal Protozoa, does not grow; after a few sub-cultures through starch-containing media, *Blastocystis* usually disappears. Inocula are put into the bottom of the tube and it is there, in the angle between the slope and the wall, that the organisms develop. The media were developed for *Entamoeba* and good strains encyst after adding *S* and excyst on transferring to fresh medium. All versions of the medium are very rich; sub-culture every 3 days above 30° C and every 5 or 6 days at room temperature. Dobell and Laidlaw's paper makes one of the best introductions to the culture of intestinal Protozoa generally.

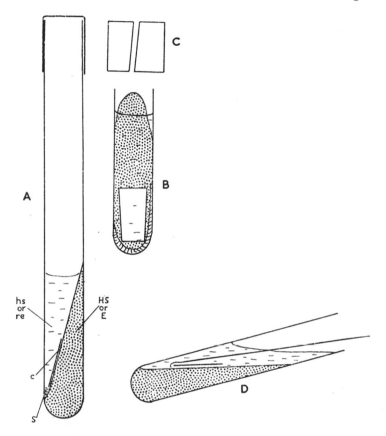

FIG. 177. A Boeck tube, showing the solid (*HS* or *E*) and liquid (*hs* or *re*) components of Boeck and Drbohlav's medium for the cultivation of entozoic amoebae, with rice starch, *S*, at the bottom of the tube, where the organisms grow. If a half cover slip, cut as in C, is placed as shown (*c* in A, face-view in B) and the tube incubated nearly flat as in D, the amoebae will populate its upper surface; the slip is withdrawn with a sterile hook (D) towards the mouth of the tube, seized with forceps, and the amoebae may be fixed in natural attitudes. (After Dobell.)

ENTAMOEBA HISTOLYTICA

E. histolytica lives on Boeck media or HSM or BALAMUTH AND SANDZA'S MEDIUM. Different strains will behave differently and their initiation and control are for experts. But the cultivation of known strains in the light of expert experience is not difficult. All media must be supplemented by solid starch to obtain encystation.

E. INVADENS

The requirements are the same as those of E. HISTOLYTICA but E. invadens also has the great advantages that it lives normally at room temperatures and is harmless to human beings. Cultures are best initiated from cysts in the livers of diseased animals, but maintenance of established strains is easier. Some strains, like some of E. histolytica, do not encyst readily, or, if so, do not excyst regularly, and for teaching purposes reliable strains with known histories obtained from research institutes are to be preferred. Sub-culturing should be done weekly. Cysts may be stored for months in the refrigerator and activated by sub-culturing at room temperature, but the author always sub-cultures monthly from stored cysts if it is important to preserve the strain.

E. RANARUM

Barret and Smith (1926) cultivated it on 1 part of inactivated human serum and 9 parts of 0·5 per cent NaCl. Remove the lower end of the large intestine of a tadpole and express the contents on to a sterile slide, mix with a drop or two of medium, and inoculate into tubes containing more medium to a depth of about 5 cm. Leave undisturbed for 10 days in the ice-box before examining. Sub-culture positives about every 10 days. Infections are uncommon (in about 1 per cent of animals) and Blastocystis and flagellates commonly accompany the amoebae and tend to overgrow them. Exposure for 1 hour to 1 : 2000 mercurochrome will sometimes get rid of the flagellates. Try adding rice starch to assist the amoebae and discourage Blastocystis.

Sanders (1931) initiated cultures in 1 part of horse serum and 19 parts of 0·5 per cent NaCl. Amoebae were observed after 6 weeks at room temperature and transferred to liver agar slopes covered with 1 : 6 horse serum and saline plus sterile rice starch. They should be maintained at room temperature and sub-cultured every 10 days.

E. THOMSONI

Smith and Barret (1928) used 1 part inactivated human blood serum and 19 parts 0·5 per cent NaCl.

Dissect out the lower end of the hind gut of a cockroach and place in a drop of medium on a sterile slide. Mix the contents of the intestine in this and inoculate into the bottoms of tubes of medium. Place in the ice-box. Amoebae appear in about 5 days. Sub-culture at fortnightly intervals and when a culture is well established maintain at room temperature in the same way. The amoebae tend to be overgrown by Blastocystis, flagellates, and yeasts inoculated with the gut contents.

ENTODINIOMORPHIDA

When mixed ciliates from the rumen of cattle were inoculated into the following medium by Hungate (1942), *Diplodinium neglectum* was the species which chiefly survived and for this species it was very successful. For slight modifications to grow other species of *Diplodinium* and *Entodinium caudatum*, see Hungate (1943).

The medium has an inorganic base to which cellulose and dry grass are added. Powdered cellulose is obtained by soaking absorbent cotton-wool for several days in strong HCl, washing, drying, and grinding in a mortar. The grass used was *Bromus catharticus* or *Lolium italicum* (but not *Medicago arabica*, which was useless) dried and ground to a powder.

The inorganic solution was:

NaCl	0·6 %
NaHCO$_3$	0·1 ,,
KH$_2$PO$_4$	0·1 ,,
MgSO$_4$ (anhydrous)	0·01 ,,
CaCl$_2$,,	0·01 ,, in tap water

To this add 0·04 per cent dried powdered grass and the same weight of cellulose. Adjust the pH to *c.* 7 (between 6·1 and 7·6) by adding NaOH or HCl. Hungate put 30 ml of this medium into a 50-ml Erlenmeyer flask and bubbled through it a mixture of 95 per cent nitrogen and 5 per cent carbon dioxide to displace oxygen. Inoculate with about 0·5 ml of rumen contents. Stopper tightly and incubate at 38° C.

Sub-culture every 2 days, as follows. Bubble the gas mixture through the inorganic medium for 15 minutes. To 20 ml of the solution add 16 mgm cellulose and 16 mgm dry grass in a 50-ml Erlenmeyer flask. Add 20 ml of a flourishing culture of ciliates. Bubble the gas through again. Stopper and incubate as before. The old culture should be rotated to mix the Protozoa before sub-culturing from it. Ciliates were maintained by Hungate in this way for 22 months, and he estimated that they divided once a day.

A method for entodiniomorphid ciliates from sheep is given by Coleman (1958).

HSM or Jones's modification of Pavlova's Medium.

This is the simplest medium to use for a great variety of intestinal parasites of vertebrate and invertebrate hosts (Jones, 1946).

Sterile horse serum	0·5	ml
1% Marmite* (yeastrol) solution	1·0	,,
Buffer saline solution (pH = 7·2)	8·5	,,
Rice starch	30	mgm†

* 'Marmite' is the name of a commercial food preparation sold in Great Britain.

† Or add one loop of starch when required (see under BOECK AND DRBOHLAV'S MEDIA).

The buffer solution is

Na$_2$HPO$_4$ (9·476 gm per litre)	375 ml
KH$_2$PO$_4$ (9·078 ,, ,,	125 ,,
NaCl (0·9%)	2,250 ,,

JONES'S MEDIUM (see *HSM*)

N.N.N. See p. 420.

OPALINATA

No good method is known. Pütter (1905) kept *Opalina* alive for some time on

Sodium chloride 0·8%	100 parts
Sodium and potassium tartrate 30%	5 ,,
Aq.D.	400 ,,

if the cultures were strengthened by adding a drop of broth made from frog intestine or, simpler, a drop of egg albumen.

The writer maintained *Opalina ranarum* for 3 months on *Ere* (see BOECK AND DRBOHLAV'S MEDIA) and there was plentiful division, especially when the cultures were started in the spring.

RINGER'S SOLUTION

Dobell and Laidlaw's Ringer for their modification of BOECK AND DRBOHLAV'S MEDIA was

NaCl	9	gm
KCl	0·2	,,
CaCl$_2$	0·2	,,
Aq.D.	1,000	ml

and it serves for most purposes.

TRICHOMONAS TERMOPSIDIS from the gut of the termite, *Zootermopsis angusticollis*.

Trager (1934*a*) successfully introduced the following media:

Salts	Soln. A gm per litre	Soln. U dist. water
NaCl	1·169	2·164
NaHCO$_3$	0·840	0·773
Na$_3$C$_6$H$_5$O$_7$. 2H$_2$O (citrate)	2·943	1·509
NaH$_2$PO$_4$. H$_2$O	0·690	0
KCl	0·745	0
KH$_2$PO$_4$	0	1·784
CaCl$_2$	0·111	0·083
MgSO$_4$	0	0·048

Trichomonas termopsidis lives indefinitely on Solution A to which 0·2 per cent Loeffler's blood-serum and a little cellulose and charcoal have been added. The cellulose is indispensable, and there is no substitute. Whole hind guts of termites are inoculated. Remove gut after sterilizing the outside of the insect by washing in 1:1000 HgCl₂ followed by 95 per cent alcohol and distilled water. Incubate at room temperature. The flagellates are found in the bottom of the tubes. Growth is usually slow in the first week and then improves. Sub-culture every 3 or 4 weeks.

To prepare the cellulose, dissolve Whatman's filter-paper No. 40 in Cross and Bevan's reagent (1 part by weight ZnCl₂, 2 parts conc. HCl), reprecipitate in water, filter on a large Buchner funnel, wash with tap water till free of chloride, then with distilled water, and allow to dry in air. Grind to a fine white powder in a mortar and many of the particles will be small enough for ingestion by the flagellates.

Trichonympha sphaerica can survive for several days in Solution A with charcoal and cellulose but does not multiply. In Solution U it grows well for 2 weeks and even in a first sub-culture but no longer.

Tricercomitus termopsidis may be cultured on liquid and solid media based on Solution A. For the liquid media add 0·1 per cent xylose or 0·2 per cent Loeffler's dehydrated blood-serum and sterilize by filtration. For solid medium, add 0·1 per cent dextrose+0·01 per cent peptone+1·5 per cent agar and autoclave for 15 minutes at 17 lb. Slants of the solid medium are most suitable for maintaining stocks. Inoculate with whole gut and a good growth results in 3 to 5 days. Sub-culture by streaking the growth on new slants and this gives a very heavy growth in 2 days. Then sub-culture every 2 or 3 weeks at room temperatures or store for 6 months at 5° C. The spherical refringent resistant bodies appear after 3 days and predominate at the centre of 4- to 5-day growths; for further information see Trager (1934*b*).

TRYPANOSOMIDAE

The standard medium is N.N.N., prepared by adding rabbit's blood to liquid agar (for details see below), allowing it to solidify in the sloped position to obtain slants of solid blood-agar, which are then incubated, partly to test for sterility and partly to collect liquid of condensation at the bottom of the tube in the angle between the end of the slant and the tube wall; it is in this that the organisms grow. On incubation with infected material the tubes are kept at 22°–25° C and the organisms display the forms exhibited in their invertebrate hosts. Successful growth is not possible if bacteria are present and all apparatus used in preparation of the medium and obtaining samples of infected material must be sterile. While it is not difficult to obtain sterile blood specimens, flagellates from insect gut must be freed from their accompanying bacteria: this is usually done by adding appropriate antibiotics to the medium. An older method takes advantage of the fact that some stages of the parasites adhere to surfaces very readily. Thus, to obtain *Leptomonas* or other flagellates from insects, drop the host into 2 per cent Lysol or other sterilizing agent for a few minutes, dissect it on flamed cork with flamed needles, straighten the gut after removal into a drop of sterile 0·6 per cent saline solution, and make smears of the contents on sterile cover slips each holding a tiny drop of sterile saline; some of the flagellates will adhere to the slide. Gently wash each smear 3 or 4 times in sterile saline and then drop the slips separately face downwards into tubes of the medium. Some will be sterile and from these good growths should be obtained.

Leishmania, Leptomonas, Trypanosoma cruzi, and the trypanosomes of the *lewisi* group may be cultivated on N.N.N., for which Hoare (*Handbook of Medical Protozoology*, 1949) gives the following recipe.

Add 1·5 gm sodium chloride and 3·5 gm agar-agar powder to 225 ml tap water in a 500 ml flask, shake well, steam for 2 hours, and filter through cotton-wool. Dispense in 5 ml lots into sterile tubes and plug with cotton-wool; the amount need not be exact. Pour the liquid into the tubes to a height of about 1 inch. Autoclave at 120° for 20 minutes. As the tubes cool, at 45–50° C, add 20 drops of fresh rabbit blood to each; the tubes may be kept in a water-bath at the required temperature if desired. Mix without forming bubbles; this is done by rubbing the hands briskly together with a tube held between the palms. Plug and slope in a position to produce a slant on solidification which will reach right to the bottom of the tube. Incubate for 24 hours at 37° C to test for sterility and also to obtain the corner of water of condensation at the bottom of the slant. Store in a dark cupboard. It is possible to make the agar slants and store these, adding the blood as required by simply melting the agar, mixing, slanting, and incubating as above.

Pathogenic trypanosomes of the *brucei* group are cultivated on Razgha's medium (see Hoare, 1949, p. 310) or Weinman's medium (for formula see Weinman, 1946; results with the medium were described by the author in 1953).

For methods of obtaining rabbit's blood, see Wenyon (1926, ii).

Drbohlav (1925*b*) found that *Leptomonas ctenocephali* from the dog flea grew best on a modification of N.N.N. medium prepared as follows.

Make up the agar base, which is agar, 14 gm; NaCl, 6·0 gm; KH_2PO_4, 3 gm; tap water, 900 ml. This is the standard base for N.N.N. plus biphosphate as a buffer. Adjust the pH to 6·6 by adding, drop by drop, the appropriate quantity of N/20 NaOH or C/1 HCl. Dispense into tubes as above and store. When cultures or sub-cultures are required, add the blood in the following way. Draw the rabbit's blood, shake to defibrinate, and dilute with an equal part of LOCKE'S SOLUTION (q.v.), which must of course be sterile. Liquefy the agar by heating, cool to 45° C and add to it in each tube half as much of the diluted blood. Rotate to mix, slant, incubate, and inoculate next day if sterile. Maintain at 18°–20° C and examine after 5 days. If pure cultures are obtained, they should be stored, after sealing with paraffin, at 10°–15° C, when they may last without transfer for months or even a year.

Herpetomonas muscarum, according to the same author (Drbohlav, 1926), did best on a similar medium but made up with a glycerine agar base adjusted to a pH of 6·2. Glycerine agar is ordinarily agar containing 0·5–1·0 per cent glycerine.

THE EXAMINATION OF LIVING PROTOZOA

The great majority of Protozoa are most profitably examined while they are alive; many, however carefully they are fixed and stained, become unrecognizable when they die. In the first instance, therefore, they should always, if possible, be studied, not only while living, but in conditions as natural as possible. For example, the characteristic rotation of *Paramecium* in a long thin spiral as it swims in a Petri dish is easily seen through the low powers of a dissecting microscope, but only with difficulty, if at all, in more restricted mounts under higher powers. The natural motion of *Euglena* as it swims in a drop of water is inhibited beneath a cover slip. If a cover slip must be used, it should be supported at the corners by fragments of another, except for very small organisms. Examination must be patient and deliberately slow. Improvement comes as the observer 'gets his eye in' and he must wait for the moment of perception. The first step towards success is persistence; it is not to change to a higher power or to fix and stain the organism. It is impossible to over-emphasize the importance of these rather platitudinous observations. The great Eugene Penard compiled most of his contributions to protozoology from studies on living organisms; his few staining methods were very simple, and during the whole of his life, which lasted for ninety-nine years, he never possessed an oil-immersion lens. We do not have to accept such limitations, but we do have to accept the fact that without cultivated powers of observation the best optical apparatus and the most proficient cytological technique will be largely wasted.

SEALING

Sealing water preparations to prevent drying or evaporation is easiest with a quick drying liquid, such as nail varnish, painted around the end of the cover slip. It kills animals which swim into it. Vaseline is better: melt the Vaseline, dip a warm needle into it and apply around the join of the slip with the slide.

SLOWING ORGANISMS FOR BETTER OBSERVATION

Sealing is sometimes enough; after a time the animals move more and more slowly. Methyl cellulose (commercially called methocel) is used, in 2 per cent aqueous solutions, to impede movement. It dissolves very slowly over about 24 hours with occasional stirring. To use, sketch a circle of methocel on the slide, fill it with water containing organisms, cover the whole with a slip.

Lund (1935) narcotized *Oxytricha* by a means adapted by a number of workers for *Euplotes* and probably applicable to other organisms. Place a thin cover slip on a dissecting microscope stage and mark with a Vaseline ring (see SEALING) about 3 mm in diameter. Add a few specimens of *Oxytricha* and remove excess fluid. Add one or two crystals of sodium amytal to the liquid. Lower a slide on to the Vaseline. The crystals dissolve slowly and it will take 20 to 120 minutes, according to the amount used, before the ciliates slow down; they maintain reduced but normal activity for about 10 minutes before they die. In the modified versions, a saturated solution of sodium amytal is used instead of crystals, and when, after some 20 to 30 minutes, the ciliates are narcotized, they are transferred to fresh medium and sealed, where they remain active for about an hour at greatly reduced rates (Pierson, 1943).

Buck (1943) reported a method which quietened *Paramecium* while enhancing observation of its feeding and cyclosis with an indicator and particles. Mix 3 gm compressed yeast, 30 mg Congo Red with 10 ml Aq.D. and boil gently for 10 minutes. Dip a needle in the stained yeast and use this for stirring a drop of a rich culture of *Paramecium* on the slide. The drop should turn pink, not red. Cover and seal. The animals feed and move rapidly at first but quieten after 10 minutes in aggregates about air bubbles or yeast clumps. When feeding, formation of food vacuoles and cyclosis may be observed. Bright orange vacuoles have a pH of 5+ and brilliant blue ones of 3−, with intermediate shades of purple.

Pantin (1946) gives tobacco smoke as a narcotic for ciliates (*Paramecium*) and flagellates. Fill a short tube with smoke and invert over it a drop containing the specimens on a slide for 15 to 60 seconds.

Vital and supravital staining

The stain is applied without previous fixation and the distinction is that vital staining does not kill but supravital staining eventually does kill the organism. The following dyes are among those most used.

BRILLIANT CRESYL BLUE

This is a basic dye staining many structures, including the skeletal apparatus of astomate ciliates. The stock solution is 1 per cent in absolute

alcohol. Dilute 10 times for use, place a drop on the slide, allow the alcohol
to evaporate, seal the organisms in a drop of water above the residue and
leave for 5 to 30 minutes.

CHINA BLUE, OPAL BLUE, NIGROSIN FOR RELIEF STAINING

Some structures are stained while the animals are alive and others after
they die by drying. A saturated solution of China Blue may be used alone,
but Bresslau (1921) preferred a mixture of Opal Blue and Phloxinrhodamin.
Add 4–6 drops of 6·5 per cent aq. solution of the latter to 1 ml of a 10 per
cent aq. solution of Opal Blue and use as follows on ciliates. Place a very
small drop containing ciliates on a slide, add an equal drop of the mixed
stain and spread lightly. The ciliates at first swim in the stain which enters
through the cytostome and colours the food and sometimes the contractile
vacuoles. On drying, the pellicular pattern, kinetosome, and cilia are blue,
the cytoplasm and sometimes the nuclei are pink. Delicate species must be
dried rapidly by waving in air. King (1928, 1935) and others have used 10
per cent solutions of China Blue, Nigrosin, or Opal Blue or a mixture of
equal parts of the first two. Add a drop of stain to a drop of culture (e.g. of
Paramecium, which reacts well) and allow to dry in air. The pellicular
pattern, somatic and buccal cilia, and contractile vacuole pores are stained.
Or make hanging drops and seal; *Paramecium trichium* survived over
2 hours in the stain. Permanent mounts of dried preparations are made by
sealing in balsam.

JANUS GREEN B

Janus Green B stains mitochondria. Use in dilutions of 1 : 10,000 or
greater; the strength varies with the organisms and some display stained
inclusions at dilution of 1 : 200,000. Or use like BRILLIANT CRESYL BLUE
(above).

NEUTRAL RED

Used usually at 1 : 10,000, or like BRILLIANT CRESYL BLUE, Neutral Red
stains, especially, vacuoles. It is an indicator and food vacuoles are first red,
then orange, and finally yellow as they pass from acid to alkaline reactions.

Rapid fixation and staining

Rapid fixation and staining may be combined to show nuclei or ectoplasmic structures, usually in temporary preparations.

ACETO–CARMINE

This is a saturated solution of carmine dissolved by boiling in 45 per cent
acetic acid, used especially for rapid demonstration of chromosomes. To

make an intense stain boil the carmine in the acid for 6 hours under a reflux condenser. Use like Methyl Green.

LUGOL'S IODINE SOLUTION is

Potassium iodine	6 gm
Iodine	4 ,,
Aq.D.	100 ml

Add a drop to a culture. It stains glycogen and other substances and shows up nuclei and is especially used for rapid determination of the cysts of entozoic amoebae. (It is also used for washing out fixatives containing mercuric chloride.)

METHYL GREEN

This is 1 per cent methyl green in 0·5–1·0 per cent glacial acetic acid. Mount specimens in it; they are killed and their nuclei displayed immediately.

NOLAND'S METHOD

Noland's method for cilia, flagella, and especially cirri of Hypotrichida uses a combined fixative and stain giving immediate results.

NOLAND'S SOLUTION is

Phenol, sat. aq. soln.	80 ml
Formalin, 40% formaldehyde	20 ,,
Glycerine	4 ,,
Gentian Violet	20 mg

Moisten the Gentian Violet with a little water to aid solution. Add the other ingredients. The phenol must not be present in excess. Mix a drop of culture with one of the solution. Flagella, cilia, membranellae, cirri, UM (of ciliates) all stain (Noland, 1928).

For Hypotrichida, Turner (1954) recommends the following modification. Mix approximately 2 parts glycerine and 1 part Lugol's Iodine Solution: the mixture should be amber. Put a single specimen in a depression slide in a tiny drop of medium. Flood with Noland's Solution. This fixes the organism at once but does not at first immerse it as it is contained in a droplet of medium. Watch, and as the dye reaches the specimen drop on it, from a height, a large drop of iodized glycerine; remove the specimen to fresh iodized glycerine. The preparation will last for 24 hours. Cirri and membranellae are jet black against a clear background.

THE EXAMINATION OF ENTOZOIC PROTOZOA

Dissect the host dry. Organs for examination must be kept moist but should not be submerged. On removal, wet them with an appropriate diluting fluid (see below). It may be necessary to withdraw the viscera of small invertebrates like insects under an invertebrate physiological solution; they may then be blotted nearly dry. All parasites of homoiothermic hosts are eventually distorted by cooling, but most preserve their shape and even movement for a time if kept warm. For example, to see the flagellates of the mouse's caecum, remove the organ by dry dissection, put it in a Petri dish, previously warmed, with a little warm Ringer's Solution, and leave the whole on a tripod very near to but not above a Bunsen flame: by 'warm' is meant 25°–30° C. Warm a slide over a flame, mix a little of the caecal contents with a small drop of warm Ringer's Solution, cover with a warm slip, and seal. The flagellates will remain active for at least an hour and may be stimulated occasionally by warming gently near, but not over, a flame. Rough and ready methods of this sort are not suitable for all parasites. Trypanosomes are fairly quickly exhausted as they cool and though they pass through a temperature range which slows but does not distort them they do not long remain in it on their way to irreversible abnormality. Some species of *Entamoeba* react more sensitively than others to cooling. For difficult species, an electrically warmed microscope stage is needed.

Diluting fluids

The contents of the gut (or other organs) may be too thick or too viscous to allow clear observation of parasites and they must then be diluted. Dilution is used only when the living parasites are to be observed; in preparing smears for fixation, dilution is very rarely necessary and nearly always detrimental. The diluting fluids commonly recommended are as follows.

RINGER'S SOLUTION (and see p. 418)

	Mammalian		*Frog*	
NaCl	0·9	gm	0·65	gm
KCl	0·042	,,	0·014	,,
CaCl$_2$	0·024	,,	0·012	,,
NaHCO$_3$	0·01–0·03	,,	0·02	,,
NaH$_2$PO$_4$	—		0·001	,,
Aq.D	100 ml		100	ml

These solutions, developed to maintain activity in the perfused heart, tend to be used because they exist; almost always, the simpler normal saline solutions may be substituted for examining parasites.

NORMAL SALINE SOLUTIONS

These are 0·9 per cent NaCl for mammals and 0·65 per cent for frogs, and the latter serves for invertebrates.

INVERTEBRATE PHYSIOLOGICAL SOLUTION

Professor L. A. Harvey informs the writer that where sea water is available a quick way of compiling an excellent physiological solution for terrestrial or freshwater invertebrates is to mix 2 parts of sea water with 9 parts of distilled water (equivalent to 0·64–0·62 per cent saline solution). Or use frog saline. For parasites of marine invertebrates, dilute with sea water itself.

Cleaning intestinal ciliates

The amount of debris accompanying gut parasites sometimes makes them difficult to examine as well as unsuitable for making permanent preparations. Sandon (1941) gives the following method for cleaning the rectal ciliates of Amphibia. Three hand centrifuge tubes are fitted into each other as in Fig. 178 after the ends of the two inner ones have been cut off and replaced by membranes of bolting silk; use moderately wide mesh for the top and finer mesh for the lower tube. Pour in Frog Ringer's Solution till the bottom of the inner tube is covered. Wash out the rectal contents with Ringer's Solution and pipette them gently into the inner tube. Within an hour the ciliates collect in a whitish mass at the base of the outer tube, but the mesh stops the passage of dirt: they may then be embedded and sectioned.

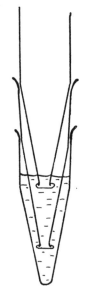

FIG. 178. Sandon's apparatus for washing rectal ciliates. The top 2 centrifuge tubes have their ends sawn off and replaced with bolting silk which retains dirt but allows the ciliates to collect in the bottom of the lowest tube. (After Sandon.)

Oocysts of Coccidia

These may be sporulated by the method given on p. 204 for *Eimeria tenella*. They will develop at room temperatures, but only if supplied with oxygen. Therefore bubble air gently through the stock, or spread the oocysts in a shallow layer of liquid in Petri dishes and prevent evaporation. The times for sporulation vary with the species. A method for excystation is given on p. 206.

Oocysts are notoriously difficult to stain. Mount a concentration beneath a cover slip. Place a few drops of glacial acetic acid next to the slip and draw it in by sucking liquid from the opposite side of the slip with filter-paper. Warm gently over a lamp bulb for 5 to 10 minutes. Do not let the acid evaporate. By a similar method of irrigation, draw under the slip freshly prepared Janus Green (1 : 1000). Leave for 10 minutes. Irrigate again, first with distilled water, then with concentrated aqueous Eosin solution. Leave for 5 minutes. Irrigate again with distilled water and seal. The jelly-like substance in the oocysts stains red; the sporozoites are unstained or tinged very light blue. It is said that if fresh, non-sporulated oocysts are used and no heat used at the acetic acid stage, development will occur (Crouch and Becker, 1931).

PERMANENT PREPARATIONS

Protozoa are too small to handle directly. They may be fixed in bulk, and sometimes they are stained in bulk, but the practice is uncertain. More

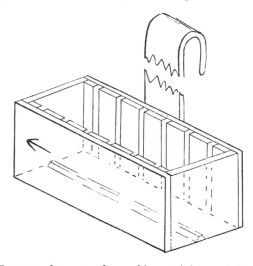

FIG. 179. Apparatus for washing, staining, and dehydrating cover-slip preparations. The box should be small enough to go comfortably into a staining jar, the handle long enough to immerse the box in a beaker for washing. There are 4 sides, 2 slotted, and no bottom but a bar to keep the slips in position. The first 6 slips are inserted all facing the arrow and any after that back to back.

usually they are attached, either before or after fixation, to cover slips or slides which are then manipulated through the reagents as if they held sections. This has the advantage that direct control of differentiation under the microscope is possible for each preparation. No. 0 slips should always be used and they break easily. To save time and minimize damage the slips should be handled singly no more than necessary. The writer collects the slips, after fixation, in a small container (Fig. 179), slotted for their reception and without a bottom to allow easy drainage, and passes the whole collection from one reagent to another. Slips are extracted for separate differentiation and again for mounting.

Adhesion methods

NATURAL METHODS

When the Protozoa themselves adhere naturally to the glass surfaces (e.g. many rhizopods) or occur in a naturally sticky substance (many entozoic species, except in blood), the ordinary method is to make a smear on a slip before fixation, e.g. of the contents of the seminal vesicles of an oligochaete to show monocystid gregarines. Smears should be thin and as even as possible, undiluted with saline or other solutions, and as soon as they are made they are dropped face downwards on to the fixative. They must never be allowed to dry either before or after fixing, except where drying is an intentional part of the technique.

Wherever possible the organisms should be fixed in expanded and natural attitudes. They must be allowed time to recover from the shock of transference to the slip before killing, and during this interval protected against evaporation. For example, withdraw a drop of sludge from a culture of *limax* amoebae or *Entamoeba* sp., mount on a No. 0 cover slip and spread very gently. Invert the slip over a polythene ring standing on a slide. The amoebae will at first be rounded up and mostly concentrated among patches of bacteria and other debris. The ring, slide, and slip form a moist chamber which can be left on the microscope stage while the amoebae recover, emerge from their concealment, and begin to wander about the glass. When they are fully expanded and well distributed (usually in 5 to 10 minutes), drop the slip face downwards on the fixative. Preparations made with this kind of preliminary care are not only far more informative but much easier to stain and differentiate, as the cytoplasm is stretched and thin.

Protozoa from homoiothermic hosts may be much more difficult to handle if they react quickly (like some entozoic amoebae) to cooling. Dobell (1942), whose paper gives full directions, inserted sterile cover slips, cut in two obliquely to distinguish the two ends, into Boeck tubes (Fig. 178). The slip is placed narrow end towards the bottom of the tube and lying flat on the solid slant, and the tubes are incubated, after inoculation, in a position so that the cover slips are almost horizontal. The amoebae populate their upper surfaces, especially towards the deeper, narrower end of the slip, which can be withdrawn as required by a sterile wire. Withdraw and fix immediately.

A great many Protozoa, especially flagellates and ciliates, live in water or other thin media and have no natural means of adhesion. Treat by one of the following methods.

IRRIGATION

The living organisms are mounted beneath a cover slip. A drop of fixative is placed at one side of the slip and liquid withdrawn from the other side with filter-paper so as to draw in the fixative. The process is repeated for every change of reagent required. If the organisms have been growing in an artificial medium, this must be replaced by water before fixation. The organisms are always disturbed before fixation, losses are heavy, and the method is extremely tedious, but it is effective with large Protozoa provided not too much is asked of the final preparation.

ALBUMEN

A circular patch of Albumen Glycerine Adhesive is rubbed on to the middle of a slide. The organisms are fixed in bulk, centrifuged, and transferred to 70 per cent alcohol and concentrated, again by centrifugation (see next technique). A small drop of the concentrate is allowed to fall from a pipette on to the albumen, which coagulates and attaches the organisms to the slide. Smyth (1945a) dropped his flagellates from a height of about 2 cm on to the slide and found that the slight force of the impact helped attachment.

To make the adhesive, drop the white only of an egg into a measuring tube. Add an equal quantity of glycerine. Whisk. Filter: this takes days. Add a crystal of thymol to stop bacterial and fungal growths.

CELLOIDIN

The writer has used the following method, which is simpler in the doing than the telling, for many years, and found it consistently reliable with a great variety of organisms. The additional steps in centrifugation are only a few more than in the last technique and the loss of material is usually nil.

Prepare a thin solution of celloidin in equal parts of absolute alcohol and ether. 1–2 per cent will serve; it should run easily over a slide without congealing in ridges, but may be rather thicker than the solution commonly used to attach sections to slides. Celloidin solutions quickly change strength by evaporation, and they are best thickened by filtering (when the solvent evaporates) and thinned by adding solvent as required. It is better to judge viscosity by practical use than to attempt to keep correctly measured solutions.

Have ready a staining set in which the 96 per cent and absolute alcohols contain 1 part of chloroform to 3 or 4 of alcohol.

1. Concentrate the organisms in the bottom of a tube by gentle centrifugation, draw off nearly all the fluid, and squirt in the fixative. Mix by pipetting. (If the organisms were cultivated in artificial medium it must first be replaced by water.) Allow to stand until fixed (for times, see below under Fixation).

2. Concentrate by allowing to settle by weight or by centrifuging again, always gently. Pipette off the fixative and wash in water or alcohol (according

to fixative employed). Washing is very slow after fixation in fluids containing bichromates (e.g. the cytological fixatives) and may be hastened by using warm water in several changes.

3. Dehydrate by concentrating in successive alcohols, mixing and centrifuging at each stage to ensure that the Protozoa are well soaked in their passage through the fluids.

4. Replace absolute alcohol by a mixture of absolute alcohol and ether in equal parts.

5. Concentrate, withdraw all but about 1–2 ml of the absolute alcohol/ether lying above the specimens, which must not be disturbed. Carefully deposit in the bottom of the tube a drop of celloidin.

6. With a very fine pipette gently and slightly disturb the Protozoa and at the same time take up a tiny drop into the pipette. Avoid any sudden or strong movement which will mix too much solvent into the celloidin at the base of the tube or disperse the Protozoa far from it. Place the drop on the centre of a clean slide. It should at once spread into an even circle about 1 cm in diameter. Wave in the air for a moment till the celloidin is tacky but not dry, dip rapidly into absolute alcohol/chloroform, then 96 per cent alcohol/chloroform, and store the slides in 70 per cent alcohol. The chloroform is to prevent solution of the celloidin film in high grade alcohols.

7. Stain and differentiate in the usual way. In dehydrating again use the high alcohols with chloroform, clear in xylol, and mount in Canada Balsam or other suitable cement.

Fixation

No subsequent treatment can repair defects in fixation. For success, the organisms must be healthy to begin with, fixation must be rapid and the fixative suitable to its purpose. Cover slips and slides must be clean,* and especially free of grease and fluff; wash them in acid alcohol and polish with a clean, dry silk rag or face tissue. The histological fixatives (Bouin or Zenker) or Schaudinn's Fluid with acetic acid give good results for general purposes, but they dissolve some structures (mitochondria, parabasal body) and distort others (axostyle, costa) and they cannot be compared for lucidity and naturalness with the cytological fixatives such as Champy and Flemming. The small size and fragile nature, as well as the complexity, of many Protozoa make them ideal objects for preparation by cytological methods, which preserve details of fine structure lost or imperfectly represented after coarser treatment. However they are fixed, Protozoa are generally improved if, after fixation (and washing, if necessary), they are hardened for several days in 70 or 96 per cent alcohol before they are stained.

* A cleaning fluid is given on p. 442, footnote.

BOUIN'S FLUID (B)

Picric acid, sat. aq. soln.	75 ml
Formalin (40% formaldehyde)	25 ,,
Glacial acetic acid	5 ,,

Fix smears for 15 to 60 minutes (or longer), transfer direct to 70 per cent alcohol. The colour of picric acid must be removed by changing the alcohol, or, for obstinate material, by immersing in a saturated solution of lithium carbonate in 70 per cent alcohol until the smear is white, and then washing again in plain alcohol. Fix tissues containing Protozoa in at least 10 times the volume of fixative for 12 hours or longer; material may be stored in Bouin indefinitely. Transfer direct to 70 per cent alcohol. Wash out the colour after sectioning, when it is easier.

DUBOSCQ-BRASIL'S FLUID (sometimes called Alcoholic Bouin)

Picric acid	1 gm
Formalin	60 ml
80% alcohol	150 ,,
Acetic acid	15 ,,

It is excellent for infected tissues fixed for sectioning.

SCHAUDINN'S FLUID

Two parts sat. aq. soln. mercuric chloride with one part 96 per cent alcohol. It is nearly always used with acetic acid (S+A): to 95 ml of the foregoing mixture add before use 5 ml glacial acetic acid. Fix smears for 15 to 60 minutes. Transfer direct to 70 per cent alcohol (not water); as a precaution this may be coloured lightly with a few drops of Lugol's Iodine Solution to remove any mercuric chloride crystals that may have formed. S+A is widely used, good for nuclei, and excellent before Feulgen.

ZENKER'S FLUID

Mercuric chloride	5	gm
Potassium bichromate	2·5	,,
Sodium sulphate	1	,,
Aq.D.	100	ml

The above is a stock solution. If, before use, there is added 5 ml glacial acetic acid, the mixture is Zenker's Fluid; if, instead, 5 ml formalin is added it is Helly's Fluid, which is a cytological fixative. The two combined (100 ml stock + 5 ml glac. acet. acid + 5 ml formalin) make an excellent tissue fixative (ZFA), sometimes used for smears, more often for infected tissue. Fix tissue for 24 hours and wash in running tap-water overnight to remove the bichromate, transfer to iodized alcohol (see under SCHAUDINN) till the liquid is colourless, repeat until one lot of liquid remains brown; this is to remove the mercuric chloride. Dehydrate slowly to remove the iodine as well as water. Smears are washed for an hour in running water and treated with iodized alcohol in the same way.

The above are histological fixatives and good for general purposes. The following cytological fixatives preserve far more detail in the cytoplasm.

CHAMPY'S FLUID

Chromic acid (1% aq.)	7 ml
Potassium bichromate (3% aq.)	7 ,,
Osmium tetroxide (2% aq.)	4 ,,

Fix for at least an hour, longer if possible. Wash out in running tap water overnight.

FLEMMING'S FLUID

Chromic acid (1% aq.)	15 ml
Osmium tetroxide (2% aq.)	4 ,,
Glacial acetic acid	1 ,,

It is often well to reduce the acetic acid to a few drops. Treat as for Champy.

OSMIUM TETROXIDE

The vapour from a 2 per cent aq. soln. may be used as a precise and delicate fixative. Twist a length of glass rod in a flame to a rough shape to fit a Petri dish and support cover slips away from the floor. Put in 1 drop of osmium tetroxide solution (osmic acid), invert the smears on the rod, put the lid on and leave for 1–2 minutes. The slips must not dry. The method is very good for cytoplasm, bad for nuclei, and is sometimes used for preliminary fixation to preserve shape before final fixation in S+A.

Staining

The choice of stain must be related to that of fixative. It is useless, for example, to apply careful methods for staining cytological details after a fixative that has destroyed them. For general purposes the best results are obtained by cytological fixation followed by prolonged staining in HEIDENHAIN'S IRON HAEMATOXYLIN. Second to this come the many varieties of haematoxylin which stain nuclei and also give a faint coloration to the cytoplasm; they may be used alone or with light cytoplasmic counterstaining in Orange G, Chromotrope 2R, or Eosin. Thirdly is a group of methods for DNA specifically, including the contents of difficult nuclei. And finally there are special methods, such as those for blood parasites, silver impregnation of ciliates, and so on.

HAEMATOXYLIN

It is used either as a general stain for nuclei and cytoplasm together, or as a nuclear stain combined with a cytoplasmic counterstain. It always requires a mordant, which is either applied separately (Heidenhain's Haematoxylin) or mixed with the dye so that the same solution mordants and stains simultaneously (Delafield's Haematoxylin). As is well known, haematoxylin itself is not a good dye, but in solution it oxidizes to haematein (i.e. it ripens), which is a powerful nuclear stain and in some solutions very precise for cytoplasmic detail. In all cases, therefore, ripened solutions must be used, as directed. For most purposes a 10 per cent solution of haematoxylin in absolute alcohol is ripened in cotton-stoppered flasks for three or four months, kept as stock, and diluted as required.

HEIDENHAIN'S IRON HAEMATOXYLIN (H.H.)

This is the classical stain of protozoologists and still the most widely useful. It is made by diluting the stock to form a 0·5 per cent aqueous solution and is used after mordanting in 4 per cent iron alum. The preparation is differentiated in the mordant after overstaining. The usual advice is to mordant in 4 per cent and differentiate in 2 per cent iron alum; the writer has not yet discovered any Protozoa in which differentiation cannot be controlled with ease in the same solution as the mordant. There are two techniques.

A. H.H. as nuclear and cytoplasmic stain, especially after cytological fixation (e.g. CHAMPY, FLEMMING).

1. Bring cover-slip smears or sections to water.
2. Immerse in mordant all day.
3. Rinse in tap water. Stain in 0·5 per cent haematoxylin all night. The subject will probably be opaque black.
4. Rinse in tap water.
5. Differentiate as follows. Have on the bench a beaker full of tap water. Immerse the slide in the mordant solution and examine. If the stain begins to come out quickly, rinse in tap water and re-examine; this stops the differentiation and allows one to work at leisure. Repeat, alternating between mordant and tap water, always examining in the latter, until the nuclei are plain and the cytoplasmic detail is clear. More commonly, the stain comes out very slowly and the material must be left in the mordant for 5 to 15 minutes running before any effect is noted; once differentiation

becomes visible it is apt to proceed more swiftly and tap water must be used frequently for examination.

6. Wash for at least an hour, or as long as overnight, in running tap water.

7. Dehydrate, clear, and mount at leisure.

The method gives the finest results with complex Protozoa such as the higher flagellates and ciliates. All the structures of *Trichomonas* (except the pelta) are revealed; cf. Fig. 75. In favourable material well-fixed ciliates show the ciliature, infraciliature, pellicular pattern, and nuclei in the same smear.

B. H.H. as a nuclear stain, with or without a counterstain; usually after B, or S+A.

1. Bring to water.
2. Mordant for 30 to 60 minutes (or 10 minutes in the 37° C oven).
3. Rinse in water.
4. Stain for the same time as in the mordant.
5. Rinse and differentiate, either in the mordant or in acid alcohol. Remove all the stain from the cytoplasm if it is intended to counterstain; alternatively leave a little colour in the cytoplasm for background.
6. Wash for 15 to 30 minutes in running tap water. ·
7. Counterstain if desired (see below, p. 436).
8. Dehydrate, clear, and mount.

The following haematoxylin variants may all be used in the same way as the second H.H. method given above, i.e. as primarily nuclear stains. They do not reveal much cytological detail and are best after B or S+A or similar fixation.

DOBELL'S TUNGSTIC HAEMATOXYLIN

Mordant in 2 per cent aq. soln. phosphotungstic acid for 10 to 30 minutes or more, wash thoroughly in distilled water, stain 0·2 per cent haematoxylin (0·5 per cent will generally serve) for 10 minutes or longer until the nuclei stand out clearly, wash for 30 minutes in tap water, dehydrate, clear, and mount. It is difficult to overstain and differentiation is usually not needed. Nuclei are purple, cytoplasm faintly stained (Dobell, 1942).

DOBELL'S MOLYBDIC HAEMATOXYLIN

Like the foregoing but the mordant is 2 per cent ammonium molybdate and the stain, which is blue, works best with freshly made haematoxylin solutions; those more than a few weeks old are generally useless (Dobell, 1942).

DELAFIELD'S HAEMATOXYLIN (D.H.)

The mordant is incorporated with the dye in one solution. Dissolve 4 gm haematoxylin in 25 ml 96 per cent alcohol and add to 400 ml sat. aq. soln. ammonia alum. Leave in a large flask or beaker for 4 days. Add 100 ml methyl alcohol and 100 ml glycerine. Filter. Ripen in a large flask plugged with cotton-wool over 3 to 4 weeks; shake occasionally. For immediate ripening, add 10 ml hydrogen peroxide.

For Protozoa it is best to dilute the stain 2 or 3 times, stain for 30 to 60 minutes, differentiate in acid alcohol, blue in running tap water. (The stain is an indicator, pink in acids, blue in alkalis, and tap water is generally alkaline enough to turn it blue.) Nuclei are dark blue, cytoplasm pale blue, or, if differentiated longer, colourless in preparation for a counterstain.

The following are more especially for nuclei and usually require counter-staining.

WEIGERT'S IRON HAEMATOXYLIN

This is a fine nuclear stain which usually does not affect cytoplasm at all deeply. It is more resistant to acids than most versions of haematoxylin and therefore especially useful before treatments which may require the use of acids after nuclear staining (e.g. Mallory's or Masson's Triple stains). It is excellent for tissues containing Protozoa. Make two solutions for stock:

Solution A	Haematoxylin	1 gm
	Absolute alcohol	100 ml
Solution B	30% aq. ferric chloride	4 ml
	Aq.D.	100 ,,
	Conc. HCl	1 ,,

Mix equal parts of the two before use and throw away at the end of the day. Stain 15 to 30 minutes, differentiate in acid alcohol, blue in tap water. Counterstain tissues in Orange G/Erythrosin or Masson's Triple Stain.

MAYER'S ACID HAEMALUM

Mayer's Acid Haemalum is useful for some sections or for whole objects with epizoic Protozoa attached to them. There are many variants of which the following has been found good.

Dissolve 50 gm potassium alum in 1,000 ml Aq.D. by heat. Add enough alcoholic solution of ripened haematoxylin to contain 1 gm. Add 20 ml glacial acetic acid. Dissolve 0·2 gm sodium iodate in Aq.D. (about 10 ml) and add this. The solution should go a dark plum colour; if it does not, heat to about 60° C. The result is

Potassium alum	50	gm
Haematoxylin (haematein)	1	,,
Glacial acetic acid	20	ml
Sodium iodate	0·2	gm
Aq.D.	1,000	ml

This is ready for use. Stain 1 hour or more, differentiate if necessary in acid alcohol, and blue thoroughly.

Counterstains for use with any of the above methods are:

CHROMOTROPE 2R

Keep a 1 per cent aq. soln. as stock. When ready to use, dehydrate cover-slip preparations to 96 per cent alcohol, place slips in a staining dish containing 96 per cent alcohol tinged pink with a few drops of stock, leave for 30 to 60 seconds, rinse in alcohol, dehydrate in absolute alcohol, clear, and mount. The stain is transparent and less clumsy than eosin, but not good for tissues.

EOSIN

Use 0·25 per cent solution in alcohol. Stain lightly for about 15 to 30 seconds. The effect is sometimes rather opaque and coarse.

ORANGE G

0·5 per cent aq. soln. for a few minutes: for smears only.

ORANGE G/ERYTHROSIN for sections

Orange G	1	gm
Erythrosin	0·25	,,
Aq.D	100	ml

Collagen, orange; muscle, brilliant red; cytoplasm, pink to red.

The following methods are for nuclei only.

THE FEULGEN NUCLEAL REACTION

When DNA is gently hydrolysed with weak acids the deoxypentose sugars which it contains release aldehydes; these are detected by Schiff's Reaction, in which the aldehyde groups combine with leuco-basic-fuchsin to turn purple. In outline, the method is to hydrolyse material with normal HCl at 60° C for a period which varies with the fixative, expose to leuco-basic-fuchsin, which stains DNA purple, and counterstain with Light Green. The technique may generally be regarded as a means of demonstrating DNA, but there are some circumstances in which error may arise, and for strictly critical work other checks are needed before the presence and distribution of DNA may be firmly established.

Have ready the following solutions:

Normal HCl (82·15 ml HCl in 1,000 ml Aq.D.) 2 baths, one at 60° C, one at room temperature.

Sulphurous acid, sat. soln.	10% anhydrous sodium bisulphite	10 ml
	Normal HCl	10 ,,
	Aq.D.	200 ,,

Leuco-basic fuchsin (Schiff's Reagent)	Boil 200 ml Aq.D. Add 1 gm basic fuchsin. Cool to 50° C and filter. Cool to 25° C and add 20 ml normal HCl and 1 gm anhydrous sodium bisulphite. Place in the dark in well-stoppered bottle for 18 to 24 hours. The solution will go pale straw colour. Add 2 gm activated charcoal, shake, and filter.

In Rafalko's modification of the technique, the leuco-basic fuchsin and the sulphurous acid solutions are prepared by slowly bubbling SO_2 from a siphon through the 0·5 per cent basic fuchsin solution and distilled water respectively. According to the author, solutions prepared in this way are more successful with difficult material. It is certainly an easy way of making them up.

1. Fix in S+A.
2. Bring to Aq.D. after washing in 70 per cent alcohol.
3. Normal HCl at room temperature, 2 min.
4. The same at 60° C, 4 min. It does not matter if the temperature varies a little to either side of 60° C, but the time for hydrolysis is important: see below.
5. Rinse in normal HCl at room temperature.
6. Rinse in Aq.D.
7. Leuco-basic fuchsin, 1–5 hours. $1\frac{1}{2}$–2 hours is long enough for most Protozoa.
8. Rinse for 1 minute each in 3 changes of sulphurous acid.
9. Wash in tap water 10–15 minutes.
10. Take up the alcohols as far as 96 per cent.
11. Counterstain 30–60 seconds in 0·25 per cent alcoholic solution of Light Green.
12. Wash in 90 per cent alcohol for a few seconds.
13. Dehydrate in absolute alcohol.
14. Clear and mount in Canada Balsam.

DNA is purple or violet; all else is pale green.
The periods for hydrolysis vary with the fixatives and are given as:

Champy	25 minutes
Flemming	16 ,,
Zenker	5 ,,

DELAMATER'S AZURE A OR THIONINE

Very small nuclei or those with little DNA may resist the Feulgen Reaction or it may be so faint that it is useless for cytological demonstrations. For these Delamater's techniques, originally developed for the DNA bodies of bacteria and fungi, may be used (Delamater, 1951). They have been successful with trypanosomids and *limax* amoebae, which are notoriously difficult subjects.

1. Fix S+A.
2. Hydrolyse as for Feulgen, after finding optimum time.
3. Rinse and stain for 2–10 hours in one of the following:

> Thionine: to 10 ml of 0·25 per cent aq. soln. thionine add, 15 minutes before use, *one* drop of thionyl chloride. Nuclei are stained intensely, cytoplasm pale violet.

> OR

> Azure A: Add *two* drops thionyl chloride to 10 ml of 0·25 per cent aq. soln. of this stain, again 15 minutes before use. Stains nuclei only.

4. After Azure A, counterstain lightly with Chromotrop 2R.
5. Dehydrate, clear and mount.

Note: Too much thionyl chloride in either stain produces a precipitate.

Huebschmann (1952) proposed the following good modification. Make up the stain as follows:

2% aq. Azure A	10	ml
Normal HCl	0·6	,,
10% Potassium metabisulphite	0·6	,,

Stain 30–60 minutes. If overstained, differentiate in 70–96 per cent alcohol. Counterstain lightly.

DELAMATER'S BASIC FUCHSIN

This is also recommended for small and difficult nuclei. The important steps are hydrolysis, as for Feulgen, and mordanting in weak formalin before staining. Without either of these preliminaries, staining with basic fuchsin is weak and diffuse; with hydrolysis but without mordanting, the nuclei stain clearly and selectively, but the stain comes out easily and it is impossible to dehydrate. With both hydrolysis and mordanting, the nuclei stain more intensely than the cytoplasm and stain is removed from the cytoplasm in the alcohols so that the nuclei remain selectively stained (Delamater, 1948).

1. Fix in S+A.
2. Hydrolysis for 5 minutes at room temperature, 5 minutes at 60° C, and 5 minutes at room temperature, in normal HCl.
3. Wash 1 to 3 times in Aq.D.
4. Mordant in 2 per cent solution of formalin for 4 minutes.
5. Wash in Aq.D.

6. Stain for 15 minutes in 0·5 per cent basic fuchsin in 0·04 normal HCl (the solution is made by adding 0·2 ml of normal HCl to 5 ml of 0·5 per cent basic fuchsin. Lower concentrations for the dye may sometimes be used with advantage).

7. Wash in Aq.D.

8. Dehydrate and simultaneously destain the cytoplasm in alcohols.

9. Clear in xylol, mount in Canada Balsam.

Triple staining for sections

To reveal the precise relations of entozoic Protozoa with their host's tissues and to show pathological pictures, MALLORY'S and MASSON'S TRIPLE STAINS are very good. The former has also been used to stain internal fibrillae in some Protozoa, e.g. archigregarines of polychaetes. Mallory was originally intended for use with Zenker-fixed material embedded in celloidin, but may be used for paraffin sections of tissues fixed in other mercuric chloride fluids. Masson is excellent after Zenker, ZFA, or Bouin.

MALLORY'S TRIPLE STAIN

1. Remove mercuric chloride crystals by soaking sections in 70 per cent alcohol turned brown with drops of LUGOL'S IODINE SOLUTION.

2. Remove iodine by washing in alcohol and bring to water.

3. Stain nuclei with WEIGERT'S HAEMATOXYLIN, which will best resist the acid in step number 6, differentiate, and blue in tap water.

4. Stain in 0·25 per cent Aq.D. fuchsin for 20 to 30 minutes. (Stronger solutions up to 1 per cent may be needed.)

5. Rinse rapidly in Aq.D. without weakening the red stain.

6. Leave in the following for 15 to 30 minutes or longer:

Aniline Blue	0·5	gm
Orange G	2·0	,,
Phosphotungstic acid	1·0	,,
Aq.D.	100	ml

The blue colour should displace the red in collagen, cartilage, and bone. If it does not, try heating gently over a flame.

7. Differentiate very rapidly as follows. Put the slide on the bench, wipe all stain from around the section, drive off the rest by squirting 96 per cent alcohol from a pipette directly on to the section, and at once.

8. Rinse in absolute alcohol, clear in xylol, and mount in Canada Balsam.

MASSON'S TRIPLE STAIN

1. Stain in WEIGERT'S HAEMATOXYLIN, differentiate, and blue. A little overstaining is good so as to resist the acids to be used later.

2. Stain in 5 per cent aq. Eosin, 5 minutes.
3. Rinse rapidly in tap water.
4. Mordant in 1 per cent phosphomolybdic acid for 2 minutes.
5. Dip in distilled water.
6. Stain for 2 minutes in one of the following solutions:

Aniline Blue Solution

Aniline Blue 2·5 gm boiled in 100 ml Aq.D.
Glacial acetic acid   1 „

Light Green Solution

Light Green   1 gm
Aq.D.   100 ml
Glacial acetic acid   1 „

7. Transfer to acetic water, which is 1 ml of glacial acetic in 100 ml Aq.D. Leave 5 to 30 minutes until excess of the blue or green stain is removed.

8. Dehydrate very rapidly. Wipe away all stain from around the section, put the slide on the bench, blot the section lightly with filter-paper, squirt absolute alcohol from a pipette on it, rinse very briefly in the absolute-alcohol jar, and then at once

9. Clear in xylol, mount in Canada Balsam. Nuclei black or dark blue; cytoplasm pink; blood red; collagen blue or green.

Stains for flagella

It is often difficult to see flagella distinctly in ordinary preparations. They may be clearly demonstrated by one of the Relief Staining Methods given under CHINA BLUE (p. 423), by BODIAN'S PROTARGOL IMPREGNATION TECHNIQUE (p. 445), or by any modifications of Loeffler's Method for bacterial flagella, of which one is given below (Couch, 1941).

COUCH'S MODIFICATION OF LOEFFLER'S STAIN

1. Mount concentrated organisms in a small drop of water.
2. Fix in osmium tetroxide fumes (p. 432) and allow to dry.
3. Heat gently in the following mordant for 30 to 60 seconds:

20% aq. tannic acid   10 parts
Ferrous sulphate, sat. aq. soln.   5 „
Basic fuchsin, sat. alc. (95%) soln.   1 „

The mordant should be filtered before use.

4. Rinse in water.
5. Stain in alkaline Gentian Violet in anilin water. This is made by shaking up 5 ml anilin oil in 95 ml water and dissolving 4 gm Gentian

Violet in it. Make alkaline with a drop or so of NaOH. Filter just before use. Warm gently in this stain for 1 to 2 minutes, wash in water, dry and mount.

The method stains flagella and shows *Flimmer*.

Couch (1941) also used the following simpler method which is good for acronematic flagella (*Peitschengeisseln*).

1. Kill with fumes of osmium tetroxide as for Loeffler.

2. Dip a needle into 0·5 per cent aq. soln. Gentian Violet and use it to stir the drop. It should go dark purple, but not too opaque to transmit light.

3. Mount and study wet as a temporary, or dry and mount as a permanent preparation.

Blood-smears

Owing to the difficulty of completing wet preparations, blood Protozoa are almost always studied in films dried on to the slide. They give informative pictures of the flagella and other cytoplasmic organellae of haemoflagellates—and, indeed, leptomonad and related parasites from the gut should first be studied by the methods for blood—but they are unreliable for nuclei, which are always seriously distorted. The essential steps (details in the schedules below) are as follows.

1. Spreading the film which may be thick or thin. Thick films are used to detect the presence of parasites in a concentration. Thin films (described below) are for indentification and cytological study; the aim here is to spread the blood so that its components are distributed over the slide in a single layer and the parasites lie clearly exposed among the erythrocytes and other elements. Films must be dried rapidly in air.

2. Fixation in alcohol. Some of the stains (Leishman's, Wright's) are dissolved in alcohol and then dye and solvent are used together first to fix and then to stain. Before water-soluble stains (Giemsa) the film is first fixed in absolute alcohol.

3. Staining by a Romanovsky method. The varieties of the Romanovsky stains (Leishman's, Wright's, Giemsa's) are formed by the partial oxidation of Methylene Blue and Eosin, and they stain erythrocytes pink, cytoplasm of parasites blue, their nuclei bright red, nuclei of leucocytes purple; flagella, kinetosomes, and kinetoplasts are red. The stains can be prepared in the laboratory but it is better to buy them in solution (or as a powder, ready mixed) from a reliable dealer.

4. The films are rinsed and dried. They need not be covered but may be used direct for oil-immersion examination; mounted in Canada Balsam, which turns acid, they fade. Not mounted, they become sticky, dirty, and scratched. It is best to mount in a neutral medium, which, like the stains, must be obtained from dealers of good reputation.

Making the film. Nearly all directions for making blood films warn the reader that there is a knack in it. This is true, but it is fair to say that the knack is commonly acquired in an afternoon. For success, the slides must be quite clean,* dipped in acid alcohol and polished with a clean, dry rag; an old silk handkerchief is useful. And they must have smooth, nicely

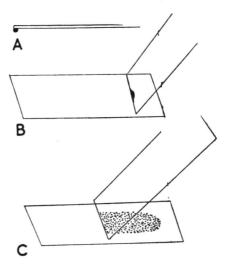

FIG. 180. Spreading a blood-smear. A drop of blood is picked up on the slide used as a spreader (A), touched down on a horizontal slide (B), and pulled out behind the spreader as the latter is slid at an angle to the horizontal (C). See text. (After Hoare.)

bevelled edges: the edge of one slide will be used to spread the blood on the surface of the other.

1. Place a slide on the bench. Pick up a drop of blood in the middle of the narrow end of another slide, which will be used as a spreader. Hold the spreader at about 45° to the horizontal slide and touching it about 2 cm from its end, so that the drop spreads along the line of contact of the two slides. Holding the spreader still at 45° to 30° push it along the length of the horizontal slide; the blood will be pulled out (not pushed) behind it into a film. What is required is a fairly swift, steady motion. If it is unsteady, the film looks wavy. And the whole process, which really is very simple, should be performed smartly.

2. As soon as it is made, dry rapidly by waving the slide in the air. Slow drying causes more distortion than is necessary. Tilt the slide face downwards against a convenient ledge.

* To clean dirty slides, leave for some days in potassium dichromate, 10 gm; sulphuric acid, 10 ml; Aq.D. 100 ml; wash in running tap-water, store in acid alcohol.

GIEMSA'S STAIN

Preparation. Add 1 drop of the solution, as purchased, to every ml of distilled water used; it is usually convenient to make up about 5 to 10 ml, i.e., 5 to 10 drops in as many ml Aq.D.

Note. Distilled water used to dilute Romanovsky stains must be neutral (pH = 7·0 to 7·2). In contact with air, Aq.D. dissolves CO_2 and becomes acid. Therefore, freshly distilled water is stored in small bottles filled to the top and firmly stoppered. If it deteriorates, boil in a hard-glass (e.g. Pyrex) flask for 15 to 30 minutes.

Method

1. Place the dried slide upright in a jar of ethyl or methyl absolute alcohol and fix for 3 minutes. Allow to dry by evaporation.

2. Place face downwards in a staining dish, or Petri dish, leaning almost flat against a rod. Run in the diluted stain. Stain for 20 to 40 minutes.

3. Rinse in tap water, shake free of moisture, lean nearly upright in a warm dry place, till dry. Mount if desired in neutral medium.

For other methods see Hoare's *Handbook of Medical Protozoology* (1949).

Silver impregnation

Silver impregnation is used extensively on ciliates and flagellates. In the former it provides very clear black and white maps of the kinetosomatic distribution. In the latter it may discover structures which otherwise cannot be demonstrated (e.g. the pelta of trichomonads) and it shows up flagella and some other organellae more reliably than stains, though not so delicately.

THE CHATTON-LWOFF TECHNIQUE FOR CILIATES

The older silver methods all required drying, and so distorted the organisms. The original version of this method, invented 30 years ago, had the great advantage that films were fixed wet and remained so throughout the process, but they were fixed in da Fano's fluid, which is not good for preserving shape. With the introduction of preliminary fixation in Champy to preserve the ordinary form of the organisms, followed by da Fano to facilitate impregnation, the last obstacles to demonstration of the infraciliature within a body presenting its natural shape were removed (Corliss, 1953). The method is indispensable to modern ciliate studies.

1. Fix preliminarily in Champy, 1 to 3 minutes. (The writer also uses OsO_4 vapour with success.)

2. Wash twice in da Fano's fixative and leave in the third change for several hours. Specimens may be stored in this for weeks.

Da Fano's Fixative is

Cobalt nitrate	1 gm
Sodium chloride	1 ,,
Formalin	10 ml
Aq.D.	90 ,,

Use sea water and omit NaCl for fixing marine organisms.

3. Concentrate the organisms by letting them settle or by centrifugation. Place 1 small drop of them on a warm slide. Add 1 drop of warm (35°–45° C) saline gelatin and mix with the tip of a warm needle. Draw off any excess fluid so as to leave the specimens grouped in a thin layer of gelatin. Do not inject bubbles into the gelatin. The whole operation should be performed briskly.

Saline gelatin is

Powdered gelatin	10	gm
Sodium chloride	0·05	,,
Aq.D.	100	ml

and it is stored in the refrigerator. Gelatin easily grows moulds. It is convenient to keep it in small, wide-mouthed, screw-topped bottles and dig out a little at a time with a warm spatula to melt in a test-tube for use.

4. Place the slide in a moist chamber (e.g. Petri dish with wet filter-paper) and put it in the refrigerator or on ice for about 2 minutes while the gelatin sets. Place in cold 3 per cent silver nitrate (5°–10° C) and keep it cold to prevent the gelatin from melting and dark to prevent premature reduction of the silver; the best place for this is the refrigerator. Keep it there for 10 to 20 minutes, depending on the organism.

5. Flush with cold distilled water and place in a white-bottomed dish (or glass vessel standing on filter-paper) containing cold distilled water to a depth of 3 to 4 cm. Expose to light. Sunlight will do, or the cheapest kind of ultraviolet health lamp. The exposure time, usually 20 to 30 minutes, is determined for the material by trial. The preparation must be kept cold to prevent melting. The writer uses an ultraviolet lamp 30 cm above the preparations, which lie in a glass dish of cold water packed at the sides with ice cubes, all standing on a large white tile.

6. Remove to 70 per cent alcohol, dehydrate, clear in xylol and mount in Canada Balsam.

Notes. (1) The technique is easy to master and gives clear, natural preparations of ciliates impregnated on all aspects. (2) A single ciliate can be fixed on the slide in a drop of Champy or in OsO_4 fumes and carried through the whole process. (3) After a little practice of step 3, it is possible to orientate organisms with a warm needle to obtain any view of them desired. (4) Preparations which are too black at the end of step 4 may be toned under the microscope by covering with a drop of 1 per cent gold chloride. Have ready a large beaker of water so that the toning may be instantly stopped at the desired stage; the gold chloride may act very rapidly.

For a defence of the 'dry' impregnation methods and their proper use, see Klein (1958).

BODIAN'S PROTARGOL (PROTEIN-SILVER) METHOD FOR PROTOZOA

The technique was originally developed for vertebrate nervous tissue but has been successfully used, especially for flagellates, in protozoology.

The preliminaries are:

1. Preparation of the stain. The specimen of protargol must be of good quality. Make a 1 per cent solution by sprinkling it on the surface of distilled water in a beaker, without heating, stirring, or otherwise disturbing, until solution is complete. The solution is freshly made before use.

2. The solution is used on the material in the presence of copper. Have ready snips of copper wire cut in lengths weighing 0·5 gm. They are eventually added to the protargol solution in the quantity of 5 gm to every 100 ml of solution.

3. Fix the Protozoa in Hollande's or Bouin's Fluid. Hollande's Fixative is:

Copper acetate, neutral	2·5 gm
Picric acid	4 ,,
Formalin	10 ml
Glacial acetic acid	1·5 ,,
Aq.D.	100 ,,

Dissolve the copper acetate in a mortar in cold water. Add picric acid little by little. This mixture keeps; add formalin and acetic acid before use.

4. Bleach, if necessary, and especially if the material has been stored for a long time in alcohol after fixation. The bleaching method is:

i. Take to water.

ii. 0·5 per cent potassium permanganate aq. soln. for 5 minutes.

iii. Wash in distilled water.

iv. 5 per cent oxalic acid for 5 minutes.

v. Wash in several changes of distilled water.

The material is now ready for treatment.

1. Place copper wire up to the amount needed in a dish, pour in the protargol solution and soak cover-slip preparations in it for 2 to 3 days. Incubate resistant material at 37° C. Change the solution on the second day. (Most slip preparations can be handled in 10 ml of solution, which requires a single 0·5 gm length of wire.)

G g

2. Wash in distilled water.

3. Reduce in 1 per cent hydroquinone in 5 per cent sodium sulphite, for 5 to 10 minutes. A weaker solution may be better.

4. Wash in several changes of distilled water.

5. Tone in 1 per cent gold chloride for 4 to 5 minutes.

6. Wash in distilled water.

7. Place in 2 per cent aq. oxalic acid till the preparation is purple, usually in about 3 minutes.

8. Wash well in distilled water.

9. 5 per cent aq. sodium thiosulphate, 5 to 10 minutes.

10. Wash in several changes of distilled water, dehydrate, clear, and mount.

Embedding for sectioning

Each of the very numerous methods described for embedding free Protozoa bespeaks dissatisfaction with the others. A general principle is to enclose the Protozoa, previously concentrated by centrifuging, in some substance such as agar, cut this to a convenient size and handle it as a piece of tissue.

Fix and wash the Protozoa and (if necessary) bring to water by centrifuging. In a block of agar cut a small cavity and deliver a concentrate of the organism into it. Remove the supernatant liquid. Seal the cavity with warm agar. Cut the block and embed in the usual way. It helps if the Protozoa are first tinted with Delafield's Haematoxylin or other easily removable dye so that they may be seen during the operations. Large Protozoa, such as *Opalina*, *Spirostomum*, may be orientated in the agar with a warm needle under the dissecting microscope. For elaborations of the method, see, for example, Hovasse in Pringsheim and Hovasse (1948) and Arnold (1952).

Rudzinska (1955) pointed out that by increasing the centrifugation after fixation preliminary embedding in agar could be avoided. Fix in the usual way and concentrate by spinning until the Protozoa form a hard pellet at the bottom of the tube; 10 minutes at 700 g is usually long enough. The pellet is removed on a scapula and is hard enough to be cut into pieces if the whole is too large. It hardens further during dehydration and clearing and may be removed from xylol with forceps and embedded in paraffin wax as if it were a piece of tissue. But observe that some Protozoa (e.g. *Paramecium*) are brittle after fixation and will not tolerate the centrifuge.

REFERENCES

SELECT LIST OF GENERAL WORKS ON PROTOZOOLOGY

CALKINS, G. N., and SUMMERS, F. M. (ed.) (1941). *Protozoa in biological research.* New York.

DOFLEIN, F., and REICHENOW, E. (1952–3). *Lehrbuch der Protozoenkunde*, 6th edn. Jena.

GRASSÉ, P.-P. (ed.) (1952–3). *Traité de zoologie*, vol. i. Paris.

GRELL, K. G. (1956). *Protozoologie.* Jena.

HALL, R. P. (1953). *Protozoology.* New York.

HOARE, C. A. (1949). *Handbook of medical protozoology.* London.

HUTNER, S. H., and LWOFF, A. *See under* LWOFF, A.

JAHN, T. L., and JAHN, F. F. (1949). *How to know the Protozoa.* Dubuque, Iowa.

JENNINGS, H. S. (1923). *Behaviour of the lower organisms.* New York.

KIRBY, H. (1950). *Material and methods in the study of Protozoa.* Berkeley and Los Angeles.

KUDO, R. R. (1954). *Protozoology*, 4th edn. Springfield, Illinois.

LWOFF, A. (1951). *Biochemistry and physiology of Protozoa*, vol. i. New York.

—— and HUTNER, S. H. (1955). Ibid., vol. ii. New York.

WENYON, C. M. (1926). *Protozoology: A manual for medical men, veterinarians and zoologists.* 2 vols. London.

LIST OF OTHER WORKS CITED IN THE TEXT

ALEXEIEFF, A. (1911*a*). Sur la morphologie et la division de *Bodo caudatus* (Duj.) Stein. *C.R. Soc. Biol., Paris*, **70**, 130.

—— (1911*b*). Notes sur les flagellés. I. Quelques flagellés intestinaux nouveaux ou peu connus. II. Quelques flagellés communs dans les infusions. *Arch. Zool. exp. gén.* **6**, 491.

—— (1912). Le Parasitisme des Eugléniens et la phylogénie des Sporozoaires *sensu stricto.* Ibid. **10** (N & R), 73.

—— (1917*a*). Sur les mitochondries à fonction glycoplastique. *C.R. Soc. Biol., Paris*, **80**, 510.

—— (1917*b*). Sur la fonction glycoplastique du kinétoplaste (= *kinetonucleus*) chez les flagellés. Ibid., p. 512.

—— (1928). Sur la question des mitochondries et de l'appareil de Golgi chez les protistes. *Arch. Protistenk.* **60**, 268.

ALLEGRE, C. F., and JAHN, T. L. (1943). A survey of the genus *Phacus* Dujardin. *Trans. Amer. micr. Soc.* **62**, 233.

ALLEN, W. E. (1946). 'Red Water' in La Jolla Bay in 1945. Ibid. **65**, 149.

AMREIN, Y. U. (1953). The mode of transmission of non-cyst-forming flagellates in the ovoviviparous yucca night lizard *Xantusia vigilis*. *Ecology*, **34**, 243.

—— and FULTON, J. D. (1959). Attempts to transfer drug-resistance of trypanosomes *in vivo*. *J. Protozool.* **6**, 120.

ANDERSON, E. (1955). The electron microscopy of *Trichomonas muris*. Ibid. **2**, 114.

—— and BEAMS, H. W. (1959). The cytology of *Tritrichomonas* as revealed by the electron microscope. *J. Morph.* **104**, 205.

448 REFERENCES

ANDERSON, E., SAXE, L. H., and BEAMS, H. W. (1956). Electron microscope observations of *Trypanosoma equiperdum*. *J. Parasit.* **42**, 11.

ANDRESEN, N. (1956). Cytological investigations on the giant amoeba *Chaos chaos* L. *C.R. Lab. Carlsberg*, Sér. chim. **29**, 435.

ANDREW, B. J. (1930). Method and rate of protozoan refaunation in the termite *Termopsis angusticollis* Hagen. *Univ. Calif. Publ. Zoöl.* **33**, 449.

ANDREWS, J. M. (1925). Morphology and mitosis in *Trichomonas termopsidis*, an intestinal flagellate of the termite, *Termopsis*. *Biol. Bull.* **49**, 69.

ANIGSTEIN, L. (1912). Über zwei neue marine Ciliaten. *Arch. Protistenk.* **24**, 127.

ARNOLD, Z. M. (1952). A rapid method for concentrating small organisms for sectioning. *Stain Technol.* **27**, 199.

—— (1955). Life history and cytology of the foraminiferan *Allogromia latticollaris*. *Univ. Calif. Publ. Zool.* **61**, 167.

BAKER, C. L. (1933). Studies on the cytoplasmic components of *Euglena gracilis* Klebs. *Arch. Protistenk.* **80**, 434.

BAKER, J. R. (1948). The status of the Protozoa. *Nature, Lond.* **161**, 548.

BAKER, W. B. (1926). Studies in the life-history of *Euglena*. I. *Euglena agilis* Carter. *Biol. Bull.* **51**, 321.

BALAMUTH, W. (1940). Regeneration in Protozoa: a problem in morphogenesis. *Quart. Rev. Biol.* **15**, 290.

—— and SANDZA, J. G. (1944). Simple, standardized culture medium for physiological studies on *Entamoeba histolytica*. *Proc. Soc. exp. Biol. Med.* **57**, 161.

BALCH, H. E. (1932). The cultivation of *Nyctotherus ovalis* and *Endamoeba blattae*. *Science*, **76**, 237.

BARKER, D. C., and DEUTSCH, K. (1958). The chromatoid body of *Entamoeba invadens*. *Exp. Cell Res.* **15**, 604.

BARKER, H. A. (1935). The culture and physiology of the marine dinoflagellates. *Arch. Mikrobiol.* **6**, 157.

—— and TAYLOR, C. V. (1931). A study of the conditions of encystment of *Colpoda cucullus*. *Physiol. Zoöl.* **4**, 620.

BARRET, H. P., and SMITH, N. M. (1926). The cultivation of *Endamoeba ranarum*. *Ann. trop. Med. Parasit.* **20**, 65.

BARRETT, J. M. (1958). Some observations on *Actinosphaerium nucleofilum* n. sp., a new fresh water Actinophryd. *J. Protozool.* **5**, 205.

BEALE, G. H. (1954). *The genetics of Paramecium aurelia*. Cambridge.

BEAMS, H. W., TAHMISIAN, T. N., DEVINE, R. L., and ANDERSON, E. (1959). Studies on the fine structure of a gregarine parasitic in the gut of the grasshopper, *Melanoplus differentialis*. *J. Protozool.* **6**, 136.

BEAUCHAMP, P. DE (1910). *Astasia captiva* n. sp., Euglénien parasite de *Catenula lemnae* Ant. Dug. *Arch. Zool. exp. gén.* **6** (N & R), 52.

BECKER, E. R. (1923a). Observations on the morphology and life-history of *Herpetomonas muscae-domesticae* in North American muscoid flies. *J. Parasit.* **9**, 199.

—— (1923b). Transmission experiments on the specificity of *Herpetomonas muscae-domesticae* in muscoid flies. Ibid. **10**, 25.

—— (1934). Coccidia and coccidiosis of domesticated, game and laboratory animals and of man. *Monogr. no. 2, Div. Industrial Sci., Iowa State College.* Iowa.

—— and HSIUNG, T. S. (1929). The method by which ruminants acquire their fauna of infusoria, and remarks concerning experiments on the host-specificity of these Protozoa. *Proc. nat. Acad. Sci., Wash.* **15**, 684.

BĚLAŘ, K. (1921a). Untersuchungen über Thecamöben der *Chlamydophrys*-Gruppe. *Arch. Protistenk.* **43**, 287.

—— (1921b). Protozoenstudien. III. Ibid. **43**, 431.

—— (1923). Untersuchungen an *Actinophrys sol* Ehrenberg. I. Die Morphologie des Formwechsels. Ibid. **46**, 1.

—— (1926a). *Der Formwechsel der Protistenkerne.* Jena, and also in *Ergebn. Zool.* **6**.

—— (1926b). Zur Cytologie von *Aggregata eberthi*. *Arch. Protistenk.* **53**, 312.

BENNETT, H. S. (1956). The concept of membrane flow and membrane vesiculation as mechanisms for active transport and ion pumping. *J. biophys. biochem. Cytol.* **2** (Suppl.), 99.

BERLIN, H. (1924). Untersuchungen über Monocystideen in den Vesiculae seminales der schwedischen Oligochaeten. *Arch. Protistenk.* **48**, 1.

BERNDT, A. (1902). Beitrag zur Kenntnis der im Darme der Larve von *Tenebrio molitor* lebenden Gregarinen. Ibid. **1**, 375.

BERNHEIMER, A. W. (1938). Fate of the crystals in Amebas. Ibid. **90**, 365.

BHATIA, B. L. (1924). Preliminary note on the mode of infection of earthworms by Monocystid parasites. *J. R. micr. Soc.* for 1924, p. 187.

—— (1929). On the distribution of gregarines in oligochaetes. *Parasitology*, **21**, 120.

—— and GULATI, A. N. (1927). On some parasitic ciliates from Indian frogs, toads, earthworms, and cockroaches. *Arch. Protistenk.* **57**, 85.

BIECHELER, B. (1934). Sur le réseau argentophile et la morphologie de quelques Péridiniens nus. *C.R. Soc. Biol., Paris*, **115**, 1039.

—— (1935). Existence d'une cyclose chromatique chez les Péridiniens. *C.R. Acad. Sci., Paris*, **201**, 503.

—— (1936a). Des conditions et du mécanisme de la prédation chez un dinoflagellé à enveloppe tabullée, *Peridinium gargantua*, n. sp. *C.R. Soc. Biol., Paris*, **121**, 1054.

—— (1936b). Observation de la capture et de la digestion des proies chez un Péridinien vert. Ibid. **122**, 1173.

—— (1952). Recherches sur les Péridiniens. *Bull. biol.* Suppl. **36**.

BIEGEL, M. (1954). Beitrag zur Peritrichenfauna der Umgebung Erlangens. *Arch. Protistenk.* **100**, 153.

BISHOP, A. (1923). Some observations upon *Spirostomum ambiguum* (Ehrenberg). *Quart. J. micr. Sci.* **67**, 391.

—— (1925). A study of the micronuclei of *Spirostomum ambiguum major* during division. Ibid. **69**, 661.

—— (1927). The cytoplasmic structures of *Spirostomum ambiguum* (Ehrenberg). Ibid. **71**, 147.

—— (1931). The morphology and method of division of *Trichomonas*. *Parasitology*, **23**, 129.

—— (1932). *Entamoeba aulostomi* Nöller. Cultivation, morphology, and method of division; and cultivation of *Hexamita* sp. Ibid. **24**, 225.

—— (1933). The morphology and division of *Hexamita gigas* n. sp. (Flagellata). Ibid. **25**, 163.

—— (1934). The experimental infection of Amphibia with cultures of *Trichomonas*. Ibid. **26**, 26.

—— (1935). Observations upon a '*Trichomonas*' from pond water. Ibid. **27**, 246.

—— (1936). Further observations upon a '*Trichomonas*' from pond water. Ibid. **28**, 443.

—— (1939). A note upon the systematic position of '*Trichomonas*' *keilini* (Bishop, 1935). Ibid. **31**, 469.

BLÄTTNER, H. (1926). Beiträge zur Reizphysiologie von *Spirostomum ambiguum* Ehrenberg. *Arch. Protistenk.* **53**, 253.

BLES, E. J. (1929). *Arcella.* A study in cell physiology. *Quart. J. micr. Sci.* **72**, 527.

BONNER, J. T. (1954). The development of cirri and bristles during binary fission in the ciliate *Euplotes eurystomus.* *J. Morph.* **95**, 95.

BOVEE, E. C. (1949). The use of the uroid as a taxonomic criterion for certain amoebas. *Anat. Rec.* **105** (3), 630.

—— (1953). Morphological identification of free-living Amoebida. *Trans. Iowa Acad. Sci.* **60**, 599.

BRADFIELD, J. R. G. (1955). Fibre patterns in animal flagella and cilia. *Symp. Soc. exp. Biol.* **9** (Fibrous proteins and their biological significance), 306.

BRAND, T. v. (1923). Die Encystierung bei *Vorticella microstoma* und hypotrichen Infusorien. *Arch. Protistenk.* **47**, 59.

BRANDT, P. W. (1958). A study of the mechanism of pinocytosis. *Exp. Cell Res.* **15**, 300.

BRASIL, L. (1905). Recherches sur la reproduction des grégarines monocystidées. *Arch. Zool. exp. gén.* **3**, 17.

—— (1907). Recherches sur le cycle évolutif des Selenidiidae, grégarines parasites d'annélides polychètes. I. La Schizogonie et la croissance des gamétocytes chez *Selenidium caulleryi* n. sp. *Arch. Protistenk.* **8**, 370.

—— (1909). Documents sur quelques sporozoaires d'annélides. Ibid. **16**, 107.

BRESSLAU, E. (1921). Die Galatinierbarkeit des Protoplasmas als Grundlage eines Verfahrens zur Schnellanfertigung gefärbter Dauerpräparate von Infusorien. Ibid. **43**, 467.

BROWN, H. P. (1945). On the structure and mechanics of the protozoan flagellum. *Ohio J. Sci.* **45**, 247.

BROWN, V. E. (1930a). The Golgi apparatus of *Amoeba proteus* Pallas. *Biol. Bull.* **59**, 240.

—— (1930b). Cytoplasmic inclusions of *Euglena gracilis* Klebs. *Z. Zellforsch.* **11**, 244.

BRUMPT, E. (1915). Cycle évolutif des Opalines. *Bull. Soc. Path. exot.* **8**, 397.

BUCK, J. B. (1943). Quietening *Paramecium* for class study. *Science,* **97**, 494.

BULLINGTON, W. E. (1925). A study of spiral movement in the ciliate Infusoria. *Arch. Protistenk.* **50**, 219.

—— (1930). A further study of spiraling in the ciliate *Paramecium*, with a note on morphology and taxonomy. *J. exp. Zool.* **56**, 423.

BURNSIDE, L. H. (1929). Relation of body size to nuclear size in *Stentor coeruleus.* Ibid. **54**, 473.

BURT, R. L. (1940). Specific analysis of the genus *Colpoda* with special reference to the standardization of experimental material. *Trans. Amer. micr. Soc.* **59**, 414.

——, KIDDER, G. W., and CLAFF, C. L. (1941). Nuclear reorganisation in the family Colpodidae. *J. Morph.* **69**, 537.

BÜTSCHLI, O. (1881). Kleine Beiträge zur Kenntnis der Gregarinen. *Z. wiss. Zool.* **35**, 384.

CALKINS, G. N. (1913). Genera and species of Amoeba. *Trans. 15th Int. Congr. Hygiene and Demography.* Washington.

—— and CULL, S. W. (1907). The conjugation of *Paramecium aurelia (caudatum).* *Arch. Protistenk.* **10**, 375.

CAMPBELL, A. S. (1926). The cytology of *Tintinnopsis nucula* (Fol) Laackmann. *Univ. Calif. Publ. Zool.* **29**, 179.

CAMPBELL, A. S. (1942). The oceanic Tintinnoina of the plankton gathered during the last cruise of the Carnegie. *Publ. Carneg. Instn.*, no. 537, p. 163.

CARINI, A., and REICHENOW, E. (1935). Über Amöbeninfektion in Zelleriellen. *Arch. Protistenk.* **84**, 175.

CARTER, L. (1957). Ionic regulation in the ciliate *Spirostomum ambiguum*. *J. exp. Biol.* **34**, 71.

CARTER, L. A. (1915). The cyst of *Amoeba proteus*. *Proc. R. phys. Soc. Edinb.* **19**, 204.

CASH, J., and HOPKINSON, J. (1905). *The British freshwater Rhizopoda and Heliozoa*, vol. i. Ray Society, London.

—— —— (1908). Idem, vol. ii.

——, WAILES, G. H., and HOPKINSON, J. (1919). Idem, vol. iv.

—— —— —— (1921). Idem, vol. v.

CAULLERY, M., and MESNIL, F. (1899). Sur quelques parasites internes des annélides. *Trav. Stat. Zool. Wimereux*, **7**, 80.

—— —— (1901). Le Parasitisme intracellulaire et la multiplication asexuée des grégarines. *C.R. Soc. Biol.*, *Paris*, **53**, 84.

—— —— (1919). Metchnikovellidae et autres parasites des grégarines d'annélides. *Ann. Inst. Pasteur*, **33**, 209.

CAUSEY, D. (1926). Mitochondria in *Noctiluca scintillans* (Macartney, 1810). *Univ. Calif. Publ. Zool.* **28**, 225.

CAVALLINI, F. (1926). The asexual cycle of development in *Arcella vulgaris*. *J. exp. Zool.* **43**, 245.

CÉPÈDE, C. (1910). Recherches sur les infusoires astomes: anatomie, biologie, éthologie parasitaire, systématique. *Arch. Zool. exp. gén.* **3**, 341.

ČERNOSVITOV, L., and EVANS, A. C. (1947). *Synopses of the British Fauna. No. 6. Lumbricidae.* Linnean Society of London.

CHADEFAUD, M. (1937). Recherches sur l'anatomie comparée des Eugléniens. *Botaniste*, sér. **28**, 85.

CHALKLEY, H. W. (1930). Stock cultures of *Ameba*. *Science*, **71**, 442.

—— (1936). The behaviour of the karyosome and the 'peripheral chromatin' during mitosis and interkinesis in *Amoeba proteus* with particular reference to the morphologic distribution of nucleic acid as indicated by the Feulgen reaction. *J. Morph.* **60**, 13.

—— and DANIEL, G. E. (1933). The relation between the form of the living cell and the nuclear phases of division in *Amoeba proteus* (Leidy). *Physiol. Zoöl.* **6**, 592.

CHAPMAN-ANDRESEN, C., and PRESCOTT, D. M. (1956). Studies on pinocytosis in the amoebae *Chaos chaos* and *Amoeba proteus*. *C.R. trav. Lab. Carlsberg*, **30**, 57.

CHARDEZ, D. (1958). Études sur les thecamoebiens d'une petite pièce d'eau. *Hydrobiologia*, **10**, 293.

CHATTON, E. (1910). Protozoaires parasites des branches des labres: *Amoeba mucicola* Chatton, *Trichodina labrorum* n. sp. *Arch. Zool. exp. gén.* **5**, 239.

—— (1920). Les Péridiniens parasites: morphologie, reproduction, éthologie. Ibid. **59**, 1.

—— (1936). Les Migrateurs horizontalement polarisés de certains peritriches. *Mem. Mus. Hist. nat. Belg.* 2ᵐᵉ sér., **3**, 913.

—— and BRACHON, S. (1936). Le Cinétome de l'*Opalina ranarum*, sa continuité génétique et son importance eu égard à l'évolution des appareils ciliaires. *C.R. Acad. Sci.*, *Paris*, **202**, 713.

—— and HOVASSE, R. (1934). L'Existence d'un réseau ectoplasmique chez les

Polykrikos et les précisions qu'il fournit à la morphologie péridinienne. *C.R. Soc. Biol., Paris*, **115**, 1036.

CHATTON, E. and LWOFF, A. (1922). Sur l'évolution des infusoires, des lamellibranches. Relations des Hypocomides avec les Ancistridés. Le Genre *Hypocomides* n. gen. *C.R. Acad. Sci., Paris*, **175**, 787.

—— —— (1934). Sur un cilié thigmotriche nouveau: *Gargarius gargarius*, n. gen. n. sp., de *Mytilus edulis*. *Bull. Soc. zool. Fr.* **59**, 375.

—— —— (1935a). La Constitution primitive de la strie ciliaire des infusoires. La desmodexie. *C.R. Soc. Biol., Paris*, **118**, 1068.

—— —— (1935b). Les Ciliés apostomes: morphologie, cytologie, éthologie, évolution, systématique. I. Aperçu historique et général. Étude monographique des genres et des espèces. *Arch. Zool. exp. gén.* **77**, 1.

—— —— (1936). Les Remaniements et la continuité du cinétome au cours de la scission chez les thigmotriches ancistrumidés. Ibid. **78** (N & R), 84.

—— —— (1949). Recherches sur les ciliés thigmotriches. I. Ibid. **86**, 169.

—— —— (1950). Idem. II. Ibid. **86**, 393.

——, LWOFF, A., and LWOFF, M. (1929). Les Infraciliatures et la continuité génétique des systèmes ciliaires récessifs. *C.R. Acad. Sci., Paris*, **188**, 273.

—— —— —— and MONOD, J.-L. (1931a). La Formation de l'ébauche buccale postérieure chez les ciliés en division et ses relations de continuité topographique et génétique avec la bouche antérieure. *C.R. Soc. Biol., Paris*, **108**, 540.

—— —— —— —— (1931b). Sur la topographie, la structure et la continuité génétique du système ciliaire de l'infusoire *Chilodon uncinatus*. *Bull. Soc. zool. Fr.* **56**, 367.

—— and Séguéla, J. (1940). La Continuité génétique des formations ciliaires chez les ciliés hypotriches: le cinétome et l'argyrome au cours de la division. *Bull. biol.* **74**, 349.

—— and VILLENEUVE, S. (1937). La Division de la bouche et la formation du péristome chez les Péritriches (*Cyclochaeta astropectinis* n. sp.). Leur continuité génétique immédiate. *C.R. Acad. Sci., Paris*, **204**, 538.

CHEISSIN, E. (1930). Morphologische und systematische Studien über Astomata aus dem Baikalsee. *Arch. Protistenk.* **70**, 531.

CHEN, T.-T. (1936a). Observations on mitosis in Opalinids. I. The behaviour and individuality of chromosomes and their significance. *Proc. nat. Acad. Sci., Wash.* **22**, 594.

—— (1936b). Idem. II. The association of chromosomes and nucleoli. Ibid. **22**, 602.

—— (1948). Chromosomes in Opalinidae with special reference to their behavior, morphology, individuality, diploidy, haploidy, and association with nucleoli. *J. Morph.* **83**, 281.

—— and STABLER, R. M. (1936). Further studies on the Endamoebae parasitizing Opalinid ciliates. *Biol. Bull.* **70**, 72.

CHEN, Y. T. (1950). Investigations of the biology of *Peranema trichophorum*. *Quart. J. micr. Sci.* **91**, 279.

CLARK, A. M. (1946). The reactions of isolated parts of *Spirostomum*. *J. exp. Biol.* **22**, 88.

CLEVELAND, L. R. (1925a). The method by which *Trichonympha campanula*, a protozoon in the intestine of termites, ingests solid particles of wood for food. *Biol. Bull.* **48**, 282.

—— (1925b). The ability of termites to live perhaps indefinitely on a diet of pure cellulose. Ibid. **48**, 289.

CLEVELAND, L. R. (1925c). The feeding habit of termite castes and its relation to their intestinal flagellates. Ibid. **48**, 295.

—— (1925d). The effects of oxygenation and starvation on the symbiosis between the termite, *Termopsis*, and its intestinal flagellates. Ibid. **48**, 309.

—— (1928). Further observations and experiments on the symbiosis between termites and their intestinal Protozoa. Ibid. **54**, 231.

—— (1947). Sex produced in the Protozoa of *Cryptocercus* by molting. *Science*, **105**, 16.

—— (1949). Hormone-induced sexual cycles of flagellates. I. Gametogenesis, fertilization and meiosis in *Trichonympha*. *J. Morph.* **85**, 197.

—— (1950a). Idem. II. Gametogenesis, fertilization and one-division meiosis in *Oxymonas*. Ibid. **86**, 185.

—— (1950b). Idem. III. Gametogenesis, fertilization and one-division meiosis in *Saccinobaculus*. Ibid. **86**, 215.

—— (1950c). Idem. IV. Meiosis after syngamy and before nuclear fusion in *Notila*. Ibid. **87**, 317.

—— (1950d). Idem. V. Fertilization in *Eucomonympha*. Ibid. **87**, 349.

—— (1951a). Idem. VI. Gametogenesis, fertilization, meiosis, oocysts and gametocysts in *Leptospironympha*. Ibid. **88**, 199.

—— (1951b). Idem. VII. One-division meiosis and autogamy without cell division in *Urinympha*. Ibid. **88**, 385.

—— (1952). Idem. VIII. Meiosis in *Rhynchonympha* in one cytoplasmic and two nuclear divisions followed by autogamy. Ibid. **91**, 269.

—— (1953). Idem. IX. Haploid gametogenesis and fertilization in *Barbulanympha*. Ibid. **93**, 371.

—— (1954a). Idem. XI. Reorganization in the zygote of *Barbulanympha* without nuclear or cytoplasmic division. Ibid. **95**, 213.

—— (1954b). Idem. XII. Meiosis in *Barbulanympha* following fertilization, autogamy and endomitosis. Ibid. **95**, 557.

—— (1955). Idem. XIII. Unusual behavior of gametes and centrioles of *Barbulanympha*. Ibid. **97**, 511.

—— (1956a). Idem. XIV. Gametic meiosis and fertilization in *Macrospironympha*. *Arch. Protistenk.* **101**, 99.

—— (1956b). Brief accounts of the sexual cycles of the flagellates of *Cryptocercus*. *J. Protozool.* **3**, 161.

—— (1957). Correlation between the molting period of *Cryptocercus* and sexuality in its Protozoa. Ibid. **4**, 168.

—— (1958a). Photographs of fertilization in the smaller species of *Trichonympha*. Ibid. **5**, 104.

—— (1958b). Photographs of fertilization in *Trichonympha grandis*. Ibid. **5**, 115.

——, HALL, S. R., SANDERS, E. P., and COLLIER, J. (1934). The wood-feeding roach *Cryptocercus*, its Protozoa, and the symbiosis between Protozoa and roach. *Mem. Amer. Acad. Arts Sci.* **17** (pp. i–x+ 185).

—— and NUTTING, W. L. (1955). Suppression of sexual cycles and death of the Protozoa of *Cryptocercus* resulting from change of hosts during molting period. *J. exp. Zool.* **130**, 485.

CODREANU, M., and CODREANU, R. (1928). Un Nouvel Euglénien (*Astasia chaetogastris* n. sp.), parasite coelomique d'un oligochète (*Chaetogaster diastrophus* Gruith). *C.R. Soc. Biol., Paris*, **99**, 1368.

COGNETTI DE MARTIIS, L. (1925). Sulla classificazione e sui caratteri tassonomici delle Monocistidee degli Oligocheti. *Monit. zool. ital.* **36**, 219.

COHEN, B. M. (1934). The effect of conjugation within a clone of *Euplotes patella*. *Genetics*, **19**, 25.

COLEMAN, G. S. (1958). Maintenance of oligotrich Protozoa from the sheep rumen *in vitro*. *Nature, Lond.* **182**, 1104.

COLLIN, B. (1912). Étude monographique sur les Acinétiens. II. Morphologie, physiologie, systématique. *Arch. Zool. exp. gén.* **51**, 1.

COLWIN, L. H. (1944). Binary fission and conjugation in *Urceolaria synaptae* (?) Type II (Protozoa, Ciliata) with special reference to the nuclear phenomena. *J. Morph.* **75**, 203.

COMFORT, A. (1956). *The biology of senescence*. London.

CONNELL, C. H., and CROSS, J. B. (1950). Mass mortality of fish associated with the protozoan *Gonyaulax* in the Gulf of Mexico. *Science*, **112**, 359.

CORLISS, J. O. (1952). Comparative studies on holotrichous ciliates in the *Colpidium–Glaucoma–Leucophrys–Tetrahymena* group. I. General considerations and history of strains in pure culture. *Trans. Amer. micr. Soc.* **71**, 159.

—— (1953*a*). Idem. II. Morphology, life cycles and systematic status of strains in pure culture. *Parasitology*, **43**, 49.

—— (1953*b*). Silver impregnation of ciliated Protozoa by the Chatton–Lwoff technic. *Stain Technol.* **28**, 97.

—— (1954). The literature on *Tetrahymena*: its history, growth, and recent trends. *J. Protozool.* **1**, 156.

—— (1955). The Opalinid infusorians: flagellates or ciliates ? Ibid. **2**, 107.

—— (1956). On the evolution and systematics of ciliated Protozoa. *Syst. Zool.* **5**, 68, 121.

—— (1957). Nomenclatural history of the higher taxa in the subphylum Ciliophora. *Arch. Protistenk.* **102**, 113.

—— (1958*a*). The systematic position of *Pseudomicrothorax dubius*, ciliate with a unique combination of anatomical features. *J. Protozool.* **5**, 184.

—— (1958*b*). The phylogenetic significance of the genus *Pseudomicrothorax* in the evolution of holotrichous ciliates. *Acta biol., Budapest*, **8**, 367.

—— (1959). An illustrated key to the higher groups of the ciliated Protozoa with definition of terms. *J. Protozool.* **6**, 265.

—— (1960). *Tetrahymena chironomi* sp. nov., a ciliate from midge larvae, and the current status of facultative parasitism in the genus *Tetrahymena*. *Parasitology*, **50**, 111.

—— (1961). *The ciliated Protozoa; classification and guide to the literature*. London and New York.

COSGROVE, W. B. (1947). Fibrillar structures in *Opalina obtrigonoidea* Metcalf. *J. Parasit.* **33**, 351.

COUCH, J. N. (1941). The structure and action of the cilia in some aquatic Phycomycetes. *Amer. J. Bot.* **28**, 704.

COUTTS, W. E., VARGAS-SALAZAR, R., SILVA-INZUNZA, E., OLMEDO, R., TURTEL-TAUB, R., and SAAVEDRA, J. (1955). *Trichomonas vaginalis* infection in the male. *Brit. med. J.* II, 885.

COWPERTHWAITE, J., WEBER, M. M., PACKER, L., and HUTNER, S. H. (1953). Nutrition of *Herpetomonas* (*Strigomonas*) *culicidarum*. *Ann. N.Y. Acad. Sci.* **56**, 972.

CRAWLEY, H. (1902). The progressive movement of gregarines. *Proc. Acad. nat. Sci. Philad.* **54**, 4.

—— (1905). The movements of gregarines. Ibid. **57**, 89.

—— (1923). Evolution in the ciliate family Ophryoscolecidae. Ibid. **75**, 393.

CROUCH, H. B., and BECKER, E. R. (1931). A method of staining the oocysts of Coccidia. *Science*, **73**, 212.

CUNNINGHAM, J. T. (1907). On *Kalpidorhynchus arenicolae*, a new gregarine, parasitic in *Arenicola ecaudata*. *Arch. Protistenk.* **10**, 199.

DANIELLI, J. F. (1958). Studies of inheritance in amoebae by the technique of nuclear transfer. *Proc. roy. Soc.* B, **148**, 321.

—— (1959). The cell-to-cell transfer of nuclei in amoebae and a comprehensive cell theory. *Ann. N.Y. Acad. Sci.* **78**, 675.

——, LORCH, I. J., ORD, M. J., and WILSON, E. G. (1955). Nucleus and cytoplasm in cellular inheritance. *Nature, Lond.* **176**, 1114.

DANIELS, M. I. (1938). A cytological study of the gregarine parasites of *Tenebrio molitor*, using the ultra-centrifuge. *Quart. J. micr. Sci.* **80**, 293.

DAVIS, H. S. (1947). Studies on the protozoan parasites of freshwater fishes. *Fishery Bulletin 41 of the Fish and Wildlife Service, Wash.* **51**, 1.

DAWSON, J. A. (1928). The culture of large free-living amebae. *Amer. Nat.* **52**, 453.

—— (1953). The culture of *Blepharisma undulans* and *Stentor coeruleus*. *Biol. Rev., College of the City of N.Y.* **15**, 13.

—— (1954). *Amoeba proteus* and *Amoeba dubia*. Ibid. **16**, 8.

—— (1955). The culture of *Amoeba proteus*. Ibid. **17**, 20.

—— and HEWITT, D. C. (1931). The longevity of encysted Colpodas. *Amer. Nat.* **65**, 181.

——, KESSLER, W. R., and SILBERSTEIN, J. K. (1937). Mitosis in *Amoeba proteus*. *Biol. Bull.* **72**, 125.

DE BRUYN, P. P. H. (1947). Theories of amoeboid movement. *Quart. Rev. Biol.* **22**, 1.

DEFLANDRE, G. (1928). Le Genre *Arcella* Ehrenberg. Morphologie–Biologie. Essai phylogénétique et systématique. *Arch. Protistenk.* **64**, 152.

—— (1929). Le Genre *Centropyxis* Stein. Ibid. **67**, 322.

—— (1934). Sur la structure des flagellés. *Ann. Protistol.* **4**, 31.

—— (1950). A propos des Eugléniens et de la structure des flagellés. *Arch. Zool. exp. gén.* **87** (N & R), 61.

DELAMATER, E. D. (1948). Basic fuchsin as a nuclear stain. *Stain Technol.* **23**, 161.

—— (1951). A staining and dehydrating procedure for the handling of micro-organisms. Ibid. **26**, 199.

DEMBOWSKI, J. (1913). Versuche über die Merotomie der Gregarinen. *Arch. Protistenk.* **29**, 1.

DE MORGAN, W. (1925). Some marine ciliates living in the laboratory tanks at Plymouth, with a description of a new species, *Holophrya coronata*. *J. mar. biol. Ass. U.K.* **13**, 600.

DIERKS, K. (1926). Untersuchungen über die Morphologie und Physiologie des *Stentor coeruleus* mit besonderer Berücksichtigung seiner kontraktilen und konduktilen Elemente. *Arch. Protistenk.* **54**, 1.

DILLER, W. F. (1936). Nuclear reorganization processes in *Paramecium aurelia*, with descriptions of autogamy and 'hemixis'. *J. Morph.* **59**, 11.

—— (1954). Autogamy in *Paramecium polycaryon*. *J. Protozool.* **1**, 60.

—— and EARL, P. R. (1958). *Paramecium jenningsi*, n. sp. Ibid. **5**, 155.

DOBELL, C. (1908). The structure and life-history of *Copromonas subtilis*, nov. gen. et nov. spec.: a contribution to our knowledge of the Flagellata. *Quart. J. micr. Sci.* **52**, 75.

456 REFERENCES

DOBELL, C. (1909). Researches on the intestinal Protozoa of frogs and toads. Ibid. **53**, 201.

—— (1911). The principles of protistology. *Arch. Protistenk.* **23**, 269.

—— (1914). Cytological studies on three species of *Amoeba*—*A. lacertae* Hartmann, *A. glebae* n. sp., *A. fluvialis* n. sp. Ibid. **34**, 139.

—— (1918). Are *Entamoeba histolytica* and *Entamoeba ranarum* the same species ? *Parasitology*, **10**, 294.

—— (1922). The discovery of the Coccidia. Ibid. **14**, 342.

—— (1925). The life-history and chromosome cycle of *Aggregata eberthi*. Ibid. **17**, 1.

—— (1927). Further observations and experiments on the cultivation of *Entamoeba histolytica* from cysts. Ibid. **19**, 288.

—— (1928). Researches on the intestinal Protozoa of Monkeys and Man.—I. General introduction, and II. Description of the whole life-history of *Entamoeba histolytica* in cultures. Ibid. **20**, 357.

—— (1931). Idem. IV. An experimental study of the *histolytica*-like species of *Entamoeba* living naturally in Macaques. Ibid. **23**, 1.

—— (1932). *Antony van Leeuwenhoek and his 'little animals'*. London.

—— (1938). Researches on the intestinal Protozoa of Monkeys and Man. IX. The life-history of *Entamoeba coli*, with special reference to metacystic development. *Parasitology*, **30**, 195.

—— (1942). Some new methods for studying intestinal amoebae and other Protozoa. Ibid. **34**, 101.

—— and JAMESON, A. P. (1915). The chromosome cycle—Coccidia and gregarines. *Proc. roy. Soc.* B, **89**, 83.

—— and LAIDLAW, P. P. (1926). On the cultivation of *Entamoeba histolytica* and some other entozoic amoebae. *Parasitology*, **18**, 283.

DOFLEIN, F. (1907). Studien zur Naturgeschichte der Protozoen. V. Amöbenstudien. Erster Teil. *Arch. Protistenk.* Suppl. I. Festb. R. Hertwig. p. 250.

—— (1918). Die vegetative Fortpflanzung von *Amoeba proteus* Pall. *Zool. Anz.* **49**, 257.

—— and REICHENOW, E. (1928). *Lehrb. d. Protozoenk.*, 5th edn. Jena.

—— —— (1952–3). Idem, 6th edn. Jena.

DOGIEL, V. (A.) (1925). Die Geschlechtsprozesse bei Infusorien (speziell bei den Ophryoscoleciden), neue Tatsachen und theoretische Erwägungen. *Arch. Protistenk.* **50**, 283.

—— (1927). Monographie der Familie Ophryoscolecidae. Ibid. **59**, 1.

DRAGESCO, J. (1952). Le Flagellé *Oxyrrhis marina*: cytologie, trichocystes, position systématique. *Bull. Micr. appl.* **2**, 148.

—— and GUILCHER, Y. (1950). Sur la structure et la fonctionnement des tentacules d'acinétiens. *Microscopie, Paris*, **2**, 17.

DRBOHLAV, J. J. (1925a). Studies on the relation of insect herpetomonad flagellates to leishmaniasis. II. The specificity of the various insect flagellates for certain hosts, as indicated by cross infection experiments. *Amer. J. Hyg.* **5**, 599.

—— (1925b). Idem. III. Cultivation requirements. Ibid. **5**, 611.

—— (1926). The cultivation of *Herpetomonas muscarum* (Leidy 1856) Kent 1881 from *Lucilia sericata*. *J. Parasit.* **12**, 183.

DUBOSCQ, O., and GRASSÉ, P. (1933). L'Appareil parabasal des flagellés: avec des remarques sur le trophosponge, l'appareil de Golgi, les mitochondries et le vacuome. *Arch. Zool. exp. gén.* **73**, 381.

DUNKERLY, J. S. (1911). On some stages in the life-history of *Leptomonas muscae domesticae*, with some remarks on the relationships of the flagellate parasites of insects. *Quart. J. micr. Sci.* **56**, 645.

DUNKERLY, J. S. (1921). Fish Myxosporidia from Plymouth. *Parasitology*, **12**, 328.

DUTTA, G. P. (1958). The cytoplasmic inclusions of *Nyctotherus macropharyngeus*: histochemical studies. *Quart. J. micr. Sci.* **99**, 517.

EDDY, S. (1930). The fresh-water armored or thecate dinoflagellates. *Trans. Amer. micr. Soc.* **49**, 277.

EDWARDS, J. G. (1925). Formation of food cups in *Amoeba* induced by chemicals. *Biol. Bull.* **48**, 236.

EHRET, C. F., and POWERS, E. L. (1959). The cell surface of *Paramecium*. *Int. Rev. Cytology*, **8**, 97.

ELLIOTT, A. M., and GRUCHY, D. F. (1952). The occurrence of mating types in *Tetrahymena*. *Biol. Bull.* **103**, 301.

—— and HAYES, R. E. (1953). Mating types in *Tetrahymena*. Ibid. **105**, 269.

—— —— (1955). *Tetrahymena* from Mexico, Panama and Columbia, with special reference to sexuality. *J. Protozool.* **2**, 75.

EL MOFTY, M., and SMYTH, J. D. (1960). Endocrine control of sexual reproduction in *Opalina ranarum* parasitic in *Rana temporaria*. *Nature, Lond.*, **186**, 559.

ELTON, C., FORD, E. B., BAKER, J. R., and GARDNER, A. D. (1931). The health and parasites of a wild mouse population. *Proc. zool. Soc. Lond.*, p. 657.

ENTZ, G. (jun.) (1909). Studien über Organisation und Biologie der Tintinniden. *Arch. Protistenk.* **15**, 93.

—— (1912). Über eine neue Amöbe auf Süßwasser-Polypen (*Hydra oligactis* Pall.). Ibid. **27**, 19.

—— (1921). Über die mitotische Teilung von *Ceratium hirundinella*. Ibid. **43**, 415.

—— (1925). Über Cysten und Encystierung der Süßwasser-Ceratien. Ibid. **51**, 131.

—— (1927). Beiträge zur Kenntnis der Peridineen. II. resp. VII. Studien an Süßwasser-Ceratien. Ibid. **58**, 344.

—— (1928). Über den Bau und über die Tätigkeit der Geißeln der Peridineen. *Ann. Protistol.* **1**, 75.

ERDMANN, R., and WOODRUFF, L. L. (1916). The periodic reorganization process in *Paramecium caudatum*. *J. exp. Zool.* **20**, 59.

FAURÉ-FREMIET, E. (1905). La Structure de l'appareil fixateur chez les Vorticellidae. *Arch. Protistenk.* **6**, 207.

—— (1908). Le *Tintinnidium inquilinum*. Ibid. **11**, 225.

—— (1910). La Fixation chez les infusoires ciliés. *Bull. sci. Fr. Belg.* **44**, 27.

—— (1924). Contribution à la connaissance des infusoires planktoniques. *Bull. biol.* suppl. **6**.

—— (1943). Étude biométrique de quelques trichodines. *Bull. Soc. zool. Fr.* **68**, 158.

—— (1948a). Les Mécanismes de la morphogénèse chez les ciliés. *Folia biotheoretica*, Ser. B, no. 3, 25.

—— (1948b). Le Rhythme de marée du *Strombidium oculatum* Gruber. *Bull. biol.* **82**, 3.

—— (1950a). Morphologie comparée et systématique des ciliés. *Bull. Soc. zool. Fr.* **75**, 109.

—— (1950b). Mécanismes de la morphogénèse chez quelques ciliés gymnostomes hypostomiens. *Arch. Anat. micr. Morph. exp.* **39**, 1.

—— (1950c). Écologie des ciliés psammophiles littoraux. *Bull. biol.* **84**, 35.

FAURÉ-FREMIET, E. (1951). The marine sand-dwelling ciliates of Cape Cod. *Biol. Bull.* **100**, 59.

—— (1953*a*). La Bipartition énantiotrope chez les ciliés oligotriches. *Arch. Anat. micr. Morph. exp.* **42**, 209.

—— (1953*b*). L'Hypothèse de la sénescence et les cycles de réorganisation nucléaire chez les ciliés. *Rev. suisse Zool.* **60**, 426.

—— (1953*c*). Morphology of Protozoa. *Ann. Rev. Microbiol.* **7**, 1.

—— (1954). Réorganisation du type endomixique chez les Loxodidae et chez les *Centrophorella*. *J. Protozool.* **1**, 20.

—— (1955). La Position systématique du genre *Balantidium*. Ibid. **2**, 54.

—— (1957). Le Macronucleus hétéromère de quelques ciliés. Ibid. **4**, 7.

——, GAUCHERY, M., and TUFFRAU, M. (1954). Les Processus de l'enkystement chez *Euplotes muscicola* Kahl. *Bull. biol.* **88**, 154.

—— and GUILCHER, Y. (1947). Les Affinités des infusoires acinétiens et la ciliature de leurs formes vagiles. *Bull. Soc. zool. Fr.* **72**, 12.

—— and ROUILLER, C. (1958). Myonèmes et cinétodesmes chez les ciliés du genre *Stentor*. *Bull. Micr. appl.* **8**, 117.

—— —— and GAUCHERY, M. (1957). La Réorganisation macronucléaire chez les *Euplotes*. Étude au microscope électronique. *Exp. Cell Res.* **12**, 135.

FAWCETT, D. W., and PORTER, K. R. (1954). A study of the fine structure of ciliated epithelia. *J. Morph.* **94**, 221.

FEO, L. G. (1956). The incidence of *Trichomonas vaginalis* in the various age groups. *Amer. J. trop. Med. Hyg.* **5**, 786.

——, VARANO, N. R., and FETTER, T. R. (1956). *Trichomonas vaginalis* in urethritis of the male. *Brit. J. ven. Dis.* **32**, 233.

FILICE, F. P. (1952). Studies on the cytology and life history of a *Giardia* from the laboratory rat. *Univ. Calif. Publ. Zool.* **57**, 53.

FINLEY, H. E. (1930). Toleration of fresh water Protozoa to increased salinity. *Ecology*, **11**, 337.

—— (1936). A method for inducing conjugation within *Vorticella* cultures. *Trans. Amer. micr. Soc.* **55**, 323.

—— (1939). Sexual differentiation in *Vorticella microstoma*. *J. exp. Zool.* **81**, 209.

—— (1943). The conjugation of *Vorticella microstoma*. Ibid. **62**, 97.

—— (1952). Sexual differentiation in peritrichous ciliates. *J. Morph.* **91**, 569.

——, McLAUGHLIN, D., and HARRISON, D. M. (1959). Non-axenic and axenic growth of *Vorticella microstoma*. *J. Protozool.* **6**, 201.

FOWELL, R. R. (1936). The fibrillar structures of Protozoa, with special reference to schizogregarines of the genus *Selenidium*. *J. R. micr. Soc.* **56**, 12.

FOX, H. M. (1921). An investigation into the cause of the spontaneous aggregation of flagellates and into the reactions of flagellates to dissolved oxygen. *J. gen. Physiol.* **3**, 483.

—— and NEWTH, H. G. (1936). On the swarming of *Vorticella*. *Proc. zool. Soc. Lond.* (1–2), 309.

FULTON, J. F. (1923). *Trichodina pediculus* and a closely related species. *Proc. Boston Soc. nat. Hist.* **37**, 1.

FURGASON, W. H. (1940). The significant cytostomal pattern of the 'Glaucoma-Colpidium group', and a proposed new genus and species, *Tetrahymena geleii*. *Arch. Protistenk.* **94**, 224.

GALL, J. G. (1959). Macronuclear duplication in the ciliated protozoan *Euplotes*. *J. biophys. biochem. Cytol.* **5**, 295.

REFERENCES

GANAPATI, P. N. (1946). Notes on some gregarines from polychaetes of the Madras coast. *Proc. Ind. Acad. Sci. B*, **23**, 228.

GARNJOBST, L. (1947). The effect of certain deficient media on resting cyst formation in *Colpoda duodenaria*. *Physiol. Zoöl.* **20**, 5.

GATENBY, J. B., and SMYTH, J. D. (1940). The Golgi apparatus and pyrenoids of *Chilomonas paramecium*, with remarks on the identification of *Copromonas subtilis*. *Quart. J. micr. Sci.* **81**, 595.

GEIMAN, Q. M., and RATCLIFFE, H. L. (1936). Morphology and life-cycle of an amoeba producing amoebiasis in reptiles. *Parasitology*, **28**, 208.

GELEI, J. von (1925). Über den Kannibalismus der Stentoren. *Arch. Protistenk.* **52**, 404.

—— (1929). Sensorischer Basalapparat der Tastborsten und der Syncilien bei Hypotrichen. *Zool. Anz.* **83**, 275.

—— (1932). Die reizleitenden Elemente der Ciliaten in naß hergestellten Silber- bzw. Goldpräparaten. *Arch. Protistenk.* **77**, 152.

—— (1934a). Der feinere Bau des Cytopharynx von *Paramecium* und seine systematische Bedeutung. Ibid. **82**, 331.

—— (1934b). Das Verhalten der ectoplasmatischen Elemente des Parameciums während der Teilung. *Zool. Anz.* **107**, 161.

—— (1934c). Die Vermehrung der Sinneshaare von *Euplotes* während des Teilungsprozesses. Ibid. **105**,   .

GEORGEVITCH, J. (1926). Sur la *Coccomyxa* de la sardine. *Arch. Zool. exp. gén.* **65** (N. & R.), 57.

GHOSH, E. (1922a). On a new ciliate, *Balantidium blattarum*, sp. nov., intestinal parasite in the common cockroach (*Blatta americana*): *Parasitology*, **14**, 15.

—— (1922b). On a new ciliate, *Balantidium ovatum*, sp. nov., an intestinal parasite in the common cockroach (*Blatta americana*). Ibid. **14**, 371.

GÖHRE, E. (1943). Untersuchungen über den plasmatischen Feinbau der Gregarinen mit besonderer Berücksichtigung der Sexualitätsverhältnisse. *Arch. Protistenk.* **96**, 295.

GOJDICS, M. (1934). The cell morphology and division of *Euglena deses* Ehrbg. *Trans. Amer micr. Soc.* **53**, 299.

—— (1953). *The genus Euglena*. Univ. Wisconsin Press, Madison, Canada.

GOLDACRE, R. J., and LORCH, I. L. (1950). Folding and unfolding of protein molecules in relation to cytoplasmic streaming, amoeboid movement and osmotic work. *Nature, Lond.* **166**, 497.

GÖNNERT, R. (1935). Über Systematik, Morphologie, Entwicklungsgeschichte und Parasiten einiger Dendrosomidae nebst Beschreibung zweier neuer Suktorien. *Arch. Protistenk.* **86**, 113.

GOODEY, T. (1913). The excystation of *Colpoda cucullus* from its resting cysts, and the nature and properties of the cyst membranes. *Proc. roy. Soc. B*, **86**, 427.

GOODRICH, E. S., and PIXELL GOODRICH, H. L. M. (1920). *Gonospora minchinii*, n. sp., a gregarine inhabiting the egg of *Arenicola*. *Quart. J. micr. Sci.* **65**, 157.

GRAHAM, H. W. (1942). Studies on the morphology, taxonomy and ecology of the Peridinales. *Carnegie Inst. Publ. no. 542*. Washington, D.C.

GRASSÉ, P. P. (1926). Contribution à l'étude des flagellés parasites. *Arch. Zool. exp. gén.* **65**, 345.

GRELL, K. G. (1940). Der Kernphasenwechsel von *Stylocephalus* (*Stylorhynchus*) *longicollis* F. Stein. (Ein Beitrag zur Frage der Chromosomreduktion der Gregarinen.) *Arch. Protistenk.* **94**, 161.

GRELL, K. G. (1950). Der Generationswechsel des parasitischen Suktors *Tachyblaston ephelotensis* Martin. *Z. Parasitenk.* **14**, 499.

—— (1952). Der Stand unserer Kenntnisse über den Bau der Protistenkerne. *Verhandl. Deutsch. Zool. Gesell. in Freiburg 1952* (p. 212). Leipzig.

—— (1953a). Die Konjugation von *Ephelota gemmipara* R. Hertwig. *Arch. Protistenk.* **98**, 287.

—— (1953b). Die Chromosomen von *Aulacantha scolymantha* Haeckel. Ibid. **99**, 1.

—— (1954). Der Generationswechsel der polythalamen Foraminifere *Rotaliella heterocaryotica*. Ibid. **100**, 268.

—— (1957). Untersuchungen über die Fortpflanzung und Sexualität der Foraminiferen. I. *Rotaliella roscoffensis*. Ibid. **102**, 147.

—— (1958a). Idem. II. *Rubratella intermedia*. Ibid. **102**, 291.

—— (1958b). Idem. III. *Glabratella sulcata*. Ibid. **102**, 449.

—— (1958c). Studien zum Differenzierungsproblem an Foraminiferen. *Naturwissenschaften*, Heft 2, 25.

—— and WOHLFARTH-BOTTERMANN, K. E. von (1957). Licht- und Elektronenmikroskopische Untersuchungen an dem Dinoflagellaten *Amphidinium elegans* n. sp. *Z. Zellforsch.* **47**, 7.

GROSPIETSCH, T. (1958). Beiträge zur Rhizopodenfauna Deutschlands. I. Die Thekamöben der Rhon. *Hydrobiologia*, **10**, 305.

GROSS, F. (1934). Zur Biologie und Entwicklungsgeschichte von *Noctiluca miliaris*. *Arch. Protistenk.* **83**, 178.

—— (1937). Notes on the culture of some marine plankton organisms. *J. mar. biol. Ass. U.K.* **21**, 753.

—— and ZEUTHEN, E. (1948). The buoyancy of plankton diatoms: a problem in cell physiology. *Proc. roy. Soc.* B, **135**, 382.

GRUCHY, D. F. (1955). The breeding system and distribution of *Tetrahymena pyriformis*. *J. Protozool.* **2**, 178.

GUILCHER, Y. (1947). *Discophrya piriformis* n. sp. et son mode de bourgeonnement. *C.R. Acad. Sci., Paris*, **225**, 72.

—— (1948). Morphogénèse chez l'acinétien *Ephelota gemmipara* Hertw. *Bull. Soc. zool. Fr.* **73**, 24.

—— (1951). Contribution à l'étude des ciliés gemmipares, chonotriches et tentaculifères. *Ann. Sci. Nat., Zool.* **13**, 33.

GÜNTHER, F. (1928). Über den Bau und die Lebensweise der Euglenen, besonders der Arten *E. terricola, geniculata, proxima, sanguinea* und *lucens* nov. spec. *Arch. Protistenk.* **60**, 511.

HAAGEN-SMIT, A. J., and THIMANN, K. V. (1938). The excystment of *Colpoda cucullus*. I. The chemical nature of the excysting factors in hay infusion. *J. cell. comp. Physiol.* **11**, 389.

HAIRSTON, N. G. (1958). Observations on the ecology of *Paramecium*, with comments on the species problem. *Evolution*, **12**, 440.

HALL, R. P. (1923). Morphology and binary fission of *Menoidium incurvum* (Fres.) Klebs. *Univ. Calif. Publ. Zool.* **20**, 447.

—— (1925a). Binary fission in *Oxyrrhis marina* Dujardin. Ibid. **26**, 281.

—— (1925b). Mitosis in *Ceratium hirundinella* O.F.M., with notes on nuclear phenomena in encysted forms and the question of sexual reproduction. Ibid. **28**, 29.

—— (1929). Reaction of certain cytoplasmic inclusions to vital dyes and their relation to mitochondria and Golgi apparatus in the flagellate *Peranema trichophorum*. *J. Morph. Physiol.* **48**, 105.

HALL, R. P. (1937). A note on the behaviour of the chromosomes in *Euglena*. *Trans. Amer. micr. Soc.* **56**, 288.

—— and JAHN, T. L. (1929). On the comparative cytology of certain Euglenoid flagellates and the systematic position of the families Euglenidae Stein and Astasiidae Bütschli. Ibid. **48**, 388.

—— and POWELL, W. N. (1928). Morphology and binary fission of *Peranema trichophorum* (Ehrbg.) Stein. *Biol. Bull.* **54**, 36.

HALL, S. R. (1931). Observations on *Euglena leucops*, sp. nov., a parasite of *Stenostomum*, with special reference to nuclear division. Ibid. **60**, 327.

HALSEY, H. R. (1936). The life-cycle of *Amoeba proteus* (Pallas, Leidy) and of *Amoeba dubia* (Schaeffer). *J. exp. Zool.* **74**, 167.

HAMILTON, M. A. (1931). The morphology of the water-scorpion, *Nepa cinerea* Linn. *Proc. zool. Soc. Lond.*, p. 1067.

HAMMOND, D. M. (1937). The neuromotor system of *Euplotes patella* during binary fission and conjugation. *Quart. J. micr. Sci.* **79**, 507.

HARRIS, T. M. (1940). A contribution to the knowledge of the British freshwater Dinoflagellata. *Proc. Linn. Soc. Lond.*, 152nd Session, Pt. 1, p. 5.

HARTMANN, M. (1928). Über experimentelle Unsterblichkeit von Protozoen-Individuen. *Zool. Jb.* **45**, 973.

HARVEY, E. N. (1952). *Bioluminescence*. New York.

HASWELL, W. A. (1907). Parasitic Euglenae. *Zool. Anz.* **31**, 296.

HAWES, R. S. (1947). On the structure, division, and systematic position of *Trichomonas vaginalis* Donné, with a note on its method of feeding. *Quart. J. micr. Sci.* **88**, 79.

HAYE, A. (1930). Über den Exkretionsapparat bei den Protisten, nebst Bemerkungen über einige andere feinere Strukturverhältnisse der untersuchten Arten. *Arch. Protistenk.* **70**, 1.

HAYES, M. L. (1938). Cytological studies on *Dileptus anser*. *Trans. Amer. micr. Soc.* **57**, 11.

HEGNER, R. (1927). Excystation and infection in the rat with *Giardia lamblia* from man. *Amer. J. Hyg.* **7**, 433.

—— (1929). Methods for cultivating and fixing clones of Arcellas. *Trans. Amer. micr. Soc.* **48**, 214.

HEIDENREICH, E. (1935). Untersuchungen an parasitischen Ciliaten aus Anneliden. Teil I: Systematik. *Arch. Protistenk.* **84**, 315.

HENTSCHEL, C. C. (1925). Notes on *Hoplitophrya* (*Anoplophrya*) *brasili* (Léger and Duboscq), an intestinal ciliate of the polychaete worm *Cirratulus*. *Parasitology*, **17**, 217.

—— (1926). On the correlation of the life-history of the acephaline gregarine, *Gonospora*, with the sexual cycle of its host. Ibid. **18**, 137.

HERTWIG, R. (1877). Über den Bau und die Entwicklung der *Spirochona gemmipara*. *Z. Naturw.* **11**, 149.

—— (1889). Über die Conjugation der Infusorien. *Abh. Bayer. Akad. Wiss.* (II. Cl.) **17**, 151.

—— (1898). Über Kernteilung, Richtungskörperbildung und Befruchtung von *Actinosphaerium eichhorni*. Ibid. **19**, 631.

HESSE, E. (1909). Contribution à l'étude des monocystidées des oligochètes. *Arch. Zool. exp. gén.* **3**, 27.

H h

HETHERINGTON, A. (1932). The constant culture of *Stentor coeruleus*. *Arch. Protistenk.* **76**, 118.

HILL, W. C. O., and NEAL, R. A. (1953). An epizootic due to *Entamoeba invadens* at the gardens of the Zoological Society of London. *Proc. zool. Soc. Lond.* **123**, 731.

HOARE, C. A. (1924). A note on the specific name of the herpetomonad of the house-fly. *Trans. R. Soc. trop. Med. Hyg.* **17**, 403.

—— (1927). Studies on coprozoic ciliates. *Parasitology,* **19**, 154.

—— (1933). Studies on some new ophidian and avian Coccidia from Uganda, with a revision of the classification of the Eimeriidea. Ibid. **25**, 359.

—— (1938). Morphological and taxonomic studies on mammalian trypanosomes. V. The diagnostic value of the kinetoplast. *Trans. R. Soc. trop. Med. Hyg.* **32**, 333.

—— (1940). Recent studies on the kinetoplast in relation to heritable variation in trypanosomes. *J. R. micr. Soc.* **60**, 26.

—— (1943). Biological races in Protozoa. *Biol. Rev.* **18**, 137.

—— (1949). The relationship of the haemoflagellates. *Proc. 4th Int. Congr. Trop. Med. and Malaria,* Washington, D.C. (1948), p. 1110.

—— (1952a). The food habits of *Entamoeba histolytica* in its commensal phase. *Parasitology,* **42**, 43.

—— (1952b). The commensal phase of *Entamoeba histolytica*. *Exp. Parasitol.* **1**, 411.

—— (1952c). The taxonomic status of biological races of parasitic Protozoa. *Proc. Linn. Soc. Lond.* **163**, 44.

—— (1954). The loss of the kinetoplast in trypanosomes, with special reference to *Trypanosoma evansi*. *J. Protozool.* **1**, 28.

—— (1956a). Classification of Coccidia Eimeriidae in a 'periodic system' of homologous genera. *Rev. bras. Malariol.* **8**, 197.

—— (1956b). Morphological and taxonomic studies on mammalian trypanosomes. VIII. Revision of *Trypanosoma evansi*. *Parasitology,* **46**, 130.

—— (1957a). The spread of African trypanosomes beyond their natural range (Essay on the historical zoogeography of the host-parasite system). *Z. Tropenmed. Parasit.* **8**, 157.

—— (1957b). The classification of trypanosomes of veterinary and medical importance. *Vet. Rev. Annotations,* **3**, 1.

—— (1957c). Symposium on the laboratory aspects of amoebiasis. I. Introduction. *Trans. R. Soc. trop. Med. Hyg.* **51**, 303.

HOFENEDER, H. (1930). Über die animalische Ernährung von *Ceratium hirundinella* O. F. Müller und über die Rolle des Kernes bei dieser Zellfunktion. *Arch. Protistenk.* **71**, 1.

HOFKER, J. (1930). Über *Noctiluca scintillans* (Macartney). Ibid. **71**, 57.

HOLLANDE, A. (1938). *Bodo perforans* n. sp. flagellé nouveau parasite externe du *Chilomonas paramaecium* Ehrenb. *Arch. Zool. exp. gén.* **79** (N. & R.), 75.

—— (1942). Étude cytologique et biologique de quelques flagellés libres. Ibid. **83**, 1.

—— (1945). Biologie et réproduction des rhizopodes des genres *Pelomyxa* et *Amoeba* et cycle évolutif de l'*Amoebophilus destructor* nov. gen. nov. sp., Chytridinée (?) parasite de *Pelomyxa palustris* Greeff. *Bull. biol.* **79**, 31.

—— (1953). Compléments sur la cytologie des Acanthaires et des Radiolaires. Addendum in Grassé's *Traité de zoologie,* vol. i, fasc. ii, p. 1089.

—— and ENJUMET, M. (1953). Contribution à l'étude biologique des Sphaerocollides (Radiolaires collodaires et Radiolaires polycyttaires) et de leurs parasites. Partie I. Thalassicollidae, Physematidae, Thalassophysidae. *Ann. Sci. Nat.* **15,** 99.

HOLLANDE, A. and GUILCHER, Y. (1945). Les Amibes du genre *Pelomyxa*: éthologie, structure, cycle évolutif, parasites (note préliminaire). *Bull. Soc. zool. Fr.* **70,** 53.

HOLTER, H. (1959*a*). Problems of pinocytosis, with special regard to amoebae. *Ann. N.Y. Acad. Sci.* **78,** 524.

—— (1959*b*). Pinocytosis. *Int. Rev. Cytol.* **8,** 480.

—— and MARSHALL, J. M. (1954). Studies on pinocytosis in the amoeba *Chaos chaos*. *C.R. trav. Lab. Carlsberg*, **29,** 7.

HONIGBERG, B. M. (1951). Structure and morphogenesis of *Trichomonas prowazeki* Alexeieff and *Trichomonas brumpti* Alexeieff. *Univ. Calif. Publ. Zool.* **55,** 337.

—— (1953). Structure, taxonomic status, and host list of *Tritrichomonas batrachorum* (Perty). *J. Parasit.* **39,** 191.

HOOGENRAAD, H. R. (1935). Studien über die sphagnicolen Rhizopoden der niederländischen Fauna. *Arch. Protistenk.* **84,** 1.

HOPKINS, D. L. (1946). The contractile vacuole and the adjustment to changing concentration in fresh water amoebae. *Biol. Bull.* **90,** 158.

HORNING, E. S. (1925). The mitochondria of a protozoan (*Opalina*) and their behaviour during the life cycle. *Aust. J. exp. Biol. med. Sci.* **2,** 167.

—— (1927). Mitochondrial behaviour during the life cycle of *Nyctotherus cordiformis*. Ibid. **4,** 69.

HORTON-SMITH, C. (1957). Factors affecting the transmission of Coccidia and the development of disease in fowls. In *Biological aspects of the transmission of disease*. London.

HOVASSE, R. (1945*a*). Trois cas d'endosymbiose bactérienne chez les ciliés astomes commensaux de l'oligochète *Lumbriculus variegatus* (Müller). *C.R. Acad. Sci., Paris,* **220,** 713.

—— (1945*b*). Endosymbiose bactérienne et astomie chez les ciliés. Ibid. **221,** 125.

—— (1946). Endosymbiose bactérienne chez les divers ciliés parasites intestinaux. Ibid. **223,** 560.

—— and BROWN, E. M. (1953). Contribution à la connaissance des Radiolaires et de leurs parasites Syndiniens. *Ann. Sci. Nat., Zool.,* 11th sér., p. 405.

HOWLAND, R. B. (1928*a*). A note on *Astasia captiva* Beauch. *Science,* **68,** 37.

—— (1928*b*). The pH of gastric vacuoles. *Protoplasma,* **5,** 127.

HUEBSCHMANN, C. (1952). A method for varying the average number of nuclei in the conidia of *Neurospora crassa*. *Mycologia,* **44,** 599.

HULL, R. W. (1954*a*). Feeding processes in *Solenophrya micraster* Penard 1914. *J. Protozool.* **1,** 178.

—— (1954*b*). The probable synonomy of *Discophrya piriformis* Guilcher and *Podophrya collini* Root. Ibid. **1** (Abs.), 6.

HUNGATE, R. E. (1939). Experiments on the nutrition of *Zootermopsis*. III. The anaerobic carbohydrate dissimilation by the intestinal Protozoa. *Ecology,* **20,** 230.

—— (1942). The culture of *Eudiplodinium neglectum*, with experiments on the digestion of cellulose. *Biol. Bull.* **83,** 303.

—— (1943). Further experiments on cellulose digestion by the Protozoa in the rumen of cattle. Ibid. **84,** 157.

—— (1955). Mutualistic intestinal Protozoa. In *Biochemistry and physiology of Protozoa* (ed. Hutner and Lwoff), vol. ii, p. 159.

464   REFERENCES

HYMAN, L. H. (1936). Observations on Protozoa: I. The impermanence of the
contractile vacuole in *Amoeba vespertilio*. II. Structure and mode of food
ingestion of *Peranema*. *Quart. J. micr. Sci.* **79**, 41.
—— (1937). *Peranema* and 'Grantia'. *Science*, **85**, 454.
—— (1938). Observations on Protozoa. III. The vacuolar system of the Euglenida. *Beih. bot. Zbl.* **58** A, 379.

ISHIKAWA, C. (1899). Further observations on the nuclear division of *Noctiluca*.
J. Sci. Coll. Imp. Univ., Tokio, **12**, 243.
IVANIĆ, M. (1926). Über die mit den Reorganisationsprozessen der Bewegungs-
und Nahrungsaufnahmeorganellen verbundenen Ruhestadien von *Paramaecium
caudatum* (Ehrbg.). *Zool. Anz.* **68**, 1.
—— (1928). Über die mit den parthenogenetischen Reorganisationsprozessen des
Kernapparates verbundenen Vermehrungscysten von *Chilodon uncinatus* Ehrbg.
Arch. Protistenk. **61**, 293.
—— (1933*a*). Die Conjugation von *Chilodon cucullulus* Ehrbg. Ibid. **79**, 313.
—— (1933*b*). Zur Kenntnis der allerersten Verschmelzungsstadien zu Beginn
der Konjugation bei *Chilodon uncinatus* u. *Chilodon cucullulus* Ehrbg. und deren
Bedeutung. *Zool. Anz.* **103**, 320.
—— (1933*c*). Neue Beiträge zur Kenntnis der mit den Reorganisationsprozessen
des Kernapparates verbundenen Vermehrungsruhestadien von *Chilodon uncinatus* Ehrbg., nebst einem neuen Beitrage zur Kenntnis der promitotischen
Teilung des Großkernes bei Infusorien. *Arch. Protistenk.* **79**, 170.
—— (1933*d*). Über die bei der Nahrungsaufnahme einiger Süßwasseramöben
vorkommende Bildung cytostomähnlicher Gebilde. Ibid. **79**, 200.
—— (1934). Über eine neue Art der ungeschlechtlichen Fortpflanzung bei *Arcella
vulgaris* Ehr. *Zool. Anz.* **108**, 233.
—— (1936*a*). Recherches nouvelles sur l'ingestion des aliments au moyen de
cytostomes chez quelques amibes d'eau douce. *La Cellule*, **45**, 177.
—— (1936*b*). Ein neuer Beitrag zur Kenntnis der multiplen Teilung bei *Arcella
vulgaris* Ehrbg. *Arch. Protistenk.* **86**, 471.
—— (1937). Körperbau, Ernährung und Vermehrung einer in Enddarme der
Küchenschabe (*Blatta* (*Periplaneta, Stylopaga*) *orientalis* L.) lebenden *Hartmannella*-Art (*Hartmannella blattae* spec. nov.). Ibid. **88**, 339.

JAHN, T. L. (1946). The euglenoid flagellates. *Quart. Rev. Biol.* **21**, 246.
JAKUS, M. A., and HALL, C. E. (1946). Electron microscope observations of the
trichocysts and cilia of *Paramecium*. *Biol. Bull.* **91**, 141.
JAMESON, A. P. (1913). A note on some Myxosporidia collected at Monaco. *Bull.
Inst. océanogr. Monaco*, no. 273.
—— (1920). The chromosome cycle of gregarines, with special reference to
Diplocystis schneideri Kunstler. *Quart. J. micr. Sci.* **64**, 207.
—— (1927). The behaviour of *Balantidium coli* Malm. in cultures. *Parasitology*,
19, 411.
JANICKI, C. (1910). Untersuchungen an parasitischen Flagellaten. I. *Lophomonas
blattarum* Stein, *L. striata* Bütschli. *Z. wiss. Zool.* **95**, 243.
—— (1911). Zur Kenntnis des Parabasalapparats bei parasitischen Flagellaten.
Biol. Zbl. **31**, 321.
JENKIN, P. M. (1927). The relation of *Spirostomum ambiguum* to the hydrogen ion
concentration (alkaline range). *J. exp. Biol.* **4**, 365.

JENNINGS, H. S. (1913). The effect of conjugation in *Paramecium*. *J. exp. Zool.* **14**, 279.

—— (1931). *Behavior of the lower organisms*. Columbia Univ. Press.

—— (1939). Genetics of *Paramecium bursaria*. I. Mating types and groups, their interrelations and distribution; mating behavior and self sterility. *Genetics*, **24**, 202.

—— (1944*a*). *Paramecium bursaria*: life history. II. Age and death of clones in relation to the results of conjugation. *J. exp. Zool.* **96**, 17.

—— (1944*b*). Idem. III. Repeated conjugations in the same stock at different ages, with and without inbreeding, in relation to mortality at conjugation. Ibid. **96**, 243.

—— and LASHLEY, K. S. (1913). Biparental inheritance and the question of sexuality in *Paramecium*. *J. exp. Zool.* **14**, 393.

JEPPS, M. W. (1942). Studies on *Polystomella* Lamarck. *J. mar. biol. Ass.* **25**, 607.

JÍROVEC, O. (1927). Protozoenstudien. II. *Arch. Protistenk.* **59**, 550.

JOHNSON, D. F. (1934). Morphology and life history of *Colacium vesiculosum* Ehrbg. Ibid. **83**, 241.

JOHNSON, H. P. (1893). A contribution to the morphology and biology of the Stentors. *J. Morph.* **8**, 467.

JOHNSON, L. P. (1944). Euglenae of Iowa. *Trans. Amer. micr. Soc.* **63**, 97.

JOHNSON, P. L. (1930). Reproduction in *Amoeba proteus*. *Arch. Protistenk.* **71**, 463.

JONES, W. R. (1946). Experimental infection of rats with *Entamoeba histolytica*. *Ann. trop. Med. Parasit.* **40**, 130.

KAHL, A. (1926). Neue und wenig bekannte Formen der holotrichen und heterotrichen Ciliaten. *Arch. Protistenk.* **55**, 197.

—— (1927). Neue und ergänzende Beobachtungen holotricher Ciliaten. I. Ibid. **60**, 34.

—— (1932). Ctenostomata (Lauterborn) n. subordo. Vierte Unterordnung der Heterotricha. Ibid. **77**, 231.

—— (1935). Urtiere oder Protozoa. I. Wimpertiere oder Ciliata (Infusoria). In Dahl's *Die Tierwelt Deutschlands*. Gustav Fischer, Jena.

KAMM, M. WATSON. *See* WATSON KAMM, M.

KANTOR, S. (1956). The infraciliature in the Ophryoscolecidae and its morphogenetic and phylogenetic significance. *J. Protozool.* **3**, Suppl., 2.

KATE, C. G. B. TEN (1927). Über das Fibrillensystem der Ciliaten. *Arch. Protistenk.* **57**, 362.

KATZIN, L. I., and KIRBY, H. (1939). The relative weights of termites and their Protozoa. *J. Parasit.* **25**, 444.

KEYSSELITZ, G. (1908). Die Entwicklung von *Myxobolus pfeifferi* Th. *Arch. Protistenk.* **11**, 252.

KIDDER, G. W. (1929). *Streblomastix strix*, morphology and mitosis. *Univ. Calif. Publ. Zool.* **33**, 109.

—— (1933*a*). Studies on *Conchophthirius mytili* De Morgan. I. Morphology and division. *Arch. Protistenk.* **79**, 1.

—— (1933*b*). Idem. II. Conjugation and nuclear reorganization. Ibid. **79**, 25.

—— (1933*c*). On the genus *Ancistruma* Strand (*Ancistrum* Maupas). I. The structure and division of *A. mytili* Quenn. and *A. isseli* Kahl. *Biol. Bull.* **64**, 1.

—— (1933*d*). Idem. II. The conjugation and nuclear reorganization of *A. isseli* Kahl. *Arch. Protistenk.* **81**, 1.

—— (1933*e*). *Conchophthirius caryoclada* sp. nov. *Biol. Bull.* **65**, 175.

—— (1934*a*). Studies on the ciliates from freshwater mussels. I. The structure and neuromotor system of *Conchophthirius anodontae* Stein, *C. curtus* Engl., and *C. magna* sp. nov. Ibid. **66**, 69.

KIDDER, G. W. (1934b). Idem. II. The nuclei of *Conchophthirius anodontae* Stein, *C. curtus* Engl., and *C. magna* Kidder during binary fission. Ibid. **66**, 286.

—— and CLAFF, C. L. (1938). Cytological investigations of *Colpoda cucullus*. Ibid. **74**, 178.

—— and SUMMERS, F. M. (1935). Taxonomic and cytological studies on the ciliates associated with the amphipod family Orchestiidae from the Woods Hole district. Ibid. **68**, 51.

KING, R. L. (1928). The contractile vacuole in *Paramecium trichium*. Ibid. **55**, 59.

—— (1935). The contractile vacuole of *Paramecium multimicronucleata*. *J. Morph.* **58**, 555.

KIRBY, H. (1927). Studies on some amoebae from the termite *Mirotermes*, with notes on some other Protozoa from the Termitidae. *Quart. J. micr. Sci.* **71**, 189.

—— (1929). *Snyderella* and *Coronympha*, two new genera of multinucleate flagellates from termites. *Univ. Calif. Publ. Zool.* **31**, 417.

—— (1930). Trichomonad flagellates from termites. I. *Tricercomitus* gen. nov., and *Hexamastix* Alexeieff. Ibid. **33**, 393.

—— (1931). Idem. II. *Eutrichomastix*, and the subfamily Trichomonadinae. Ibid. **36**, 171.

—— (1932). Flagellates of the genus *Trichonympha* in termites. Ibid. **37**, 349.

—— (1937). Host-parasite relations in the distribution of Protozoa in termites. Ibid. **41**, 189.

—— (1939). Two new flagellates from termites in the genera *Coronympha* Kirby, and *Metacoronympha* Kirby, new genus. *Proc. Calif. Acad. Sci.* **22**, 207.

—— (1941). Devescovinid flagellates of termites. I. The genus *Devescovina*. *Univ. Calif. Publ. Zool.* **45**, 1.

—— (1942a). Idem. II. The genera *Caduceia* and *Macrotrichomonas*. Ibid. **45**, 93.

—— (1942b). Idem. III. The genera *Foaina* and *Parajoenia*. Ibid. **45**, 167.

—— (1944). Some observations on cytology and morphogenesis in flagellate Protozoa. *J. Morph.* **75**, 361.

—— (1945a). The structure of the common intestinal trichomonad of man. *J. Parasit.* **31**, 163.

—— (1945b). Devescovinid flagellates of termites. IV. The genera *Metadevescovina* and *Pseudodevescovina*. *Univ. Calif. Publ. Zool.* **45**, 247.

—— (1947). Flagellate and host relationships of trichomonad flagellates. *J. Parasit.* **33**, 214.

—— (1949). Devescovinid flagellates of termites. The genus *Hyperdevescovina*, the genus *Bullanympha*, and undescribed or unrecorded species. *Univ. Calif. Publ. Zool.* **45**, 319.

—— (1950). *Materials and methods in the study of Protozoa.* University of California Press. Berkeley and Los Angeles.

—— and HONIGBERG, B. (1949). Flagellates of the caecum of ground squirrels. *Univ. Calif. Publ. Zool.* **53**, 315.

KITCHING, J. A. (1934). The physiology of contractile vacuoles. I. Osmotic relations. *J. exp. Biol.* **11**, 364.

—— (1936). Idem. II. The control of body volume in marine Peritricha. Ibid. **13**, 11.

—— (1938). Idem. III. The water balance of fresh-water Peritricha. Ibid. **15**, 143.

—— (1939). Idem. IV. A note on the sources of water evacuated, and on the function of contractile vacuoles in marine Peritricha. Ibid. **16**, 34.

—— (1951). Idem. VII. Osmotic relations in a suctorian, with special reference to the mechanism of control of vacuolar output. Ibid. **28**, 203.

KITCHING, J. A. (1952a). Observations on the mechanism of feeding in the suctorian *Podophrya*. Ibid. **29**, 255.

—— (1952b). The physiology of contractile vacuoles. VIII. The water relations of the suctorian *Podophrya* during feeding. Ibid. **29**, 363.

—— (1952c). Contractile vacuoles. *Symp. Soc. exp. Biol.* **6** (*Structural aspects of cell physiology*), p. 145. Cambridge.

—— (1954a). The effects of high hydrostatic pressures on a suctorian. *J. exp. Biol.* **31**, 56.

—— (1954b). The physiology of contractile vacuoles. IX. Effects of sudden changes in temperature on the contractile vacuole of a suctorian; with a discussion of the mechanism of contraction. Ibid. **31**, 68.

—— (1954c). Idem. X. Effects of high hydrostatic pressure on the contractile vacuole of a suctorian. Ibid. **31**, 76.

—— (1954d). On suction in Suctoria. *Proc. 7th Symp. Colston Res. Soc., Colston Papers*, **7**, 197.

KLEBS, G. (1893). Flagellatenstudien. I. *Z. wiss. Zool.* **55**, 265.

KLEIN, B. M. (1928). Die Silberliniensysteme der Ciliaten. Weitere Resultate. *Arch. Protistenk.* **62**, 177.

—— (1929). Weitere Beiträge zur Kenntnis des Silberliniensystems der Ciliaten. Ibid. **65**, 183.

—— (1936). Beziehungen zwischen Maschenweite und Bildungsvorgängen im Silberliniensystem der Ciliaten. Ibid. **88**, 1.

—— (1958). The 'dry' silver method and its proper use. *J. Protozool.* **5**, 99.

KOFOID, C. A. (1907). The plates of *Ceratium* with a note on the unity of the genus. *Zool. Anz.* **32**, 177.

—— (1909). On *Peridinium steini* Jörgensen, with a note on the nomenclature of the skeleton of the Peridinidae. *Arch. Protistenk.* **16**, 25.

—— (1920). A new morphological interpretation of the structure of *Noctiluca*, and its bearing on the status of the Cystoflagellata (Haeckel). *Univ. Calif. Publ. Zool.* **19**, 317.

—— and CAMPBELL, A. S. (1929). A conspectus of the marine and fresh-water Ciliata belonging to the suborder Tintinnoinea, with descriptions of new species principally from the Agassiz Expedition to the Eastern Tropical Pacific 1904–1905. Ibid. **34**, 403.

—— and CHRISTIANSEN, E. B. (1915). On binary and multiple fission in *Giardia muris* (Grassi). Ibid. **16**, 30.

—— and MACLENNAN, R. F. (1930). Ciliates from *Bos indicus* Linn. I. The genus *Entodinium* Stein. Ibid. **33**, 471.

—— —— (1932). Idem. II. A revision of *Diplodinium* Schuberg. Ibid. **37**, 53.

—— —— (1933). Idem. III. *Epidinium* Crawley, *Epiplastron* gen. nov., and *Ophryoscolex* Stein. Ibid. **39**, 1.

—— and ROSENBERG, L. E. (1940). The neuromotor system of *Opisthonecta henneguyi* (Fauré-Fremiet). *Proc. Amer. phil. Soc.* **82**, 421.

—— and SWEZY, O. (1915). Mitosis and multiple fission in trichomonad flagellates. *Proc. Amer. Acad. Arts Sci.* **51**, 289.

—— —— (1919a). Studies on the parasites of the termites. I. On *Streblomastix strix*, a polymastigote flagellate with a linear plasmodial phase. *Univ. Calif. Publ. Zool.* **20**, 1.

—— —— (1919b). Idem. III. On *Trichonympha campanula* sp. nov. Ibid. **20**, 41.

—— —— (1921). The free-living unarmored Dinoflagellata. *Mem. Univ. Calif.* **5**.

KONSULOFF, S. (1922). Untersuchungen über *Opalina*. *Arch. Protistenk.* **44**, 285.

468 REFERENCES

KORMOS, J., and KORMOS, K. (1957a). Neue Untersuchungen über den Geschlechtsdimorphismus der Prodiscophryen. *Act. biol. hung.* **7**, 109.

—— —— (1957b). Determination in der Entwicklung der Suctorien. I. Die Determination der Stelle der Embryoorganisierung. Ibid. **7**, 366.

—— —— (1958). Äußere und innere Konjugation. Ibid. **8**, 103.

KOZLOFF, E. N. (1945a). *Cochliophilus depressus* gen. nov., sp. nov. and *Cochliophilus minor* sp. nov., holotrichous ciliates from the mantle cavity of *Phytia setifer* (Cooper). *Biol. Bull.* **89**, 95.

—— (1945b). *Heterocineta phoronopsidis* sp. nov., a ciliate from the tentacles of *Phoronopsis viridis* Hilton. Ibid. **89**, 180.

—— (1946a). Studies on ciliates of the family Ancistrocomidae Chatton and Lwoff (Order Holotricha, Suborder Thigmotricha). I. *Hypocomina tegularum* sp. nov. and *Crebricoma* gen. nov. Ibid. **90**, 1.

—— (1946b). Idem. II. *Hypocomides mytili* Chatton and Lwoff, *Hypocomides botulae* sp. nov., *Hypocomides parva* sp. nov., *Hypocomides kelliae* sp. nov. and *Insignicoma venusta*, gen. nov., sp. nov. Ibid. **90**, 200.

—— (1946c). Idem. III. *Ancistrocoma pelseneeri* Chatton and Lwoff, *Ancistrocoma dissimilis* sp. nov., and *Hypocomagalma pholadidis* sp. nov. Ibid. **91**, 189.

—— (1946d). Idem. IV. *Heterocineta janickii* Jarocki, *Heterocineta goniobasidis* sp. nov., *Heterocineta fluminicolae* sp. nov., and *Enerthecoma properans* Jarocki. Ibid. **91**, 200.

—— (1948). The morphology of *Cryptobia helicis* Leidy, with an account of the fate of the extranuclear organelles in division. *J. Morph.* **83**, 253.

—— (1956). Experimental infection of the gray garden slug, *Deroceras reticulatum* (Müller), by the holotrichous ciliate *Tetrahymena pyriformis* (Ehrenberg). *J. Protozool.* **3**, 17.

KRANEVELD, F. C., HOUWINK, A. L., and KEIDEL, H. J. W. (1951). Electron microscopical investigations on trypanosomes. I. Some preliminary data regarding the structure of *Trypanosoma evansi*. *Proc. K. Nederl. Akad. Wetensch.* **54** (Ser. C), 393.

KRASCHENINNIKOW, S., and WENRICH, D. H. (1958). Some observations on the morphology and division of *Balantidium coli* and *Balantidium caviae* (?). *J. Protozool.* **5**, 196.

KRICHENBAUER, H. (1937). Beitrag zur Kenntnis der Morphologie und Entwicklungsgeschichte der Gattungen *Euglena* und *Phacus*. *Arch. Protistenk.* **90**, 88.

KROGH, A. (1939). *Osmotic regulation in aquatic animals*. Cambridge.

KRÜGER, F. (1934). Untersuchungen über die Trichocysten einiger *Prorodon*-Arten. *Arch. Protistenk.* **83**, 275.

KUCZYNSKI, M. H. (1914). Untersuchungen an Trichomonaden. Ibid. **33**, 119.

—— (1918). Über die Teilungsvorgänge verschiedener Trichomonaden und ihre Organisation im allgemeinen. Ibid. **39**, 107.

KUDO, R. (R.) (1918). Experiments on the extrusion of polar filaments of Cnidosporidian spores. *J. Parasit.* **4**, 141.

—— (1920). Studies on Myxosporidia; a synopsis of genera and species of Myxosporidia. *Illinois biol. Monogr.* **5**, 1.

—— (1921). On the nature of structures characteristic of Cnidosporidian spores. *Trans. Amer. micr. Soc.* **40**, 59.

—— (1926a). Observations on *Lophomonas blattarum*, a flagellate inhabiting the colon of the cockroach, *Blatta orientalis*. *Arch. Protistenk.* **53**, 191.

—— (1926b). A cytological study of *Lophomonas striata* Bütschli. Ibid. **55**, 504.

—— (1926c). Observations on *Endamoeba blattae*. *Amer. J. Hyg.* **6**, 139.

Kudo, R. (R.) (1933). A taxonomic consideration of Myxosporidia. *Trans. Amer. micr. Soc.* **52,** 195.

—— (1936). Studies on *Nyctotherus ovalis* Leidy, with special reference to its nuclear structure. *Arch. Protistenk.* **87,** 10.

—— (1947). *Pelomyxa carolinensis* Wilson. II. Nuclear division and plasmotomy. *J. Morph.* **80,** 93.

—— (1952). The genus *Pelomyxa*. *Trans. Amer. micr. Soc.* **71,** 108.

—— (1957). *Pelomyxa palustris* Greef. I. Cultivation and general observations. *J. Protozool.* **4,** 154.

—— (1959). *Pelomyxa* and related organisms. *Ann. N.Y. Acad. Sci.* **78,** 474.

—— and Meglitsch, P. A. (1938). On *Balantidium praenucleatum* n. sp., inhabiting the colon of *Blatta orientalis*. *Arch. Protistenk.* **91,** 111.

Kühn, A. (1915). Über Bau, Teilung und Encystierung von *Bodo edax* Klebs. Ibid. **35,** 212.

Kümmel, G. (1958). Die Gleitbewegung der Gregarinen. Elektronenmikroskopische und experimentelle Untersuchungen. Ibid. **102,** 501.

Kuschakewitsch, S. (1907). Beobachtungen über vegetative, degenerative und germinative Vorgänge bei den Gregarinen des Mehlwurmdarms. Ibid. Suppl. I. Festb. R. Hertwig, p. 202.

Lackey, J. B. (1933). Studies in the life history of Euglenida. III. The morphology of *Peranema trichophorum* Ehrenberg, with special reference to its kinetic elements and the classification of the Heteronemidae. *Biol. Bull.* **45,** 238.

Lapage, G. (1922). Cannibalism in *Amoeba vespertilio* (Penard). *Quart. J. micr. Sci.* **66,** 669.

Lauterborn, R. (1894). Über die Winterfauna einiger Gewässer der Oberrheinebene. Mit Beschreibungen neuer Protozoen. *Biol. Zbl.* **14,** 390.

—— (1908). Protozoen-Studien. V. Teil. Zur Kenntnis einiger Rhizopoden und Infusorien aus dem Gebiete des Oberrheins. *Z. wiss. Zool.* **90,** 645.

Lebour, M. V. (1925). *The dinoflagellates of northern seas.* Plymouth.

Le Calvez, J. (1938). Recherches sur les Foraminifères. I. Développement et reproduction. *Arch. Zool. exp. gén.* **80,** 163.

—— (1940). Une Amibe, *Vahlkampfia discorbinis*, n. sp., parasite du foraminifère *Discorbis mediterranensis* (d'Orbigny). Ibid. **81,** 123.

—— (1950). Recherches sur les foraminifères. II. Place de la méiose et sexualité. Ibid. **87,** 211.

Leedale, G. F. (1958). Nuclear structure and mitosis in Euglenineae. *Arch. Mikrobiol.* **32,** 32.

—— (1959). Periodicity of mitosis and cell division in the Euglenineae. *Biol. Bull.* **116,** 162.

Léger, L. (1902). Sur la structure et le mode de multiplication des flagellés du genre *Herpetomonas* Kent. *C.R. Acad. Sci., Paris,* **134,** 781.

—— and Duboscq, O. (1904*a*). Nouvelles recherches sur les grégarines et l'épithélium intestinal des trachéates. *Arch. Protistenk.* **4,** 335.

—— —— (1904*b*). Notes sur les infusoires endoparasites. II. *Anoplophrya brasili* Léger et Duboscq. Parasite d'*Audouinia tentaculata*. *Arch. Zool. exp. gén.* **2,** 337.

—— (1909). Études sur la sexualité chez les grégarines. *Arch. Protistenk.* **17,** 19.

Leidy, J. (1879). Fresh-water rhizopods of North America. *U.S. Geological Survey,* **12.** Washington.

LEINER, M., and WOHLFEIL, M. (1953). *Pelomyxa palustris* Greeff und ihre symbiotischen Bakterien. *Arch. Protistenk.* 98, 227.

LEVINE, L. (1959). Axenizing *Vorticella convallaria*. *J. Protozool.* 6, 169.

LEWIS, W. H. (1931). Pinocytosis. *Johns Hopkins Hosp. Bull.* 49, 17.

LIESCHE, W. (1938). Die Kern- und Fortpflanzungsverhältnisse von *Amoeba proteus* (Pall.). *Arch. Protistenk.* 91, 135.

LIST, T. (1913). Über die Temporal- und Lokalvariation von *Ceratium hirundinella* O.F.M. *Arch. Hydrobiol. Planktonk.* 9, 81.

LOOPER, J. B. (1928). Observations on the food reactions of *Actinophrys sol*. *Biol. Bull.* 54, 485.

LORCH, I. J., and DANIELLI, J. F. (1950). Transplantation of nuclei from cell to cell. *Nature, Lond.* 166, 329.

—— —— (1953a). Nuclear transplantation in amoebae. I. Some species characters of *Amoeba proteus* and *Amoeba discoides*. *Quart. J. micr. Sci.* 94, 445.

—— —— (1953b). Idem. II. The immediate results of transfers of nuclei between *Amoeba proteus* and *Amoeba discoides*. Ibid. 94, 461.

LOUBATIÈRES, R. (1955). Contribution à l'étude des Grégarinomorphes Monocystidae parasites des oligochètes du Languedoc-Rousillon. *Ann. Sci. Nat., Zool.* 17, 73.

LOWNDES, A. G. (1936). Flagella movement. *Nature, Lond.* 138, 210.

—— (1941a). Mechanics of a flagellum. Ibid. 148, 198.

—— (1941b). On flagellar movement in unicellular organisms. *Proc. zool. Soc. Lond.* 111 (Ser. A), 111.

—— (1943). The swimming of unicellular flagellate organisms. Ibid. 113 (Ser. A), 99.

—— (1944). The swimming of *Monas stigmatica* Pringsheim and *Peranema trichophorum* (Ehrbg.) Stein and *Volvox* sp. Additional experiments on the working of a flagellum. Ibid. 114, 325.

—— (1945). Swimming of *Monas stigmatica*. *Nature, Lond.* 155, 579.

LUCAS, C. L. T. (1927). Two new species of amoeba found in cockroaches: with notes on the cysts of *Nyctotherus ovalis* Leidy. *Parasitology*, 19, 223.

—— (1928). A study of excystation in *Nyctotherus ovalis* with notes on other intestinal Protozoa of the cockroach. *J. Parasit.* 14, 161.

LUCAS, M. S. (1932a). A study of *Cyathodinium piriforme*. An endozoic protozoan from the intestinal tract of the guinea-pig. *Arch. Protistenk.* 77, 64.

—— (1932b). The cytoplasmic phases of rejuvenescence and fission in *Cyathodinium piriforme*. II. A type of fission heretofore undescribed for ciliates. Ibid. 77, 407.

LUDWIG, W. (1928). Der Betriebsstoffwechsel von *Paramaecium caudatum* Ehrbg. Zugleich ein Beitrag zur Frage nach der Funktion der kontraktilen Vacuolen. Ibid. 62, 12.

LUND, E. E. (1930). The effect of diet upon the intestinal fauna of *Termopsis*. *Univ. Calif. Publ. Zool.* 36, 81.

—— (1933). A correlation of the silverline and neuromotor systems of *Paramecium*. Ibid. 39, 35.

—— (1935). The neuromotor system of *Oxytricha*. *J. Morph.* 58, 257.

—— (1941). The feeding mechanisms of various ciliated Protozoa. Ibid. 69, 563.

LWOFF, A. (1923). Sur la nutrition des infusoires. *C.R. Acad. Sci., Paris*, 176, 928.

—— (1936). Le cycle nucléaire de *Stephanopogon mesnili* Lw. (cilié homocaryote). *Arch. Zool. exp. gén.* 78 (N. & R.), 117.

Lwoff, A. (1950). *Problems of morphogenesis in ciliates; the kinetosomes in development, reproduction and evolution.* New York and London.

—— and Dusi, H. (1935). La Suppression expérimentale des chloroplastes chez *Euglena mesnili. C.R. Soc. Biol., Paris,* **119**, 1092.

—— and Lwoff, M. (1931*a*). Recherches morphologiques sur *Leptomonas ctenocephali* Fanth. (Trypanosomide). Remarques sur l'appareil parabasal. *Bull. biol.* **65**, 170.

—— and Lwoff, A. (1931*b*). Recherches sur la morphologie de *Leptomonas oncopelti* Noguchi et Tilden et *Leptomonas fasciculata* Novy, MacNeal et Torrey. *Arch. Zool. exp. gén.* **71** (N. & R.), 21.

McDonald, B. B. (1958). Quantitative aspects of deoxyribose nucleic acid (DNA) metabolism in an amicronucleate strain of *Tetrahymena. Biol. Bull.* **114**, 71.

McDonald, J. D. (1922). On *Balantidium coli* (Malmsten) and *Balantidium suis* (sp. nov.), with an account of their neuromotor apparatus. *Univ. Calif. Publ. Zool.* **20**, 243.

MacDougall, M. M. (1942). A study of temperature effects on gregarines of *Tenebrio molitor* larvae. *J. Parasit.* **28**, 233.

MacDougall, M. S. (1925). Cytological observations on gymnostomatous ciliates, with a description of the maturation phenomena in diploid and tetraploid forms of *Chilodon uncinatus. Quart. J. micr. Sci.* **69**, 361.

—— (1929). Modifications in *Chilodon uncinatus* produced by ultraviolet radiation. *J. exp. Zool.* **54**, 95.

—— (1931). Another mutation of *Chilodon uncinatus* produced by ultraviolet radiation, with a description of its maturation processes. Ibid. **58**, 229.

—— (1936). Étude cytologique de trois espèces du genre *Chilodonella* Strand. Morphologie, conjugaison, réorganisation. *Bull. biol.* **70**, 308.

MacKinley, R. B. (1936). Observations on *Nebela collaris* Leidy (*pro parte*), a testate amoeba of moorland waters. Part I. *J. R. micr. Soc.* **56**, 307.

Mackinnon, D. L. (1910). Herpetomonads from the alimentary tract of certain dungflies. *Parasitology,* **3**, 255.

—— (1914*a*). Observations on amoebae from the intestine of the crane-fly larva, *Tipula* sp. *Arch. Protistenk.* **32**, 267.

—— (1914*b*). Alteration of name. Ibid. **34**, 340.

—— and Adam, D. I. (1924). Notes on four astomatous ciliates from oligochaete worms. *Quart. J. micr. Sci.* **68**, 211.

—— and Ray, H. N. (1933). The life cycle of two species of '*Selenidium*' from the polychaete worm *Potamilla reniformis. Parasitology,* **25**, 143.

Maier, H. N. (1903). Über den feineren Bau der Wimperapparate der Infusorien. *Arch. Protistenk.* **2**, 73.

Mainx, F. (1928). Beiträge zur Morphologie und Physiologie der Euglveninen. I. Teil. Morphologische Beobachtungen, Methoden und Erfolge der Reinkultur. Ibid. **60**, 305.

Mangin, L. (1907). Observations sur la constitution de la membrane des Péridiniens. *C.R. Acad. Sci., Paris,* **144**, 1055.

Manton, I. (1952). The fine structure of plant cilia. *Symp. Soc. exp. Biol.* **6** (*Structural aspects of cell physiology*), 307.

—— (1953). Number of fibrils in the cilia of green algae. *Nature, Lond.* **171**, 485.

—— (1956). Plant cilia and associated organelles. *14th Symp. Soc. Study Develop. Growth* (*Cellular mechanisms in differentiation and growth*), 61.

MARSHALL, J. M., SCHUMAKER, V. N., and BRANDT, P. W. (1959). Pinocytosis in amoebae. *Ann. N.Y. Acad. Sci.* **78**, 515.

MAST, S. O. (1909). The reactions of *Didinium nasutum* (Stein) with special reference to the feeding habits and the function of trichocysts. *Biol. Bull.* **16**, 91.

—— (1912). The reactions of the flagellate *Peranema*. *J. Anim. Behav.* **2**, 91.

—— (1931). Movement and response in *Difflugia* with special reference to the nature of cytoplasmic contraction. *Biol. Bull.* **61**, 223.

—— (1934). Amoeboid movement in *Pelomyxa palustris*. *Physiol. Zoöl.* **7**, 470.

—— (1938a). The contractile vacuole in *Amoeba proteus* (Leidy). *Biol. Bull.* **74**, 306.

—— (1938b). Factors involved in the process of orientation of lower organisms in light. *Biol. Rev.* **13**, 186.

—— (1947). The food-vacuole in *Paramecium*. *Biol. Bull.* **92**, 31.

—— and DOYLE, W. L. (1934). Ingestion of fluid by *Amoeba*. *Protoplasma*, **20**, 555.

—— —— (1935a). Structure, origin and function of cytoplasmic constituents in *Amoeba proteus*. I. Structure. *Arch. Protistenk.* **86**, 155.

—— —— (1935b). Idem. II. Origin and function based on experimental evidence; effect of centrifuging on *Amoeba proteus*. Ibid. **86**, 278.

—— and JOHNSON, P. L. (1931). Concerning the scientific name of the common large amoeba, usually designated *Amoeba proteus* (Leidy). Ibid. **75**, 14.

—— and LASHLEY, K. S. (1916). Observations on ciliary current in free-swimming Paramecia. *J. exp. Zool.* **21**, 281.

MATTHES, D. (1950). Die Kiemenfauna unserer Landasseln. *Zool. Jb.* **78**, 573.

—— (1954). Beitrag zur Kenntnis der Gattung *Discophrya* Lachmann. *Arch. Protistenk.* **99**, 187.

MATTHEY, R. (1923). Contribution à l'étude de *Trypanoplasma helicis* Leidy. *Rev. suisse Zool.* **30**, 425.

MAUPAS, E. (1889). Le Rajeunissement karyogamique chez les ciliés. *Arch. Zool. exp. gén.* **7**, 149.

MAYER, M. (1920). Zur Cystenbildung von *Trichomonas muris*. *Arch. Protistenk.* **40**, 290.

MEGLITSCH, P. A. (1940). Cytological observations on *Endamoeba blattae*. *Illinois biol. Monogr.* **17**, no. 4.

MEIER, M. (1956). Die Monocystideenfauna der Oligochaeten von Erlangen und Umgebung. *Arch. Protistenk.* **101**, 335.

MERCER, E. H. (1959). An electron microscope study of *Amoeba proteus*. *Proc. roy. Soc.* B, **150**, 216.

METCALF, M. M. (1909). *Opalina*. Its anatomy and reproduction, with a description of infection experiments and a chronological review of the literature. *Arch. Protistenk.* **13**, 195.

—— (1918a). *Opalina* and the origin of the ciliate Infusoria. *J. Wash. Acad. Sci.* **8**, 427.

—— (1918b). *Opalina* and the origin of ciliates. *Anat. Rec.* **14**, 88.

—— (1923). The Opalinid ciliate infusorians. *Smithsonian Inst. U.S. Nat. Mus. Bull.*, no. 120, pp. 484.

—— (1940). Further studies on the Opalinid ciliate infusorians and their hosts. *Proc. U.S. Nat. Mus.* **87**, 465.

METZ, C. B., PITELKA, D. R., and WESTFALL, J. A. (1953). The fibrillar systems of ciliates as revealed by the electron microscope. I. *Paramecium*. *Biol. Bull.* **104**, 408.

—— and WESTFALL, J. A. (1954). Idem. II. *Tetrahymena*. Ibid. **107**, 106.

MICHRLSON, E. (1928). Existenzbedingungen und Cystenbildung bei *Paramecium caudatum* Ehrb. *Arch. Protistenk.* 61, 167.

MILLER, C. A., and JOHNSON, W. H. (1957). A purine and pyrimidine requirement for *Paramecium multimicronucleatum*. *J. Protozool.* 4, 200.

MINCHIN, E. A., and THOMSON, J. D. (1915). The rat-trypanosome, *Trypanosoma lewisi*, in its relation to the rat-flea, *Ceratophyllus fasciatus*. *Quart. J. micr. Sci.* 60, 463.

MOHR, J. L. (1940). On the orientation of Opalinids. *J. Parasit.* 26, 236.

MORRIS, S. (1936). Studies on *Endamoeba blattae* (Bütschli). *J. Morph.* 59, 225.

MOSES, M. J. (1950). Nucleic acids and proteins of the nuclei of *Paramecium*. Ibid. 87, 493.

MUGARD, H. (1948). Contribution à l'étude des infusoires hyménostomes histiophages. *Ann. Sci. Nat., Zool.* 11me sér., 10, 171.

—— and LORSIGNOL, L. (1957). Étude de la division et de la régénération chez deux Ophryoglenidae d'eau douce: *Ophryoglena pectans* et *Deltopylum rhabdoides*. *Bull. biol.* 90, 446.

MÜHL, D. (1921). Beitrag zur Kenntnis der Morphologie und Physiologie der Mehlwurmgregarinen. *Arch. Protistenk.* 43, 361.

MULSOW, W. (1913). Die Conjugation von *Stentor coeruleus* und *Stentor polymorphus*. Ibid. 28, 363.

MYERS, E. H. (1936). The life-cycle of *Spirillina vivipara* Ehrenberg, with notes on morphogenesis, systematics and distribution of the Foraminifera. *J. R. micr. Soc.* 56, 120.

—— (1938). The present state of our knowledge concerning the life-cycle of the Foraminifera. *Proc. nat. Acad. Sci., Wash.* 24, 10.

—— (1940). Observations on the origin and fate of flagellated gametes in multiple tests of *Discorbis* (Foraminifera). *J. mar. biol. Ass. U.K.* 24, 201.

NANNEY, D. L. (1953). Nucleo-cytoplasmic interaction during conjugation in *Tetrahymena*. *Biol. Bull.* 105, 133.

NEAL, R. A. (1948). *Entamoeba histolytica* in wild rats caught in London. *J. Hyg.* 46, 90.

—— (1950). An experimental study of *Entamoeba muris* (Grassi, 1879); its morphology, affinities and host-parasite relationship. *Parasitology*, 40, 343.

—— (1953). Studies on the morphology and biology of *Entamoeba moshkovskii* Tshalaia, 1941. Ibid. 43, 253.

NEFF, R. J. (1957). Purification, axenic cultivation, and description of a soil amoeba, *Acanthamoeba* sp. *J. Protozool.* 4, 176.

—— (1958). Mechanisms of purifying amoebae by migration on agar surfaces. Ibid. 5, 226.

NERESHEIMER, E. R. (1903). Über die Höhe histologischer Differenzierung bei heterotrichen Ciliaten. *Arch. Protistenk.* 2, 305.

NICOL, J. A. C. (1958). Observations on luminescence in *Noctiluca*. *J. mar. biol. Ass. U.K.* 37, 535.

NIE, D. (1950). Morphology and taxonomy of the intestinal Protozoa of the guinea-pig, *Cavia porcella*. *J. Morph.* 86, 381.

NIESCHULTZ, O. (1922). Über eine *Astasia*-Art aus dem Süßwassernematoden *Trilobus gracilis* Bst. *Zool. Anz.* 54, 136.

NOBLE, A. E. (1932). On *Tokophrya lemnarum* Stein (Suctoria) with an account of its budding and conjugation. *Univ. Calif. Publ. Zool.* 37, 477.

NOBLE, E. R. (1938). The life cycle of *Zygosoma globosum* sp. nov. a gregarine parasite of *Urechis caupo*. Ibid. **43**, 41.

—— (1941). Nuclear cycles in the life history of the Protozoan genus *Ceratomyxa*. *J. Morph.* **69**, 455.

—— (1944). Life cycles in the Myxosporidia. *Quart. Rev. Biol.* **19**, 213.

—— (1955). The morphology and life cycles of trypanosomes. Ibid. **30**, 1.

——, McRARY, W. L., and BEAVER, E. T. (1953). Cell division in trypanosomes. *Trans. Amer. micr. Soc.* **72**, 236.

NOLAND, L. E. (1928). A combined fixative and stain for demonstrating flagella and cilia in temporary mounts. *Science*, **67**, 534.

—— (1937). Observations on marine ciliates of the gulf coast of Florida. *Trans. Amer. micr. Soc.* **56**, 160.

—— (1957). Protoplasmic streaming: a perennial puzzle. *J. Protozool.* **4**, 1.

—— and FINLEY, H. E. (1931). Studies on the taxonomy of the genus *Vorticella*. *Trans. Amer. micr. Soc.* **50**, 81.

NUTTING, W. L., and CLEVELAND, L. R. (1958). Effects of glandular extirpations on *Cryptocercus* and the sexual cycles of its Protozoa. *J. exp. Zool.* **137**, 13.

OKADA, Y. K. (1930). Über den Bau und die Bewegungsweise von *Pelomyxa*. *Arch. Protistenk.* **70**, 131.

—— (1932). Über die Zentralachse von *Pelomyxa*. Ibid. **77**, 529.

OVERBEEK DE MEYER, G. A. W. VAN (1929). Beiträge zu Wachstums- und Plasma-differenzierungs-Erscheinungen an *Opalina ranarum*. Ibid. **66**, 207.

OWEN, H. M. (1947). Flagellar structure: I. A discussion of fixation and staining of the protozoan flagellum. *Trans. Amer. micr. Soc.* **66**, 50.

—— (1949). Idem. II. The flagellum as a taxonomic character. Ibid. **68**, 261.

OXFORD, A. E. (1955). The rumen ciliate Protozoa: their chemical composition, metabolism, requirements for maintenance and culture, and physiological significance for the host. *Exp. Parasit.* **4**, 569.

PADNOS, M., and NIGRELLI, R. F. (1942). *Trichodina spheroidesi* and *Trichodina halli* spp. nov. Parasitic on the gills and skin of marine fishes, with special reference to the life-history of *T. spheroidesi*. *Zoologica, N.Y.* **27**, 65.

PAI, K.-T., and WANG, C.-C. (1948). The variation of *Nyctotherus ovalis* Leidy, and its fibrillar system. *Sinensia*, **18**, 43.

PANTIN, C. F. A. (1946). *Notes on microscopical technique for zoologists.* Cambridge.

PAPPAS, G. D. (1954). Structural and cytochemical studies of the cytoplasm in the family Amoebida. *Ohio J. Sci.* **54**, 195.

—— (1959). Electron microscope studies on amoebae. *Ann. N.Y. Acad. Sci.* **78**, 448.

PÁRDUCZ, B. (1939). Körperbau und einige Lebenserscheinungen von *Uronema marinum* Duj. *Arch. Protistenk.* **92**, 283.

—— (1940). Verwandtschaftliche Beziehungen zwischen den Gattungen *Uronema* und *Cyclidium*. Bau und Lebensweise von *Cyclidium glaucoma* Müll. Ibid. **93**, 185.

PARISI, B. (1912). Primo contributo alla distribuzione geografica dei Missosporidi in Italia. *Att. Soc. ital. Sci. nat.* **50**, 283.

PATEFF, P. (1926). Fortpflanzungserscheinungen bei *Difflugia mammillaris* Penard und *Clypeolina marginata* Penard. *Arch. Protistenk.* **55**, 516.

PENARD, E. (1902). *Faune rhizopodique du bassin du Léman.* Geneva.

—— (1904). *Les Héliozoaires d'eau douce.* Geneva.

PENARD, E. (1905). Observations sur les amibes à pellicule. *Arch. Protistenk.* **6**, 175.

—— (1909). Sur quelques rhizopodes des mousses. Ibid. **70**, 258.

—— (1922). *Études sur les infusoires d'eau douce.* Geneva.

PÉRARD, C. (1924). Recherches sur les coccidies et les coccidioses du lapin. *C.R. Acad. Sci., Paris,* **178**, 2131.

—— (1925). Idem. Thèse pour le doctorat vétérinaire. Paris.

PETERS, N. (1929). Über Orts- und Geißelbewegung bei marinen Dinoflagellaten. *Arch. Protistenk.* **67**, 291.

PETERSEN, J. B. (1929). Beiträge zur Kenntnis der Flagellatengeißeln. *Bot. Tidsskr.* **40**, 373.

PHELPS, A. (1947). A method for isolating from natural water those Protozoa which can live in pure culture. *Anat. Rec.* **99**, 605.

PHILLIPS, N. E., and MACKINNON, D. L. (1946). Observations on a monocystid gregarine, *Apolocystis elongata* n. sp., in the seminal vesicles of *Eisenia foetida* (Sav.). *Parasitology,* **37**, 65.

PICKARD, E. A. (1927). The neuromotor apparatus of *Boveria teredinidi* Nelson, a ciliate from the gills of *Teredo navalis. Univ. Calif. Publ. Zool.* **29**, 405.

PIEKARSKI, G. (1939). Cytologische Untersuchungen an einem normalen und einem Micronucleus-losen Stamm von *Colpoda steini* Maupas. *Arch. Protistenk.* **92**, 117.

PIERSON, B. F. (1943). A comparative morphological study of several species of *Euplotes* closely related to *Euplotes patella. J. Morph.* **72**, 125.

PITELKA, D. R. (1945). Morphology and taxonomy of flagellates of the genus *Peranema* Dujardin. Ibid. **76**, 179.

—— (1949). Observations on the flagellum structure in Flagellata. *Univ. Calif. Publ. Zool.* **53**, 377.

—— (1956). An electron microscope study of cortical structures of *Opalina obtrigonoidea. J. biophys. biochem. Cytol.* **2**, 423.

—— and SCHOOLEY, C. N. (1955). Comparative morphology of some protistan flagella. *Univ. Calif. Publ. Zool.* **61**, 79.

—— —— (1958). The fine structure of the flagellar apparatus in *Trichonympha. J. Morph.* **102**, 199.

POCHMANN, A. (1942). Synopsis der Gattung *Phacus. Arch. Protistenk.* **95**, 81.

PORTER, A. (1909). The life-cycle of *Herpetomonas jaculum* (Léger), parasitic in the alimentary tract of *Nepa cinerea. Parasitology,* **2**, 367.

POUNDEN, W. D., and HIBBS, J. W. (1950). The development of calves raised without Protozoa and certain other characteristic rumen microorganisms. *J. Dairy Sci.* **33**, 639.

PRATJE, A. (1921*a*). *Noctiluca miliaris* Suriray. Beiträge zur Morphologie, Physiologie und Cytologie. I. Morphologie und Physiologie. (Beobachtungen an der lebenden Zelle). *Arch. Protistenk.* **42**, 1.

—— (1921*b*). Die verwandtschaftlichen Beziehungen der Cystoflagellaten zu den Dinoflagellaten. Zugleich ein Referat über Kofoid's neue *Noctiluca*-Arbeit (1920). Ibid. **42**, 422.

PRELL, H. (1921). Zur Theorie der sekretorischen Ortsbewegung. II. Die Bewegung der Gregarinen. Ibid. **42**, 157.

PRESCOTT, D. M. (1955). Relations between cell growth and cell division. I. Reduced weight, cell volume, protein content, and nuclear volume of *Amoeba proteus* from division to division. *Exp. Cell Res.* **9**, 328.

—— (1956). Mass and clone culturing of *Amoeba proteus* and *Chaos chaos. C.R. Lab. Carlsberg, Sér. chim.* **30**, 1.

PRESCOTT, D. M. (1959). Microtechniques in amoebae studies. *Ann. N.Y. Acad. Sci.* **78**, 655.

PRINGSHEIM, E. G. (1936). Zur Kenntnis saprotropher Algen und Flagellaten. I. Mitteilung. Über Anhäufungskulturen polysaprober Flagellaten. *Arch. Protistenk.* **87**, 43.

—— (1942). Contributions to our knowledge of saprophytic Algae and Flagellata. III. *Astasia, Distigma, Menoidium* and *Rhabdomonas*. *New Phytol.* **41**, 171.

—— (1946a). *Pure cultures of algae: their preparation and maintenance.* Cambridge.

—— (1946b). The biphasic or soil-water culture method for growing Algae and Flagellata. *J. Ecol.* **33**, 193.

—— (1948). Taxonomic problems in the Euglenineae. *Biol. Rev.* **23**, 46.

—— (1953). Salzwasser-Eugleninen. *Arch. Mikrobiol.* **18**, 149.

—— (1956). Contributions towards a monograph of the genus *Euglena*. *Nova Acta Leopoldina* (*Abh. Dtsch. Akad. Naturforsch.*), **18**, Nr. 125, 168 pp.

—— and HOVASSE, R. (1948). The loss of chromatophores in *Euglena gracilis*. *New Phytol.* **47**, 52.

—— —— (1950). Les Relations de parenté entre Astasiacées et Euglènacées. *Arch. Zool. exp. gén.* **86**, 499.

PROVASOLI, L., HUTNER, S. H., and SCHATZ, A. (1948). Streptomycin-induced chlorophyll-less races of *Euglena*. *Proc. Soc. exp. Biol. Med.* **69**, 279.

——, MCLAUGHLIN, J. J. A., and DROOP, M. R. (1957). The development of artificial media for marine Algae. *Arch. Mikrobiol.* **25**, 392.

PÜTTER, A. (1905). Die Atmung der Protozoen. *Z. allg. Physiol.* **5**, 566.

PUYTORAC, P. DE (1954). Contribution à l'étude cytologique et taxonomique des infusoires astomes. *Ann. Sci. Nat., Zool.* 11me sér. **16**, 85.

—— (1955a). A propos de deux nouvelles espèces de ciliés astomes: *Radiophrya intermedia* sp. nov. et *Juxtaradiophrya enchytraeoidei* sp. nov. Cinétodesme et cytosquelette chez les astomes. *Bull. Soc. zool. Fr.* **80**, 92.

—— (1955b). Sur *Hovasseiella polydorae* nov. gen., n. sp., cilié astome endo-parasite de *Polydora giardi* Mesn. *Arch. Zool. exp. gén.* **93** (N. & R.), 20.

—— (1956a). Détermination de certaines des conditions écologiques propres aux différents ciliés parasites du tube digestif d'*Allolobophora savignyi* G. et H. (Oligochète). *Bull. Biol. Fr. Belg.* **90**, 122.

—— (1956b). L'"argyrome" chez les grégarines Monocystinae. *C.R. de l'Assoc. des Anatomistes*, 43rd Reunion, Lisbon, 1956, p. 694.

—— (1957a). *Elliptothigma limnodrili* Meier. Intérêt de ce cilié dans une recherche des parentés phylétiques de certains infusoires astomes. *C.R. Acad. Sci., Paris*, **244**, 1079.

—— (1957b). L'Infraciliature de quelques ciliés Haptophryidae. Comparaison avec celle de certains thigmotriches. Ibid. **244**, 1962.

—— (1957c) Nouvelles données sur les ciliés Hoplitophryidae. *Arch. Zool. exp. gén.* **94** (N. & R.), 89.

—— (1959). Les *Lubetiella* nov. gen., ciliés endoparasites des vers Megascolecidae sont la preuve de l'origine trichostomienne de certains infusoires astomes. *C.R. Acad. Sci., Paris*, **248**, 1579.

RAABE, H. (1946). L'appareil nucléaire d'*Urostyla grandis* Ehrbg. Pt. I. Appareil micronucléaire. *Ann. Univ. M. Curie-Sklodowska*, **1**, 1.

—— (1947). Idem. II. Appareil macronucléaire. Ibid. **1**, 133.

RAABE, Z. (1934). Über einige an den Kiemen von *Mytilus edulis* L. und *Macoma balthica* (L.) parasitierende Ciliaten-Arten. *Ann. Mus. zool. polon.* **10**, 289.

RAABE, Z. (1936). Weitere Untersuchungen an parasitischen Ciliaten aus dem polnischen Teil der Ostsee. I. Ciliata Thigmotricha aus den Familien Thigmophryidae, Conchophthiridae und Ancistrumidae. Ibid. **11**, 419.

—— (1938). Idem. II. Ciliata Thigmotricha aus den Familien Hypocomidae Bütschli und Sphenophryidae Ch. & Lw. Ibid. **13**, 41.

—— (1949). Studies on the family Hysterocinitidae Diesing. Ibid. **14**, 21.

—— (1950). Recherches sur les ciliés Thigmotriches (Thigmotricha Ch. Lw.). V. Ciliés thigmotriches du lac Balaton (Hongrie). *Ann. Univ. M. Curie-Sklodowska*, **5**, 197.

RAFALKO, J. S. (1947). Cytological observations on the amoebo-flagellate, *Naegleria gruberi. J. Morph.* **81**, 1.

RAIKOV, I. B. (1958). Der Formwechsel des Kernapparates einiger niederer Ciliaten. I. Die Gattung *Trachelocerca. Arch. Protistenk.* **103**, 129.

—— (1959a). Idem. II. Die Gattung *Loxodes.* Ibid. **104**, 1.

—— (1959b). Tsitologicheskie i tsitokhimicheskie osobennosti yadernogo apparata i deleniya navnoresnichinoi infusorii *Geleia nigriceps* Kahl. (Cytological and cytochemical peculiarities of the nuclear apparatus and division in the holotrichous ciliate *Geleia nigriceps* Kahl). In Russian. *Tsitologiya*, **1**, 566 (Izdat. Akad. Nauk SSSR, Moskva).

RANDALL, J. T. (1956). Fine structure of some ciliated Protozoa. *Nature, Lond.* **178**, 9.

—— (1957). The fine structure of the protozoan *Spirostomum ambiguum. Symp. Soc. exp. Biol.* **10** (*Mitochondria and other cytoplasmic inclusions*), p. 185.

—— (1958). New light on Leeuwenhoek's 'little animals'. *The Times Science Review*, Autumn 1958.

—— and JACKSON, S. F. (1958). Fine structure and function in *Stentor polymorphus. J. biophys. biochem. Cytol.* **4**, 807.

RAY, C. (1956). Meiosis and nuclear behaviour in *Tetrahymena pyriformis. J. Protozool.* **3**, 88.

RAY, H. N. (1930a). Studies on some Sporozoa in polychaete worms. I. Gregarines of the genus *Selenidium. Parasitology*, **22**, 370.

—— (1930b). Idem. II. *Dorisiella scolelepidis*, n. gen., n. sp. Ibid. **22**, 471.

REED, N. (1933). Sporogony in *Selenidium mesnili* Brasil, a sporozoan parasite of *Myxicola infundibulum* Mont. Ibid. **25**, 402.

REES, C. W. (1922). The neuromotor apparatus of *Paramecium. Univ. Calif. Publ. Zool.* **20**, 333.

REICH, F. (1912). Das Kaninchencoccid *Eimeria stiedae* (Lindemann 1865) nebst einem Beitrage zur Kenntnis von *Eimeria falciformis* (Eimer 1870). *Arch. Protistenk.* **28**, 1.

REICHENOW, E. (1921). Die Hämococcidien der Eidechsen. Vorbemerkungen und Teil I: Die Entwicklungsgeschichte von *Karyolysus.* Ibid. **42**, 179.

—— (1932). Sporozoa. In Grimpe's *Die Tierwelt der Nord- und Ostsee*, II. g. Leipzig.

REYNOLDS, B. D. (1926). Cavallini's 'Asexual Cycle in Arcella'. *Science*, **63**, 545.

REYNOLDSON, T. B. (1950). Natural population fluctuations of *Urceolaria mitra* (Protozoa, Peritricha) epizoic on flatworms. *J. anim. Ecol.* **19**, 106.

—— (1951). The dispersal of *Urceolaria mitra* (Peritricha) epizoic on flatworms. Ibid. **20**, 123.

ROBERTSON, M. (1927). Notes on certain points in the cytology of *Trypanosoma raiae* and *Bodo caudatus. Parasitology*, **19**, 375.

RODHAIN, J. (1934). *Entamoeba invadens* n. sp., parasite de serpents. *C.R. Soc. Biol., Paris,* **117,** 1199.

ROOT, F. M. (1914). Reproduction and reactions to food in the suctorian, *Podophrya collini* n. sp. *Arch. Protistenk.* **35,** 164.

ROSENBERG, L. E. (1938). Cyst stages of *Opisthonecta henneguyi. Trans. Amer. micr. Soc.* **57,** 147.

ROSKIN, G. (1925). Über die Axopodien der Heliozoa und die Greifentakeln der Ephelotidae. *Arch. Protistenk.* **52,** 207.

—— (1929). Neue Heliozoen-Arten. I. Ibid. **66,** 201.

—— and LEVINSON, L. B. (1929). Die Kontraktilen und die Skelettelemente der Protozoen. I. Der Kontraktile und der Skelettapparat der Gregarinen (Monocystidae). Ibid. **66,** 353.

ROSSOLIMO, L. L. (1926). Parasitische Infusorien aus dem Baikal-See. Ibid. **54,** 468.

—— and PERZEWA, T. A. (1929). Zur Kenntnis einiger astomen Infusorien: Studien an Skelettbildung. Ibid. **67,** 237.

ROTH, L. E. (1957). An electron microscope study of the cytology of the protozoan *Euplotes patella. J. biophys. biochem. Cytol.* **3,** 985.

—— (1959). An electron-microscope study of the cytology of the protozoan *Peranema trichophorum. J. Protozool.* **6,** 107.

ROUILLER, C., FAURÉ-FREMIET, E., and GAUCHERY, M. (1956). Les Tentacules d'*Ephelota*; étude au microscope electronique. Ibid. **3,** 194.

RUDZINSKA, M. A. (1955). A simple method for paraffin and plastic embedding of Protozoa. Ibid. **2,** 188.

—— and CHAMBERS, R. (1951). The activity of the contractile vacuole in a suctorian (*Tokophrya infusionum*). *Biol. Bull.* **100,** 49.

—— and PORTER, K. R. (1954). Electron microscope study of intact tentacles and disc in *Tokophrya infusionum. Experientia,* **10,** 460.

RUMJANTZEW, A., and WERMEL, E. (1925). Untersuchungen über den Protoplasmabau von *Actinosphaerium eichhorni. Arch. Protistenk.* **52,** 217.

RYCKEGHEM, J. VAN (1928). *Hexamitus Tubifici* nov. sp. *Ann. Soc. sci. Bruxelles,* sér. B, **48** (2nd Pt.), 139.

SAMUELS, R. (1941). The morphology and division of *Trichomonas augusta* Alexeieff. *Trans. Amer. micr. Soc.* **60,** 421.

—— (1957). Studies of *Tritrichomonas batrachorum.* I. The trophic organism. *J. Protozool.* **4,** 110.

SANDERS, E. P. (1931). The life-cycle of *Entamoeba ranarum* Grassi (1879). *Arch. Protistenk.* **74,** 365.

SANDON, H. (1934). Pseudopodial movements of Foraminifera. *Nature, Lond.* **133,** 761.

—— (1941). A method of cleaning intestinal ciliates. *Turtox News,* **19.**

—— (1949). Opalinids from Nile fish. *Nature, Lond.* **164,** 410.

SASSUCHIN, D. (1931). Zum Studium der Darmprotozoenfauna der Neger im Süd-Osten RSFSR. I. Darmprotozoen des *Citellus pygmaeus* Pallas. *Arch. Protistenk.* **74,** 417.

SAXE, L. H. (1954). Transfaunation studies on the host specificity of the enteric Protozoa of rodents. *J. Protozool.* **1,** 220.

SCHAEFFER, A. A. (1910). Selection of food in *Stentor cæruleus* (Ehr.). *J. exp. Zool.* **8,** 75.

—— (1916a). On the feeding habits of Ameba. Ibid. **20,** 529.

SCHAEFFER, A. A. (1916b). Notes on the specific and other characters of *Amoeba proteus* Pallas (Leidy), *A. discoides* spec. nov. and *A. dubia* spec. nov. *Arch. Protistenk.* **37**, 204.

—— (1926). *Taxonomy of the amebas.* Carnegie Inst., Washington.

SCHEEL, C. (1899a). Über die Fortpflanzung der Amöben. *Sitzber. Ges. Morph. Physiol. Munich,* **15**, 86.

—— (1899b). Beiträge zur Fortpflanzung der Amöben. *Festschr. zum 70. Geb. von K. v. Kupffer,* Jena, p. 569.

SCHEWIAKOFF, W. (1894). Über die Ursache der fortschreitenden Bewegung der Gregarinen. *Z. wiss. Zool.* **58**, 340.

—— (1926). Acantharia. *Fauna e flora del Golfo di Napoli*: **37**. Monografia. Naples.

SCHILLER, J. (1933). *Dinoflagellatae*: 1. Teil. In Rabenhorst's *Kryptogamen-Flora von Deutschland, Österreich und der Schweiz.* 10.iii.1. Leipzig.

—— (1937). Ibid. 2 Teil. Idem. 10.iii.2.

SCHINDERA, M. (1922). Beiträge zur Biologie, Agglomeration und Züchtung von *Trypanoplasma helicis* Leidy. *Arch. Protistenk.* **45**, 200.

SCHMIDT, W. (1920). Untersuchungen über *Octomitus intestinalis truttae.* Ibid. **40**, 253.

SCHRÖDER, O. (1906). Beiträge zur Kenntnis von *Campanella umbellaria* L. sp. (*Epistylis flavicans* + *grandis* Ehrbg.) Ibid. **7**, 75.

—— (1907). Beiträge zur Kenntnis von *Stentor coeruleus* Ehrbg. und *St. roeselii* Ehrbg. Ibid. **8**, 1.

SCHUMAKER, V. N. (1958). Uptake of protein from solutions by *Amoeba proteus.* *Exp. Cell Res.* **15**, 314.

SCHWARTZ, V. (1935). Versuche über Regeneration und Kerndimorphismus bei *Stentor coeruleus* Ehrbg. *Arch. Protistenk.* **85**, 100.

SCOTT, M. J. (1927). Studies on the *Balantidium* from the guinea-pig. *J. Morph.* **44**, 417.

SEDAR, A. W., and PORTER, K. R. (1955). The fine structure of cortical components of *Paramecium multimicronucleatum.* *J. biophys. biochem. Cytol.* **1**, 583.

SENN, G. (1911). *Oxyrrhis, Nephroselmis* und einige Euflagellaten, nebst Bemerkungen über deren System. *Z. wiss. Zool.* **97**, 605.

SESHACHAR, B. R. (1950). The nucleus and nucleic acids of *Chilodonella uncinatus* Ehrbg. *J. exp. Zool.* **114**, 517.

—— and PADMAVATHI, P. B. (1956). The cytology of a new species of *Spirostomum.* *J. Protozool.* **3**, 145.

SEYD, E. L. (1936). Studies on the regulation of *Spirostomum ambiguum* Ehrbg. *Arch. Protistenk.* **86**, 454.

SHARP, R. G. (1914). *Diplodinium ecaudatum* with an account of its neuromotor apparatus. *Univ. Calif. Publ. Zool.* **13**, 43.

SIEGEL, R. W. (1958). Hybrid vigor, heterosis and evolution in *Paramecium aurelia.* *Evolution,* **12**, 402.

SINGH, B. N. (1938). The cytology of *Amoeba proteus* 'Y' and the effects of large and small centrifugal forces. *Quart. J. micr. Sci.* **80**, 601.

—— (1948a). Studies on giant amoeboid organisms. 1. The distribution of *Leptomyxa reticulata* Goodey in soils of Great Britain and the effect of bacterial food on growth and cyst formation. *J. gen. Microbiol.* **2**, 8.

—— (1948b). Idem. 2. Nuclear division and cyst formation in *Leptomyxa reticulata* Goodey with remarks on the systematic position of the organism. Ibid. **2**, 89.

SINGH, B. N. (1952). Nuclear division in nine species of small free-living amoebae and its bearing on the classification of the order Amoebida. *Phil. Trans. roy. Soc.* B, **236**, 405.

SKOCZYLAS, O. (1958). Über die Mitose von *Ceratium cornutum* und einigen anderen Peridineen. *Arch. Protistenk.* **103**, 193.

SKVORTZOW, B. W. (1928). Die Euglenaceengattung *Phacus* Dujardin. Eine systematische Übersicht. *Ber. Dtsch. Bot. Ges.* **46**, 105.

SLEIGH, M. A. (1956). Metachronism and frequency of beat in the peristomial cilia of *Stentor*. *J. exp. Biol.* **33**, 15.

—— (1957). Further observations on co-ordination and the determination of frequency in the peristomial cilia of *Stentor*. Ibid. **34**, 106.

SMETANA, H. (1933a). Coccidiosis of the liver in rabbits. I. Experimental study on the excystation of oocysts of *Eimeria stiedae*. *Arch. Path. (Lab. Med.)*, **15**, 175.

—— (1933b). Idem. II. Experimental study of the mode of infection of the liver by sporozoites of *Eimeria stiedae*. Ibid. **15**, 330.

—— (1933c). Idem. III. Experimental study of the histogenesis of coccidiosis of the liver. Ibid. **15**, 516.

SMITH, G. M. (1950). *The fresh-water Algae of the United States*. New York.

SMITH, N. M., and BARRET, H. P. (1928). The cultivation of a parasitic amoeba from the cockroach. *J. Parasit.* **14**, 272.

SMYTH, J. D. (1945a). Structure and osmiophilic inclusions of *Astasia harrisii*. *Quart. J. micr. Sci.* **85**, 117.

—— (1945b). Morphology of the osmiophil material of *Rhabdomonas costata*, and its behaviour during division. Ibid. **85**, 329.

SOKOLOW, B. (1912). Studien über Physiologie der Gregarinen. *Arch. Protistenk.* **27**, 260.

—— (1923). Hunger and regeneration. *J. R. micr. Soc.*, p. 183.

—— (1924). Das Regenerationsproblem bei Protozoen. *Arch. Protistenk.* **47**, 143.

SONDHEIM, M. (1915). Über *Actinophrys oculata* Stein. Ibid. **36**, 52.

SONNEBORN, T. M. (1937). Sex, sex inheritance and sex determination in *Paramecium aurelia*. *Proc. nat. Acad. Sci., Wash.* **23**, 378.

—— (1940). The relation of macronuclear regeneration in *Paramecium aurelia* to macronuclear structure, amitosis and genetic determination. *Anat. Rec.* **78** (Abs.), 53.

—— (1947). Recent advances in the genetics of *Paramecium* and *Euplotes*. *Advanc. Genet.*, **1**, 263.

—— (1954). The relation of autogamy to senescence and rejuvenescence in *Paramecium aurelia*. *J. Protozool.* **1**, 38.

—— (1957). Breeding systems, reproductive methods, and species problems in Protozoa. In *The species problem*. Amer. Ass. Adv. Sci., Wash.

—— and DIPPELL, R. V. (1956). Giant *Paramecium aurelia* (?). *J. Protozool.* **3**, Suppl. 9.

SOROURI, P. (1955). The nuclear cytology of *Leishmania tropica*. *J. Morph.* **97**, 393.

SOUTHWOOD, E. C., and SOUTHWOOD, A. J. (1958). The breeding of *Arenicola ecaudata* Johnston and *A. branchialis* Aud. and Edw. at Plymouth. *J. mar. biol. Ass. U.K.* **37**, 267.

SPECHT, H. (1934). Aerobic respiration in *Spirostomum ambiguum* and the production of ammonia. *J. cell. comp. Physiol.* **5**, 319.

—— (1935). The culture of *Spirostomum ambiguum*. *Arch. Protistenk.* **85**, 150.

SPRAGUE, V. (1941). Studies on *Gregarina blattarum* with particular reference to the chromosome cycle. *Illinois biol. Monogr.* **18**, no. 2, pp. 57.

SPRUGEL, G. (1951). Vertical distribution of *Stentor coeruleus* in relation to dissolved oxygen levels in an Iowa pond. *Ecology*, **32**, 147.

ŠRAMEK-HUŠEK, R. (1954). Neue und wenig bekannte Ciliaten aus der Tschechoslowakei und ihre Stellung im Saprobiensystem. *Arch. Protistenk.* **100**, 246.

STABLER, R. M., and CHEN, T.-T. (1936). Observations on an Endamoeba parasitizing Opalinid ciliates. *Biol. Bull.* **70**, 56.

STEIN, F. (1851). Neue Beiträge zur Kenntnis der Entwicklungsgeschichte und des feineren Baues der Infusionsthiere. *Z. wiss. Zool.* **3**, 475.

—— (1859). *Der Organismus der Infusionsthiere*, vol. i, pp. 206. Leipzig.

—— (1867). Idem, vol. ii, pp. 355. Leipzig.

STEINECKE, F. (1932). Algologische Notizen. II. *Heterodendron pascheri, Euglenocapsa ochracea, Stylodinium cerasiforme. Arch. Protistenk.* **76**, 589.

STEVENS, N. M. (1904). Further studies on the ciliate Infusoria, *Licnophora* and *Boveria*. Ibid. **3**, 1.

STILLER, J. (1939). Die Peritrichenfauna der Nordsee bei Helgoland. Ibid. **92**, 415.

—— (1940). Beitrag zur Peritrichenfauna des Grossen Plöner Sees in Holstein. *Arch. Hydrobiol.* **36**, 263.

STORM, J., and HUTNER, S. H. (1953). Nutrition of *Peranema. Ann. N.Y. Acad. Sci.* **56**, 901.

STRICKLAND, C. (1911). Description of a *Herpetomonas* parasitic in the alimentary tract of the common greenbottle fly, *Lucilia* sp. *Parasitology*, **4**, 222.

SUMMERS, F. M. (1935). The division and reorganization of the macronuclei of *Aspidisca lynceus* Müller, *Diophrys appendiculata* Stein, and *Stylonychia pustulata* Ehrbg. *Arch. Protistenk.* **85**, 173.

SWARCZEWSKY, B. (1928). Zur Kenntnis der Baikalprotistenfauna. Die an den Baikalgammariden lebenden Infusorien. V. *Spirochonina.* Ibid. **64**, 44.

SWEENEY, B. M. (1951). Culture of the dinoflagellate *Gymnodinium* with soil extract. *Amer. J. Bot.* **38**, 669.

SWEZY, O. (1915). Binary and multiple fission in *Hexamitus. Univ. Calif. Publ. Zool.* **16**, 71.

SWINGLE, L. D. (1911). The transmission of *Trypanosoma lewisi* by rat fleas (*Ceratophyllus* sp. and *Pulex* sp.), with short descriptions of three new herpetomonads. *J. inf. Dis.* **8**, 125.

SZABÓ, M. (1935). Neuere Beiträge zur Kenntnis der Gattung *Halteria. Arch. Protistenk.* **86**, 307.

TALIAFERRO, W. H. (1921*a*). Variation and inheritance in size in *Trypanosoma lewisi.* I. Life-cycle in the rat and a study of size and variation in 'pure line' infections. *Proc. nat. Acad. Sci., Wash.* **7**, 138.

—— (1921*b*). Idem. II. The effects of growing 'pure lines' in different vertebrate and invertebrate hosts and a study of size and variation in infections occurring in nature. Ibid. **7**, 163.

—— (1923). A study of size and variability, throughout the course of 'pure line' infections, with *Trypanosoma lewisi. J. exp. Zool.* **37**, 127.

—— (1926). Variability and inheritance of size in *Trypanosoma lewisi.* Ibid. **43**, 429.

TANNREUTHER, G. W. (1926). Life history of *Prorodon griseus. Biol. Bull.* **51**, 303.

TARTAR, V. (1953). Chimeras and nuclear transplantations in ciliates, *Stentor coeruleus* × *S. polymorphus. J. exp. Zool.* **124**, 63.

—— (1954). Reactions of *Stentor coeruleus* to homoplastic grafting. Ibid. **127**, 511.

TAYLOR, C. V. (1920). Demonstration of the function of the neuromotor apparatus in *Euplotes* by the method of microdissection. *Univ. Calif. Publ. Zool.* **19**, 403.

—— (1928). Protoplasmic reorganization in *Uronychia uncinata*, n. sp., during binary fission and regeneration. *Physiol. Zoöl.* **1**, 1.

—— and FURGASON, W. H. (1938). Structural analysis of *Colpoda duodenaria* sp. nov. *Arch. Protistenk.* **90**, 320.

—— and GARNJOBST, L. (1939). Reorganization of the 'silverline system' in the reproductive cysts of *Colpoda duodenaria*. Ibid. **92**, 73.

TAYLOR, M. (1925). *Amoeba proteus*: some new observations on its nucleus, life-history and culture. *Quart. J. micr. Sci.* **69**, 119.

—— (1947). *Amoeba kerrii* (n. sp.): morphology, cytology and life-history. Ibid. **88**, 99.

—— (1956a). Spores of the large free-living amoebae. *Nature, Lond.* **178**, 100.

—— (1956b). Some new observations on the development of the *proteus* group of amoebae. Ibid. **178**, 1478.

—— and HAYES, C. (1944). *Amoeba lescherae* (nov. spec.)—its morphology, cytology, and life-history. *Quart. J. micr. Sci.* **84**, 295.

TCHAKOTINE, S. (1936). La Fonction du stigma chez le flagellé *Euglena*, étudiée au moyen de la micropuncture ultraviolette. *C.R. Soc. Biol., Paris*, **121**, 1162.

TCHANG–TSO RUN (1931). L'Infraciliature et l'enkystement de l'*Anoplophrya brasili* Léger et Duboscq. *Bull. Soc. zool. Fr.* **56**, 547.

TERRA, N. DE, and RUSTAD, R. C. (1959). The dependance of pinocytosis on temperature and aerobic respiration. *Exp. Cell Res.* **17**, 191.

THÉLOHAN, P. (1895). Recherches sur les Myxosporidies. *Bull. sci. Fr. Belg.* **26**, 100.

THIMANN, K. V., and BARKER, H. A. (1934). Studies on the excystment of *Colpoda cucullus*. II. The action of the encystment inducing substance. *J. exp. Zool.* **69**, 37.

THOMPSON, D'A. W. (1942). *Growth and form*, 2nd edn. Cambridge.

THOMPSON, J. C. (1958). Experimental infections of various animals with strains of the genus *Tetrahymena*. *J. Protozool.* **5**, 203.

—— and Corliss, J. O. (1958). A redescription of the holotrichous ciliate *Pseudomicrothorax dubius*, with particular attention to its morphogenesis. Ibid. **5**, 175.

THOMSON, J. G. (1925). A *Giardia* parasitic in a bursate nematode living in the viscacha. *Protozoology*, **1**, 1.

—— and LUCAS, C. L. T. (1926). A preliminary note on the study of *Endamoeba blattae* (Bütschli, 1878) Leidy, 1879, found parasitic in the intestine of *Blatta orientalis* in England, with some remarks on its generic status. *J. trop. Med. Hyg.* **29**, 41.

TRAGER, W. (1932). A cellulase from the symbiotic intestinal flagellates of termites and of the roach, *Cryptocercus punctulatus*. *Biochem. J.* **26**, 1762.

—— (1934a). The cultivation of a cellulose-digesting flagellate, *Trichomonas termopsidis*, and of certain other termite Protozoa. *Biol. Bull.* **66**, 182.

—— (1934b). A note on the cultivation of *Tricercomitus termopsidis* and its method of cyst formation. *Arch. Protistenk.* **83**, 264.

TROISI, R. A. (1933). Studies on the acephaline gregarines of some oligocheate annelids. *Trans. Amer. micr. Soc.* **52**, 326.

—— (1940). Further studies on *Nematocystis elmassiani* from oligocheate annelids. *J. Morph.* **66**, 561.

TSCHENZOFF, B. (1916). Die Kernteilung bei *Euglena viridis* Ehrb. *Arch. Protistenk.* **36**, 137.

TUFFRAU, M. (1952). La Morphogénèse de division chez les Colpodidae. *Bull. biol.* **86,** 309.

—— (1953). Les Processus cytologiques de la conjugaison chez *Spirochona gemmipara* Stein. Ibid. **87,** 314.

TURNER, H. J. (1954). An improved method of staining the external organellae of hypotrichs. *J. Protozool.* **1,** 18.

TURNER, J. P. (1930). Division and conjugation in *Euplotes patella* Ehrenberg with special reference to the nuclear phenomena. *Univ. Calif. Publ. Zool.* **33,** 193.

—— (1933). The external fibrillar system of *Euplotes* with notes on the neuromotor apparatus. *Biol. Bull.* **64,** 53.

TYZZER, E. E. (1929). Coccidiosis in gallinaceous birds. *Amer. J. Hyg.* **10,** 269.

—— (1932). Criteria and methods in the investigation of avian coccidiosis. *Science,* **75,** 324.

——, THEILER, H., and JONES, E. E. (1932). Coccidiosis in gallinaceous birds. II. A comparative study of species of *Eimeria* of the chicken. *Amer. J. Hyg.* **15,** 319.

UZMANN, J. R., and STICKNEY, A. P. (1954). *Trichodina myicola* n. sp., a peritrichous ciliate from the marine bivalve *Mya arenaria* L. *J. Protozool.* **1,** 149.

VALKANOV, A. (1935). Untersuchungen über den Entwicklungskreis eines Turbellarienparasiten (*Monocystella arndti*). *Z. Parasitenk.* **7,** 517.

—— (1940). Die Heliozoen und Proteomyxien. Artbestand und sonstige kritische Bemerkungen. *Arch. Protistenk.* **93,** 225.

VERWORN, M. (1899). *General physiology* (Engl. trans. by F. S. Lee), p. 184.

VILLENEUVE-BRACHON, S. (1940). Recherches sur les ciliés hétérotriches. Cinétome, argyrome, myonèmes. Formes nouvelles ou peu connues. *Arch. Zool. exp. gén.* **82,** 1.

VLK, W. (1938). Über den Bau der Geissel. *Arch. Protistenk.* **90,** 448.

VOLKONSKY, M. (1931). *Hartmannella castellanii* Douglas et classification des Hartmannelles (Hartmannellinae nov. subfam., *Acanthamoeba* nov. gen., *Glaeseria* nov. gen.). *Arch. Zool. exp. gén.* **72,** 317.

VOLZ, P. (1929). Studien zur Biologie der bodenbewohnenden Thekamöben. *Arch. Protistenk.* **68,** 349.

WAGTENDONK, W. J. VAN (1955). *Encystment and excystment of Protozoa.* In *Biochemistry and physiology of Protozoa,* vol. **2** (ed. Hutner, S. H., and Lwoff, A.). New York and London.

WAILES, G. H. (1934). Freshwater dinoflagellates of North America. *Mus. Art Notes Vancouver,* **7,** Suppl. 2, 1.

WALLACE, F. G., and CLARK, T. B. (1959). Flagellate parasites of the fly, *Phaenicia sericata* (Meigen). *J. Protozool.* **6,** 58.

WALLENGREN, H. (1896). Einige neue ciliate Infusorien. *Biol. Zbl.* **16,** 547.

WATSON, J. M. (1946). On the coprophilic habits of a ciliate—*Glaucoma piriformis.* *J. trop. Med. Hyg.* **49,** 44.

WATSON, M. E. (1916). Studies on gregarines, including descriptions of twenty-one new species and a synopsis of the eugregarine records from the Myriapoda, Coleoptera and Orthoptera of the world. *Illinois biol. Monogr.* **2,** no. 3, pp. 258.

WATSON KAMM, M. (1922). Studies on gregarines. II. Synopsis of the polycystid gregarines of the world, excluding those from the Myriapoda, Orthoptera and Coleoptera. Ibid. **7,** no. 1, pp. 104.

WEDEKIND, G. (1927). Zytologische Untersuchungen an *Barrouxia schneideri*. (Gametenbildung, Befruchtung und Sporogonie), zugleich ein Beitrag zum Reduktionsproblem. (Coccidienuntersuchungen I.) *Z. Zellforsch.* **5**, 505.

WEINMAN, D. (1946). Cultivation of African sleeping sickness trypanosomes on improved, simple, cell-free medium. *Proc. Soc. exp. Biol. Med.* **63**, 456.

—— (1953). African sleeping sickness trypanosomes: cultivation and properties of the culture forms. *Ann. N.Y. Acad. Sci.* **56**, 995.

WEISZ, P. B. (1949a). The role of specific macronuclear nodes in the differentiation and the maintenance of the oral area in *Stentor*. *J. exp. Zool.* **111**, 141.

—— (1949b). A cytochemical and cytological study of differentiation in normal and reorganizational stages of *Stentor coeruleus*. *J. Morph.* **84**, 335.

—— (1950). On the mitochondrial nature of the pigmented granules in *Stentor* and *Blepharisma*. Ibid. **86**, 177.

—— (1954). Morphogenesis in Protozoa. *Quart. Rev. Biol.* **29**, 207.

WENRICH, D. H. (1921). The structure and division of *Trichomonas muris* (Hartmann). *J. Morph.* **36**, 119.

—— (1924). Studies on *Euglenamorpha hegneri* n. g., n. sp., a euglenoid flagellate found in tadpoles. *Biol. Bull.* **47**, 149.

—— (1928). Eight well-defined species of *Paramecium*. *Trans. Amer. micr. Soc.* **47**, 275.

—— (1954). Sex in Protozoa; a comparative review. In *Sex in Microorganisms* (ed. Wenrich, D. H., Lewis, I. F., and Raper, J. R.). Washington, D.C.

—— and SAXE, L. H. (1950). *Trichomonas microti*, n. sp. *J. Parasit.* **36**, 261.

WENYON, C. M. (1907). Observations on the Protozoa in the intestine of mice. *Arch. Protistenk.* Suppl. I, p. 169.

—— (1913a). Observations on *Herpetomonas muscae domesticae* and some allied flagellates. Ibid. **30**, 1.

—— (1913b). Experiments on the behaviour of *Leishmania* and allied flagellates in bugs and fleas, with some remarks on previous work. *J. Lond. Sch. trop. Med.* **2**, 13.

WESCHENFELDER, R. (1938). Die Entwicklung von *Actinocephalus parvus* Wellmer. *Arch. Protistenk.* **91**, 1.

WEST, G. S., and FRITSCH, F. E. (1927). *A treatise on the British freshwater Algae.* Revised edn. Cambridge.

WETZEL, A. (1925). Vergleichende cytologische Untersuchungen an Ciliaten. *Arch. Protistenk.* **51**, 209.

WHITTINGTON, M. J. (1951a). Observations upon a trichomonad from the gut of the snake, *Vipera ammodytes* L. *Parasitology*, **41**, 274.

—— (1951b). The survival of *Trichomonas vaginalis* at temperatures below +37° C. *J. Hyg., Camb.* **49**, 400.

—— (1957). Epidemiology of infections with *Trichomonas vaginalis* in the light of improved methods. *Brit. J. ven. Dis.* **33**, 80.

WICHTERMAN, R. (1937). Division and conjugation in *Nyctotherus cordiformis* (Ehr.) Stein (Protozoa, Ciliata) with special reference to the nuclear phenomena. *J. Morph.* **60**, 563.

—— (1953). *The biology of Paramecium.* New York.

WILLIAMSON, J. W. (1944). Nutrition and growth studies of *Amoeba*. *Physiol. Zoöl.* **17**, 209.

WILLMER, E. N. (1956). Factors which influence the acquisition of flagella by the amoeba, *Naegleria gruberi*. *J. exp. Biol.* **33**, 583.

WILSON, C. W. (1916). On the life-history of a soil amoeba. *Univ. Calif. Publ. Zool.* **16**, 241.

WOHLFARTH-BOTTERMANN, K.-E. von (1950). Funktion und Struktur der *Paramecium*-Trichocysten. *Naturwissenschaften*, **37**, 562.

—— and PFEFFERKORN, G. (1952–3). Protistenstudien. I. Pro- und Nesselkapsel-trichocysten der Ciliaten-Gattung *Prorodon*. *Z. wiss. Mikr.* **61**, 239.

WOLCOTT, G. B. (1952). Mitosis in *Trypanosoma lewisi*. *J. Morph.* **90**, 189.

WOLKEN, J. J., and PALADE, G. E. (1953). An electron microscope study of two flagellates. Chloroplast structure and variation. *Ann. N.Y. Acad. Sci.* **56**, 873.

WOOD, E. J. F. (1954). Dinoflagellates in the Australian region. *Austr. J. mar. freshw. Res.* **5**, 171.

WOODCOCK, H. M. (1914). Further remarks on the flagellate parasites of *Culex*. Is there a generic type, *Crithidia*? *Zool. Anz.* **44**, 26.

WOODRUFF, L. L., and ERDMANN, R. (1914). A normal periodic reorganization process without cell fusion in *Paramecium*. *J. exp. Zool.* **17**, 425.

WORLEY, L. G. (1933). The intracellular fibre systems of *Paramecium*. *Proc. nat. Acad. Sci., Wash.* **19**, 323.

YOCUM, H. B. (1918). The neuromotor apparatus of *Euplotes patella*. *Univ. Calif. Publ. Zool.* **18**, 337.

—— (1934). Observations on the experimental adaptation of certain fresh-water ciliates to sea water. *Biol. Bull.* **67**, 273.

YUSA, A. (1957). The morphology and morphogenesis of the buccal organelles in *Paramecium* with particular reference to their systematic significance. *J. Protozool.* **4**, 128.

ZAHL, P. A., and MCLAUGHLIN, J. J. A. (1957). Isolation and cultivation of zooxanthellae. *Nature, Lond.* **180**, 199.

ZELIFF, C. C. (1933). A new protozoan from the larva of the beetle *Osmoderma scabra*. *Proc. U.S. Nat. Mus.* **82**, Art. 23, 1.

ZERLING, —. (1933). Une *Astasia* sans flagelle, *Astasia doridis* n. sp., parasite des pontes de nudibranches. *C.R. Soc. Biol., Paris*, **112**, 643.

ZUELZER, M. (1927). Über *Amoeba biddulphiae* n. sp., eine in der marinen Diatomee *Biddulphia sinensis* Grev. parasitierende Amöbe. *Arch. Protistenk.* **57**, 247.

AUTHOR INDEX

SUBJECT INDEX

The page numbers in italic refer to illustrations.

Attention is drawn to the two *host-lists*, one of parasites described, and one of those mentioned, in the text.

D2